OTTAWA ▲

WASHINGTON ▲

MEXICO
CITY ▲

Waterfowl Tomorrow

Waterfowl

Editor: JOSEPH P. LINDUSKA

Managing Editor: ARNOLD L. NELSON

Artist: BOB HINES

THE UNITED STATES DEPARTMENT OF THE INTERIOR

Tomorrow

Bureau of Sport Fisheries and Wildlife • Fish and Wildlife Service

Produced by the Department of the Interior with the assistance of officials and representatives of State, Provincial, and National Governments and private enterprise in Canada, Mexico, and the United States.

L. C. card no. 64-60084

UNITED STATES
GOVERNMENT PRINTING OFFICE
WASHINGTON : 1964

FOR SALE BY THE SUPERINTENDENT OF DOCUMENTS, WASHINGTON, D.C., 20402 - PRICE $4.00
AVAILABLE IN CANADA FROM THE QUEEN'S PRINTER, OTTAWA, CANADA - PRICE $4.00

Foreword

I SEE A BOY alone at dusk on Dundas Hill. He sees a V of geese headed south, and he hears their haunting call. His heart leaps up; where they come from, where they fly, he does not know; nor can he tell you what he feels in the immensity of a waning autumn day.

The same kind of feeling may return later in his lifetime, but now in his boyhood he cannot know that.

Someday he will know how a poet tried to put these emotions into words:

> The world is too much with us;
> late and soon
> Getting and spending, we lay
> waste our powers;
> Little we see in Nature that is
> ours;
> We have given our hearts away,
> a sordid boon:

and,

> Ye blessed creatures, I have
> heard the call
> Ye to each other make; I see
> The heavens laugh with you in
> your jubilee;
> My heart is at your festival.

Any one of us who reads this book could have been that boy who, not many years ago, heard the wild geese call, and saw the mallards on Jessup's Pond.

The present prospect is that most of our sons will not have that adventure, that feeling of oneness with the natural world. That is the price we will pay for poorly planned "progress," for a world of concrete and speed and unceasing sound.

We and our children will be the losers if we do not care enough to save from exploitation some hills and dunes and swamps and woods and lakes where we can renew our ties to Nature and where God's other creatures can live and move and have their being.

Let us not delude ourselves, or be content with sentimentality or mere words. The time has come when men must choose what kind of permanent relationship they want to have with their land and her creatures.

There is a growing uneasiness and deep concern for the preservation of the wildlife of this Continent. This book is a manifest of the ceaseless work for the perpetuation and wise use of North America's magnificent migratory bird resources—resources that Canada, the United States, and Mexico must share and manage for the benefit of mankind. It is both encouraging and gratifying that officials and citizens of the three countries have combined efforts to make possible the writing of this volume.

It is for us to give conservation a new focus, a specific application not only to the broad fields of lands, forests, and water but also to the living creatures that inhabit them.

This book does just that, and I commend it to the study and enjoyment of all peoples of the Continent.

STEWART L. UDALL,
Secretary of the Interior.

Preface

Waterfowl Tomorrow is a book about the needs of the 48 species of ducks, geese, and swans that live on the North American Continent. Especially it is a book about the lands and waters that sustain these wildfowl in Canada, the United States, and Mexico. From early colonial days, migratory waterfowl have been hunted, sometimes wisely, sometimes not. But hunting them is only a part of the story. Millions of people in all walks of life see in these creatures a great natural asset, a treasure that must be perpetuated at all cost.

Largely because of the interest and support of sportsmen, we have witnessed in our time an intensive effort to learn what we need to know if waterfowl are to have a chance of flourishing tomorrow. In this book we present a digest of knowledge that has been accumulating over a span of scarcely more than 3 decades. We seek through this book to help all thinking people to a better understanding of the needs of waterfowl and of the things in our way of life that are affecting them adversely. The extent to which the volume helps in achieving this goal will determine its usefulness.

Much of the information presented here is in print for the first time; some of it will undergo modification as further work reveals new facts or better methods. Lack of the final word has not been considered a reason for avoiding subjects that have important bearing on waterfowl management; we hope that readers will find a minimum of qualification and hedging.

Space limitations have made it necessary to leave many things unsaid. Suggestions for additional reading have been omitted; most of the pertinent literature is not generally available in libraries. Readers desiring more detail are encouraged to communicate directly with the authors or to write to the Bureau of Sport Fisheries and Wildlife, Washington, D.C., 20240, or to the Canadian Wildlife Service, Ottawa, Canada.

Logically we can expect *Waterfowl Tomorrow* to be of help in shaping governmental policy. But it should not be inferred that the text is in any sense a statement of policy of any government whose employee or employees may be among the contributing authors.

Names of marsh and water plants follow those used by Neil Hotchkiss in *Marsh Wealth*. Bird names, in general, are those appearing in the *Check List of North American Birds* published by the American Ornithologists' Union in 1957. However, well-known synonyms and common colloquial names have been allowed to remain where the identity of the species is clear. Classification for the Canada goose follows the one proposed by Jean Delacour in *Waterfowl of the World*.

Because of their free movement between States and Nations, waterfowl are subjects always for broad cooperative attention. The 103 authors are from all sections of the United States and Canada. Many have dedicated most of a lifetime to the subjects on which they are writing.

Aside from the authors, a great many individuals and organizations have participated in numerous ways. They are deserving of high praise and sincere thanks even though, regrettably, it is impossible to single all of them out for individual attention. The staff at the Patuxent Wildlife Research Center in particular is to be commended for providing many essential services.

Special acknowledgement and thanks are due: To Walter F. Crissey, Arthur S. Hawkins, Ray C. Erickson, John W. Aldrich, and Neil Hotchkiss for technical review of manuscripts; to Fred H. Dale for assistance in preparing biographical sketches and legends for photographic illustrations; to Emma Charters for the index; to Gertrude King, Katherine DePriest, Polly Clarke, Ellen Warren, and Joan Bakker for painstaking work on manuscripts and galley proofs; to Frank H. Mortimer and Clifford W. Shankland of the United States Government Printing Office for design and typography and for other assistance; and to Clayton F. Matthews for many services that expedited publication greatly.

To Alfred Stefferud of the United States Department of Agriculture we are grateful for guidance, encouragement, and editorial assistance. His help was sustaining throughout.

Credit and thanks are due also to George W. Cain, Daniel L. Leedy, C. Edward Addy, Winston E. Banko, Harvey K. Nelson, Lee E. Yeager, and C. Edward Carlson. All rendered assistance that contributed to the completion of the book.

JOSEPH P. LINDUSKA,
Editor.

Contents

More Duck Factories

Goose and Swan Factories

Down the Flyways

Nature at Work

Men at Work

Places to Hide—and Seek

A Helping Hand

Waterfowl Tomorrow

WATERFOWL TOMORROW

SCAUP

Introduction

AMERICAN WIDGEON

Waterfowl in a Changing Continent

THREE LIFETIMES—yours is one of them—span the major changes in population, industry, science, the use of land, and public policy that have made the America we live in. All those changes bear strongly on the numbers of our waterfowl, because man and waterfowl often have the same need for land, water, air, space, and food. We know the importance of the changes men have made; we may not know their importance to waterfowl or, indeed, the importance of waterfowl to all of us.

In your grandfather's lifetime, wide marshes and uncounted lakes, ponds, potholes, and rivers teemed with ducks, geese, and other fowl. Adventurers and settlers as they moved westward saw great flights of birds, flocks of a size and of kinds beyond the power of most of them to describe but within the power of all to appreciate as sources of meat and pleasure and as tokens of a land on which God and Nature smiled.

One explorer who did put his experience in words was Capt. Howard Stansbury. When he arrived on the Bear River Marshes in the Great Basin of Utah in 1849, he reported: "The marshes were covered by immense flocks of wild geese and ducks among which many

3

swans were seen, being distinguishable by their size and whiteness of their plumage. I had seen large flocks of these birds before, in various parts of our country and especially on the Potomac, but never did I behold anything like the immense numbers here congregated together. Thousands of acres, as far as the eye could reach, seemed literally covered with them, presenting a scene of busy animated cheerfulness, in most graceful contrast with the dreary, silent solitudes by which we were immediately surrounded."

Others in your grandfather's time and earlier used terms like "great clouds of ducks" and "the sound made by the flushing of immense flocks of birds was like thunder" to tell of the wonder before their eyes. But most men then were too busy with ax, plow, hammer, and crowbar to make note, except in mind and heart, of the wild bounty; too busy building homes and farms and cities to foresee that they endangered the homes and lives of the wild things with whom they had shared the land. The realization of the need to save and share was to come later, in your father's day and ours.

Wetlands continued for a time to yield abundant game. There was little pressure to use them for any other purpose, to drain them for farming. It was easier then to break the sod for crops or clear off trees. Digging drainage ditches, besides, was hard work, which had to be done with pick and shovel or crude, horse-drawn implements. The perfection of excavating machinery in the latter part of the 19th century brought great change. Wetlands previously used almost exclusively by wild creatures could now be drained quickly and easily for dryland uses. Millions of acres have since been drained by machines.

Once there were about 127 million acres of wetland in the United States. Drainage had reduced our area of wetland to about 82 million acres in the 1950's. Its extent has dropped much more since then.

Of particular concern to naturalists is the draining of the prairie pothole country in the North Central States, a section that abounds in waterfowl. More than a million acres of it were drained between 1943 and 1961. It is an example of the steady removal of waterfowl habitat in the United States. The trend continues, sometimes wisely, sometimes unwisely, but always questionably.

Questionably because of the growth of our population which has more than doubled in a half century. At the same time, the need for the type of outdoor recreation supplied by watching and hunting migratory waterfowl has increased even faster than the population because of an increase in leisure time, the greater ease and speed of travel, and a desire to escape for a time the tensions of modern living.

THE NUMBERS OF WATERFOWL vary year to year and decade to decade, depending largely on natural conditions. Lows and highs are normal and are to be expected. No one can say for sure how the highs of a generation ago compare to the highs of later years. Many of us believe, though, that the general trend in peak populations is downward. It could hardly be otherwise in view of the disappearance of breeding places.

More hunters and fewer birds make it necessary to reduce the length of the hunting season and the number of ducks in a bag. The first Federal regulations for hunting migratory waterfowl provided for a season that averaged 100 days and bag limits of 25 ducks and 8 geese. That was in 1918. The regulations indicated no shooting hours and no possession limits or prohibitions on methods of hunting. How different were conditions in 1962: The hunting season for ducks ranged from 25 to 65 days and for geese from 60 to 75 days in the various flyways; bag limits for ducks and geese were 2 to 5 birds, and the season for canvasback and redhead was closed, because there were too few to permit hunting; and shooting hours and methods of hunting were resricted so as to control the number taken.

The situation has become serious, it is true, but I do not mean to say that all people have been apathetic about it. Individuals, groups, and governments have taken constructive, helpful action.

ONE FORWARD STRIDE in the conservation of migratory fowl occurred in 1916. The United States and Britain signed a treaty for the protection of birds moving seasonally between the United States and Canada. It drew attention to the international and legal status of

Life begins—a day-old wood duck.

many groups of migratory birds and established a basis for protecting them. This was indispensable to the regulation of the birds under law. The treaty, still the foundation for managing migratory birds in North America, set the pattern for negotiation in 1936 of a comparable treaty with Mexico. The two treaties link Canada, the United States, and Mexico in efforts to preserve a common resource that Nature had intended them to share, not monopolize.

Another step followed a severe drought in the thirties, which demonstrated that laws alone, or treaties, or regulations, however well-intentioned, cannot save waterfowl.

Everything suffered then for lack of rain—people, livestock, crops, the soil itself, and waterfowl. The heart of our waterfowl nursery, the prairies of central Canada and the United States, became a vast dust bowl that yielded neither crops nor ducklings.

The numbers of waterfowl dwindled to the lowest level in history. Among the many lessons the great drought brought home to all of us was that we cannot disturb or remove wildlife habitat and then expect wild things to fend entirely for themselves and survive. An effort began therefore to acquire lands to help safeguard the production and overwinter survival of waterfowl. Nothing like it had happened before on behalf of migratory birds.

Its outcome is told in a few figures. Before the big drought, the Federal Government had managed by one means or another to acquire

744 thousand acres for the conservation of all kinds of wildlife. By 1942, nearly 3 million acres had been set aside for the preservation of waterfowl alone. Much of the land was acquired with money received from the sale of dollar duck stamps, which all hunters of waterfowl had bought under the Migratory Bird Hunting Stamp Act, passed by the Congress in 1934. Allocations came also from other sources.

THEN HISTORY REPEATED ITSELF. By the late fifties it became clear that the water cycle in the prairies was heading downward. Potholes and marshes were drying up. The numbers of ducks fell alarmingly. Waterfowl authorities were even more deeply concerned than before. Why? Birds had rebounded from the previous drought, but the situation was not the same now. Irreversible changes had been taking place on the prairies. New drainage programs were destroying more habitat than was being restored. The meaning was clear: For millions of acres of prime waterfowl-producing marsh there would be a permanent drought and no return to production. A time for constructive action had come again.

Out of much discussion came many recommendations, some of which were put into action—to curtail hunting seasons in some places and close them entirely for critically affected species; to take special precautions to protect brood stock; to offset, compensate for, or prevent unnecessary drainage; to reserve more wetlands for waterfowl. The upshot was a widespread agreement that more wetlands should be acquired publicly. For that, money was needed. The Congress responded in 1961 by authorizing under Public Law 87–383 a loan fund of 105 million dollars repayable from receipts of the sales of migratory waterfowl hunting stamps.

The completion of this new acquisition program, well underway by 1962, was set for 1968. The increasing costs of land and the growing difficulty of acquiring the needed land are major obstacles.

We hope for the best from the program—for another substantial recovery. We hate to think of what otherwise may happen—a further loss of critical nesting habitat at a pace faster than replacement can be provided.

A vital factor is the determination among many citizens of the whole continent that migratory waterfowl must not vanish as a recreational resource—drought, drainage, and progress of man notwithstanding.

If we really want to save our waterfowl, we must prepare now. We must expand and use fully our experience and knowledge of ways to manage waterfowl. We need new, imaginative approaches to preservation, utilization, and management. Yesterday's answers may not meet the problems and requirements of tomorrow.

The background of the new requirements is clear enough. A population of 300 million in the United States by 2000 is predicted. Automation in industry and agriculture means that fewer workers may produce and fabricate our necessities. More leisure time for millions of people will make it possible for many more of them to enjoy the outdoor environment, including wildlife resources. We must be prepared to help those millions to do so without jeopardy to the wildlife resources. A large order, that.

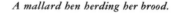

A mallard hen herding her brood.

Trumpeter swans in the rugged country of their home territory—Red Rocks Lake, Montana. The white birds are adult—the grayish ones are immature. The ducks fraternizing with them are Barrow's goldeneyes.

The entire task of waterfowl preservation and management cannot be left to government. The larger share of land in the United States is privately owned, and much can be done on it to insure the welfare of waterfowl. Ways to help private landowners foster great production of waterfowl need to be explored to the end that private lands, like public lands, may serve the recreational needs of all citizens.

A great American conservationist, the late Aldo Leopold, in 1931 foresaw this need. He wrote: "The only fundamental remedy [to shrink-age of breeding grounds] is to recognize the fact that undrained private marshland performs a public service in producing migratory birds, and to give the owner an incentive for keeping, continuing or restoring that service by according them a preferential tax status, such as is now accorded in some States to private forests on the same principle of public service. The public (agencies) can never acquire enough of the small marshes to offset the ones which are being taxed out of existence, nor can science show how to grow ducklings in a cornfield. The steamroller of economic self-interest must somehow be steered so that it will work with, not against, the feeble palliatives so far employed to avert spiritual calamity—a duckless America."

Thirty years later another dedicated conservationist, Stewart Udall, Secretary of the U.S. Department of the Interior, renewed the plea for greater public awareness of the place of waterfowl in our lives and their needs. On March 31, 1961, he inaugurated the after-season sale of migratory waterfowl stamps with these words:

"First, all America has a stake in our migratory birds—we must establish while we can, islands of natural habitat and havens where our wildlife can rest and reproduce. We must have funds to buy these lands while the opportunity still exists, and I believe that each citizen should have a chance to contribute directly to the cause.

"Secondly, I know no better way to make our youth conscious of our wonderful country than to give them the chance to share, even if only slightly, in the preservation of its resources. There is no better way to fix the eyes of youth on the vistas of tomorrow than to give them an opportunity to take some responsibility today.

"Because I believe that conservation is a program essential to the physical and psychological wellbeing of our people, I have approved this program, not only for its material values but for the understanding it will generate."

I mention two related points, as important as the others.

The new science of waterfowl management needs and deserves public support. During the years since the crisis of the thirties, we have gone far in scientific inquiry into waterfowl populations and wetlands management. Much of what we have learned already has been applied. Evidence thereof is given throughout this book. Evidence is given also that tomorrow's programs of waterfowl management will be only as strong as the technology back of them. Every sportsman and every interested citizen, therefore, can help in the conservation of waterfowl by backing management based on facts rather than expediency.

A SPORTSMAN can do much more. His conduct is a critical element in survival of waterfowl. Because greed, selfishness, and indifference can harm or destroy the best-planned program of waterfowl management, a true sportsman respects regulations as necessary to the preservation of his sport. He puts his responsibilities as a sportsman and conservationist before his demands for hunting seasons, bag limits, and hunting practices. He knows his part in the survival of waterfowl. He knows the many rewards of being afield with dog and gun, whether the bag limit is 10 birds or 2, whether the season is 75 days or 25. He, no more than anyone else, likes hunting restrictions, but he accepts them, knowing they are necessary.

He appreciates what the late President John F. Kennedy said in a message to the Congress in 1962:

"As our population expands, as our industrial output increases, and

Come closer if you dare!   The Canada goose is fearless when defending its nest.

as rising productivity makes possible increased enjoyment of leisure time, the obligation to make the most efficient and beneficial use of our natural resources becomes correspondingly greater. The standard of living we enjoy—greater than any other nation in history—is attributable in large measure to the wide variety and rich abundance of this country's physical resources. But these resources are not inexhaustible—nor do they automatically replenish themselves.

"We depend on our natural resources to sustain us—but in turn their continued availability must depend on our using them prudently, improving them wisely, and where possible, restoring them promptly. We must reaffirm our dedication to the sound practices of conservation which can be defined as the wise use of our natural environment; it is, in the final analysis, the highest form of national thrift—the prevention of waste and despoilment while preserving, improving and renewing the quality and usefulness of all our resources. Our deep spiritual confidence that this nation will survive the perils of today—which may well be with us for decades to come—compels us to invest in our nation's future, to consider and meet our obligations to our children and the numberless generations that will follow.

"Our national conservation effort must include the complete spectrum of resources: air, water, and land; fuels, energy, and minerals; soils, forests, and forage; fish and wildlife. Together they make up the world of nature which surrounds us—a vital part of the American heritage."—FRANK P. BRIGGS.

CANVASBACKS

The World of
Waterfowl

Cousins by the Dozens

THE 48 SPECIES of swans, geese, and ducks that frequent continental North America all belong to one family—the *Anatidae.* They share certain broad similarities: all have webbed feet; more or less wide, flat bills; short legs and tails; and rather long necks. All can live in a watery environment of one sort or another.

But we may get into difficulties if we generalize more than that about waterfowl and lump webfeet into one group of different-sized, different-colored, and different-voiced, but still much alike, birds. If we do, we may be in for mis- understandings about bag limits, of what drought may mean to water- fowl, and of the whole "duck situation."

Waterfowl come in many sizes (30 tiny green-winged teal would barely balance a good-sized trum- peter swan) and a full palette of colors, from the frosty snow goose through the multihued drake wood duck to the drab and sooty scoters. They have a complete chorus of voices—honking, trumpeting, quack- ing, whistling, purring, and croak- ing. Beyond these broad family resemblances, we can distinguish certain subgroups.

15

THE SWANS sort out reasonably well. Our three species (including the mute, an introduced European) are all large and white and have extremely long necks. The whistling swan, the commonest, is a giant bird whose wingspread reaches 82 inches. It mates for life, nesting on shorelines in the open tundra and along the coasts of the Arctic. Accompanied by soft trumpetings and loud whoops, whistlers migrate in October and November to both east and west coasts, often moving at great heights and great speed. The two species native to North America (trumpeter and whistler) were listed as game species in the Migratory Bird Treaties but no open seasons were declared from the time of the first treaty in 1918 until a limited season on whistling swans in Utah was permitted in 1962.

THE GEESE, too, make up a reasonably distinct group. They are intermediate in shape and size between swans and ducks. Their bodies are less flattened and their necks are longer than those of the ducks. Both sexes are alike in coloration, as is true of the swans. Geese, however, have a wider range of colors and sizes.

The Canada goose is the best known—and usually the most sought after by the hunter. It breeds over a wide area, from the northern States through the Arctic tundra. Canadas often construct rather bulky nests of reeds, grass, and other vegetation on the ground near water. But not all—some birds may utilize a shallow depression on a barren beach, the roof of a muskrat house, an abandoned osprey nest 40 feet up a dead tree, rock cliffs along the Snake River, or in wash tubs nailed on trees in Missouri.

While his mate incubates an average of five or six eggs, the gander does sentry duty nearby. He will stay on the job until the young are reared, and the defense a pair of enraged adults can put up against would-be gosling gulpers has much to do with the success of the species.

The legs of the Canada and other geese are farther forward under the body than those of ducks and swans. They therefore have better balance for travel on land and can forage away from water, working over green grass and grain shoots in spring and farm crop-residues in fall and winter. Aquatic plants, insects, and crustaceans get attention, too.

If geese share certain physical features that set them somewhat apart from other waterfowl, can we generalize that they are pretty much the same, and that the life history of one holds true for all? We can— but we would be wrong. The little group of eight species of geese in North America includes some that are truly maritime and others that seldom see salt water; some that breed in one place or another over nearly half the continent; and one species that nests only on a small group of lakes north of the Arctic Circle.

Here is one example of the diversity of the group: The largest species in North America is the Canada goose. The smallest? Also the Canada goose.

A lone blue goose in quiet water.

The ring-necked duck, a diving species that likes woodland lakes and ponds.

A green-winged teal (upper right)—the midget of waterfowl—in company with the long-necked—long-tailed pintail (2 males and a female).

There are 11 presently recognized subspecies of *Branta canadensis*. They vary in size from the giant form up to 18 pounds or more, to the tiny cackling Canada, which has the heft of a mallard. They range in color from dark races in humid coastal areas to light forms in the dryer interior.

But surely this physical variation is important only to a few bifocaled museum curators? Not at all. Along with physical variation goes variation in habits, behavior, habitat, and distribution. Some races therefore thrive on untouched, remote breeding grounds, but others are endangered by loss of nesting habitat to civilization.

Here, reflected in one species, is the story of all waterfowl—a story of almost endless diversity within a framework of general similarity. For, different as they are, the geese are alike as peas in a pod compared to the largest subgroup of waterfowl, the ducks.

To ACHIEVE SOME MEASURE of order, the 37 species of ducks regularly found in continental United States can be grouped by certain structures and habits. The surface-feeding ducks—the "dabblers" or "puddle ducks"—favor, as their name implies, the smaller, shallower inland lakes, ponds, and marshes. To make a fast getaway from such restricted waters, they bound vertically into flight. Legs set farther forward than most ducks give the dabblers good locomotion on land.

Their ability to forage ashore, to feed efficiently in the shallows, and to dive moderately well makes the dabbling ducks the most versatile feeders of all waterfowl. As a group, they make use of dozens of submerged and emergent aquatic plants; such forest mast as acorns and sweet-gum; scores of aquatic and terrestrial animals, from insects to clams; and many kinds of farm crops, grasses, and weeds. Food preferences range from the 40 percent animal material of the mottled duck to 90 percent vegetation of the wood duck.

Beyond these, few generalizations hold for the dabblers. The mallard, for example, is prized by gunners from coast to coast; most hunters have never heard of the mottled duck. The pintail has the widest breeding range of any North American duck; the northern race of the Mexican duck is confined to part of the valley of the Rio Grande. The blue-winged teal spends the summer as far north as northern Canada and may winter in central Chile; the Florida mottled duck never leaves the southern half of its namesake State. The American widgeon always nests on dry land; the black nests anywhere from the ground to a duck-blind roof or a treetop crow's nest; wood ducks seek out tree holes and nest like woodpeckers. Yet these are dabblers all.

THE CANVASBACK—the prize of the hunter and gourmet—is a member of the second major group of ducks, the divers. They usually feed underwater, aided by larger feet and shorter legs; which are farther to the rear of the body than the dabbling ducks. These features make the divers awk-ward on land, and they seldom visit crop fields.

The "can" and his close relative, the redhead, display a strong affinity for the prairie potholes and sloughs, the redhead often preferring the larger, more open marshes. Both nest over water, in clumps of reeds or cattails. This is important, for drought and drainage in the pothole country hit first and hardest the species oriented to such habitat.

Not all species of divers are equally affected by dryness because they show the same diversity from species to species that is true to a greater or lesser degree for each subfamily of waterfowl. The canvasback and redhead generally nest early, over water; the lesser scaup and ring-neck nest late, often on the ground. The goldeneyes and the bufflehead nest in tree hollows. The redhead breeds in drought-subject southern Canada. The lesser scaup nesting range includes a portion of the droughty prairies but most of it is much farther to the north. All these species live mostly on inland waters, but many other divers, including the oldsquaw, the scoters, and the eiders, nest chiefly in the Arctic and are largely maritime species.

While some divers seek the warmth of Mexico in winter, a common eider's concept of a winter resort is any Arctic water kept open by current or tidal rip, even though the air temperature may be 50° below zero.

All divers feed chiefly on aquatic foods, but diversity among species is still the rule. Redheads and canvasbacks dine mainly on plants. Scaup divide their attention equally between plants and animals. The maritime divers concentrate almost exclusively on animals; a listing of their mollusc and crustacean diet is as varied as the menu of a seacoast restaurant.

EVEN MORE SPECIALIZED for the underwater pursuit of aquatic animals are members of a third group of ducks, the mergansers. Their streamlined bodies are tipped by a narrow bill, whose edges are serrated with backward-pointing "teeth" that are ideal for grasping the fish that make up much of their food. We have three species of mergansers in North America. All breed from coast to coast across the Northern States and Canada, but subtle variations reduce competition. The little hooded merganser nests in tree-holes and prefers wood-bordered streams and ponds. The two larger species seek more open waters, but the red-breasted merganser always nests on the ground, generally farther north than the common merganser, which may nest in tree cavities, cliffs, or on the ground.

When winter arrives, the red-breasted species strikes out for the coastlines, the common merganser visits both inland lakes and coastal waters, and the hooded remains almost entirely inland.

IT WOULD SEEM that all possible diversities have been exploited by the waterfowl we have already discussed. Hardly. Tucked away in his own subfamily, along with a South American relative seldom seen on our shores, is a sprightly, stiff-tailed, little bird called the ruddy duck. All by himself he makes a paradox.

The ruddy is so specialized for diving, with stubby legs set far astern, that he is helpless on land. A better submariner than any diving duck or merganser, he feeds largely on plants, not fish. Though he dives so well and nests among overwater reeds like a redhead, he loves muddy creeks and little ponds. Like a gander, but like no other duck, the male ruddy helps care for the youngsters, but they hardly need him, because they can dive from the first day and are inde-

A brood of canvasbacks on Agassiz Refuge, Minnesota. These ducks nest in the prairie pothole region and periodically are hard hit by drought.

pendent when only half-grown. He is blessed with a voiceless mate, yet he and his whole family seem to be bad-tempered from the day they hatch. Ruddy has more colloquial names than any other duck, and they express his paradoxical nature— "butter duck," because of his fat and juicy table qualities, and "hickory" and "leather duck," for his shot-turning armor of dense feathers.

Most Yankees never heard of a tree duck, and those that have probably discount it as another tall tale from Texas. That's understandable, for birds with duck-sized bodies, goose-length legs, and swanlike necks are a bit unbelievable. But two such species do occur along our southern borders.

The black-bellied tree duck is common in Mexico, visits Texas regularly, and other southern States occasionally. The fulvous tree duck frequents southwestern parts of the United States from Texas to southern California, as well as northern Mexico. Both species are mainly vegetarians, grazing like geese and "tipping up" in shallow waters as do the dabbling ducks. They often feed at night and spend the days in reed-grown lagoons and ponds.

Of the two, the black-bellied most deserves the name "tree" duck, for it nests in forks of branches and in tree holes and frequently perches on limbs, like songbirds.

THESE, THEN, are North America's waterfowl—our own 48 species of the family *Anatidae*. They have been perpetuated not by their similarities, but by their differences. Over countless centuries they have reduced competition and insured survival by an amazing diversification on the common theme of their physical adaptation to water.

Among them, the 48 species utilize nearly every available aquatic habitat, from ocean surf to inland pothole; from arctic sea to semitropical lagoon. Each species has its own unique set of habits and adaptations, of food preferences, nest sites, migration pattern, general distribution, and local habitat. Each has traits

Blue-winged teal. This little duck is seldom hunted heavily in the North because it migrates early in the fall before the opening of the hunting season.

overlapping those of others, but each species combination is as individual as a fingerprint.

A far-reaching significance attaches to this. Diversification means the perpetuation of the family. Local or regional drought, drainage, disease, and die-offs of food organisms may endanger some species, but not all. Thus the canvasback and redhead have been hard hit by the drought of the late fifties and early sixties in the prairie potholes. But the wood duck, the geese, the maritime divers, and many others have been unaffected.

The waterfowl that achieve uniqueness through great specialization in habits or range generally are hardest hit by manmade or natural changes.

The "perky" appearance of the male ruddy duck is characteristic of this species.

Redheads and lesser scaup both breed on prairie potholes. But drought deals more severely with the redheads, since their nest-side needs are more specific and their breeding range is narrower. The wide-ranging Canada goose is much less susceptible to catastrophe than the highly localized Ross' goose.

THE SAME DIVERSITY that perpetuates the *Anatidae* and permits the existence of so many species vastly complicates the task of waterfowl management. Preserving waterfowl takes much more than simply preserving water or wetlands. It takes the preservation of a great variety of specific kinds of wetlands. Saving a breeding ground may entail thousands of square miles of pothole country or one lake on a tributary of an arctic stream. Providing food on wintering grounds may mean planting corn along a midwestern river or halting pollution of a tidewater bay. Curtailing a harvest may involve closing hunting in two counties or diplomatic exchanges with half a dozen foreign countries.

Diversity is the essence of waterfowl. If they are to be maintained in variety and abundance, diversity must be the essence of their management.—DONALD H. BALDWIN, GEORGE V. BURGER, and FRANCIS H. KORTRIGHT.

Tundra to Tropics

TO THE Bird Banding Laboratory at the Patuxent Wildlife
Research Center at Laurel, Maryland, came a letter from Sullana,
Peru. Sr. Rodolfo Cruz Marino, a
pharmacist, wrote us he shot a blue-
winged teal in a marsh 2 miles from
his home. He enclosed with his letter
the tiny strip of metal he had removed from the bird's left leg. The
letters and figures stamped on the
band

Avise F & Wildlife Service
– 565 – 78432 –
Write Washington D.C. USA

told us that it had been put on the
teal 6 months earlier by Robert
Meyerding, a United States Game
Management Agent, near Renoun,
Saskatchewan, Canada. It told us

also that the teal, a very early migrant that flies swiftly in small, compact flocks and has a pale-blue patch
on the forewing, had flown 7 thousand miles across a dozen international boundaries in the 6 months.

We obtained more information
about the flights of blue-winged teal
in a letter from Sr. Roberto Flores S,
the mayor of Quito, Ecuador. He
reported the recovery of a band from
a teal shot on a lake 13 thousand
feet above sea level on the slopes of
Cotopaxi Volcano. It had been
banded at the Delta Waterfowl Research Station in Manitoba, Canada.
It had flown over 4 thousand airline
miles.

To our ever-growing file of facts
on the migration of waterfowl the
letters added several useful details—

23

the distance between the points at which the teal were banded and at which the bands were recovered, the length and time of the flights, their destination, and the nature of the marsh or wetland where they were taken.

The letters from Peru and Ecuador are samples of the tens of thousands received at the Patuxent Bird Banding Laboratory through the cooperative efforts of banders and hunters. They become a part of the thousands of case histories we compile each year by means of statistical cards, which are sorted, grouped, and regrouped by machines and all together reveal many of the mysteries of the migration of birds.

The South American Indian who turns over a band to a missionary or a local constable and the Eskimo who shows one to a fur trader in the Arctic may regard the band with passing curiosity. He might much rather keep it as a good luck piece or an ornament. (He would be astonished indeed if he could see the intricate machines that prepare the detailed acknowledgment reports or the printed tabulations of the banding results.) The Latin American neighbor who sends in a band and in return expects "Sr. Fish and Wildlife" to supply him with a .22 rifle may have little interest in flyways, regulations, and bag limits in the United States. But whatever their motive and whatever their knowledge of the purpose of the bands, all are vital links in our research on waterfowl.

The migration of birds has been observed with awe or curiosity or a kind of poetic excitement over the centuries—as, for example, did the ancient Greeks, who saw occasional birds silhouetted against the moon at night, noted their absence the next day, and reasoned that they made their way to the moon each winter and returned safely with the coming of spring. The North American Indian was keenly aware that waterfowl migrated, for getting game was part of his daily life. Only in this century, however, when it became painfully clear that Nature's bounty was in serious danger of depletion, did we begin to take inventory of this resource, to give thought to preserving its habitat, and to study the many aspects of the requirements and values of waterfowl.

Banding of waterfowl is no longer done haphazardly but according to the need for specific types of information about each species. Biologists of the Migratory Bird Populations Station at the Patuxent Wildlife Research Center know what banding information is already available on each species and the most urgent needs for additional information. They assign "quotas" of birds to be banded at specified times of the year in various parts of the continent. Then State, Federal, and Canadian biologists and game management agents set about to do the required tagging. All official banding on this continent, whether in Canada, the United States, or Mexico, is part of one coordinated system. The procedure simplifies greatly the keeping of records, which now number about 11 million. About 4 million are for waterfowl. Slightly fewer than half of the 600 thousand birds banded each year are waterfowl. About four-

A setup for capturing waterfowl alive for banding operations at Swan Creek Experiment Station in Michigan. The folded net is projected over feeding birds by the thrust of explosives. Note 3 small cannons camouflaged behind the net.

A catch of Canada geese at Oak Orchard National Wildlife Refuge, Basom, New York, in a cannon projected net. The captured birds are being readied for banding.

fifths of the recoveries, which average close to 40 thousand a year, concern waterfowl.

ONLY TWO SPECIES of waterfowl in the United States and Canada are essentially nonmigratory—the mottled duck and the Mexican duck which is better known as the New Mexican duck. Members of all other species of ducks, geese, and swans cross international boundaries twice annually.

Surveys by the Bureau of Sport Fisheries and Wildlife of the breeding grounds showed that four-fifths of the ducks important to hunters were produced in Canada and Alaska in 1962. Only a small number winter in Canada. Data from waterfowl surveys made each January show that about 85 to 90 percent of the waterfowl observed each winter

are in the United States, and about 10 percent in Mexico. Any abuse of the waterfowl resource in one country therefore affects directly the utilization and enjoyment by citizens of the other countries. Accordingly, the United States, Canada, and Mexico have entered into treaties—the first in 1916—to insure the wise management, protection, and utilization of migratory birds. The banding of waterfowl was started in a small way at the same time to get essential information about the movements of the various species.

Thousands of waterfowl were banded on Federal refuges, private sanctuaries, and Canadian breeding grounds in the thirties and forties. The first work to determine movement of waterfowl populations from breeding areas to wintering grounds was done then.

Waterfowl raised on the North American continent migrate far and wide. These pintails were trapped on the Island of Oahu in Hawaii.

THE RECOVERED BANDS SHOWED
that each species has its own routes
and its own destinations. Different
species raised in the same slough may
winter in entirely different parts of
the continent. At the same time all
members of the same species utilizing the same nesting slough will not
have the same wintering grounds.
Birds that share one wintering
ground may have been hatched
thousands of miles apart from each
other. For example, recoveries from
the Bahama Islands in the British
West Indies show that blue-winged
teal fly there to winter from the
prairies of Canada; pintails from
North Dakota, Ontario, and Quebec; lesser scaup from Michigan;
wood ducks from Vermont; American widgeon from Saskatchewan,
Manitoba, and Prince Edward Island; and American coot from Minnesota.

We have learned also that the
general direction of movement for
many North American waterfowl
from breeding to wintering grounds
is northwest to southeast. One of
the best defined routes is the one the
scaup follows from Alaska southeastward toward Lake Manitoba, the
Upper Mississippi Valley, and the
Great Lakes. There the route splits,
one fork extends to Chesapeake Bay
and thence down the coast to Florida. The other proceeds down the
Mississippi Valley to the Gulf of
Mexico. Five percent of the recoveries of scaup banded in Alaska have
come from Mexico, the West Indies,
and the Latin American countries.

We have notable exceptions to the
northwest-southeast migratory movement. Most of the sea ducks follow
either the Pacific or Atlantic coast
for the greater part of their migration routes. Black ducks and smaller

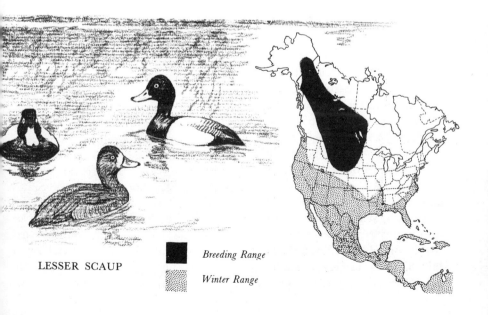

LESSER SCAUP

◼ *Breeding Range*

▨ *Winter Range*

A biologist of the Florida Game and Fresh Water Fish Commission records the number of the band attached to the leg of a mallard—the date and place of banding, the name of the bander, and other details.

bays. In spring, however, the brant dawdle on their northward flight. They stop often at coastal bays and pastures, seemingly aware that their breeding ground will not be free of its icy cloak until late May.

The route of the blue goose is generally north-south. From breeding grounds on Baffin and Southampton Islands in northern Canada at a longitude of about 72°, the route swings along the eastern shore of Hudson Bay to James Bay. Then, on what is practically a direct nonstop flight, the birds arrive on the coastal marshes of Louisiana at a longitude of about 92°. On the northward trip they tend to go westward and fly through eastern South Dakota and southeastern Manitoba.

The well-known Canada goose, which occurs throughout Canada, every American State, and much of northern Mexico, has an acute homing instinct. It breeds on lakes, muskegs, and along rivers throughout the northern "bush", especially near Hudson Bay. Several hundred thousand Canada geese move southward in the fall. They winter mainly in California, Texas, the Mississippi Valley, and along the Atlantic coast. To many Americans their return flight northward is a sign that spring is coming.

numbers of other dabbling species follow the Atlantic coast from the Maritime Provinces of Canada to their wintering grounds in the Southeastern States. Many of the pintails, widgeon, and shovelers that breed in southern Alberta and southern Saskatchewan move southwestward to winter in the Pacific States.

Black brant in their southward flight from Alaskan Arctic nesting areas first swing toward the Aleutian chain. Later they alter their course along the coasts of British Columbia, Washington, and Oregon and finally reach a southern terminus in Baja California, Mexico. The fall flight is largely offshore, and minor stops are made at protected

The mallard, to many hunters the most important duck, has a vast breeding range and spends part of each year in the contiguous 48 States and Alaska. Most mallards are raised in the Prairie Provinces of Canada. During migration they visit wetlands in all parts of the United States, but they are most numerous in the Mississippi Valley and the

Pacific States. Very few winter south of the United States.

Most of the blue-winged teal winter south of the United States. They start southward so early in the fall that most of them have gone before the hunting season opens. We therefore are not surprised to find that about one-third of the recoveries from blue-winged teal banded in the Prairie Provinces of Canada have come from south of our border. A typical nester of the potholes of Canada and the United States, the blue-winged teal is known to the fur-bedecked Indian of the Athabaska and the almost naked native in the marshes of Lake Maracaibo, Venezuela. Hundreds of bands put on blue-wings in Canada during the summer, and later returned to us, indicate they arrive in Central and South America about mid-September, reach a peak in numbers in November, remain there until March and early April, and then start the return journey northward before the first week of May.

The redhead makes one of the most remarkable migrations of all North American waterfowl. Redheads breed abundantly in the Bear River marshes at the north end of Great Salt Lake in Utah as well as other large western marshes. Many from Bear River take a westerly route and winter in California. Others leave the same breeding grounds and fly northeastward across North Dakota and Minnesota to join other redheads coming from the Canadian prairie. The Bear River birds, in crossing from west to east, are actually flying almost at right angles to the majority of their kind that are following routes from the Canadian prairie and parkland habitat. Most of these

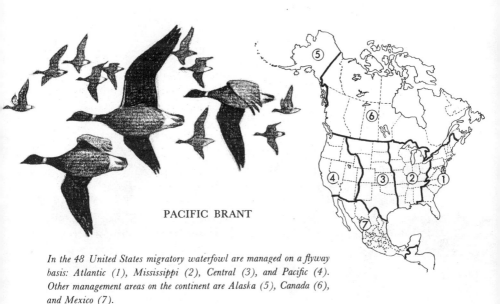

PACIFIC BRANT

In the 48 United States migratory waterfowl are managed on a flyway basis: Atlantic (1), Mississippi (2), Central (3), and Pacific (4). Other management areas on the continent are Alaska (5), Canada (6), and Mexico (7).

birds continue down the Mississippi and winter along the lower Texas coast. Others continue eastward from the Upper Mississippi across Michigan to the Finger Lakes of New York and finally to the tidal bays of Maryland, Virginia, and North Carolina.

IN THE EARLY DAYS of bird banding, the late Frederick C. Lincoln, of the United States Biological Survey, observed that recovery localities of banded waterfowl are not scattered at random. The records of a given species from a given place tend rather to fall in more or less well-defined sections, indicating that large numbers of birds use certain routes regularly. Some of their travel lanes are like a narrow path close to some definite geographical feature, such as a river valley or a coastline. Other lanes may resemble a broad boulevard alongside a land mass or body of water. A migration

route usually is a generalized pattern, rather than an exact course followed by individual birds, and may vary because of local storms, water conditions, and many other factors.

If you were to plot all major migration routes of several species of waterfowl on a single map, you would see a confusing criss-cross pattern through much of Canada and States along the Canadian border. As they move southward, however, the birds tend to separate into four distinct geographic groups, which Dr. Lincoln designated as flyways.

Two kinds of flyways are recognized by waterfowl specialists: (1) biological flyways—those established by the birds themselves, and (2) administrative flyways—those delineated by people for efficient management of the resource. The four biological flyways carry the same

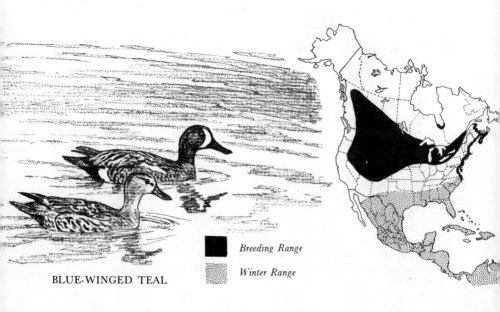

Breeding Range

Winter Range

BLUE-WINGED TEAL

Readying equipment to be used for banding waterfowl in Alberta, Canada. Flightless young will be "herded" into traps and banded.

names as the administrative flyways but there is an important difference. Whereas biological flyways include the entire range of the birds, administrative flyways are confined to the United States.

Biological flyways are older than mankind. They ignore political boundaries. They reflect the whimsey of living things. The Atlantic Flyway, for instance, draws birds from all across northern Canada, from the mouth of the Mackenzie River and even part of Yukon Territory and Alaska east to Labrador and Greenland. As the birds move gradually southward and southeastward, thousands of others join them, all moving towards the eastern Great Lakes and the Atlantic Coast States. The Great Lakes birds make an overland flight to Chesapeake Bay, but the birds from the northeastern

part of the continent fly down the coast. Most of the eiders and some of the Canada geese and black ducks end their migration in New England waters. Most of the waterfowl, however, go at least as far south as Delaware or Chesapeake Bay. The migratory path becomes quite narrow as the birds move south of Maryland and Virginia and then broadens out as the birds disperse from Florida to various destinations in the West Indies and farther south.

In the same way, the Mississippi Flyway draws birds from clear across the Arctic part of the Continent and funnels them into a fairly narrow pathway in the lower Mississippi Valley, from which point they disperse both eastward and westward along the shores of the Gulf of Mexico.

The Central Flyway covers much

of the interior of the continent from the Rocky Mountains east through the Great Plains.

The Pacific Flyway birds come mainly from west of the Rocky Mountains and from the Great Basin and adjacent parts of the Prairie Provinces of Canada.

The natural, or biological, flyways overlap considerably; their boundaries cannot be defined precisely; and they vary from year to year according to weather conditions. For efficiency in management the Bureau of Sport Fisheries and Wildlife has adopted four administrative flyways that agree generally with the biological flyways. The administrative flyways date from 1948, the first year that waterfowl hunting was regulated on a flyway basis. Waterfowl management since then has been related directly to the administrative

flyways. Regulations for hunting waterfowl are generally the same throughout a flyway. Different flyways have different sets of regulations because the number of birds available in relation to the number of hunters differs from flyway to flyway and from year to year. The annual regulations are adjusted in each flyway to reflect the number of birds available for harvest.

Each flyway has its own combination of characteristic waterfowl species. The Atlantic Flyway, for example, is preponderantly a route for the black duck, scaup, American widgeon, pintail, and Canada goose. The Mississippi Flyway is used by the Canada goose, blue goose, mallard, blue-winged teal, and ring-necked duck. The Central Flyway is a thoroughfare for mallard, pintail, teal, and white-fronted geese. The

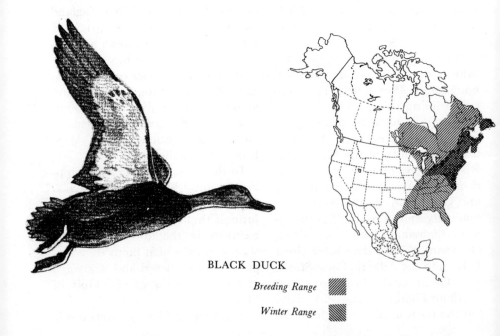

BLACK DUCK

Breeding Range

Winter Range

Pacific Flyway is noted for pintails, mallards, American widgeon, shovelers, teal, and several species of geese.

MIGRATION FOLLOWS a definite, predictable pattern, which reminds one of a hunter's preparation for a trip to his favorite marsh on opening day of the hunting season. The hunter lays in a supply of suitable clothing, buys ammunition, cleans his gun, gets his duck stamp and hunting license—all in advance of the trip. Physically and psychologically he is ready for the big day well before the season opens. Finally, the evening before the opening, sandwiches are put up and there is much activity, chatter, and boasting while the car is packed. The trip to the marsh may be slowed by red lights, a traffic jam, and perhaps a detour, but the destination finally is reached, and the mission is accomplished.

Waterfowl prepare for migration by donning a new or partly new suit of clothing. If the trip is to be a long one, they lay in a supply of fuel in the form of fat under the skin. In spring, a chain of physiological changes takes place, stimulated at least partly by increasing day length. The reproductive organs enlarge, and the urge to migrate becomes strong.

The birds are finally ready, physically and psychologically. But the releasing mechanism for their journey is not their condition. Rather, it is the condition of the great and erratic sea of atmosphere through which they must ply their way. Water currents can be treacherous,

but air currents and storm systems can be even more so. Nevertheless birds sometimes start out before open water and ample food are ready to support them at their destination. Wells W. Cooke, of the former Bureau of Biological Survey, long ago observed that Canada geese in spring advanced northward with the isotherm of 35° F., which coincides closely with the melting of the ice. Before there were any human aviators, waterfowl were taking advantage of pressure-pattern navigation.

Most species are not so regular. Many stay in their winter homes until spring has come. Then they move rapidly to their breeding grounds. Typical late migrants in spring are brant, snow geese, blue-winged teal, shovelers, gadwalls, and ruddy ducks.

Once migration begins, the advance of late starters may be rapid enough to overtake early migrants, such as buffleheads, goldeneyes, mallards, and pintails, which for a month or more have been pressing northward.

In migration, waterfowl neither loaf nor hurry. They move along at a speed normal for the species, pausing as they go to feed and rest. The cruising speeds vary for different species, but for ducks and geese they generally are about 40 to 60 miles an hour. The intervals reported between banding in the north and recovery in southern regions indicate that a month or more may be taken to cover an airline distance of a thousand miles.

Some birds fly faster. A black duck banded in Ontario was killed 12 days later in Mississippi, a dis-

Budding wildlife biologists of tomorrow—Cornell University students discuss bird banding while on a field trip to Patuxent Wildlife Research Center at Laurel, Maryland!

tance of slightly more than a thousand miles. Many blue-winged teal, banded on their breeding grounds on the prairies of the United States and Canada, have covered 2 thousand to 3 thousand airline miles in 30 days. An immature male bluewing traveled 3,800 miles from the Athabaska Delta in northern Alberta to Maracaibo, Venezuela, in a month. Another immature bluewing banded at Delta, Manitoba, on August 19, 1951, was shot at Rio Hacha, Magdalena, Colombia, just 16 days later.

We have learned from many studies that waterfowl return repeat-

edly to the marsh where they were hatched. Data we have gathered from bands show that ducks and geese tend to migrate over the same route year after year. This predictability of movement is the foundation of the present international management of waterfowl.

Flying a particular course to a specific area is thought to be an inherited faculty, but some naturalists believe that older, experienced birds teach the route to the young. Such an explanation may apply to geese, which travel in family groups. But it would not apply to all ducks, because adult and young ducks may migrate at different times. Immature ducks generally are the first to start their southward migration from the breeding grounds. The pintail and blue-winged teal are exceptions, as adult drakes of those species start the southward trip early. Adults of many duck species come south later than the immature ones. Hunters refer to this late mass movement as the "big northern" flight.

Canada geese, white-fronted geese, brant, snow geese, and blue geese tend to travel in flocks composed of many families. Mallards and black ducks often pair off during the winter, and mated pairs migrate north together. In general, however, waterfowl migrate together as individuals of a species. There is a tendency for the males of some duck species to arrive on the breeding grounds ahead of the females.

Investigations by Frank Bellrose and William J. Hamilton III, have told us much about how waterfowl orientate themselves to celestial bodies and use them as navigational aids. The scientists have used radar and miniature radio transmitters (carried by the birds themselves), to gather data that may finally answer many questions about the habits and instincts of waterfowl that men have pondered for countless centuries.

The secrets of migration are yielding to research conducted in many countries. From Pacific atolls to the rocky cliffs of Labrador, from muskegs of the Arctic to mangrove swamps of the Tropics, men and organizations are gathering information that gives us new understanding about the travels of waterfowl, where they nest and winter, and how they live and die.

The science of waterfowl management is becoming more and more technical and a growing amount of research is done by highly trained scientists who use the most intricate of modern equipment. Yet, the sportsman is still a vital, productive, indispensable, and deeply appreciated part of our efforts to uncover new knowledge about waterfowl. The banding of birds in great quantity over many parts of the globe is but the spade work to new knowledge of the travels and affairs of waterfowl. Only when the bird is recovered, and the place and data of recovery is reported by the hunter, is the story complete. Here is an area of waterfowl research and management where scientist and sportsman can work hand in hand toward the goal of a sure, continuing, and ample supply of waterfowl.

—FRED A. GLOVER.

AVOCET
BLUE-WINGED TEAL

Duck Factories—
The Big Three

MALLARDS

Prairie Potholes and Marshes

PRAIRIE POTHOLES are the backbone of duck production in North America. Filled with water, they constitute the most fruitful duck producing medium in the world. Given a few wet years, the prairie country can pyramid duck numbers to startling proportions. Several successive drought years bring an inevitable crash. Populations dwindle almost in direct proportion to the decline in water. For some species intimately tied to prairie habitat, it means dangerously low numbers and tightened hunting regulations.

The prairie pothole region makes up only 10 percent of the total waterfowl breeding area of this continent, yet it produces 50 percent of the duck crop in an average year—more than that in bumper years.

This region covers about 300 thousand square miles in south-central Canada and north-central United States. It extends in a great arc from Edmonton in Alberta, eastward to Prince Albert in Saskatchewan, south and east to Winnepeg in Manitoba, and across the border to include the western parts of Minnesota and South Dakota. There the Missouri River marks the western and southern border as it crosses western North

39

Dakota and northern Montana to Great Falls. At that point, it extends northward along the foothills of the Rockies to Calgary and Edmonton.

Averaging 300 miles in width, this great expanse of prairie is about a thousand miles in length from northwest to southeast. It is bounded by mountains on the northwest, forests on the north and east, and unglaciated, well-drained prairies on the south.

This pock-marked country was created by the advancing and retreating glaciers of the recent Ice Ages. Scattered throughout are moraines in various stages of erosion; in them the most permanent and desirable waterfowl habitats are concentrated.

Just outside of the glaciated pothole region, and too important to overlook, is the duck-rich lake region of north-central Nebraska, the Sandhills. Most of the lakes or potholes there occur in grassy basins or troughs, which resulted from wind erosion after the disappearance of an early inland sea. For centuries, food-filled lakes and adjacent vegetation over these 20 thousand square miles have been unusual duck factories. Where bison once roamed and Hereford and Angus now flourish, mallards and blue-winged teal abound.

The pothole area includes flat and undulating and steeply rolling and hilly terrain. Scattered hills, not yet leveled by erosion rise 700 to 3500 feet above lowlands, but otherwise much of the area has little pronounced relief except where prehistoric rivers carved deep coulees.

The southern two-thirds are grassland prairie. The northern third is being invaded by aspen. On the southern edge of this zone, aspen appear as islands and later merge into a solid forest. Because of the parklike appearance of these clumps of aspen, this portion of the prairie is known as parklands.

Millions of shallow depressions are filled with water in years of normal spring runoff. The parklands have a slightly higher annual rainfall, lower mean summer temperatures, and lower rates of evaporation than the grasslands. Therefore they are a more dependable area of duck production during droughts. They provide a wider range of cover, water, and nesting and brooding sites than the more intensively cultivated grassland prairies. Drought in the thirties, late fifties, and early sixties demonstrated the greater stability of the parklands.

Some of the pothole prairie in northern Montana, southeastern Alberta, and southwestern Saskatchewan still remains uncultivated. Cattle have replaced the shaggy buffalo, but if properly managed they are but a slight disturbance to waterfowl.

To be useful to ducks, potholes must have water. Not all of them do—at least not all summer. We use several terms to describe them.

Sheet water is a shallow depression, temporarily flooded by melting snows or heavy rains. The water may disappear in a few days, but vegetation in the basin usually is not altered.

Temporary potholes are covered in spring with as much as 18 inches

of water, which usually disappears in 4 to 6 weeks in all but wet years, but often that is enough for plants like rushes, sedges, and cattails. These ponds attract upland nesters and early broods, which must, however, move later in the season to places where there is water.

Semipermanent or intermediate potholes are basins filled with 2 to 5 feet of water in the spring. Some do not dry out for several years and usually have both aquatic and emergent vegetation. They provide nesting sites for diving ducks and are also used by upland nesting ducks. In terms of broods per unit area, they are the most productive of all types of potholes.

Permanent potholes may have as much as 10 feet of water. Rushes and water plants may grow in the shallower parts. These potholes often exist in the most recent and least eroded morainal areas of the prairies. Adult ducks often use the larger water areas after nesting when they moult and replace most of their feathers.

We use the term marsh to describe a large body of water that has an irregular shape, completely or partly grown with rushes, sedges, and other emergent vegetation, and frequently with moderate or heavy growths of submerged plants. Prairie lakes are deeper than marshes, may have a band of vegetation along the shoreline, but otherwise are open and windswept.

MELTING SNOW is the major source of water for nearly all prairie potholes and marshes. Widely scattered and infrequent heavy rains may also fill them. Of the many factors that affect the amount of water that may reach a pothole, some begin to operate a year or two before the spring in which migrating birds seek them out for breeding sites. The amount of moisture in the soil in late fall determines how deep it freezes. A frozen wet soil allows runoff from snowmelt to flow into depressions rapidly. But dry soil absorbs water before it can reach the depressions. Depending on soil moisture at the time of freezeup, a thick snow cover may provide less runoff than a light snow cover.

Many combinations of snowfall, rainfall, soil moisture, temperature, and winds cause wide fluctuations in water conditions in the prairies.

Good runoff may raise pond water levels more than 10 feet in a season, but drought in the fifties dried up some potholes that were 10 feet deep. In an average year, about a third of the prairie potholes dry up between May and July; in a dry year, as many as two-thirds may disappear. Even during a normal spring and summer, several inches of water may be lost in a week.

In the parklands, where the evaporation rate is lower than in the grasslands, the summer loss of water is smaller. In May, the density of potholes in parklands is twice that in the grasslands, but by July the differential in drying is such that the parklands usually have three times as many. In May, the total surface area of potholes in the grasslands is greater than that in parklands, but grassland potholes more frequently are dry or are too

No matter where this pintail is brought to hand the number on her leg band will identify her as being reared in the Sandhills of Nebraska.

shallow by midsummer to be of value to waterfowl.

By no means do potholes occur in neat patterns or regular numbers. Sometimes you can count 100 of them in a square mile but only 10 in another section a few miles away. The Regina Plains in Saskatchewan are so flat that only temporary, shallow sheets of water occur immediately after heavy rains or sudden melting of snow, and the whole area may look like one big lake, dotted with farm buildings and crisscrossed with roads. Blocks of prairies as large as 20 thousand square miles in the Dakotas average fewer than 10 potholes to a square mile. Other stretches of prairie in southeastern Saskatchewan may average 100 per square mile. The entire prairie pothole region averages about 30 potholes per square mile in a normal year. Not in drought years, however. In the block in Saskatchewan, for example, water-filled potholes averaged 101 per square mile in 1955, 50 in 1956, and only 3 (after 3 years of drought) in 1961.

FARMING HAS CHANGED the number and location of potholes in some parts of the prairies. Thousands of potholes have been drained in Minnesota and eastern North and South Dakota so as to create more tillable land. Similar drainage is starting on a smaller scale in parts of south-central Manitoba and on scattered farms in the Canadian parklands and grasslands. In rolling parklands, a pothole may be drained into a nearby stream. In the grasslands, several small ponds may be drained into a larger one. The methods of drainage differ, but the result is the same.

Drought makes it possible to destroy potholes in another way. More and more aspen is cut and burned every year. In years of normal rainfall, farmers prefer to clear aspen in upland places, but in drought years more clearing can be done in and around dried potholes. Sometimes when a pond dries up, the aspen and willows near it are cut, pushed into the basin, and burned. The cleared place is then plowed, and if the basin is not too deep it is filled with earth. Once filled and seeded to grain, little remains but a small depression, which will hold only sheet water. Through the years these spots and the shallow potholes on the open prairies are gradually filled by repeated plowing and by drifting soil. So another valuable habitat for breeding waterfowl disappears.

During drought periods a pothole may be plowed, but this does not necessarily destroy the utility of the habitat. A basin that is so deep it cannot be entirely filled with earth will refill with water during a wet year. The reappearance of water brings a rapid renewal of emergent and submergent vegetation. Ducks can use the pothole again. However, after holding water several years a dense growth of sedges and cattails may develop which reduces the value of the pothole to ducks.

WHY HAVE DUCKS made these droughty prairies their favorite breeding grounds? The answer is that they like and need the num-

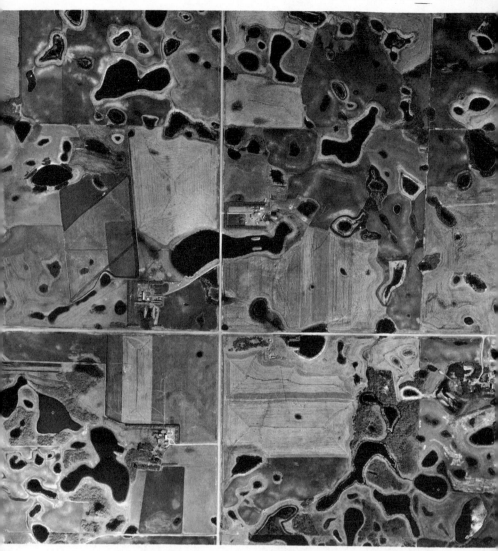

Typical pothole country of the Canadian prairies, near Minnedosa, Manitoba. This is one of the best waterfowl production areas of North America.

ber, variety, and quality of the millions of potholes available. Such species as the mallard, pintail, blue-winged teal, and canvasback often use several ponds of varied types for mating and for rearing young. At the start of the breeding season,

paired ducks seek isolation. The very number and variety of prairie potholes give large populations of ducks the privacy they need to rear their families.

Potholes, even those separated by only a few feet, are all different.

One pothole may have plants that provide escape cover for broods. Another may provide loafing places for adults and young. Still others may have deeper water or a dense growth of submerged vegetation or an abundance of animal and plant foods. Not that one pond cannot fulfill all waterfowl requirements— it can and often does. But in localities of small potholes of limited utility, one pair of ducks may require and utilize four or five ponds in a day.

Often we do not see any difference in the drainage basins and soil types of associated ponds, but we can see differences in ways waterfowl use them. We see that parkland potholes differ from grassland potholes in the aspen and willow that grow near them and in their greater average depth and permanence. But many less obvious differences relate to land-use practices near them and the kinds and amounts of plants and invertebrate life in them.

WATERFOWL in all stages of life need many kinds of plants. On the breeding grounds they serve many needs of adult and young ducks.

Duckweed is the commonest floating plant in parkland and grassland potholes. When water levels are high, it may cover the surface, blot out the sun's rays, and hinder or stop the growth of submerged aquatics. Ducks may eat it, and it favors the growth of a variety of aquatic life that ducks feed on.

The main submergent plants of the more permanent prairie potholes are pondweeds and watermilfoil. Seeds, leaves, and tubers of pondweeds are of such importance as food for ducks that their presence or absence affects the use of areas by waterfowl during fall migration.

Common emergent plants of major importance to ducks in grassland potholes are cattails, bulrushes, spikerushes, smartweeds, and whitetop. There are more cattails, bulrushes, and many species of sedge in parkland potholes. All emergents are used as escape cover, and some—the cattails, bulrushes, sedges, and whitetop—are used for nesting sites by diving species, like redheads, canvasbacks, ruddy, and ring-necked ducks. Mallards, too, often nest over water in these stands of emergent vegetation.

Of the emergent plants, only bulrushes and smartweeds offer quantities of food for waterfowl. Older ducklings and adults also select waste grain from stubble fields and a great variety of weed seeds. The chief food of ducklings is aquatic insects, such as the larval forms of mosquitoes, mayflies, midges, dragonflies, damselflies, and caddisflies, and many beetles and spiders. Snails, tadpoles, leeches, and freshwater shrimps make up a large part of the summer diet of adults and young. Prairie potholes are rich in small animal life—a fact which helps explain their attractiveness to waterfowl.

For ducks that do not nest in emergent vegetation, upland cover for several hundred yards around a pothole is an important feature in a duck's breeding environment.

Grasses, sedges, and weeds along fence rows and roadsides, hayfields, clumps of buckbrush, silverberry, rose, aspen, raspberry gooseberry, and currant are used by such species as mallard, pintail, gadwall, American widgeon, blue- and green-winged teal, and shoveler. Buffleheads and common goldeneyes nest in cavities in trees and sometimes in chimneys of abandoned farm houses.

THE CLEARING and burning of aspen and associated shrubs in the parklands have reduced nesting cover of waterfowl on many farms. The opening of new land in the northern parklands and the use of more efficient machinery for clearing and working the land have brought closer the day when northern prairies will be as intensively cultivated as those to the south.

Such developments eliminate some of the original prairie nesting places, but they also create a new cropland type. Hayfields especially provide good nesting cover if they are not mowed too early in the season. The clearing of trees from the edges of densely vegetated ponds and moderate grazing of potholes choked with emergent vegetation also make for more attractive waterfowl habitat. The clearing of dense parklands in central Alberta has increased greatly the use of potholes that once were unattractive to ducks.

Some effects of agriculture are good, but others are not. Intensive farming and extensive drainage of wetlands are harmful to waterfowl. But if potholes are spared and grazing is not excessive, the total farming operation is not perilous to nesting waterfowl and may even offer some advantage. Unfortunately, these differences in farm management invariably are based on economics and factors other than a consideration of the needs of waterfowl.

MOST WATER AREAS are frozen when adult ducks arrive on the prairies in spring. Only the edges of the larger lakes and fast streams provide open water. Early arrivals and even nesting mallards and pintails often feed on waste grain in the stubble fields. As ice thaws on the potholes, breeding pairs scatter over the countryside and establish their territories in the ponds. Plants grow rapidly. Invertebrate life multiplies at a tremendous rate, and ducks soon find food in great quantity.

The first mallards, pintails, and canvasbacks begin to arrive on prairie potholes in late March or early April, depending upon the severity of the weather. On the western prairies, spring usually arrives earlier than in eastern sections because of warm Chinook winds. Mallards and pintails may appear in Alberta and northern Montana in mid-March, while great concentrations of the same species may be held up in the Dakotas for another month by snow and freezing temperatures.

American widgeons, gadwalls, shovelers, green-winged teal, lesser scaup, and redheads usually follow the mallards and pintails in a few weeks. They appear in the Dakotas in early April and on the Canadian prairies by the last week of the month. Blue-winged teal, normally the last to migrate, may appear anytime from late April to mid-May.

Fifteen species of ducks nest commonly in the prairie pothole region. Most abundant are the mallard, pintail, and the blue-winged teal. Pintails, shovelers, and gadwalls seek the grasslands. Gadwalls utilize ponds of higher salinity than do the other species. Green-winged teal, lesser scaup, buffleheads, ring-necked ducks, common goldeneyes, and white-winged scoters are more abundant in the parklands. Mallards, blue-winged teal, widgeons, redheads, canvasbacks, and ruddy ducks seem content with either prairie location. Rarely, the wood duck, cinnamon teal, and black duck occur in both grasslands and parklands.

SPRING brings feverish activity. Most waterfowl are paired on arrival, but many more engage in the courtship antics in which the female selects her mate for the breeding season. Nuptial flights and displays on water and in the air occur in April and early May. There will be little rest thereafter until frost comes, and the birds again move south.

Here are the sequences in the life of a pintail pair in the prairie pothole country—if all goes well.

Weather permitting, the mated pair begins to seek a nesting site within a week of arrival on the breeding grounds. They spend many daylight hours flying to and fro, examining fence rows, roadsides, shrubby areas, and stubble fields, until the female finally selects the place. Then, after much scratching, turning, and twisting and pulling of vegetation, she makes a small depression in the ground, similar to the dusting site of a grouse. Now, laying begins—one egg each day until the clutch is complete. It will number 6 to 12 eggs. Early in egg laying the hen is sparing of time at the nest and gives it but a few minutes a day. Later, more time is given to building and conditioning; by the time the last egg is laid, the nest is a deep, well-shaped bowl, composed of leaves, dry grass, sticks, and earth interspersed with down she plucks from her breast. The down becomes a part of the nest itself and forms a protective covering for the eggs when she is away. The eggs begin to hatch about 24 days after incubation starts.

Activities associated with nesting occupy the time between late April and late May. During the incubation period, the male is alone for longer periods each day. With growing restlessness, he finally departs from the breeding territory and joins other males to form small bachelor groups. These flocks search out large, shallow lakes, where they begin their annual eclipse moult. These are traditional areas and are used each year by moulting males, which are flightless and vulnerable to predators for about a month. So they seek the protection of large expanses of open water or the dense cover of heavy growths of emergent

48

vegetation. At the completion of this major moult, the males take on the somber colors of the females.

Many prairie pintail drakes move southward, even into the marshes of the Bear River in Utah and into the Klamath Basin of Oregon-California before beginning their summer moult. Many more, as well as males of other species, moult in large lakes near the breeding potholes. Late-nesting species follow the same pattern. However, egg laying begins as much as a month or 6 weeks after that of the pintails. The males of some diving species, such as canvasbacks and lesser scaup, may fly further north into the forested areas to moult, leaving their females and broods behind.

Hatching takes place in June, July, and August. New broods appear daily on prairie ponds. For 6 weeks, they are confined to water areas near the nest site, while their natal down is replaced gradually by body feathers and flight feathers. The earliest-hatched broods are flying by mid-July. At that time females cease to care for their young and begin their postnuptial moult. They do not join the males in large concentrations, but more

An ideal pothole for nesting waterfowl located in western Minnesota. Millions of areas of this type are the "backbone" of the prairie duck factory.

commonly stay in or near the brood pond to wait out their flightless period.

Beginning with the arrival of early pintails in April until the last brood of diving ducks reaches flight stage in September, the grassland and parkland potholes are scenes of constant activity, which ends only with the frosts and snow of October and November.

BUT THIS ACCOUNT of annual replenishment is largely a success story. Not often does it happen just this way. Ducks are born to adversity, and the nesting birds that fail will outnumber—even in good years—those that succeed. The causes of failure are many and varied.

Man is responsible for many of them. He has burned and plowed upland nesting cover, drained and polluted potholes, and allowed his stock to eat away cover of all types. But wild animals are no less a threat. Marauding dogs and cats, coyotes, foxes, skunks, raccoons, minks, weasels, ground squirrels, gulls, crows, magpies, and bull snakes—all are destroyers of eggs. If the eggs do hatch, more hazards attend the journey from upland nest to pothole. But even there, security is not guaranteed. A pond offers safety from some land predators, but overhead are hawks and owls; below are voracious pike. Those that survive may be stricken by botulism, algal poisoning, or parasitic infestations. Leeches will suffocate some. Hail storms, as only the prairies can produce, may kill thousands more.

But all these dangers, important as they are, do not compare in total effect with the one great regulator of prairie duck numbers—drought.

DROUGHT is the greatest single disaster than can overtake a waterfowl population on our prairies. Vast areas of grasslands may lose all potholes and lakes except the ones fed by irrigation water or springs. In a series of drought years, like those during the late fifties and early sixties, even the parklands suffer. Breeding populations drop to a fraction of normal, and brood production falls accordingly. Plant and animal food disappears as potholes dry up, and ducks are forced into new, strange, and often unsuitable areas outside the prairies.

Thousands of pairs of ducks of all species failed to nest at all in 1959 and 1961. Large concentrations remained on breeding grounds on permanent lakes. They were still there until mid-June, when many moved southward, even into southern California, at a time when they ordinarily would have been in Canada and the Northern States. Several successive drought years can reduce the number of hens that raise broods to about half that of good years.

But with all these hazards, the duck population usually doubles between May and August and, when the prairies are wet, may more than double. It therefore pays to send sufficient stock back to the breeding grounds each spring to utilize fully the wetlands having a high productive potential. Equally important is preservation of habitat capable of producing dozens of broods per square mile, perhaps the most challenging goal of waterfowl management today.—ALLEN G. SMITH, JEROME H. STOUDT, and J. BERNARD GOLLOP.

SCAUP

Northern Watersheds and Deltas

MANY OF US think of it as a far country, a land of snow, ice, Eskimos, reindeer, barren wastes, and millions of square miles of boreal forests, muskeg, and tundra. What we may not know is that in this top half of our continent great rivers have made rich, wide deltas, which are among the most spectacular waterfowl producing areas in North America.

The major drainage systems of the north all have their beginnings on the Continental Divide. All drain to Arctic or sub-Arctic regions. The Saskatchewan flows east-north-east to Hudson Bay, the MacKenzie north to the Beaufort Sea, and the Yukon west to the Bering Sea. All carry huge loads of silt, which is deposited wherever the rivers reach base level.

Some northern rivers are clear-water streams. They are spawned in and flow through the rock-ribbed Laurentian Shield, which was scoured clean of topsoil by the continental icecap thousands of years ago. Carrying no silt, they merely spill their waters into the sea and maybe form a few sandbars at their mouths. Some of them harbor large populations of geese along their main stems or lower reaches, but they do not have deltas.

NORTHERN DELTAS are important in the year-to-year production of waterfowl. They are especially important when drought hits the prairies and parklands. Then the displaced prairie ducks seek out the deltas, for here they find conditions most like those from which they

51

fled in search of water. The deltas never go dry. Too much water at the wrong time actually may be a threat to waterfowl because of flooding.

Floods usually occur during spring breakup. Damage to nesting waterfowl is light then, because nesting has not yet begun or has just started. Later in the summer, floods from heavy snowmelt in the mountains hit the deltas when they are most vulnerable—just before or during the hatch of early nesting puddle ducks and the early incubation period of divers. Hens flooded from nests at this time will probably not try again, because little time remains. Freezeup comes early in the Far North.

THE SASKATCHEWAN, most southerly of the northern rivers, flows mainly eastward through Cedar Lake and Lake Winnipeg and terminates in Hudson Bay. Beyond Lake Winnipeg, it loses its identity as the Saskatchewan and is known as the Nelson. We are concerned with its course only as far as Cedar Lake, however, for that is the terminus of its sprawling delta.

Two main forks, the North Branch and the South Branch, rise within a half mile of each other, among the high peaks of the Continental Divide—Alberta's western boundary. After flowing nearly 900 miles, they meet to form the main stem at the "Forks" below Prince Albert, Saskatchewan. The two branches, nearly equal in size, flow through entirely different types of country.

The South Branch, a combination of the waters of the Bow and the Old Man, has cut its way through the short-grass prairie country of the high plains, carving a trench nearly 300 feet deep. As it proceeds east and then north, the surrounding countryside gradually lowers and changes from open prairie to parklands.

After breaking through the last mountain barrier, the North Branch flows through rolling country clothed throughout its course with boreal forest and parklands. Below the "Forks" the main stem of the Saskatchewan enters boreal forest again before spreading its muddy flood over the delta.

The amount of silt transported by the Saskatchewan has been prodigious. Rich topsoil of the high plains and parklands has been deposited annually over the basin of the delta to form a fertile marshland, a water world of shallow lakes and winding channels. The lake beds are mere depressions in the marsh contained by natural levees along channel banks. Deeper lakes contain large areas of open water, which support lush growths of aquatic vegetation, as well as islands of floating bog. Many of the plants are first-class waterfowl foods, among them sago pondweed, a preferred food of divers. In shallower places are dense stands of hardstem bulrush, softstem bulrush, phragmites, and cattails. Bordering the lakes and extending to the natural levees are wet meadows of sedges, grasses, and horsetail. Channel banks are high enough to support growths of willow and balsam poplar, the only woody plants of any consequence in the delta proper.

In such a diversity of habitat, it is small wonder that aerial survey teams have tallied between 100 thousand and 150 thousand ducks during the early breeding season. Those are minimum figures, since many neutral-colored ducks escape detection in the heavy cover; consequently, the figures are treated as indices for year-to-year comparison only. Also, many ducks seeking refuge in northern areas during prairie droughts are unsuccessful nesters. Were this not so, prairie droughts would not be synonymous with reduced duck populations.

All species common throughout west-central Canada are represented. Typical of northern breeding grounds, lesser scaup are predominant and make up slightly more than a third of the total. Blue-winged teal account for approximately a fifth. The rest are mallards, common goldeneyes, canvasbacks, American widgeons, redheads, ruddy ducks, ring-necked ducks, shovelers, white-winged scoters, buffleheads, green-winged teal, pintails, mergansers, and gadwalls, in that order of abundance. Coots are common throughout the delta. There is a small population of breeding Canada geese.

Besides being a prime production area, it is a place where migrant waterfowl gather to rest and feed during the long hauls to and from northerly nesting grounds. During early fall, waterfowl hunting is an important feature of the local economy. It provides food for the people and furnishes sport for an ever-increasing number of nonresident hunters.

THE DELTA of the Saskatchewan has the usual predators commonly encountered in the north. The voracious jackfish, or northern pike, is an abundant and constant menace to young ducklings. Crows and ravens pilfer eggs at every opportunity. Mink hunt the marshes nightly. Foxes and skunks prowl the meadows and channel banks. Predators probably are no more numerous here than elsewhere throughout the north, but they constitute a serious drain on production of waterfowl.

The most southerly of the northern deltas, the Saskatchewan has the heaviest human usage. The town of The Pas, Manitoba, a community of some 4,600 people, straddles The Pas Ridge midway in the delta. It is a distribution point for the region, a hub for the local fur and fish industry, and a center for the manufacture of forest products. Some 3,500 Cree Indians and Metis live in or near the delta and depend on the fur harvest and hunting and fishing for their livelihood. Agriculture, unimportant until recently, has become more prevalent with drainage.

Originally the delta covered roughly 3,500 square miles of prime waterfowl nesting territory, divided into two nearly equal parts by the esker on which the town of The Pas is situated. Then man began to alter the natural features of the marsh, for better or worse.

On the credit side, the Manitoba Game Branch began a program of water conservation to maintain constant water levels in the principal basins. The judicious placement of low-head dams in key areas kept them from draining into the main channels during low river stages. Much of the work was done mainly to increase muskrat production, but the side benefits to waterfowl were considerable.

On the debit side, 135 thousand acres of waterfowl habitat in the western half of the delta were diked and drained by The Pas Reclamation Project. This project, never a great success agriculturally because of poor drainage and a short growing season, ruined a large part of the marsh for waterfowl. Despite the marginal nature of the farming, however, more land is being put to agricultural use each year.

The Grand Rapids Hydroelectric Project was begun in 1960. It includes a dam below Cedar Lake, which will flood 1.6 million acres of the eastern part of the marsh and will eliminate or seriously damage all of the best waterfowl habitat in the half of the delta east of The Pas. Studies have been completed to determine how losses to wildlife might be lessened, but even if recommendations are followed, the loss of waterfowl habitat will be tremendous.

After 1964, when the reservoir created by the Grand Rapids Hydroelectric Project is filled to capacity, slightly less than one-fourth of the original Saskatchewan delta will remain as prime waterfowl habitat. At a time when wetlands are dwindling throughout the more populous regions of North America, this is indeed a serious blow to the future of North American waterfowl and to the sport of wildfowling.

THE MACKENZIE RIVER system, second longest in North America, is a complex of several major rivers that finally gather in Great Slave Lake to form the MacKenzie proper. Its watershed drains all of Northwestern Canada east of the Continental Divide and north of the Saskatchewan, with the exception of the lesser streams that drain directly to the Arctic Sea or to Hudson Bay. The system may be likened to a giant staircase with multiple branches and landings, each branch being a tributary and each landing a delta. All of the major tributaries rise on the east face of the Continental Divide. All are murky with heavy loads of silt "too thick to drink and too thin to plow."

THE ATHABASKA, the most southerly tributary, rises in the melt waters of the Columbia Glacier, only a few miles from the source of the North Saskatchewan. It flows northwest to Jasper as a tumbling mountain stream. There it swings to the northeast through a deep, narrow valley across the front range of the Rockies. After breaking through the mountains, it continues on through rolling foothills and low benchlands clothed in boreal forest, just brushing the edge of the parklands and cultivation. At Ft. McMurray it picks up the Clearwater, then heads due north to Lake Athabaska and its delta. At the northern edge of the delta, its waters merge with that of the Peace, which gathers its headwaters in the rift of the Rocky Mountain Trench in British Columbia.

Beyond that junction, the com-

Great Slave Lake, Northwest Territories, is frequently frozen over in June. Duck nesting in this severe climate is a battle against the elements and a race against time.

bination of the two rivers is called the Slave. Flowing north-northwest, the Slave skirts the Laurentian Shield on the east and its own fossil delta, the Slave River Parklands, on the west. At the rapids of the Slave, a roaring 15-mile stretch of white water, it enters the Northwest Territories, at which point it has completed about one-half its journey to Great Slave Lake. Here it swings in gargantuan meanders through the Slave River Parklands to its active delta on Great Slave Lake near Ft. Resolution. Great Slave Lake is also a collection point for other rivers coming out of the forest tundra and rock barrens. It receives the Snare, the Lockhart, the Snowdrift, the Taltson, and the Hay, which drains a considerable area of boreal forest land north of the Peace.

At the outlet of Great Slave Lake, the MacKenzie proper begins, clear now but soon to pick up the turbid waters of the Liard and other silt-laden mountain streams flowing off the east face of the Continental Divide. It passes through the MacKenzie lowland, flat to gently rolling lands of low relief, covered with boreal forests or forest tundra and dotted with innumerable lakes and ponds. It has one last encounter with the mountains where it has cut through the gap between the Franklins and the main mass of the Rockies near Ft. Wriggly. It skirts the Franklins on the east bank to the San Sault rapids and continues northwestward where it has carved a gorge at the Ramparts. From here it swings west to Arctic Red River and finally north again to Point Separation, where its muddy flood spreads out over the MacKenzie delta.

THE ATHABASKA delta was formed where the silt-laden river found its base level at Lake Athabaska. During the course of time this silt, the topsoil of northern Alberta, was spread over a vast area, gradually filling the west end of Lake Athabaska. Now it extends entirely across the west end of the lake, pinching off Lake Claire, a shallow bay at the extreme western end.

The delta, during its formation, has had a history almost exactly parallel to that of the Saskatchewan. Innumerable meandering channels have been formed. Some are sealed off by silt and debris. Others are actively cutting away at the silt banks, and the accelerated deposition of silt along the channel banks has sealed off numerous shallow basins. These basins are shallow lakes or grassy meadows, depending on the degree of siltation. The end-product of ages of delta building is a marsh of some 1,625 square miles of prime waterfowl habitat.

The Peace River, bordering the delta on the north, has also affected its formation and to some extent influences its water levels. When the Peace is in flood and its waters higher than the marsh level, it flows back "uphill" through various channels into the marsh. This spreads an enriching layer of silt, but it also doubles the flood threat. Either river is capable of causing flood damage to some parts of the marsh, but when both flood simultaneously the entire delta may be under water. This has occurred a number of times; when it happens in June or July, waterfowl production is curtailed seriously.

The Athabaska delta is the most northerly "prairie type" marsh and the last outpost of many food and cover plants, among them hardstem, softstem, and alkali bulrushes and sago pondweed. Herds of wild bison graze the meadows bordering Lake Claire. Sharp-tailed grouse can be flushed from the grasslands. Yellow-headed blackbirds nest in the marsh, as do coots, ruddy ducks, redheads, and gadwall.

The species composition of Athabaska ducks also has a prairie flavor. The mallard is number one. The pintail is second. These two make up more than half of the total. The remainder, in order of abundance, are canvasback, lesser scaup, shoveler, common goldeneye, redhead, American widgeon, bufflehead, green-winged teal, blue-winged teal, ring-necked ducks, gadwall, ruddy ducks, common and red-breasted mergansers, and white-winged and surf scoters. Besides the nesting population, the delta is host to hordes of ducks and geese migrating to and from more northerly breeding areas. Probably the entire population of Ross' geese gather here on their journeys between the Arctic coast and California.

AERIAL SURVEYS of the Athabaska delta have been made each spring since 1947. Counts are made on approximately 2 percent of the marsh, and from this sample a population index is computed for the entire delta. Counts have been highest in years of drought on the prairies. Then prairie ducks move north in search of water. In the drought year of 1961, we recorded a quarter million ducks on the marsh. By way of contrast, we tallied only 84 thousand ducks on the delta in 1955, a year of abundant prairie surface water. Probably this lower figure represents the hardcore population that prefers nesting in the delta regardless of conditions elsewhere.

The Athabaska delta has its quota of predators that take their annual toll of eggs and ducklings. Ravens, mink, and the ubiquitous jackfish exert a constant pressure. In years following a rabbit die-off, foxes and lynx resort to the marsh to fill their empty bellies.

FT. CHIPEWAYAN, at the northeast corner of the delta, is its only settlement. The village includes a few hundred Indians and whites, most of whom subsist on the commercial fishery and from muskrat hunting and trapping. To these people, waterfowl are an important part of their yearly food supply. At the northern edge of the delta, on the banks of the Peace, there has been some logging, but this has been a small operation, as the supply of merchantable timber is limited. Thus, for the forseeable future at least, it appears that the delta will continue to be of prime importance to waterfowl and a haven for ducks displaced by drought on the prairies.

IN THE DISTANT Past, perhaps shortly after the last ice age, an arm of Great Slave Lake extended south through the Slave River parklands. It is possible that Great Slave Lake and Lake Athabaska may have been connected at that time. Over countless years this trough was silted in by the combined waters of the Athabaska, the Peace, and the Slave. Then, after the water level dropped or the land raised, the Slave carved its present channel through what was once its own delta. The delta of the Slave is still building a wide lobe into Great Slave Lake.

After the change in base level, an area of approximately 7,500 square miles of rich alluvial soil was left stranded. Bounded on the east by the Precambrian Shield and on the west by a low escarpment of limestone, much of this now lies within the boundaries of Wood Buffalo Park, Canada's largest National Park. It is the original range of the wood bison and the only known nesting ground of the whooping cranes presently used.

The Slave River parklands are as flat as a floor, with numerous shallow lakes and extensive meadows. Between the shallow basins are groves of aspen and thickets of willow. On better-drained sites are spruce and jack pine. Most lakes within this fossil delta are so shallow that the water entirely disappears during dry years. Some ponds, however, are deep enough to support lush aquatic vegetation and provide high-grade waterfowl nesting habitat.

Near Great Slave Lake, where the river reaches base level, the parklands gradually merge into an active delta-building complex. Here, numerous channels of the delta fan have changed course again and again, resulting in a maze of long, shallow lakes separated by low, timbered ridges. The lakes are extremely rich in aquatic vegetation and consequently are highly productive waterfowl nurseries.

THE SLAVE RIVER PARKLANDS, together with the present delta of the Slave, have breeding population indices ranging between 40 thousand and 230 thousand ducks, the high figure reflecting waterfowl displacement by prairie drought. Species, in order of numerical importance, are the pintail, American widgeon, lesser scaup, bufflehead, mallard, green-winged teal, common goldeneye, ring-necked duck, and shoveler.

Most lakes are too shallow for jackfish, and predators are almost entirely terrestrial. Ravens, mink, foxes, and lynx are all present but probably no more abundant than in other deltas. As late as 1955, timber wolves were plentiful, but recent predator-control programs, largely to protect the buffalo, have cut their numbers to a remnant.

Settlement along the Slave is sparse. Ft. Fitzgerald and Ft. Smith, at opposite ends of the rapids. are the only settlements between Lake Athabaska and Ft. Resolution on Great Slave Lake. These villages were established as convenient links in the river transport system and as fur trading posts. But with the advent of low-cost air freight and the building of the MacKenzie highway, river traffic has dwindled. Ft. Smith is the administrative center of the Northwest Territories and its second largest town.

There is agricultural potential in the Slave River parklands, depending on future population needs and the development of early maturing crops. Hydroelectric possibilities exist at the rapids of the Slave. A lead mining development was started at Pine Point, only a few miles west of the northern end of the Slave delta. The mining project proposed to bring in a railroad. A new highway is to link Ft. Smith with the MacKenzie highway and the "Outside." And, so, changes will alter the wilderness status of the Slave River parklands. Whether or not this will be detrimental to waterfowl and other wildlife in the region depends upon how wisely man can integrate "progress" with wildlife.

After a journey of 1,100 miles from Great Slave Lake, the MacKenzie makes a final flourish before disappearing into Beaufort Sea, where its muddy flood presses against ice flows of the Arctic. At Point Separation the main stem divides into multiple channels, which fan out across its delta like the roots of a tree. Many channels unite, then divide again, creating a labyrinth of waterways. The result is a maze where a traveler in a small boat can easily become lost. Between channels, innumerable lakes and ponds are separated by low ridges covered with a dense growth of willow and spruce.

From the air, one square mile looks exactly like every other square mile, and navigation by map from a low elevation is virtually impossible. This jumble of channels, lakes, ponds, and low ridges of willow and spruce is superposed over delta silt and permafrost. Below the top few inches, the silt never thaws.

Toward the lower end of the delta, spruce becomes smaller and sparser and finally is replaced by willows. Still lower down, willows disappear, and many interior basins become sedge meadows rather than lakes. At the extreme edge, where the delta meets the sea, only mud flats are exposed at low tide.

The limits of the delta are definite; the lines of demarcation, pencil-sharp. At its upper end, and along the southeast, forest tundra slopes down to its edge. Farther down on the east side, the tundra-mantled Caribou Hills abut abruptly in a pronounced escarpment. On

Near Aklavik, Northwest Territories, and beyond, is the famous delta of the MacKenzie River, renowned as a waterfowl producer of the Far North. When the prairies go dry, the duck population of this area increases markedly.

the west, tundra slopes downward in a series of benches from the Richardson Mountains to the delta flats. In all probability, the present delta was once a shallow bay of the Beaufort Sea. It is being extended annually by the MacKenzie silt and is enriched with each spring breakup, when high water and ice jams combine to spread water and mud over all but its highest parts.

THIS CONSTANT ENRICHMENT produces the best of waterfowl habitat. Here, 150 to 200 miles above the Arctic Circle, submerged aquatic vegetation is abundant, and associated with it are swarms of minute animal life—ideal food for ducklings. Indeed, food must be abundant to produce fully-fledged ducks in the short arctic summer. Breakup does not occur until early June and shallow ponds may have shell ice by mid-September.

All phases of production, from the laying of the first egg to achievement of flight by the young, must be telescoped into this short period. There is little time for broods hatched in late July or early August to mature and leave before freezeup. This short season also eliminates the possibility of a successful second nesting attempt should the first nest be lost to predators or flood waters. Under conditions of constant light, which is characteristic of arctic summers, ducklings undoubtedly feed more frequently than do those reared in southern latitudes, where night interrupts activity. Growth, therefore, is faster. Predators of the Far North include

a few typically arctic species uncommon or absent on more southerly deltas. In addition to mink foxes, lynx, ravens, and jackfish there are glaucous gulls and three species of jaegers, all notorious thieves of eggs and ducklings. Barren Ground grizzly bears, though relatively rare, occasionally raid a nesting colony of snow geese. Loons, while not actually predators, compete with other waterfowl for living space, and, being strongly territorial, they will not tolerate other waterbirds upon their domain. Consequently, ducks are seldom seen on a pond where a pair of loons has set up housekeeping.

The MacKenzie delta is huge—almost 5 thousand square miles. Aerial surveys have revealed breeding population indices of 80 thousand to 335 thousand ducks. The difference reflects conditions on the prairies, being highest in drought years and lowest when prairie potholes are water-filled. In the wooded delta, the greater scaup is the number one duck. The pintail is the most abundant in the open habitat of the treeless delta. Other species are American widgeon, white-winged scoter, mallard, common goldeneye, green-winged teal, red-breasted merganser, shoveler, and canvasback. A colony of snow geese, numbering 4 to 5 thousand birds, occupies a group of low islands near Kendall Island on the outer delta. Occasionally small numbers of black brant are associated with them. A few hundred each of Canada and white-fronted geese occur as scattered nesters on the lower portion of the delta, and

2 to 3 thousand whistling swans nest regularly in the same open type of habitat.

Flooding is the worst hazard to waterfowl nesting on the delta. It has been almost completely under water three times in the 15 years from 1948 to 1962. High water of less than flood proportion has inundated many low-lying lake margins and meadows, particularly on the outer delta. The snow goose colony near Kendall Island is especially susceptible to flooding, for the nests are barely above the high-tide zone. When exceptionally high tides occur during periods of high water, the destruction of nests is inevitable.

THE DELTA has a high human population compared to other arctic regions. There are five villages in or near the delta: Arctic Red River, just a few miles above Pt. Separation; Ft. MacPherson, on the Peel River near the southwest corner; Inuvik, on the east side; Aklavik, in the delta; and Tuktoyaktuk, just beyond the mouth of the east channel on the Arctic coast. Altogether, more than 3 thousand persons, most of them Eskimos and Indians, live in this relatively "congested" area.

Muskrat hunting and trapping are the principal activities on the delta and were probably the prime reasons for the establishment of some settlements. All delta lands are allocated by parcel to individual families. The parcels are passed down from generation to generation. Most of the 'rats are shot during spring breakup, which coincides with the arrival of waterfowl, but the hunt is largely completed before nesting begins.

Oil exploration crews have been active in the delta, and much of the area is under permit to oil companies. If oil should be found in commercial quantities, it will have considerable impact on the local economy, but under proper safeguards it should not seriously affect waterfowl.

ALASKA IS A PATCHWORK of vast mountain ranges parted by wide, fertile river valleys, the largest and most important of which is the renowned Yukon.

The Yukon River and one of its major tributaries, the Porcupine, arise in Canada from the western slopes of the Continental Divide. They enter Alaska from the northeast and join at Ft. Yukon. From there, the Yukon bisects the State in a southwesterly direction, spilling its silt-laden water into the Bering Sea. From the western slope of the lower Alaska Range, innumerable streams merge in a short distance and quickly form Alaska's second largest river, the Kuskokwim, which flows toward the lower Yukon. These two rivers come within 25 miles of each other, then diverge abruptly, and continue at right angles over the last 100 miles of their journey to the Bering Sea.

The delta of 26 thousand square miles that lies between these two river mouths has been nurtured through centuries with organic-rich silt from the interior valleys. It is one of the continent's great waterfowl nurseries and is the major or sole breeding ground for several species of Pacific Flyway waterfowl.

The highly gregarious cackling Canada goose and black brant restrict themselves to a narrow fringe of coastal tundra. Although several thousand brant continue to the deltas of the MacKenzie, Anderson, and lesser rivers along the Canadian Arctic coast, most of them nest on the Yukon-Kuskokwim, and all of the cacklers remain there. Practically all the emperor geese nest there, as do most of the whistling swan from the Western States. White-fronted geese, Taverner's Canada geese, and lesser sandhill cranes also occur commonly. Among the ducks, greater scaup and pintail are most abundant, followed by common scoter, mallard, oldsquaw, and several species of eider. The common snipe is an important nester. Many other species of shorebirds are present in numbers beyond credibility along the tide-swept mud flats.

We have used aerial surveys to learn trends from year to year, expressed as a breeding population index. Since 1956, when comparable coverage has been made, the breeding population index of ducks has fluctuated between 500 thousand and 750 thousand birds. Ground studies indicate that approximately half of the ducks actually present are tallied from the air in this type of open habitat. In a year of average abundance, all species of geese together probably contribute another 500 thousand summer residents to the Yukon-Kuskokwim Delta.

Several hundred miles upriver, the Yukon and Porcupine join. This is the center of Alaska's second largest duck factory, the Upper Yukon Basin or the Fort Yukon Flats. The area has been referred to as the Rampart Dam impoundment area, and in connection with that project intensive studies have provided a thorough understanding of production and distribution of waterfowl from this area of 11 thousand square miles.

In contrast with the open, treeless tundra of the coast, Fort Yukon Flats is a spruce-muskeg climax, so fire-scarred that willow and aspen are far more predominant now than spruce. The incredible fertility of some lakes may in fact be due to deep-burning fires, which have released minerals and other nutrients locked up in the undecayed peat bogs. The lakes and potholes in this broad, crescent-shaped valley exceed 30 thousand. The aerial breeding population index averages about 170 thousand ducks annually. This is a minimum figure, since ground studies indicate that in this wooded habitat only about one-third of the ducks present are seen from the air. At least 15 species of ducks (plus Canada and white-fronted geese) nest in the area. Pintail, lesser scaup, American widgeon, scoter, shoveler, mallard, canvasback, and green-winged teal are the dominant species.

The banding of 18 thousand waterfowl of 11 species has demonstrated the far-flung distribution of birds from the upper Yukon. Recoveries of 578 included returns from 29 States, six Provinces of Canada, Mexico, Panama, and the Dominican Republic. Scaup and widgeon have the widest distribution across the continent, many returns coming from the Atlantic and Gulf Coast States. Mallards are most restricted, being confined largely to the Pacific Northwest and migrating only as far south as the Willamette Valley of Oregon.

There is good evidence that birds of many species displaced from the drought-stricken prairies have moved as far as eastern Alaska to nest. Breeding records of blue-winged teal, redheads, ruddy ducks, and ring-necked ducks were recorded for the first time in Alaska in 1960–1962. The canvasback also has become much more abundant and widespread in Alaska than at any time previously. Several recoveries also have been made of ducks banded in earlier years as downy young on the Canadian breeding grounds.

Although the Yukon-Kuskokwim Delta and Fort Yukon Flats produce about half of Alaska's annual waterfowl crop, there are many smaller spots of high productivity. They all are associated with deltas along the seacoast or those created by a geological block in an interior river valley. Old Crow Flats in Canada's Yukon Territory is one of them. It is actually a fossil delta of the Old Crow River, a tributary of the upper Porcupine, which was left stranded when the Old Crow cut down to its present base level. The Flats lie just across the divide from the MacKenzie Delta and occupy a basin of almost 2 thousand square miles, surrounded by mountains of the Richardson Range. The basin is studded with shallow lakes and ponds that are bordered by tundra and forest tundra.

In 1960, a drought year on the prairies, we recorded an all-time high of slightly more than 170 thousand ducks on the Flats. During years of plentiful surface water on the prairies, this index of numbers has dropped to 77 thousand. Species, in order of abundance, are white-winged scoter, scaup, pintail, American widgeon, oldsquaw, mallard, goldeneye, green-winged teal, canvasback, shoveler, and red-breasted merganser. There are also a few Canada and white-fronted geese and an occasional pair of whistling swans.

INDIANS from Old Crow village, at the junction of the Old Crow and Porcupine, hunt the Flats for muskrats in the spring but return to the village shortly after breakup. During the waterfowl nesting season, the Flats are left in solitude.

The possibility of large-scale agricultural ventures deleterious to wetlands in Alaska seems remote. There has been intensive oil exploration in many northern areas.

This activity together with mining could be harmful in some areas without proper controls, but we believe that such industrial development can be conducted without destruction of waterfowl habitat. It will require constant vigilance on the part of all conservationists, however, to assure that wildlife values are properly recognized.

THE HYDROELECTRIC POTENTIAL of Alaska is fabulous. Development could seriously threaten many valuable duck factories. A physiography that creates great duck marshes, on the one hand, creates the means for destroying them on the other. At the downstream end of all broad valleys between mountain ranges, the rivers are constricted through narrow, deep canyons. Each is an ideal power site; each, if developed, can easily destroy its upstream valley. Less spectacular, but equally destructive, is the effect of sedimentation. Behind the dams, mineral- and organic-rich silt settles out, leaving relatively clear water to flow seaward. Then rivers spew lifeless to the sea, while the soil to develop and regenerate the deltas works to shorten the lifespan of impoundments.

The proposed Rampart Canyon Dam alone would wipe out the entire upper Yukon basin all the way to the Canadian border, an area that distributes annually 1.5 million ducks among all four flyways. That would be the immediate loss. How long before the effects would be felt on the outer delta is problematic, but the potential there is even greater than the immediate result from flooding.

Rampart is the first and most imminent but by no means the sole hydroelectric threat. Nine potential sites, with a generating capacity of about 11.3 billion kilowatts, have been earmarked for the Yukon and Kuskokwim river basins. Some of the smaller projects would affect little or no waterfowl habitat, but all the larger dams would eliminate or seriously harm major production areas. Important wildlife values will be traded for kilowatts of questionable need.

We believe the best means to forestall the more destructive of these projects is a well-informed public that has a thoroughly aroused conscience. If, in the final analysis, the welfare of the Nation were dependent upon Yukon River power and there were no alternative, no loyal American could rightfully object. We question, however, whether the Nation is now faced, or ever will be, with this hard choice. Excellent alternate sites of negligible threat to fish and wildlife are available; they should be promoted in lieu of the devastating Yukon Basin developments.

Of the lesser arctic drainages, the Anderson is significant. It drains much of the rolling forest tundra country north of Great Bear Lake and the Hare Indian River. The Anderson is small by comparison with the MacKenzie or the Yukon, and the amount of silt it transports is proportionally much less. Nonetheless, it has built a delta of some 70 square miles, which is extending annually into Wood Bay. On its outermost islands, barely above high tide, colonies of snow geese and black brant number 5 thousand to 7 thousand birds. Along with them and over the delta generally are whistling swans, white-fronted geese, and many ducks common to the Arctic, principally greater scaup, pintail, American widgeon, mallard, shoveler, and green-winged teal.

Of the smaller streams flowing east to Hudson Bay, the Boas and the Thelon are noteworthy. The Boas has built a delta of some 30 square miles, on which there is a colony of about 25 thousand snow and blue geese. The upper Thelon has a population of 8 thousand to 10 thousand Canada geese.

Along the Arctic Coast between Bathurst Inlet and Chantrey Inlet are a series of short-stemmed, north-flowing rivers, which lack deltas but are important nevertheless as brooding areas for snow geese, white-fronted geese, Canada geese, Ross' geese, and some black brant. These are the Ellice, Perry, Armac, and an unnamed river, which the Eskimos call Kugaruk. Judging by populations tallied on the Perry and the Ellice, upwards of 10 thousand geese use the lower parts of these rivers as brooding areas.

Probably the greatest single snow goose production area in North America is the lower basin and delta of the Egg River on Banks Island, the western outpost of land in the Arctic Archipelago. Although snow geese have been banded there, the number nesting is not definitely known, and estimates vary considerably. The most reliable information suggests that there may be 120 thousand snow geese on Banks Island, most of them on the Egg River.

NORTHERN WATERSHEDS AND DELTAS constitute a relatively small part of the total duck production areas, yet they produce a great abundance and variety of ducks and geese. The total area of the deltas, past and present, is about 55,700 square miles. From these areas, we have obtained indices varying between 981 thousand and 2.08 million breeding ducks. The marked difference is a reflection of surface water conditions on the prairies. When prairie surface water is abundant, northern breeding grounds support a minimum population of native ducks that prefer northern habitats. When the prairies are dry, northern deltas are swarmed over by prairie ducks seeking water, but only a small percentage of these displaced birds are successful in producing broods. If this were not the case, prairie droughts would hardly affect overall duck numbers. And yet some are successful in nesting, an accomplishment which permits rapid repopulation of the prairies when surface water returns. But by any yardstick the northern deltas make a solid contribution to the continent's total of waterfowl. In a favorable year, even the minimum breeding index of 981 thousand could represent a fall total of 6 million, when visibility factors and production of young are taken into account.

In addition to being regular and important contributors to the continental waterfowl population, the deltas assume special significance when drought in the southland forces ducks north in search of suitable habitat. Some displaced ducks probably do not even attempt to nest and in effect are sitting out the drought. But they must have a suitable environment even to do that, since adult ducks cannot get by on a sun-baked alkali flat or the parched bed of a parkland pothole. The deltas, therefore, function as waterfowl reservoirs that are never completely drained and that maintain a nucleus of breeding stock that would be hard pressed to survive the adversity of prolonged drought on the prairies.

Deltas along with the northern watershed are the principal nurseries for all geese, except some Canadas and whitefronts. Being traditionally Arctic or sub-Arctic nesters, their numbers are more stable than duck populations, although there are year-to-year variations in the numbers of young produced. The total breeding populations of all the northern deltas and watersheds is estimated at 675 thousand geese.

AND, NOW, WHAT IS THE OUTLOOK for the continuing productivity of the deltas? It can be stated in a few words.

The Saskatchewan—three-fourths of it will be defunct or seriously damaged by the mid-sixties; the Yukon is threatened by the Rampart dam project; oil field development looms as a detriment on the MacKenzie and Old Crow Flats. As man continues to exploit the north at an ever-accelerated pace, we can expect further shrinkage of waterfowl habitat. Unless the maintenance and perpetuation of waterfowl breeding areas gain recognition in Government planning as necessary and desirable national assets, fall flights from the Far North will grow smaller—rapidly.

We can have kilowatts and canvasbacks—but not from the same place.—ROBERT H. SMITH, FRANK DUFRESNE, and HENRY A. HANSEN.

RED-BREASTED MERGANSERS

Northern Forests and Tundra

NORTH AND EAST of the
fertile prairies and parklands
is a primitive area of woodlands
and tundra. It covers more than
two-thirds of the Canadian land
mass, most of Alaska, and a portion of northeastern United States.
It has rather poor soils, a large
amount of exposed bedrock, not
much farming, and totals about 3.5
million square miles. Most of the
area can be reached only by aircraft and canoe. Its very shortcom-
ings, if that is what they are, may
be values for the future of waterfowl.

Waterfowl densities of the woodlands and tundra are comparatively
low, but the expanse of land and
the myriad lakes and streams make
possible a substantial contribution
to the total waterfowl population.
Although the climate is severe and
the summers are short, waterfowl
breed even in the most northern
parts. Habitat for waterfowl is
stable; it changes little from year
to year—a noteworthy point, for no
doubt this land for ages played a
vital part in the survival of waterfowl during severe droughts on the
prairies. Perhaps, then, northern
forests and tundra are the real
backbone of the continental waterfowl population, even though the
prairies produce far more waterfowl to the square mile in wet
years. Furthermore, it seems unlikely
that man will exert any great adverse influence on these northern
areas as places for waterfowl to live

67

and breed. Here, perhaps, is one land that we can bequeath unspoiled to those who follow us.

Temperature, wind, rainfall, evaporation rate, and basic geological formation have alined its southernmost boundary in a northwest-southeast direction. The woodland part, therefore, extends southward into northeastern Minnesota, northern Michigan, northern Pennsylvania, New York State, and Massachusetts. To the west, the north woods extend through most of northern and central Alberta, the northeastern two-thirds of British Columbia, and northward into Alaska. From this southern line, the area extends northward to include the Arctic Islands of Banks, Victoria, Baffin, and others.

Most of this vast area has a low density of breeding waterfowl, averaging between 1 and 5 birds per square mile. Exceptions are several large river flats and deltas, such as the Yukon delta in Alaska and the MacKenzie delta in Canada, but these areas have been described in a previous chapter. Included here is more than a third of the North American continent whose chief claim to fame as a waterfowl production area is its size and dependability.

THE NORTH COUNTRY has two major life zones or habitat types—the forest to the south and the tundra to the north. The tree line divides the two zones. It runs just inland along the southern coast of Labrador, along the line of the Torngat uplift to Ungava Bay, then cuts across the Ungava Peninsula at approximately the valley of the Leaf River, extends northwestward from Churchill to north of Great Bear Lake, and thence to the coast of Alaska at about Kotzebue Sound.

The tundra, or barren land, has been described as a land of desolation. Woodland Indians fear the treeless country, as the Eskimos fear the forest. Its climate is, indeed, formidable. Even in mid-July, many of the bays of the larger lakes are still icebound, and the soil remains frozen throughout the year. There are no trees, and from an aircraft, the landscape in summer may remind one of parts of the prairie pothole country of the Great Plains. A closer look on the ground, however, discloses a completely different flora.

The northern forest may be classified into three rather broad zones running east and west. In a north to south sequence, the three zones are open boreal, closed boreal, and mixed forest. Adjacent to the tundra on the south is the open boreal, characterized by widely spaced conifer trees and ground covered with picturesque colorful lichens.

It is a transition zone between forest and tundra. Along the northern border of the zone the valleys are wooded and the hills are tundra. Dwarfed black spruce and many of the plants and animals common to both broad zones occur here. Barren ground caribou and ptarmigan migrate across the zone into the woodlands in the fall. They return to the barren grounds in the spring.

The closed forest is a dense association primarily of spruce, fir, and other conifers, and with considerable birch, aspen, and willow interspersed. The mixed forest zone occurs primarily from Minnesota east across the Northern States and southern Canada to Nova Scotia. It is a dense forest composed of a mixture of conifers and broad-leaved soft and hard woods.

Extensive muskegs and bogs are prominent, particularly in the open boreal area. Throughout the lowlands in the closed forest, sphagnum is the dominant ground cover. Lakes, ponds, and streams are abundant in all three zones, although most contain little food to support waterfowl. It is a land of moose and woodland caribou, beautiful rocky lakes, and excellent fishing.

THE BOREAL FOREST or woodland lake country is rich in history. It caught the white man's attention in the early 1600's. A group of Englishmen formed a Company of Adventurers in 1670 to trade into Hudson Bay and exploit the fur resources. It was the beginning of the great fur trading era, which gave much impetus to the exploration of what is now Canada and the United States. Shortly thereafter, Hudson's Bay Company trading posts were established in James Bay. Beaver fur was then in great demand in European markets, and so the woodland lake country, which is the natural habitat for aspen- and willow-loving beaver, was invaded first by fur traders. They established trading posts far inland. Canadian history abounds with records of incredible explorations and journeys by trappers, traders, and voyagers long before the opening of the West was even begun. In 1772, for example, Samuel Hearne walked 1,800 miles from Churchill to Coppermine on the Arctic Sea, visiting Great Slave Lake on the return trip.

THE INTERIOR of the woodland lake country in eastern Canada is a comparatively unproductive land, which consists mainly of bedrock, usually referred to as the Pre-Cambrian Shield. The Pre-Cambrian is the oldest geological formation. During millions of years of glaciation, any topsoil previously present was scraped off and deposited to the south in the form of glacial drift. Lakes and rivers are normally clear and have low dissolved total solids (a rough indication of fertility). They offer some of the finest sports fishing on the continent. This is the land of the loon whose weird call symbolizes the wildness for which this country is noted.

HERE AND THERE in this rocky land are deltas formed by small streams as they empty into lakes, shallow bays caused by endless action of wind and water, and beaver ponds, where aquatic plant and animal life are quite abundant and water levels are fairly constant. At each of them, a pair or two of ducks may set up housekeeping and rear a brood. Each of these "Microhabitats" can produce only a few ducks, but many of them over a wide country make a large total contribution.

West of Hudson Bay, the scaups,

mallard, green-winged teal, and ring-necked duck are the main breeders, in about that order. To the east in the Quebec, Labrador, and Maritime area, the black duck replaces the mallard and is the most abundant puddle duck. Here, also, red-breasted mergansers and goldeneyes are common, and many thousands of eiders nest along tidal shorelines. The densities of breeding ducks inland, as estimated from aerial surveys, may be 1 to 5 to the square mile. Breeding pairs of Canada geese are thinly scattered over the suitable habitats of the forest country on both the east and west side of Hudson Bay.

ALONG the west coast of Hudson and James Bays is the largest bog in the world. It extends about 800 miles from Churchill, Manitoba, to Eastmain, Quebec. It is 200 miles wide in the Albany River drainage. Its general slope is only about 4 feet to the mile, and the portion along the coast is flat as a pancake. Further inland, the northern part of the Pre-Cambrian Shield is just as flat. Only the low hills in which the Sutton River originates and the Sachigo hills, on the border between Ontario and Manitoba, break the dull flatness.

The Great Muskeg, as this swamp is called, is young geologically. After the glaciers retreated, most of the present Hudson and James Bay lowlands lay under the sea for hundreds of years. A mantle of heavy blue marine clay was gradually deposited over the glacial till until about 5 thousand years ago, when a rise in land levels occurred.

The Grumman Goose, a dependable amphibious plane, on a waterfowl survey transect near Yellowknife, Northwest Territories. No roads or fences here to guide the pilot!

Old beach lines indicate that a rapid initial retreat of the seas occurred from the first postglacial coast to within 30 miles of the present Hudson Bay shore. This adjustment in land levels is continuing today. New beaches are forming constantly as the sea retreats.

Generally speaking, the areas within the Shield most attractive to waterfowl are those adjacent to tidal shorelines or those capped with marine or other deposits of more recent formation. In addition to the western shore of Hudson and James Bays mentioned above, other examples are such locations as southern Southampton Island, the Bowman Bay area of Baffin Island, and the flat tundra of the Ungava Peninsula.

Studies of fossil pollens reveal that the marine clay first grew sedge marsh, with some black spruce, tamarack, and jack pine on the better drained sites. When plant debris built up and peat formed, sites suitable for spruce and tamarack increased. Today many shallower sedge marshes and even old lakes have been filled and support a muskeg bog, which cone-bearing trees are taking over.

THE COASTAL lowlands of Hudson and James Bays have a boreal forest fauna. In the Ontario-Manitoba area are woodland caribou, black bears, timber wolves, red foxes, beaver, otter, marten, mink, and fisher. Moose, recent invaders of much of this zone, have become abundant in some places. Wolverines are rare. Red-backed mice are

common. Skunks and woodchucks are rare.

Those parts of the Hudson Bay and James Bay lowlands which were submerged beneath the sea after the glaciers retreated are now major breeding areas for Canada geese. The chief muskeg type for nesting geese contains small, deep ponds with many islands and peninsulas. This pothole-type muskeg generally has clean shorelines, unchoked by sedge or sphagnum. Spruces may grow close to the water's edge, and lichens may cover much of the ground.

Geese also nest on shores of some of the larger lakes and in ponds between old beachlines close to the coast. They do not breed in muskeg dry enough to support trees, however. Neither do they breed in places where ponds have become choked with sphagnum and other vegetation. After nesting, most geese remain in the muskeg until the young can fly, but the ones that breed near medium-sized rivers may come out to graze on the banks. They drift downstream until they reach the coast, where they may remain feeding on the sedge flats until fall.

The highest breeding densities of dabbling ducks in this area of the Shield probably occur in the relatively fertile headwater lakes of the Shagami, Shamattawa, and Sutton Rivers. Waterfowl do nest in muskeg, however, and broods of mallards occasionally are seen in this type of habitat. The presence of American widgeons, ring-necked ducks, and common goldeneyes indicates that they also may breed here. Surf scoters breed in some of the headwater lakes, and it is likely that white-winged and common scoters are also nesters.

Local residents do not take many Canada geese in this area. The total kill in Ontario is between 9 thousand and 10 thousand Canadas a year—about 4 to 5 percent of the total number bagged each year. Most sportsmen who hunt in this general area remain on the coast, where snow geese are their main quarry. Their bag of Canada geese is small—about 400 birds.

The northern woodlands may become a major summer recreational area. Each year growing numbers of people vacation here and enjoy excellent and varied sport fishing. Float-equipped aircraft carry sportsmen to remote areas in a few hours. Accommodations for visitors are good. All this activity does not destroy waterfowl habitat and so probably will have little detrimental effect on waterfowl production. White men have been in this land nearly four centuries and have not spoiled it.

THE TUNDRA, which extends northward from the woodlands, is thought of by most of us as a bleak and lonely land. It has no trees, little fuel for fires, and plants that Nature has dwarfed and disciplined so they can survive the severest conditions. Yet the land has beauty to those whose eyes can see it. Lichens flourish—orange, red, brown. Because the growing season is short, most plants blossom at about the same time and make an endless carpet of multicolored brilliance. To the Eskimo, to whom this land really belongs, this is the most beautiful place on earth. If he should leave it, his only wish is to return. Only the strong can exist in the barrens; maybe that is why the Eskimo is happy with his lot and proud that he can survive here. All others who travel in this land are wise to take all precautions, for even airplanes, modern weather forecasting, and the fancy "survival" gadgets may not be enough.

Much of the tundra is wet and swampy. Not because of rainfall, which varies from about 4 to 10 inches, but because of permafrost. The soil, except a few inches of topsoil that thaws during the short summer, remains permanently frozen. The resulting impermeability of the soil, poor drainage, and low evaporation rate make a soggy surface.

The tundra was the last area to be released from continental glaciation. Its surface geology, therefore, is primitive and interesting. Great eskers, formed by glacial rivers that deposited soil on the ice, are common. They often pass through large lakes or parallel a river in the present drainage system for miles. Rivers usually are fast and straight and have few large inland deltas, as in the woodlands. Compared to the prairies, which the tundra superficially resembles, most of the land is not highly productive. The exceptions, as mentioned previously, are the coastal portions which until recently remained beneath the sea and received a deposit of silt.

THE BRIEF summer of the barrens demands that living things waste no time if they are to survive and perpetuate their kind. But the long arctic days and their many hours of sunlight compensate somewhat for the shortness of the season. All biological processes are incredibly dynamic; here, the rapidity of change in natural events is astounding. When breeding waterfowl arrive here in June, they settle down at once to the business at hand. Nesting and brooding cannot be delayed if the young are to be on the wing before freeze up.

THE INTERIOR TUNDRA contributes little to the production of ducks. Old squaw and eiders occur in low densities, but are mostly in the coastal areas. Geese breed over the entire area in scattered pairs or groups. The Canada goose is the main breeder and occasionally one sees white-fronted geese and snow geese of both white and blue phases. Great rivers, such as the Thelon, Back, Perry, Payne, and Ellice, influence the behavior of brooding geese. Soon after hatching, the geese begin moving down tributaries into major drainage basins; by late July, fairly large numbers of geese, young and old, concentrate along major streams. Biologists who band waterfowl in the Far North make use of this trait.

TUNDRA along the coastline and the coastal plain, both on the mainland and on the Arctic Islands, provides the most attractive waterfowl habitat in the tundra zone. High densities of breeding waterfowl exist there, especially colonial nesters such as the snow goose. Not only do all species of geese nest in one or another of the many coast-al tundra situations, but, collectively, these areas produce most of the North American geese. Coastal tundras in Alaska and in the western Arctic produce all of the emperor geese, cackling geese, black brant, and most of the white fronts. Coastal areas in the Northwest Territories and in the Arctic Islands produce the bulk of the American brant, the smaller races of the Canadas, and the blue and snow geese. Even among the large Canadas a significant portion of the population is produced in coastal tundras of the Ungava Peninsula in northern Quebec.

Blue and snow geese were long regarded as separate species. They are now considered as color phases of the same species. The blue phase has its center of abundance in the Foxe Basin region of Baffin Island. The two phases intergrade in the colonies on the Boas River delta on Southampton Island, on Cape Henrietta Maria, and at Eskimo Point. Further west the white phase birds dominate in the important breeding colonies located along the Perry River, on Victoria and Banks Islands, and in the Wrangel Island colony in eastern Siberia.

During the early 1950's the colonies on Boas River, Cape Henrietta Maria, and Eskimo Point were composed mostly of white birds. Since that time the number of blue phase birds has increased markedly in these colonies and the number of white birds has decreased. We often have seen a white and a blue phase goose guarding the same nest and tending the same brood.

The breeding ground of the Ross'

A Labrador Retriever helps Dick Vaught of the Missouri Conservation Commission capture flightless Canada geese on the coast of Hudson Bay. Birds so captured are banded and released.

goose, once a mystery, is a rather confined inland area just west of Perry River. In the summer of 1962, we observed from an airplane many groups of these rather scarce, little geese. We readily told them from snow geese because of the yellowish cast of the white plumage.

The Arctic Coast and associated islands are also breeding grounds for the whistling swan. This great bird nests from Alaska to Baffinland and often goes far inland.

COASTAL TUNDRA on the southern shore of Hudson Bay is confined to two areas of about 1,500 square miles each on Cape Henrietta Maria and on Cape Churchill. Between them is a broken, narrow strip, less than a few miles wide, along the coast. On the west shore of James

Bay, tundra does not extend south of Ekwan Point. Here the coastal tundra consists mostly of beach lines, which support a ground cover dominated by lichens and low willows. Long, narrow ponds and sedge marshes are formed between the old beaches. Only on Cape Churchill and Cape Henrietta Maria do the sedge marshes give way to a drier grass tundra, studded with willow-rimmed lakes.

Land mammals are not abundant. Arctic foxes are few in number and absent in some years. There are no lemmings or arctic hares. Barren-ground caribou still visit the Cape Churchill area in numbers but have not penetrated as far as Cape Henrietta Maria since the late 1800's. Woodland caribou use the coastal tundras seasonally.

A few snow geese may have nested in this coastal tundra for many years, but not until 1947 was a colony established near Cape Henrietta Maria. These geese now breed in three main concentrations in the braided mouths of three rivers along a 30-mile strip of coast. More than 17 thousand breeding adult, sub-adult, and young snow geese were in this colony in 1957. About a third were of the white color phase; the rest were blue.

Snow geese occasionally may breed elsewhere on the southern Hudson Bay coast. Our air surveys disclosed two broods on Cape Churchill in 1962 and a number of broods on Akimiski Island in James Bay in 1959 and 1960. Nonbreeding snow geese may moult at localities other than the Cape Henrietta Maria area, but the numbers are never large.

Many pintails and black ducks summer on these coasts. Most of them appear to be males, which probably have abandoned their mates busy with incubating and brood duties at scattered inland points. Some pintails breed in the coastal ponds, however, and may achieve high densities on Cape Churchill and Cape Henrietta Maria.

Greater scaup and oldsquaws nest along the entire coast on ponds between the beach ridges. Their total number is not large. A few other species can be considered rare or occasional breeders. Whistling swans nested on Cape Churchill in 1962. A few swans occasionally remain for the summer without nesting at other points. At a few localities, shoveler, king eider, and the rare Hudson Bay race of the common eider can be found breeding.

THE AREA between Fort Severn and Churchill lies within the migration route of populations of small Canada geese, which breed in the Arctic. During migration, they are eagerly hunted by coastal Indians, because they are generally fatter and better tasting than snow geese. Several thousand fall to native guns each year. When geese are available, the coastal Indians pay little attention to ducks, but nevertheless, they take 7 thousand to 10 thousand a year.

Snow geese are an important food for the coastal Indians. They eat them fresh, dried, and smoked, consuming not only the meat but also sometimes the cleaned intestines. They save the feathers for stuffing bedrolls and the fat for making bannock. In the old days, even the bones were used; one may still see spoons made from the sternum. Between 30 thousand and 38 thousand snow geese are taken each year by the coastal Indians of Ontario and Manitoba. This constituted about 6 to 8 percent of the total population in the Mississippi Flyway in 1962.

That the tundra is vital to the continental goose population was proved when drought on the prairies in 1959–1962 severely depressed the duck populations, goose populations held up well. Duck populations in 1962 were the lowest in 15 years, and bag limits were the lowest in the history of waterfowling, but it was unnecessary to reduce bag limits on geese. An experimental hunting season on whistling swan was also permitted in the fall of 1962—an indication of the comparative stability of the far northern waterfowl breeding grounds.

When we sum up and assess the place of the Canadian North in the future of waterfowl management, we have to consider several points. Densities of waterfowl breeding populations are low and except for colonial nesters are never as spectacular as on the prairies, but the total contribution to the fall flight is sizable. The habitat is more stable than farther south. Weather and predators probably are the greatest variables.

Drought and drainage are seldom problems in the North. The North, therefore, will continue to be a dependable reservoir for breeding waterfowl and thus be a factor in the preservation of waterfowl even if habitats elsewhere are destroyed. Furthermore, it is unlikely that mining, fishing, and lumbering will soon adversely influence the usefulness of this area to breeding waterfowl except along major rivers where the potential exists for hydro-electric development. On the other hand, the factors that reduce detrimental effects will also make it hard to change and improve habitats in programs of waterfowl management.

We believe, though, that several actions are feasible to improve waterfowl management. We should undertake further exploration, especially in the Arctic Islands, to complete our knowledge of all breeding populations of geese. Well-designed studies of selected areas and in different types of habitat are needed to get information on the basic biology of waterfowl production. Research like this will give us information on the annual reproduction rates of northern nesting waterfowl and the environmental factors that limit reproduction. Banding should be increased so as to evaluate the contribution of northern waterfowl habitat to various hunting areas. Weather is an important factor controlling breeding success in the Far North and more detailed weather data are required to help us predict the likelihood of good or bad breeding seasons.

Knowledge is the basis of intelligent management. We must have it to insure sustained maximum utilization of the waterfowl resource by the people of our continent.—
EDWARD G. WELLEIN and
HARRY GORDON LUMSDEN.

PINTAILS

More Duck Factories

REDHEAD AND BROOD

Western Production Areas

THE WESTERN SLOPE of our continent is a land of big sky, sagebrush, mountains, fertile valleys, rolling croplands, deserts, and in most parts (except a section of the Pacific Northwest) a land of less than 20 inches of precipitation a year. Moisture here is the essence of life—in cities, on farms, in the drylands, and over the western marshes. It is the home—if there is water—of many waterfowl.

Here you can see examples of all that people have done to land and water in 100 years. The American Indians lived off the land, but their activities (except their use of fire) made little change in the natural habitat used by waterfowl and other wildlife. Then came white explorers, fur traders, and gold seekers to open new vistas to exploitation and development. Grazing, agriculture, and industry followed, and with them the intensive use of lowlands, irrigation, diversion of water, and drainage of wetlands for crops. The better watered, more level, and productive areas were developed earliest; later, the less fertile places as pressures of population and demands of people increased.

People live in close association with water. So do ducks. The fortunes of waterfowl are linked closely with the needs and deeds of men. Where man monopolizes water, little is left for waterfowl. Where man diverts or stores water, it becomes a potential benefit to

79

waterfowl. Special requirements and conditions must be met before maximum use by ducks can occur, but such situations have occurred or have been purposefully developed.

We can group the habitats of waterfowl in several ways. Because our main interest is in the production areas of the West, we classify them in two broad types, which we designate here as unmanaged and managed.

Managed areas for waterfowl production are mostly owned or controlled by State or Federal wildlife conservation agencies. On them, a primary objective of management is to maintain or improve wetland habitat for the production of waterfowl.

Few of the unmanaged areas retain any semblance of natural, undisturbed conditions. Most have felt the influence of human activity either in the form of grazing by cattle or modification of the water supply.

The unmanaged ones in the Pacific Flyway can be put in two subtypes—modified natural areas and man-created areas, usually associated with irrigation projects. Natural areas modified by man's activities include a wide range of wetland habitat. Let us look at some to see what they are like, what they once were, and what they may become in future years.

THE BEST EXAMPLES of larger production sections that man has modified only slightly are in central and eastern British Columbia. The Cariboo parklands and the Chilcotin in the intermountain region are roll-ing country, with an interspersion of grassland, Douglas-fir, and aspen. It is the most densely populated waterfowl producing area of the Province. The many shallow lakes and smaller bodies of water are essentially alkaline and produce an abundance of aquatic plants attractive to ducks. Modification, if any, has been by grazing. Density of breeding ducks is 10 to 20 a square mile.

Another in British Columbia is the Rocky Mountain Trench. This valley, bounded on east and west by lofty granite mountains, is spectacularly scenic. Here the mighty Columbia and Kootenay Rivers originate. Densities of breeding ducks approximate 20 a square mile. Canada geese, whistling swans, deer, moose, and elk help create a wildlife paradise.

Nearby forests make the water areas particularly attractive to the smaller diving ducks. Barrow's goldeneye, lesser scaup, and bufflehead are among the primary breeders. Most of the common dabbling species also occur.

WARNER VALLEY, in southeastern Oregon, is another example of an undisturbed production area. Its southern end has been developed toward a livestock economy of meadow hay and small grain. The northern end has extensive sage- or greasewood-covered sandhills, interspersed with alkali lakes. In wet years, when high water floods the lakes and sandy knolls, the valley is commonly used by breeding ducks, principally mallards, gadwalls, cinnamon teal, and pintails. We have

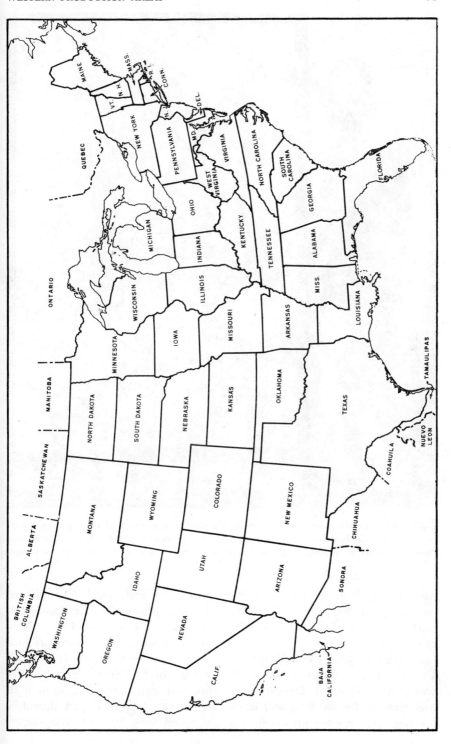

Ducks raised on the Bear River National Wildlife Refuge, Utah, disperse widely.   Pins marking the northernmost and southernmost recovery records are pointed out by Refuge Manager Vanez T. Wilson.   Each pin represents recovery of a duck banded at the refuge.

no good records of duck nesting densities, but they seem to be comparable to some of our best managed marsh habitat.

In Washington is the well-watered Puget Sound country, which once was heavily forested. Development and clearing for dairying and truck farming have opened up much of it and enhanced original conditions for the production of waterfowl. Sloughs, ditches, shallow lakes, beaver ponds, and streams produce good numbers of mallards and wood ducks. Small numbers of blue-winged teal, cinnamon teal, American widgeon, and shovelers also nest here. Western Washington produces about 10 percent of the State's total. We estimate that 60 thousand ducks comprise the fall flight from this section.

The Willamette Valley in Oregon in some ways is like the Puget Sound country. Land clearing for agriculture has created fair nesting habitat for mallards and wood ducks along streams and river channels.

The Sacramento-San Joaquin Valley in California was an important production and wintering area for ducks. Intensive agricultural development and water control reduced the waterfowl production capabilities to a fraction of the former value. A survey in 1906 showed over 3 million acres of wetlands. Today less than 15 percent of these areas are so classified.

This Central Valley once provided nesting sites for gadwalls, pintails, mallards, shovelers, cinnamon teal, redheads, and ruddy ducks. Gradually, the changes in habitat no longer suited the requirements of several of these species. Mallards now are dominant. Gadwalls and cinnamon teal run poor seconds. The other species are gone or are extremely uncommon as nesting birds.

Irrigated ricefields and summer-dry marsh now form the primary breeding habitat aside from permanent watercourses. Summer surveys covering about 3 thousand square miles of the remaining habitat show the density of breeding ducks to be about 20 to the square mile. Estimated production is about 60 thousand young birds each year.

Gray's Lake in southeastern Idaho is a hardstem bulrush marsh of 22 thousand acres. It was once an open marsh, but water levels have been lowered artificially so that emergent vegetation has become denser. Nesting success was high (70 percent) in the fifties, and nest densities were about 40 per acre on some edge segments. Nesting species include mallards, pintails, redheads, cinnamon and green-winged teal, canvasbacks, gadwalls, lesser scaup, and ruddy ducks. The lake could be made vastly better for waterfowl by opening dense bulrush stands to give better balance between emergent vegetation and open water.

The Humboldt River in Nevada rises in the eastern mountain ranges, traverses an otherwise arid country, and ends in the Carson Sink. This low-gradient stream has many oxbows bordered by willows or wetland meadows. Most of the water is intensively utilized for livestock and farming, but nesting ducks, principally mallards, gadwalls, and cinnamon teal, occur in densities of about 10 to the square mile.

The Flathead and nearby mountain valleys in Montana, have uneven valley floors which were caused by residual glacial deposits. They have many potholes which are well supplied with aquatic foods and are partly surrounded by fields of cereal grains. Densities of breeding ducks are about 50 a square mile. Mallards, shovelers, and blue-winged teal are the chief nesting species. Areas like these are not easily drained and so have a fair degree of stability.

These unmanaged duck-producing

84   WATERFOWL TOMORROW

habitats exemplify a wide variation in nesting density and total area. We also could cite streams, lakes, isolated ponds, and other wetland habitat, all of which produce waterfowl in varying numbers. Their future depends on an assured supply of water. History and current trends dictate that the use of water for purposes other than the production of waterfowl will increase. Ducks will have less water.

A NEW TYPE of waterfowl habitat has become more and more important in the West—created upon land usually without surface water. Irrigation projects and stock ponds are examples. We mention a few of the best.

The Columbia Basin Irrigation Project in east-central Washington was made possible by the construction of Grand Coulee Dam. By 1960, when the project was half completed, about 500 thousand acres of what was once sagebrush and grassland were under intensive diversified agriculture. In addition to many miles of canals and drainage ditches, large tracts of rough, sandy wasteland have become flooded either inadvertently by return flows or as part of a water distribution system. The results were excellent places for waterfowl production and they are used by increasing numbers of mallards, blue-wings, and cinnamon teal.

The nearby Yakima Valley has had a longer development history. The flat or gently rolling bottom land is a checkerboard of irrigation canals and about 250 miles of drainage ditches. Populations of breeding ducks average 15 to 30 and 5 to 10

broods a square mile. Some of the drainage canals in good years harbor 200 broods per lineal mile. There are many similar but smaller irrigation projects in the West. Where arid land is being supplied with water in this way, the habitat so created usually is on the credit side of the ledger.

Many ranchers have built stock watering ponds in the arid West in recent years. The practice, which permits livestock to utilize open range better, can be useful to waterfowl. Many watering holes and ponds dry up in late summer or are used so heavily by cattle that their value to ducks drops, but the ones that persist through the brooding season and have adequate marginal cover may be beneficial to waterfowl. All in all, an expansion of stock ponds offers excellent possibilities of creating and maintaining additional habitat.

MANAGED MARSH AREAS of the West, according to a survey in 1962, produce an estimated 300 thousand ducklings a year. Acre for acre managed marshes, largely State or Federally controlled, rank among the best waterfowl-producing lands of the continent. The most important of them deserve special mention. We should keep in mind that some of the best habitat on the Canadian prairies may produce 30 to 50 broods to the square mile.

Near the head of the list are the marshes adjacent to the Great Salt Lake in Utah; they are premium-grade waterfowl producers. Terminal water from the Bear and Weber Rivers and water from smaller streams is impounded or spread over a onetime lakebed. The marsh created here is highly favored with nesting waterfowl during the spring and summer.

Impoundments and waterspreading devices have created almost 60 thousand acres of high-quality production habitat. One to three ducklings are produced per acre—a total of about 100 thousand young birds. On select areas this production amounts to more than a thousand ducklings or about 200 to 250 broods per square mile. Within these managed areas nest densities run as high as 60 to 80 nests per acre. The leading species produced are gadwalls, cinnamon teal, redheads, and mallards.

Assured water supply throughout the growing season is the key to their present management and further development. Diversion of water into upstream reservoirs for irrigation and hydroelectric plants has proceeded to a point where continued existence of this wetland in Utah is becoming critical. The development of additional sections could more than double the waterfowl habitat, but an adequate water supply is lacking for this purpose.

THE KLAMATH BASIN, along the Oregon-California border, is another excellent example of a managed waterfowl production area in the West. Once Tule and Lower

A good water year at Malheur National Wildlife Refuge, Oregon, provides favorable plant and water conditions for waterfowl; the usual result—a bumper crop of waterfowl.

Klamath Lakes were expansive marshes and overflow lands of the Lost and Klamath River drainages. They produced large numbers of waterfowl. How many, no one really knows.

In the early 1900's, Oregon and California ceded interest in these lands to the Federal Government. They were to be reclaimed for agricultural purposes. Much of this has been accomplished and the land is well developed for farming. Waterfowl habitat developments have been incorporated into the total project, and today more than 25 thousand acres of high-quality duck production habitat exists on Tule Lake and Lower Klamath National Wildlife Refuges. They produce about 50 thousand ducklings, mainly gadwalls, redheads, and mallards. Density of breeding ducks and production is closely comparable to the Utah areas. The future of the Tule-Klamath area depends on satisfactory allocations of land and water for waterfowl.

Oregon has two fine areas that are managed largely for waterfowl production. The larger is Malheur National Wildlife Refuge. The Federal Government owns it. Summer Lake, State owned, is smaller but perhaps is more productive on a per acre basis. Both Malheur and Summer Lake, in the southeastern part of Oregon, are closed basins with no outlets. Such shallow alkaline lakes supplied with fresh water from tributary streams become highly productive for waterfowl. Ducklings on these areas number 300 to 700 a square mile. In years with ample water Malheur may produce as many as 30 thousand ducklings

and Summer Lake 10 thousand. The primary nesting species are gadwall, mallards, cinnamon teal, and redheads.

Like the borders of Great Salt Lake, the productivity of most Oregon marshes depends on yearly precipitation. Malheur Refuge particularly has had wide fluctuations in water levels in wet and dry years.

STILLWATER National Wildlife Refuge and associated Wildlife Management Area in Nevada are under State and Federal management in conjunction with the Truckee-Carson Irrigation District. These areas, formerly a part of the lower Carson River and Carson Sink, depend on return-flow irrigation water. As in Utah and Oregon, the water is spread over soils of alkaline nature through a series of distribution channels and dikes. The result is a marsh habitat that produces about one duck per acre, a total of 20 thousand ducklings annually. Inadequate water supplies in drought years may lower total waterfowl production markedly. The chief nesting species are mallards, redheads, and cinnamon teal. Other puddle ducks and diving ducks occur in smaller numbers.

These five areas—Malheur, Tule-Klamath, Summer Lake, Stillwater, and the Great Salt Lake units— produce more than 200 thousand young ducks annually—more than two-thirds of the production from all western marshes managed by State and Federal conservation agencies.

THE TOTAL PRODUCTION of all habitat in the Western States has not been measured accurately, but a reasonable estimate would place the yearly yield at about a million ducks. That number plus the parent birds may comprise about 5 percent of the total fall flight of ducks to the Pacific Flyway.

Nearly all ducks from the Western wetlands remain within the Pacific Flyway. Recoveries of bands from locally reared birds indicate that the bulk of the harvest occurs on these same natal marsh areas. In most instances, except for divers, ducks produced in any particular State will, to a large degree, be harvested in that State.

As to the Future: Perhaps no other section has had such great changes in the use of land and water in so short a time. Growth and development are far from complete. As our population increases, the demand for products of the soil will keep pace, and a more intensive use of land and water will be necessary. We doubt whether technological progress will come quickly enough to forestall increasing losses of wetland habitat on private lands. We

Bear River National Wildlife Refuge, near Brigham City, Utah, is an outstanding area for migratory waterfowl.

look forward to an expansion of irrigation projects in the West. Many of them, with adequate planning, can be developed to include features that will enhance the production of waterfowl. For some years, the projects may balance losses that occur elsewhere, but ultimately we foresee a net loss.

The acquisition and development of private land for waterfowl production offer possibilities. Good wetlands can continue to be placed in public trust and improved by special management techniques. A greater use of subsurface water can be expanded in some localities to improve habitat, although that is expensive and very likely may some day exhaust or seriously deplete the supply of ground water.

The situation is not particularly promising. If we are to retain the waterfowl production we now have in the West, it is essential that large marshes be maintained. Efforts also must be made to encourage private landowners to maintain wetland habitat. A continuation of the present trend will mean that breeding habitat in the Western Region some day will consist of widely scattered acreages controlled by Federal and State agencies, and only the mallards will remain to seek out the springs, the ditches, and artificially developed water areas as places to nest and rear their young.—G. HORTIN JENSEN and JOHN E. CHATTIN.

Conservation mistaught is worse than conservation untaught.
—RUDOLF BENNITT.

BLACK DUCKS

Eastern Production Areas

COME SPRING, it's up from the wintering grounds and off to the breeding grounds—a tough ordeal for most waterfowl. Many, wintering in the Deep South, have a thousand miles to go. But it is a short hop compared with the flight of others heading for arctic tundra; they may traverse half the continent—5 thousand miles—before settling down to the task at hand. But whatever the origin, whatever the destination, they all reach for waters where they first learned to fly. There, with luck, a new generation will mature and fulfill the same destiny.

Some birds are spared, or denied, this great adventure. Their wintering and nesting ranges nearly coincide, and the migratory urge is satisfied with local excursions. These birds are few, less than 5 percent of the ones considered here, and are largely restricted to coastal marshes.

EASTERN PRODUCTION AREAS include States in the upper halves of the Atlantic Flyway (Maryland and West Virginia and north) and the Mississippi Flyway (Missouri and Tennessee and north) except Minnesota and northern Wisconsin, Michigan, New York and Maine. Here we have 9 million acres of wetlands—one-eighth of those in the Nation—but only 10 percent provide good breeding habitat. About 85 percent of the total and nearly three-fourths of the good nesting areas are in the Mississippi Flyway. More than half of these wetland acres are

89

swamp or bog. Only stream channels or pockets of water make them usable by breeding ducks. Other wetlands of little value for breeding birds include seasonally flooded flats, marshes without standing water, and shallow water devoid of emergent plants.

THIS IS THE LAND of wood ducks, mallards, black ducks, and blue-winged teal, but mostly woodies. They outnumber all other species two to one. Moreover, they occur almost everywhere, in small creeks and large rivers, farm ponds and lakes, marshes, and swamps. They are indigenous to wooded bottomlands and impenetrable swamps, yet they will nest in towns. Most wood ducks in North America breed in the eastern third of the continent. Banding and kill data indicate a total of 400 thousand pairs in 1962, and, of that number, we estimate nearly half breed in the area with which this chapter is concerned. Human beings and wood ducks reach their peak densities in the deciduous forest region. Consequently, woodie habitat has suffered seriously from the accompaniments of civilization. Drainage, lumbering, and urbanization have eliminated more than one-half of its breeding habitat.

COASTAL MARSHES support thousands of ducks in winter, but this habitat often carries low nesting populations. Marine and brackish habitat, backed by fresh-water marshes, is black duck domain. Wood ducks find few good niches in the coastal belt. In Delaware and

New Jersey one wood duck brood may be seen to five black duck broods. From coastal Maine to Long Island, wood duck broods are rare.

Black ducks nest in meadows or woods, a mile from water or directly over it, on muskrat houses, old stumps, abandoned hawk nests, or choice spots under beach plum. Offshore duck blinds provide excellent sites. The adaptable black is the dominant breeding species of the North Atlantic coastal belt.

Other species are present along coastal marshes. Mute swans are naturalized from New Jersey to Massachusetts, and Long Island winter populations exceed 500 birds. Canada goose colonies are established on some inland waters. Mallards, perhaps of domestic ancestry, occur throughout the coastal belt. Blue-winged teal nest regularly but sparsely, and there are breeding records for red-breasted mergansers and shovelers. Gadwall breeding units occur in Somerset County in Maryland, Bombay Hook in Delaware, Egg Island in New Jersey, and Jones Beach Pond on Long Island, where 19 broods were observed in one season. On Fire Island barrier beach on Long Island, where beachgrass and beach plum blend, 13 black duck nests were located in 1935. These were nests of 25 pairs established around 200 acres of fresh and salt marsh. Since that time, the area has been altered, and breeding populations have declined. But it is clear that a potential exists.

Human activities have tremendous impact on coastal wetlands. Ditching for mosquito control—for drainage or tidal flushing—has damaged many marshes. Dredging for boat channels and filling for housing developments have destroyed others. And hardly a coastal marsh exists that is not traversed regularly by people from spring to fall. Pity the duck that seeks a secluded corner for rearing a family.

Coastal fresh and saline areas approach a million acres, 1 percent of the Nation's wetlands. All Atlantic Coast States have some of this habitat, but New Jersey, Maryland, and Delaware are most richly endowed. Salt meadows, salt marshes, and coastal fresh marshes are the best for breeding waterfowl. Some coastal areas support 10 pairs per 100 acres, but fewer than 100 thousand acres approach this level of productivity. Densities may be less than one pair per 100 acres and average three to five. We estimate annual production at 10 thousand to 20 thousand young.

INTERIOR NEW ENGLAND contains 250 thousand acres of wetlands, mainly swamps and bogs. There are few marshes and natural ponds. But men and beaver create areas that produce waterfowl even though few large units exist where breeding birds may concentrate. In New England, tussock sedge is more frequent than bulrushes and cattails. Pond borders are oftener wooded than open.

Wood ducks and black ducks in about equal numbers are the chief species in this country. Mallards are scarce but increasing. Blue-winged teal nest here but contribute little to production. Green-winged teal occur rarely. Excellent production

units exist on the Lake Champlain marshes. Massachusetts has made some swamps into top producers through the use of wood duck boxes. Other units may not average a pair of ducks on 100 acres, although some poor habitat may be enhanced by the creation of small openings. Open water or a stream channel will encourage both black and wood ducks to use wooded swamp. We estimate this region produces 15 thousand to 25 thousand ducks annually.

THE ALLEGHENY PLATEAU includes the Piedmont and unglaciated Allegheny areas of West Virginia, western Maryland and Pennsylvania, and New York's southern tier, Catskill, and Mohawk sections. Water areas are few and consist mainly of scattered small marshes, wooded swamps, beaver ponds, and old millponds. Big water areas, reservoirs, and flood-control dams attract few nesting ducks. Waterfowl are correspondingly scarce. Wood duck and black duck are the commonest species, and there is limited nesting by blue-winged teal, mallards, and hooded mergansers. Few water units in this area are highly productive. Two pairs of breeders per 100 acres is our estimate for the 100 thousand acres of wetlands. If so, the Allegheny Plateau produces 5 thousand to 10 thousand ducks a year.

THE ERIE-ONTARIO LOWLAND includes the level part of western New York and northwestern Pennsylvania. Glaciation has left many water areas, some of the best known being the Finger Lakes. These are

Look out below! Young wood duck dives to its future as it leaves the security of the nest box.

Apartment living for mallards. Two-compartment nesting box used by mallards at Blackwater National Wildlife Refuge, Maryland.

deep lakes, important as migration and wintering areas but of little value for nesting. Along the old Erie Canal from Syracuse to Buffalo, rich farmland stretches from the Finger Lakes north to the former shoreline of Lake Ontario. Along sluggish streams, and squeezed between drumlins, are marshes, swamps, and bogs. The most important of these are the Montezuma Swamp-Seneca River complex and the Oak Orchard-Tonawanda Creeks swamps, both of which have State and Federal refuges. Many acres were drained for mucklands, but what remains is some of the most productive waterfowl habitat in the East.

New York's Lake Erie shoreline, pressed by the Allegheny Plateau, has no big marshes. Nearby Chautauqua Lake is not a breeding area, but Pennsylvania's arm to Lake Erie is more level; here Pymatuning and Conneaut marshes provide good breeding habitat. Mallards, wood ducks, black ducks, and blue-winged teal are the main species. Shovelers, hooded mergansers, green-winged teal, and gadwalls occur in lesser numbers. Canada geese and redheads have been introduced as nesting populations. The section includes 30 thousand acres of breeding habitat; breeding pair densities are 25 to 50 per square mile. Annual production is estimated at 3 thousand to 10 thousand young.

St. lawrence lowlands differ from Canadian waters across the river and Adirondack ponds to the southeast. Favored with limestone outcrops and many water pockets, the area includes 22 thousand acres of high-value wetlands, including small marshes, potholes, beaver ponds, and large water areas and productive streams. New York State has two managed areas here—Wilson Hill and Perch River—and more wetlands are being purchased. Black and wood ducks make up two-thirds of the production. Blue-winged teal, ring-necked ducks, and three species of mergansers also nest. Breeding pairs reach 15 to 30 per square mile of marsh. We estimate that a thousand pairs produce 3 thousand young annually.

THE MISSISSIPPI RIVER with its tributaries is breeding range for wood ducks. Wetland surveys show from 1,250,000 to 1,750,000 acres of overflow bottomland hardwoods, swamps, streams, ponds, and small lakes—ideal nesting, feeding, and rearing areas for wood ducks. Thousands of miles of uninventoried small streams add niches suitable for breeding woodies. Density of breeding birds is low along most small streams, but the extent of this habitat allows for many broods.

The famous delta country is the southern edge of this region. Here, a touch of Deep South prevails with cypress, cotton, and cottonmouths. Bottomland hardwoods provide 400 thousand acres of wood duck habitat. Noteworthy areas are the Hatchie and Obion River swamps and Reelfoot Lake in Tennessee, the restored Mingo Swamp and newly-created Duck Creek in Missouri, and Horseshoe Lake in Illinois. Flanking the Mississippi River from Memphis to Cairo are numerous timber-bordered sloughs and ponds. Streams

in Tennessee and Kentucky show 0.3 wood duck broods per mile, which is about the same as for Midwest waterways. It appears low for the quality of habitat, but nest predation may be a critical factor. Yearly production is estimated at 15 thousand to 20 thousand wood ducks.

The Wabash Lowlands of Illinois and Indiana lie northeast of the Delta Country. Bottomland hardwood flanks parts of the Wabash River and its tributaries and provides 150 thousand acres of breeding habitat, mainly oxbows and sloughs. Stream surveys show 0.7 wood duck broods per mile—twice that of the delta area. The estimated annual production is 10 thousand to 15 thousand.

Three-fourths of Ohio drains into the Mississippi Basin by way of the Ohio River. Most notable streams for wood ducks are the Miami, Olentangy, and Scioto. Natural and artificial impoundments in Ohio provide 120 thousand wetland acres. Bottomland woods, which are flooded in some years, add 25 thousand acres of value to wood ducks. Bottomlands are less extensive than in the Wabash Lowlands, and the streams drop more rapidly and have higher banks. Lower breeding densities result, and 0.3 to 0.4 wood duck broods are produced per mile of stream. Annual production is estimated at 8 thousand to 12 thousand young.

The Illinois River System provides the best wood duck habitat we know of. There are 75 thousand acres of bottomland lakes flanking the river channel. Bordered by buttonbush and black willow, and containing beds of marsh smartweed, lotus, and river bulrush, these bottoms constitute ideal wood duck environment. Oak trees in upland woodlots, some a mile from water, provide quality nesting sites, and nesting houses made proof against most predators augment the production, which probably totals 7 thousand to 10 thousand annually.

The Upper Mississippi from Cairo to St. Louis provides meager habitat for wood ducks. Drainage has eliminated most lateral water areas, and a broad channel with sand bars makes the main stem unattractive. From Alton, Ill., to Lake Pepin, Minn., the river changes character and has hundreds of wooded islands, many containing ponds and sloughs.

From Lake Pepin to Dubuque, Iowa, broadleaf arrowhead, bulrushes, big burreed, and lotus occur along the margins of navigation pools. Marshes and wooded sloughs, ponds, and chutes provide excellent wood duck habitat. Nesting sites abound on the wooded islands. No other unit produces as many wood ducks as the upper Mississippi River with its 300 thousand acres of excellent habitat. A few other ducks nest here, such as mallards, blue-winged teal, and black ducks, but they make up only 5 percent of the yearly production of 20 thousand to 30 thousand.

Elsewhere in the Mississippi Basin, significant breeding habitat occurs on the Des Moines, Iowa, Cedar, and Wapsipinicon Rivers in Iowa, the Rock River in Illinois, and the Wisconsin, Black, and Chippewa Rivers in Wisconsin. The lower Chariton River in central Missouri and the Kaskaskia River in southwestern Illinois also are important streams. Combined, these streams contain 200 thousand acres of wood duck habitat; and 10 thousand to 15 thousand young are produced.

THE INTERLAKE AREA embraces most of Wisconsin, northeastern Illinois, southern Michigan, and northern Indiana. Rounded hills, smooth to rolling plains, lakes, swamps, and marshes are remainders of the Wisconsin period of glaciation. Extinct glacial lakes, moraines, outwash and till plains, drumlins, and eskers mark the advances and retreats of the great ice sheet.

Most duck production accrues from potholes and from small, scattered marshes. In Wisconsin a few large marshes remain in basins of extinct glacial lakes. All this adds up to 400 thousand wetland acres suitable for breeding waterfowl. Another 1.2 million acres are little used; open-water lakes and isolated wet meadows have little value for breeding ducks.

Drainage has eliminated innumerable wetlands and threatens many more that overlie good soils. The greatest single blow to production in this area occurred when the Kankakee Marsh of 400 thousand acres in northern Indiana was drained late in the 19th century. Large marshes in central and northwestern Wisconsin were also drained in this period, although the Wisconsin Conservation Department and the Fish and Wildlife Service have restored parts of them.

The most extensive duck habitat

in this area today is along the Michigan-Indiana line. Despite drainage, potholes and small marshes still abound, aggregating 90 thousand acres. Shallow, open-water lakes, bordered by strips of cattails, bulrushes, and arrowheads, cover 108 thousand acres. Sedge and grass meadows cover 430 thousand acres.

Michigan biologists report 10 pairs of breeding ducks and nearly 0.5 broods per lineal mile of marsh. About equal numbers of mallards, black ducks, and blue-winged teal compose three-fourths of the breeding ducks in southern Michigan. Wood ducks are next in abundance. Their breeding density is about 0.5 pairs per lineal mile. Ring-necked

ducks, mergansers, pintails, and goldeneyes also are present as breeding birds.

Southeast Wisconsin and northeast Illinois contain 45 thousand acres of potholes and small marshes and 75 thousand acres of sedge and grass meadows. Horicon Marsh—31 thousand acres of cattails, river bulrush, big burreed, and open water— is the largest and most productive marsh in the region. Surveys during 1958 to 1962 suggest a production of 1,500 to 12,000 ducks. One blue-winged teal nest to 2 acres and one mallard nest to 4 acres were found in hayfields around Horicon. Brood surveys showed that blue-winged teal made up one-half of the crop and mallards one-third.

The male wood duck is one of the most beautiful of our North American waterfowl. Once seriously reduced in numbers, it is now a common breeding duck.

Redhead broods formed 7 percent of the total; ruddy ducks, 3 percent; and black ducks, 2.5 percent.

In Wisconsin, the peat-newton soil type provides 155 acres of wetlands per square mile, but these are shrub-swamps of limited value for ducks. Necedah National Wildlife Refuge and Meadow Valley State Conservation Area represent partial restoration of wetlands drained some years ago. Mallards are the abundant breeding duck, followed by wood ducks, blue-winged teal, and ring-necked ducks.

The restored Crex Meadow, 8,500 acres in northwestern Wisconsin, is part of the once extensive marshes that were present. Other remnants bring the total acreage of shallow and deep marsh to 20 thousand and wet meadows to 25 thousand. Mallards, ring-necked ducks, and blue-winged teal are the most common breeders.

There are more than 5 thousand active beaver ponds and several thousand inactive beaver ponds in northern Wisconsin. These average 3.5 acres but range to 75 acres. On 333 beaver ponds he studied, George Knudsen found 115 duck broods. Michigan's lower peninsula contains about 2,500 beaver ponds. The total of these impoundments in the Interlake region probably produce 15 thousand to 20 thousand ducklings.

Surveys in Wisconsin show one pair of breeding ducks for 8 acres of habitat. One-half are blue-winged teal. One-fourth are mallards. About 9 percent are ring-necked ducks. Four percent each are wood ducks and black ducks.

American widgeon, redhead, pintail, hooded merganser, shoveler, and gadwall make up the remainder, in that order. Total production of ducks in the Interlake region is probably in the range of 120 thousand to 150 thousand young.

THE GREAT LAKE MARSHES, of all our areas, have suffered the least from human abuse and misuse. Only small portions have been drained, but important losses include the famous marshes around Wolf and Calumet Lakes near Chicago, some along the Detroit River and Lake St. Clair, and others bordering Lake Erie and Lake Ontario. In many areas, marsh margins are being destroyed in favor of cottages, boats, swimmers, and water-skiers. Nevertheless there are 120 thousand acres of wetlands along the Great Lakes which extend from Green Bay, Wisc., along both shores of Michigan's lower peninsula and include Ohio's Lake Erie shore and New York's Lake Ontario shore.

Geologists point out that the Great Lakes region is gradually tilting, and land slopes are slight. This has resulted in the drowning of mouths of streams and the creation of many marshes and bays, such as Maumee and Sandusky Bays in Ohio.

The southwest and west shores of Lake Erie include 40 thousand acres of good marsh, most of which is owned by duck clubs and is valued at 250 dollars an acre. Some duck clubs have improved their marshlands by installation of water-control structures. Other large marshes occur at Saginaw Bay, Lake St. Clair, and Green Bay.

The composition of the breeding population varies by marsh and by year. Mallards comprise one-half of the nesting ducks. Blue-winged teal and black ducks are next in abundance. Wood ducks nest on islands in the marsh or along its borders and form 10 percent of the breeding population on the Lake Erie marshes. Locally, on Lake Ontario, nesting boxes have increased wood ducks from a rare pair to two to four pairs per square mile. Pintails are regular breeders on many marshes but constitute only 1 to 2 percent of the nesting total. Marshes connected directly to the Great Lakes do not produce many ducks. Wind tides inundate many nests and are an important factor in limiting production. Water levels may vary several feet within hours with changes in wind direction and velocity.

The most productive marshes are along the southwest shore of Lake Erie in Ohio. Water levels on many are controlled by levees, which reduce the flooding of nests. At privately owned Winous Point marsh in Ohio, breeding ducks reach 50 pairs per square mile. On the nearby State-owned Magee Marsh, 16 pairs of breeding ducks were found per square mile. With uncontrolled water levels, densities are much lower. A fair estimate of the breeding ducks for all Great Lake marshes would be 5 to 15 pairs per square mile. With 1 thousand to 3 thousand pairs of ducks, the annual crop probably is 3 thousand to 10 thousand young.

ALL TOLD, eastern production areas do not approach self-sufficiency when the total waterfowl harvest is stacked against total production. A fair guess, for all species for the entire region, would be that 10 percent of the harvest is home-

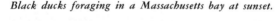

Black ducks foraging in a Massachusetts bay at sunset.

grown; the other 90 percent are migrants from the North and West. New England, Michigan, and New York produce about one in six of the black ducks their hunters shoot. Elsewhere, local nesting accounts for an even smaller portion of the black duck kill. But wood ducks are another matter. A conservative estimate of total production is a half million, and it could be nearly double that number. With a probable annual take of about 250 thousand, we are paying our own way on this one species.

Plainly enough, production in the East is not of a dimension to influence fall flights appreciably. And yet it is a contribution to the whole, and prospects appear to be good to enlarge upon it. Wood ducks, in particular, are susceptible to management. In many areas they have responded to simple measures and further improvements will add to the prosperity of this species. For others, simple expedients to increased production are not available. But manmade impoundments help, and in due time techniques should appear to make such areas even more effective. Planning for self-sufficiency is probably an unreasonable and unnecessary objective for this region, but to strive for substantial improvement is not. Studies and developmental programs now underway should add to the production capacity of the area.—

DIRCK BENSON and
FRANK C. BELLROSE.

WOOD DUCKS

Ducks in Dixie

FOR THE southern hunter wood ducks and mottled ducks are as southern as hominy grits. A million ducks were bagged in 1961 in the 12 Southern States. About 14 percent of them were wood ducks and mottled ducks. The production areas in Alabama, Arkansas, Florida, Georgia, Louisiana, Mississippi, New Mexico, North Carolina, Oklahoma, South Carolina, Texas, Virginia, and Mexico may produce 650 thousand wood ducks, 100 thousand mottled ducks, 50 thousand black-bellied tree ducks, 10 thousand fulvous tree ducks, and 10 thousand Mexican ducks each year.

As elsewhere, water determines how many ducks hatch, grow, and reproduce. Water makes marshes and swamps. Water keeps up the wetlands. It regulates the kinds and amounts of food and cover ducks need. And, as elsewhere, water in the South is subject to use and abuse—sometimes to the benefit of waterfowl but oftener not.

THE WOOD DUCK is more dependent on forests than any other American waterfowl. Wood ducks prefer to breed in places where trees provide nesting cavities and food; in permanent fresh-water lakes and streams that offer brushy borders for nesting and rearing young and swampy areas for roosting. The best and most extensive type of habitat in the South is the hardwood bottomland that borders streams and contains permanent fresh-water lakes. Next are the swamps, usually dominated by cypress and tupelo gum, in the Atlantic and Gulf coastal plains.

A survey in 1955 listed 53 million acres of wetlands, in units of 40 acres or more, in the Southern States. Not all produced wood ducks or ducks of any kind. But 20 million acres of seasonally flooded woodland, 14 million acres of wooded swamp, and 1 million acres of flooded brushland from Virginia to eastern Texas had value for webfoot Beau Brummell.

Thirty-five million acres of habitat is a lot. Already, however, much has been eliminated through drainage and leveeing along rivers and streams. We estimate that one-third of the original wetlands has been converted to dryland uses. Nest trees may remain, but water for rearing, feeding, and resting usually is eliminated or reduced and quality impaired.

LAND CLEARING AND FARMING, which normally follow drainage, have further eliminated much of the habitat. Logging has reduced the value of other areas by removing trees needed for nesting and mast production. Forestry practices, such as culling wolf or deformed trees and girdling or poisoning species of no economic value, have further reduced the environment of wood ducks.

Current land-use patterns in the South make the outlook uncertain for wood ducks. Much of the remaining habitat has timber of low value on poor land. Other acres for other reasons are unsuitable for development now. Manmade changes will reduce the habitat further, but some developments have helped the species.

Impoundments that flood forest land often create or improve the habitat of wood ducks. Watershed programs to conserve soil and water as well as farm ponds have been largely beneficial. The protection and management of beavers in Georgia and Alabama have aided the birds, as has the erection of nest boxes.

Natural enemies can limit the numbers of wood ducks. Raccoons, fox squirrels, and rat snakes are the main predators of nests in the South. Even though the habitat is essentially unchanged, predation often varies year to year because of changing populations of predators, wood ducks, and other prey species.

We lack satisfactory ways to determine the number of wood ducks over sizable territory, and we can make only crude estimates. Biologists in Alabama make float trips down selected streams each year and tally the number of ducks they see. In 1962, a year of high populations, they estimated that 58 thousand wood ducks were raised in the State.

Surveys by the Bureau of Sport Fisheries and Wildlife in 1959 and 1960 showed that the wood duck was third in numbers shot by hunters in the Atlantic Flyway and fourth in the Mississippi Flyway. The species accounted for 8 percent of the total number of ducks taken in the United States; more than one-fourth of them were shot in the South.

THE MOTTLED DUCK is the commonest nesting waterfowl in the marshes and coastal prairies of central and southern Florida, Louisiana, Texas, and Tamaulipas and Veracruz, Mexico. Two races, the Florida mottled duck and the western Gulf mottled duck, are recognized. It is an inconspicuous bird and not often is seen in large numbers, but it bulks large in sport hunting throughout its range.

Nesting starts in February in some years and extends through September. The peak comes in May and June. The mottled duck resembles the mallard in accepting a variety of nesting sites. But, like the northern black duck, it is secretive and sensitive to disturbance by people.

Nesting mottled ducks have many enemies. Raccoons, opossums, skunks, boat-tailed grackles, dogs, and snakes destroy eggs and nests. Ducklings contend with them and with turtles, alligators, gar and other large fish, and swarms of blue crabs, when water levels are low in coastal marshes. The long nesting season of the mottled duck limits the number of eggs available to predators at any one time. The pressure of predators, therefore, is not concentrated, as with other species.

The burning of marshes, trampling by cattle, flooding, and other factors also reduce nesting success severely. J. R. Singleton reported a 28-percent nesting success of 108 nests during a 3-year study of the mottled duck in Texas.

THE RANGE of the western Gulf mottled duck is about 50 thousand square miles of the coastal regions of Louisiana and Texas and Tamaulipas and Veracruz in Mexico. It breeds and winters all over its range, at least as far south as Tampico. It is known to winter in small numbers in Veracruz. It lives at some seasons on the offshore islands of the Gulf of Mexico, in brackish or fresh-water marshes, ricefields, and farm ponds. Its center of abundance is the coastal marshes of Louisiana and southeastern Texas.

The western Gulf mottled duck sometimes numbers fewer than 50 thousand, but favorable conditions may mean a tremendous increase. A single post-nesting concentration of 50 thousand mottled ducks was observed in Cameron Parish in Louisiana in August 1942, after a series of years of abundant rainfall. It was one of five large flocks in that region that summer.

THE RANGE of the Florida mottled duck includes 15 thousand square miles in central and southern Florida. It inhabits ponds and lakes of pine flatwoods, everglades, cultivated and fallow fields, brackish and fresh-water marshes, mangrove swamps, and cypress-tupelo gum hammock. Its center of abundance is on or near Lake Okeechobee in Hendry, Lee, Charlotte, and Glades Counties.

A wood duck banded and ready for release.

Annual inventories, conducted by the Florida Game and Fresh Water Fish Commission since 1948, have indicated populations of fewer than 50 thousand. Summer drought from 1953 through 1956 dried up the Everglades, the pine flatwoods ponds, and the marshes of Lake Okeechobee, the St. Johns River Valley, and the Kissimmee River Valley. Then populations of Florida mottled duck dwindled from 30 thousand to 6 thousand. The return of normal rainfall in the late fifties and a drop in hunting pressure by delaying the opening of waterfowl hunting seasons have assisted its recovery.

Both races of the mottled duck are under heavy hunting pressure. The western Gulf mottled duck in 1961 accounted for 7.4 percent of the duck kill in Louisiana and Texas, with a harvest of 20 thousand and 18 thousand in those States, respectively. Only a few hundred were killed in Mississippi and fewer than 100 in Alabama. The harvest of Florida mottled duck in 1961 was 21 percent of the statewide duck kill—27 thousand.

Environment and heavy hunting are of first importance in determining the numbers. Cultivation, drainage, impoundment of marshes, construction of deepwater reservoirs, real estate development, and industrial activities are altering the homes of the species. Not all of these inroads on habitat are detrimental, though.

More than 10 thousand acres of prime habitat in Brevard and Indian River Counties in Florida have been diked and impounded with water to control the breeding of mosquitoes. Water birds of many species utilize the impoundments.

Rice farming in Texas and Louisiana and certain types of truck crop farming in Florida have also created habitats, although in Florida more habitat has been destroyed by truck crop and sugarcane farming than has been created. Deepwater reservoirs have been proposed for Lake Okeechobee and parts of the Kissimmee Valley and St. Johns River Valley in Florida,

the three major fresh-water systems in the range of the Florida mottled duck. These developments may adversely affect the population and distribution of the Florida mottled duck by eliminating shallow zones, important to the birds.

THE BLACK-BELLIED TREE DUCK is a tropical duck, mainly of Mexico and Central America. A few small nesting colonies exist in southern Texas and along the lower Rio Grande Valley. In the United States it is less common than the fulvous tree duck. Small reservoirs, cattle tanks, and other manmade water areas have created habitat in the semiarid region of southern Texas. Small nesting colonies are becoming established along the Texas coast as far north as Corpus Christi. Unlike the fulvous tree duck, the black-bellied tree duck builds its nest in tree cavities or hollow trunks. The bird is not important to American sportsmen, but it has considerable interest for aviculturists. It is one of the more heavily shot species in Mexico, but it seems to be maintaining its numbers.

THE MEXICAN DUCK in the United States occurs in the Rio Grande Valley from the Bosque del Apache Refuge, N. Mex., to southwestern Texas, and in the Pecos Valley north to Bitter Lake Refuge, and the San Simon Marshes of the Gila River in Hidalgo County in New Mexico. Its range extends southward through the highlands of Mexico as far as Morelos and Puebla. It is commonest in the volcanic Cordillera in the central uplands of Mexico. A second center of distribution is in New Mexico, occupied by a population classified by some as a separate race called the northern Mexican duck. Formerly it was a common nester within its New Mexico range, but since about 1940 this northern Mexican duck has been of such rare occurrence in New Mexico as to be considered an endangered subspecies. Both the State and Federal governments have taken special action to try to restore its numbers. The number in Mexico probably does not exceed 10 thousand birds.

Because of its limited range, scarcity, and resemblance to the mallard, with which it is known to cross north of Albuquerque, N. Mex., little is known of the habits of this interesting and wary duck.

In the arid land that comprises its range, the Mexican duck is con-fined to mudflats, bars, and marshes of river bottomlands. Marshes of cattail, common three-square, and phragmites interspersed among willow and cottonwood make up most of its habitat along the Rio Grande River south of Albuquerque and in the San Simon Marshes along the Gila River. The birds frequently feed at night in irrigated fields of grain and alfalfa.

The few nests that have been found were in marsh and grassy zones below the zone of mesquite scrub and in close proximity to open water. Alton A. Lindsey reported in 1945 that the San Simon Marshes. of Hidalgo County supported the greatest known nesting concentration of Mexican ducks in New Mexico. During that summer he estimated that six pairs were nesting in a small marsh of 200 acres. Ten years before, in 1935, J. Stokley Ligon found 12 pairs nesting in the same marsh. A.

The fulvous tree duck is a common nester in parts of Louisiana, Texas, and California.

Starker Leopold expressed concern that it may become a rare species in Mexico because of the loss of habitat through water diversion and drainage.

On the Bosque del Apache National Wildlife Refuge on the Rio Grande River, there were 250 Mexican ducks in 1946, and 200 young were produced in May 1947. The refuge, which contains about 13 thousand acres of bottomland, is the only one that furnishes nesting grounds for this duck. The Mexican duck was uncommon in that area in the midfifties and by the sixties it had disappeared as a breeding species.

Marsh drainage, cattle grazing, and human disturbance throughout its range have markedly reduced the number of the Mexican duck. As recently as 1961, Ligon believed that most Mexican ducks breeding in the United States migrated into Mexico before the hunting season. There they may be subjected to heavy hunting, because few other ducks are available at that time.

The preservation of habitat, particularly at the San Simon Marshes and Bosque del Apache Refuge, is considered essential for its survival. Efforts to reestablish the Mexican duck as a breeding species on the Bosque del Apache Refuge were begun in 1962.

THE FULVOUS TREE DUCK has been the most successful southern species of waterfowl to nest in the Gulf coast region of Texas and Louisiana. This fascinating bird is ducklike in having a flat bill and webbed feet, but its duck traits end there. The "tree duck" shuns trees, has the general aspect of a small swan and the behavior of a tame goose, looks like an ibis or heron in flight, and cannot quack.

Its normal range in the United States had been thought to be the Gulf States and California, but since 1960 they have appeared in numbers in the fall along the Atlantic seaboard, even as far north as New Brunswick. They have also been recorded in Ohio and Michigan. Such straying from traditional ranges is nothing new, for it has an extraordinary global distribution. It occurs in eastern Africa, India, southeastern and northeastern South America, besides Mexico and the United States. This unusual range could only mean an inherent wanderlust.

While coastal lowlands of Mexico south to Campeche and Oaxaca are the stronghold of the fulvous tree duck in North America, it can no longer be considered abundant. In April, part of the Mexican population moves north into Texas and Louisiana. Nesting, in June, July, and August, is confined to ricefields and nearby shoalwater marshes. In Mexico, it nests in marshy vegetation or on adjacent dry ground.

When the young are mature they flock together at various assembly points in early fall. Most northern birds move south into Mexico when the weather turns cool in September and October. Few therefore are taken during the hunting season in Louisiana and Texas.

THE MUSCOVY DUCK occurs in Mexico on the coastal plains south through Central and South America to Peru on the Pacific and Argentina on the Atlantic. It dwells in bottomland timber along rivers and streams. It nests and roosts in trees. The problem of inventorying woodland waterfowl applies to this species, and we have no estimates of numbers. In some years, not a single muscovy duck is seen on midwinter inventories in Mexico.

A. Starker Leopold said of the muscovy in Mexico: "Although the bottomland timber required by this species is being reduced by clearing, many areas so far undisturbed have lost their populations of muscovies. Hunting is the only logical explanation."

OTHER WATERFOWL occasionally find suitable conditions and rear young in the Southern States and Mexico. Among them are most of the ducks that winter there, plus the American coot. Blue-winged teal, black ducks, gadwall, hooded merganser, common merganser, cinnamon teal, shoveler, mallard, and ruddy duck are well-known species whose southern limits of breeding range borders the Southland. The blue-winged teal maintains a fair-sized, but undetermined, nesting population in the Gulf coast area of Louisiana and Texas. Several hundred gadwalls have nested since 1940 on the Pea Island National Wildlife Refuge on the outer banks of North Carolina. Nesting mal-

lards are scattered through the South. They frequently cross with mottled ducks and Mexican ducks and become obscured in those populations.

The masked duck, a relative of the ruddy, is a tropical bird, chiefly of the West Indies and northern South America. It has been recorded occasionally in Mexico, Texas, Florida, and other distant places in North America. It is known to nest in limited numbers along the Texas coast and probably along the Gulf coast of Mexico.

THE SOUTHLAND CONTRIBUTION to the continental production of waterfowl does not bulk large. Yet we offer fair variety, and some species are exclusively southern—nesting here, then staying on to round out the year. Two species, the wood duck and mottled duck, are produced in quantities to provide considerable hunting. Others are of interest mainly because of limited numbers and distribution.

Whatever the uncertain status of the South as a production area, one thing is evident: Here, as elsewhere, habitat is the basis for numbers, and habitat in many areas is yielding to other developments. Preservation of this resource will require more attention in the future than it has received in the past.—
JOHN L. SINCOCK,
MORTON M. SMITH, and
JOHN J. LYNCH.

CANADA GEESE

Goose and Swan
Factories

GIANT CANADA GEESE
CACKLING CANADA GEESE

Honkers Large and Small

CANADA GEESE are the big game of North American waterfowl—the kings, aristocrats, trophy species—to all who hunt them with gun or camera. Wary and keen of eye, the Canadian honker walks proudly, and flies with marvelous grace. Few voices in Nature quicken man's pulse more readily or cock his head more surely than the clear, deep call of a honker high above.

Few North American birds exhibit greater racial variation than is found in Canada geese. In fact, so great is the variation in size and relative proportions that the largest and one of the smallest of all geese are found within the many subspecies. The tiny dark-colored cackling Canada goose of the Pacific coast averages a scant 3 pounds, the size of a big mallard. The pale-colored giant Canada goose of the northeastern prairies may go 18 pounds or more, the weight of a whistling swan. Regardless of size and color variation in the different races of Canada geese, the hallmark of the clan is a black neck and head and a prominent white cheek patch. This is the silhouette on signs of the national wildlife refuges all over the United States.

109

Canada geese breed across Canada and Alaska with smaller localized wild breeding populations still existing, and newly established breeding flocks now developing in many sections of the United States. The greatest racial variation is shown in the northwestern part of this big territory. Seven of the subspecies considered in this chapter nest in the Arctic and subarctic. Canada geese originally lived only in North America and the islands of northeastern Asia. They were introduced into Europe in the 18th century and into New Zealand in recent years.

Biologists have studied the variation among Canada goose populations for many years but are still unable to agree on how to classify them. The chief reason for this is that much of the breeding range is inaccessible except by air and collection of specimens of the various breeding populations has been difficult. At present, the total specimens of Canada geese in all museum collections combined are not sufficient to work out the true racial determination in all parts of the species' range. Another confusing factor is that yearlings and other nonbreeding birds tend to wander northward from their breeding grounds, and often it is hard to determine if idle geese in the summer are subadults far from their native haunts or unmated adults on their own breeding grounds. For many years the larger races of honkers which domesticate readily have been shipped back and forth across the continent between game breeders, State conservation departments, and refuges of the Bureau of Sport

Fisheries and Wildlife. These may have produced populations with mixed racial characters and confused further the distribution of racial types of Canada geese in the United States. Subspecies mix on the wintering areas but rigid natural selection of adapted individuals, strong family bonds which tend to prevent excessive interbreeding and intermingling, and geographic isolation on the breeding grounds have served to maintain the identity of the various subspecies.

There is a gradual change from north to south in size and color of the subspecies. The small, short-billed, short-necked geese nest in the arctic tundra, while the birds become progressively larger in the forested and prairie regions to the south. The darkest birds occur in the extreme northwestern coastal portions of the breeding range and lighter forms in interior and northeastern North America. Birds of the central Arctic are intermediate in size and color.

Recoveries of banded geese have made it possible to recognize several well-defined populations or flocks within some subspecies. Major migrant concentrations and wintering populations, however, have yet to be related to specific production areas. The strong affinity of individual populations of Canada geese for specific migration routes and wintering areas offers unusual opportunities for scientific management of these aristocrats of the waterfowl clan.

CANADIAN HONKER, or just honker, is the name hunters often apply to Canada geese, especially to the larger races with deep, vibrant voices. It is unlikely that everyone will agree on any set of names, scientific or common. In this chapter we have used the taxonomic classification proposed by Delacour (1954) in *Waterfowl of the World*. This authority recognizes 11 North American subspecies. The common names for subspecies used by Delacour are followed in all but one instance. The appropriate name, western Canada goose, used by Roger T. Peterson in his *Field Guide to Western Birds,* for *Branta canadensis moffitti* has been adopted for that race.

Additional study is providing facts that eventually may lead to further subdivision or consolidation of the subspecies. As Delacour so aptly stated in 1954, "The last word on taxonomy of the Canada geese will be said only when all breeding populations have been carefully investigated." Canada goose nomenclature is currently undergoing further revision. Specimens in museums throughout the continent are being studied more critically and collections are being expanded. More intensive work is being done on the breeding grounds.

The range for each of the major populations of Canada geese is based on present knowledge of breeding, migration, and wintering areas. For the sake of standardizing terminology, "population" is used to designate all components of a

PRINCIPAL RANGES OF LARGE CANADA GEESE *(Branta canadensis)*

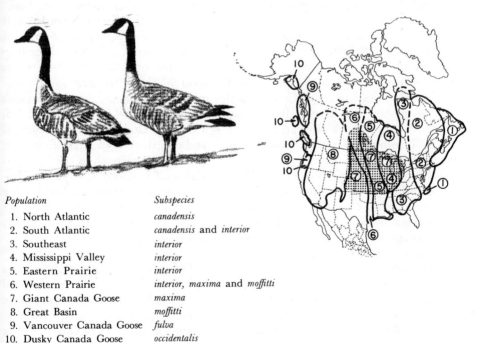

Population	Subspecies
1. North Atlantic	*canadensis*
2. South Atlantic	*canadensis* and *interior*
3. Southeast	*interior*
4. Mississippi Valley	*interior*
5. Eastern Prairie	*interior*
6. Western Prairie	*interior, maxima* and *moffitti*
7. Giant Canada Goose	*maxima*
8. Great Basin	*moffitti*
9. Vancouver Canada Goose	*fulva*
10. Dusky Canada Goose	*occidentalis*

given group utilizing fairly well defined breeding grounds, migration routes, and wintering grounds. Each population may be made up of several "flocks" associated with specific concentration areas, usually north of the primary wintering grounds. Because the proper names sometimes differ from common names often used in some sections of the country, they are listed for clarification, along with the presently accepted scientific name, in the discussion of populations.

From the hunter's viewpoint Canada geese come in two sizes, large and small. The following are generally considered to be "large Canadas."

THE WESTERN CANADA GOOSE (*Branta canadensis moffitti*) is the second largest of all the races. A 13 pounder is a big one but now and then a bird reaches 15 pounds— rarely if ever any more, even though a hunter, hefting his prize at arm's length, would like to think so.

Western Canada geese nest mostly west of the Continental Divide in the Great Basin and north into the headwaters of the Columbia River, but also in the western Great Plains in Alberta, Montana, and Wyoming. They comprise what is commonly referred to as the *Great Basin Population.* Recent work indicates that some of the eastern segments of this group are intermediate toward the giant Canada race found in its most typical form in the eastern prairies. Like Canada geese elsewhere, yearlings tend to wander northward after the family bond has loosened.

Some of the more eastern groups join subarctic races and migrate down the eastern side of the Rockies to winter in the Plains States.

Western Canadas have developed several distinct flocks within their range.

A rather stay-at-home group nests on the Columbia and Snake Rivers in eastern Washington and northward into the Okanogan Valley of British Columbia. Most of them winter in south-central Washington in sanctuaries on the Snake and Columbia Rivers.

A small group breeds in the Flathead Valley of Montana and winters along the Snake River in southern Idaho. Geese that breed in southern Idaho and around Great Salt Lake in northern Utah spend the winter along the lower Colorado River.

The largest number of western Canadas nest in northeastern California, northwestern Nevada, and south-central Oregon. Some of them winter on their breeding grounds, but bad weather sends most of them toward the Sacramento Valley. Some western Canadas from breeding areas in Idaho, Montana, Utah, Wyoming, Alberta, and southwestern Saskatchewan migrate as far south as the Imperial Valley of California, Arizona, New Mexico, and northern Mexico. The population of the western Canada goose is estimated to total about 115 thousand birds.

TWO RACES OF large, dark Canada geese breed along the Alaska and British Columbia coasts. These geese range in size from 6 to 13 pounds. The Dusky Canada Goose (*Branta canadensis occidentalis)*, the smaller of the two, nests primarily on the Copper River Delta on the south-central Alaska coast. A few are scattered across Prince William Sound and the Cook Inlet area near Anchorage. They migrate close offshore, leapfrogging southeast Alaska, touching on the Queen Charlotte and Vancouver Islands of British Columbia, and coming to rest for the winter in a small district of the Willamette Valley in western Oregon.

The Vancouver Canada Goose *(Branta canadensis fulva)* breeds in coastal southeastern Alaska and southward along the British Columbia coast. They are largely non-migrant. Ten percent or fewer go to the Willamette Valley of Oregon. Each race numbers only about 20 thousand.

TODD'S OR INTERIOR CANADA GOOSE *(Branta canadensis interior)*, nests in a wide zone of forested muskeg around Hudson Bay, from the 60th parallel on the west side, south through Manitoba and Ontario across James Bay, through Quebec and to Hudson Strait north to southern Baffin Island. In all this region, geese prefer the Hudson Bay lowlands, or isolated pockets of similar muskeg habitat farther inland, rather than the rocky Canadian shield. These are fairly large, medium colored geese, the males weighing 6–11 pounds, females 6–9 pounds.

Four distinct populations have been delineated that include geese principally of this subspecies. The *South Atlantic Population* nests east of Hudson Bay to the Atlantic coast, and winters from southern New Jersey to Lake Mattamuskeet in North Carolina. They intermingle with geese of the *North Atlantic Population* on the wintering grounds. The *Southeast Population* nests in a rather small area inland from the south coast of James Bay north along the east side of Hudson Bay to southern Baffin Island, and on Akamiski Island. They winter in the inland regions of the Southeastern States and at points on the Atlantic and Gulf coasts. The *Mississippi Valley Population* nests in Ontario, inland from the west coast of James Bay and Hudson Bay, almost to the Manitoba border. Others may also come from breeding areas east of Hudson Bay. The major migration route swings down over Ontario, around both sides and over the Great Lakes from Minnesota and Wisconsin, east to Ohio, funneling into southern Illinois. Principal concentration areas are the Horicon and Necedah National Wildlife Refuges in Wisconsin, State areas in southwestern Michigan, the Crab Orchard National Wildlife Refuge, and famed Horseshoe Lake and Union County State areas in southern Illinois. The majority now winter primarily in southern Illinois. Lesser numbers move south to Kentucky, Tennessee, and Alabama. The *Eastern Prairie Population* nests in northwestern Ontario and northern Manitoba along the west coast of Hudson Bay. They migrate down through western Ontario, the inter-lake region of Manitoba, eastern Dakotas, western Minnesota, and over much of Iowa, congregating in large numbers at the Swan Lake National Wildlife Refuge and the nearby Fountain Grove Management Area in north-central Missouri. A major portion of these birds now winter at the Swan Lake Refuge and the remainder move south to the Texas-Louisiana coast. While it is difficult to determine the size of this entire group, fall populations of 130 thousand have been recorded at the Swan Lake Refuge.

One additional group, the *Western Prairie Population,* completes the picture of large Canada geese in the central United States. These geese probably breed in central Canada mostly west of the 100th meridian, but some may originate within the breeding range of the *Eastern Prairie Population.* They migrate through Saskatchewan, western Manitoba, the Dakotas, and southward to central and east Texas. A large segment of this population is represented by geese using the Missouri River in South Dakota. A portion of them winter there. It was previously assumed that these were largely Western Canada geese *(B. c. moffiitti)* but recently both Todd's Canada goose *(B. c. interior)* and the Giant Canada *(B. c. maxima)* were identified in wintering populations at the Lake Andes National Wildlife Refuge and the Fort Randall Reservoir in South Dakota. This population comes from a breeding area where a mixture of racial types would be expected to occur.

Populations of Todd's geese are the most abundant of all Canadas. These birds, together with the Atlantic Canada goose population, with which they intermingle on the wintering grounds in the Southeast, totaled nearly one million birds in the January 1964 midwinter survey.

THE ATLANTIC CANADA GOOSE *(Branta canadensis canadensis)* comprises the *North Atlantic Population.* These geese, similar to Todd's in size, but whiter on the under parts, nest in eastern Labrador and Newfoundland. They winter chiefly from Nova Scotia south to Chesapeake Bay and beyond along the coast. They overlap with Todd's Canada goose on the wintering grounds and their characteristics intergrade with that race over an extensive breeding area in central Quebec. It is estimated that they number more than 300 thousand birds in midwinter.

THE GIANT CANADA GOOSE *(Branta canadensis maxima),* was believed to have become extinct about 1920. The original breeding grounds extended over most of the eastern prairie States, portions of the western Great Lakes area, and into southern Canada. However, this largest of all honkers was rediscovered, in 1960, when Harold C. Hanson of the Illinois Natural History Survey identified members of this race in the flock of Canadas wintering near Rochester, Minn. Additional numbers have been identified in breeding flocks on national wildlife refuges and game management areas in Minnesota, South Dakota, North Dakota, Michigan, and Saskatchewan. Many midwestern game breeders also have substantial numbers of the giant Canada that they have perpetuated for years, although their identity was obscure until the mystery began to unravel.

Members of this race reach the maximum size for the species. They have relatively elongated bodies, long necks, large broad bills, and light colored plumage. Weights range from 10 to 18 pounds, with captive birds exceeding 20 pounds.

The largest remnant of this race winters at Rochester, Minnesota. Some of these birds breed in a locality between Lake Winnipeg and Lake Manitoba in south-central Manitoba. Several banded at Rochester in the winters of 1960–1962, and others banded in Saskatchewan, South Dakota, Missouri, and Texas, were retrapped in the Aberdeen Lake area along the Thelon River in the Northwest Territories during the summer of 1963. This is about 14 hundred airline miles from their winter home. These birds were moulting and were believed to be nonbreeders.

We do not know the full extent of the breeding range and total population size of the giant Canada. Many game breeders in the north-central States raise significant num-bers of these geese. This race is now being used throughout the Midwest by Federal and State conservation agencies engaged in restoration of local breeding flocks of Canada geese.

Smaller nesting geese from the Arctic and subarctic are generally referred to as "small Canada's."

THE CACKLING CANADA GOOSE *(Branta canadensis minima)* is the smallest of all races and weighs 3 to 4 pounds. It has relatively long wings which serve it well on its lengthy trek between Alaska and California. Cacklers nest in a small district in Alaska along the Bering Sea chiefly between the Yukon and Kuskokwim Rivers. They have been seen as far south as northwestern Mexico and in Hawaii and Japan.

Cacklers move leisurely down the coast near the base of the Alaska Peninsula, where they fatten on tundra berries until early October.

PRINCIPAL RANGES OF SMALL CANADA GEESE *(Branta canadensis)*

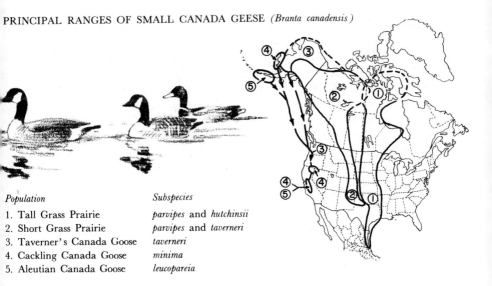

Population	Subspecies
1. Tall Grass Prairie	*parvipes* and *hutchinsii*
2. Short Grass Prairie	*parvipes* and *taverneri*
3. Taverner's Canada Goose	*taverneri*
4. Cackling Canada Goose	*minima*
5. Aleutian Canada Goose	*leucopareia*

From there they fly offshore over the Pacific and make landfall near the mouth of the Columbia River. They turn abruptly up the Columbia through the Cascades and then turn south again down the eastern side of the mountains to the Klamath Basin and northeastern California. Most of them linger there until late November before going to the Sacramento and San Joaquin Valleys and beyond. Their route has few detours. Some, taken along the Alaska coast, are presumed to be birds forced in from the open ocean by strong onshore winds. In autumn, before hunting, this race of small geese may number 250 thousand.

THE ALEUTIAN CANADA GOOSE (*Branta canadensis leucopareia*) also is from Alaska. It is small, with a relatively large amount of white plumage mixed with the brown, forming a broken ring at the base of the black neck. Only a remnant remains of what once may have been a sizable population. The birds nest on a few of the Aleutian Islands. Robert D. Jones, manager of the Aleutian Islands National Wildlife Refuge, located a colony of a few hundred on Buldir Island in the summer of 1962. Old records indicate that they wintered along the coast of Washington and Oregon, in the interior valleys of California, and down to northwestern Mexico. They also migrated down the western side of the Pacific to Japan.

TAVERNER'S CANADA GOOSE (*Branta canadensis taverneri*) is intermediate in size between the large Pacific coastal races and the tiny cackler. Taverner's goose nests in western and northern Alaska and eastward into Canada along the arctic coast. Its eastern limits have not been defined, but it intergrades with the lesser Canada goose on the Old Crow Flats in Yukon Territory and very likely in eastern Alaska as well.

Recoveries of Taverner's Canada geese banded at five places in Alaska show that they migrate close inshore along the Pacific coast. From northern Puget Sound they cross the Cascades into eastern Washington. Most of them winter in south-central Washington and eastern Oregon. Some go as far as the interior valleys of California. Others, probably of the eastern edge of their range, migrate down the Great Plains to west Texas. Taverner's Canada geese may number as many as 100 thousand in an average year.

THE LESSER CANADA GOOSE (*Branta canadensis parvipes*) includes a complex group of intermediate size birds of which the true identity and range are not yet fully known.

Typical examples of these geese are light colored like the western and giant Canadas. In size they are an intermediate form between the large Canadas of the southern forested or prairie regions and the smallest tundra forms, which range from 4 to 8 pounds in weight. They nest in widely scattered groups, usually inland, in pockets of suitable habitat across the Northwest Territories of Canada and eastern Alaska between the 60th and 70th parallels. Depending upon the portion of the breeding grounds from which they originate, lesser Canadas follow rather well-defined migration routes on their way to wintering areas. Those coming out of north-central Canada appear to follow closely the short grass prairie, stopping in sizable number at staging areas in eastern Alberta and western Saskatchewan, then moving on to wintering areas at Two Buttes, Colo., and the vicinity of Waggoner Ranch and Buffalo Lake in northwestern Texas. This group is referred to as the *Short Grass Prairie Population.*

Others coming from more easterly portions of the breeding grounds, the 100th meridian east to Hudson Bay, move down over Manitoba, through the tall grass prairie of eastern Dakotas, western Minnesota, Iowa, and Missouri, to wintering areas in Oklahoma, Texas, and Mexico. This group is considered to be a part of the *Tall*

Grass Prairie Population and individuals are found in close company with the smaller Richardson's Canada geese.

RICHARDSON'S CANADA GEESE *(Branta canadensis hutchinsii)* are eastern counterparts of the tiny cackler but are slightly larger weighing 3 to 7 pounds. They nest on the coastal tundra of Southampton Island, southwestern Baffin Island, and portions of the Melville and Boothia Peninsulas. They mingle and move south with the neighboring lesser Canada geese along the western coast of Hudson Bay, through Manitoba and northwestern Ontario, along the eastern edge of the Plains States to winter in Oklahoma, Texas, and Mexico.

Because Richardson's and lesser Canada geese intermingle so freely on migration and wintering grounds, it is difficult to determine the numbers of each. In combination, the

A family of Canada geese on parade.

winter population may total 200 thousand to 300 thousand in an average year.

There are differences of opinion among students of Canada goose speciation as to the geographical location and extent of intergradation between lesser Canadas *(parvipes)* of north-central Canada, the Richardson's *(hutchinsii)* of eastern Arctic, and Taverner's *(taverneri)* of the western Arctic. Some individuals, in fact, question that there are distinct racial differences between these populations. Charles MacInnes, based on his work in the eastern Arctic and analysis of museum specimens, suggests that all of the small Canadas using the Tall-Grass Prairie migration route constitute a single interbreeding population. He believes all three of the above subspecies should be considered as one subspecies, *Branta canadensis hutchinsii.* Others, including Jean Delacour, whose classification concepts we are following here, believe that these populations are devisable as described.

CANADA GEESE are essentially grazing birds and are more land-based than ducks, particularly when the goslings are growing. It is no accident that many of them have chosen Arctic regions as their summer home. Much of the Far North is flat, treeless tundra of lush meadows of sedge and other grass-like plants, ideal for grazing geese. The North also offers long hours of daylight during much of the summer, few predators, and little disturbance by people.

Northern weather is variable. In many places along the Pacific coast,

as far north as Prince William Sound in Alaska, rain and snow exceed 100 inches a year. In the rest of Alaska and most of northern Canada, precipitation is about 6 to 20 inches and rarely exceeds 30. And yet, the high-rainfall belt contains little standing water, whereas the low-rainfall zone has much surface water. The latter condition is due to a layer of permafrost which prevents percolation. There is relatively little evaporation; the greatest water loss is due to transpiration by the lush vegetation. In high latitudes there is more apt to be too much rather than too little surface water.

High latitudes offer advantages other than lush pastures interspersed with stable water. Almost continuous daylight from mid-May to late July creates conditions for a fantastic growth of plants and invertebrate animals and subsequently of the birds. Geese from 60° latitude and northward are fledged and on the wing in about two-thirds the time it takes in the northwestern States. This fast rate of growth permits the birds to mature in a brief summer period and it shortens the time when, as downy youngsters, they are most vulnerable to enemies.

PREDATORS in the Far North are generally less dangerous to nesting waterfowl than they are in the southern part of the breeding range. Jaegers sometimes destroy many eggs when other food is scarce. Gulls may take young when broods are scattered by storms and disturbance from people. Foxes take a toll of nests and goslings, especially when lemmings and hares are scarce.

Raccoons and skunks, common waterfowl nest predators in the prairies, are not found in the Far North.

CANADA GEESE ARRIVE EARLY on the breeding grounds. In south-central Washington, warm Pacific air funnels up the Columbia gorge to trigger an earlier spring. Here, western Canadas on the Columbia River select territories in mid-February and begin laying early in March. The peak comes in the third week or so. The Westerns average a week or 10 days later in northeastern California and about a month later in southeastern Idaho. Large geese start nesting about mid-April in the Canadian Prairie Provinces. Arctic races follow the retreating ice line north and start to lay early in June as soon as suitable nest sites are free of snow.

All Canada geese mate for life in their second to fourth year. If either member of a pair is killed, the other usually remates. The usual clutch is five eggs but two to nine may be laid. There are indications that birds nesting for the first time lay fewer eggs than older birds. Incubation takes about 25 days.

Canada geese, unlike most ducks, usually select nest sites that permit an open view around them. The large races that breed in Canada and the United States nest on islands in rivers and lakes at points away from dense cover. They often use muskrat houses on large marshes. In the cattle country of the Northwest, they often nest on haystacks near water. They sometimes select a site on a cliff or use the abandoned nest of an osprey or a blue heron. Nests on cliffs also are common along many rivers in northern Alaska and parts of Canada. The Arctic races use tiny hummocks in the soggy tundra. The dusky Canadas of Alaska's Copper River Delta nest on slightly elevated ridges of silt, which parallel the banks of tidal sloughs on land that otherwise is as flat as a floor. In certain localities in the southern part of the breeding range, where flooding and predators limit production, geese use artificial nesting structures, such as tubs placed in trees or nesting platforms built over water and provided with nesting material.

CANADA GEESE are highly gregarious from late summer through winter, but nesting adults dislike crowding. There are exceptions. Cecil S. Williams found 11 nests of geese on a single haystack in southern Oregon and densities of 60 nests to the acre have been observed on small islands in Idaho and Washington. Two geese are known to have nested within 15 feet of each other on opposite sides of a gnarled tree, while a third was incubating a mixed clutch of eggs in a blue heron nest 9 feet above. Several herons were nesting in the same tree. As a rule, though, honkers need more space than that. Some eastern nesting populations are scattered one pair to a lake or island, rarely reaching a density over one pair per 2 square miles. In the best range on the west side of Hudson Bay, Canada geese average only five or six nests per square mile, rarely "crowding" to 20. Colonies of cackling Canada geese may be rather evenly distrib-

Canada geese feeding in shallow water. They often do this. Grazing in upland fields is a habit common to them also.

uted to densities up to 146 nests per square mile, or an average of one nest to 4.4 acres. Dusky Canadas have been found in densities of one nest to 5.7 acres but seldom closer than 100 yards to each other.

ONCE THE GOSLINGS HAVE HATCHED the inborn sociability of geese reasserts itself. Then family groups gather in small flocks and move to green pastures. Usually geese nest on or very near suitable feeding areas but sometimes they move several miles downstream or around a lakeshore to reach good grazing. Insects supplement the diet of grass, sedge, and other tender plants. One often sees large flocks made up of many broods attended by no more than half a dozen adult geese. Now and then other geese replace these "babysitters" so they can join adults elsewhere. Should a person intrude, however, there is bedlam as the youngsters scatter and adult geese appear from all directions to reclaim their offspring.

When goslings are half grown the parents lose their flight feathers and become grounded for about 3 weeks until they grow new pinions. This molt is timed so that parents and young begin to fly at about the same time. For a week or so, as new quills harden, the birds do not fly far. When full flight has been attained, family groups desert the feeding grounds, join others, and move leisurely to staging areas in Canada part way down their fall flight route. Here most of the geese feed through September and into October before pushing on to winter quarters, although some escape hunters in northern States by mov-

ing south ahead of the hunting season as early as September 20.

CANADA GEESE are more successful than most species of ducks in maintaining a stable population on a continental scale, mainly because they are widely distributed in remote areas and their nesting habitat is more stable. Nesting success, however, is dependent upon climatic factors such as time of ice break-up, rate of thaw and duration of flooding, and severity of prolonged freezing temperatures. Over their broad nesting range, poor production in one area or for a given population may be counterbalanced by good production in another. The result is that the overall number of Canadas is fairly constant from one year to the next. The average continental wintering population was slightly over 1,800,000 for the 7 years, 1954–1960. The greatest fluctuation was only 10 percent of this average.

Biologists who made studies of four subspecies in the southern breeding areas learned that nesting success averaged 64 percent—that is, of 100 nests, 64 hatched goslings. The low was 24 percent and the high was 87. Failure was due to poor (overcrowded) nesting sites, flooding, predators, and desertion. Those conditions are more likely in agricultural and hydro-development regions where the larger southern races breed. Nesting success in northern California was 52 to 79 percent in 1942–1954. Success on the Columbia River in south-central Washington varied only 71 to 78 percent in 1953–1955 but dropped to 62 percent in 1956. A premature flood crest, caused partly by the release of stored water behind Grand Coulee Dam, destroyed 12 percent of the nests in 1956. Unseasonable release of impounded water has been the cause of low production on other western rivers and reservoirs.

Only a few detailed studies have been made on remote northern breeding grounds. Cacklers hatched 73 percent of their nests in 1951 on the Yukon-Kuskokwim. Dusky Canadas brought off 87 percent on the Copper River Delta in 1959. In the eastern Arctic, MacInnes reported 64 and 81 percent success for nests under observation at the mouth of the McConnell River, Northwest Territories in 1959 and 1960.

Richardson's Canada geese had a near failure in 1961 on Southampton Island in northern Hudson Bay. An exploding lemming population which reached a peak in 1960 produced many arctic foxes on nesting grounds along the coast. The lemmings had disappeared by the time geese arrived in 1961 and foxes turned to tundra nesting birds for food. In some places foxes took 90 percent of the eggs. An event like this usually concerns only a small district, and rarely most of the eastern Arctic as occurred in 1961. In 10 seasons of study on Southampton Island, biologists reported foxes to be a major problem only in 1961.

The Aleutian Canada goose has been eliminated as a breeding bird on a number of islands where fox farming was introduced. Efforts are being made to eradicate the free-roaming foxes from some of the major islands and to restore breeding geese in these areas.

IT IS HARD TO SAY how much the numbers of Canada geese can be increased but it is a good bet that a substantial gain is possible. Some subspecies—for instance, the giant Canada and the Aleutian Canada goose—are undoubtedly far below their peak numbers of a century ago. Others, like the western Canada goose and the medium-sized geese that winter in eastern Washington, may be more abundant than formerly. Todd's Canada goose has been increasing steadily in eastern United States since the low of the mid-1940's. The extensive far northern tundra and muskeg habitat does not seem to be carrying as many nesting geese as it could. Although some races frequently occur in colonies most Canadas resist crowding.

The factors that limit expansion of some populations are complex and hard to pinpoint. An example is the small population of nonmigrant Vancouver Canada geese of southeastern Alaska. Few of them winter south of their breeding grounds in the Alexander Archipelago. It is perhaps the most lightly harvested population of all Canada geese, because few people live where they winter and the hunting grounds are hard to reach. Yet this subspecies does not expand much beyond 15 or 20 thousand. A full scale investigation would probably be required to find out why the number does not increase.

Aleuts, Eskimos, and Indians, who live off the land, do not take many Canada geese, although people near some villages gather the eggs. Species that nest in colonies suffer more from egg-taking than the more solitary Canadas, except maybe the cackler. In a few localities people organize to capture flightless geese, but the practice has become less frequent as opportunities for work and education have improved. We have no indication that utilization of Canada geese by natives on the breeding grounds is a limiting factor in the expansion of any subspecies, but it is quite evident that sport hunting in Canada and the United States can quickly reduce populations if not controlled closely.

The Canada goose responds well to present game management techniques. One outstanding example is the *Mississippi Valley Population* which slumped to a low of less than 30 thousand birds in 1946 when the season was closed on Canada geese in the Mississippi Flyway. Strict regulations, intensive refuge management programs in Illinois, Wisconsin, and Michigan, and seasonal kill quotas initiated in 1960 have resulted in marked increases in this population. A peak of nearly 450 thousand Canadas was reached in the Mississippi Flyway in January 1963. Present management plans are geared to the carrying capacities of major migration and wintering areas. Annual nesting success, of course, determines the size of annual harvest permitted in the respective States. Just how large this population may ultimately grow will depend on future management problems and hunting demands.

There is considerable effort being made by State conservation departments and the Bureau of Sport Fisheries and Wildlife to establish more local breeding populations of Canadas, especially in the former breeding range of races native to the northern tier of States. These programs have good potential for projects of local interest. However, these new flocks may present problems in management. In many cases newly established flocks have not migrated, thus causing serious wintering problems. Such projects, in the main, however, have wide public appeal, and there is little doubt that local breeding populations can eventually be restored over much of the former range of the Canada goose providing that the proper breeding stock is introduced, the proper habitat is maintained, and public agencies or private organizations are willing to bear the cost.

FUTURE MANAGEMENT programs need a better foundation of more intensive research, especially on the breeding biology and specific habitat requirements of subspecies. Additional collecting of representative specimens and banding on the breeding and wintering grounds are needed to relate more accurately the given races of geese to specific breeding areas, migration routes, and wintering areas. The adequacy of migration and wintering habitat for each population requires constant surveillance to prevent deterioration or loss of habitat in certain localities and to assure adequate provisions for increased goose populations in the future.

IN THIS DAY of increasing demands on the land, Canada geese hold a trump card in the chancy game of survival. Their breeding grounds, deep in the Arctic and subarctic vastness, are mostly out of reach to those who might exploit them. That is important. All other adversities considered, none can spell doom faster than the loss of a place to reproduce. Without suitable areas to nest and brood young, all other needs of wildlife cease to be.

Other waterfowl that have nesting grounds closer to civilization may be put in jeopardy by drainage, pollution, and a host of developments that destroy and erode their nurseries. For the moment, those dangers do not threaten the Canadas over much of their range, but—the time could come. The remoteness that now protects nesting geese from the harassment of civilization also makes impractical the management of their far-flung breeding areas. Our greatest opportunity then is to safeguard these Arctic habitats against developments that would destroy them.

—HENRY A. HANSEN and
HARVEY K. NELSON

Suddenly out of the north came the sound I had been waiting for, a soft, melodious gabbling that swelled and died and increased in volume until all other sounds were engulfed by its clamor. Far in the blue I saw them, a long skein of dots undulating like a floating ribbon pulled toward the south by an invisible cord tied to the point of its V.

—SIGURD F. OLSON.

SNOW GEESE

Snows and Blues

FROM BEYOND the north wind come the snow geese. Each summer they vanish from settled regions. Some go clear off the topside of the North American mainland to nest on the islands of the Arctic Archipelago. When the brief summer wanes in that remote, icy world, the greater snow geese come to the Atlantic coastal marshes to winter, and many lesser snow geese lose themselves each fall in the marshes and prairies along the western Gulf of Mexico. Others of the breed spend the winter placidly pulling grass in ricefields and farmlands of the Pacific and Gulf coasts, be-

having not at all like the wilderness bird the Cree Indians know as "wa-wa" or "wavy" until some citizen tries to bag one.

We can argue about the identity of snow and blue geese and get confused over "lesser" and "greater" snow geese. For our purpose now, though, it is enough to point out that lesser snows and blues interbreed freely and that some family groups include both colors. That would seem to make them color phases, one of the other, and not much more.

The white bird apparently was the original stock, and the blue

125

followed along later. Therefore, I refer to them both as lesser snow geese—white and blue phases. The greater snow geese have no blue phase. Here they are considered a separate subspecies, closely related to the lesser yet distinct from them. However, we are more interested now in where they come from, where they go, and what they do along the way.

FIFTY YEARS AGO, the "blue" snow goose was relatively rare. Now these blue-phase individuals are increasing at the rate of 2 percent a year, and they are gradually extending their way westward. They were restricted to colonies on Baffin and Southampton Islands in 1930. Since then they have spread south and westward to other places in the Northwest Territories—Eskimo Point, Perry River, and Banks Island. The increase has been somewhat at the expense of white-phase birds. If the present trend continues until 1975, all nesting colonies in North America should contain at least 1 percent blue-phase birds, and all colonies around Hudson Bay should have 35 to 98 percent.

Blue-phase birds occur in wintering flocks in much the same pattern as is evident on the nesting grounds. Blues now dominate winter flocks in southeastern Louisiana. The white phase of the lesser snow is becoming scarce in that region, and has been a mere 5 percent of wintering flocks in recent years. Westward along the Gulf coast,

only 6 percent to 15 percent of wintering snows in the Vermilion marshes, and 20 percent to 30 percent of snows in the Cameron marshes of southwestern Louisiana, are now of the white phase. On the Texas coast, white- and blue-phase geese are equal in numbers north of Galveston. South of that point, white snow geese dominate. Blue-phase birds make up about 20 percent of mixed flocks at Victoria and become relatively uncommon in extreme south Texas and Mexico. A few blue-phase birds show up each winter on the Atlantic coast—about one-third of 1 percent of the snow geese there. The "blue" snow goose is a rarity on the Pacific coast.

Blue-phase birds have a higher rate of survival on the breeding grounds. At Boas River and Eskimo Point, I found that predators caused 50 percent of all nesting loss. In the seasons that were delayed 10 days, more than 40 percent of all eggs were taken by predators. White-phase birds are more likely to lose their eggs because they nest slightly earlier than blue or mixed pairs. More of their nests therefore are available to predators at a time when other food is scarce. Flooding is more apt to occur early in the nesting season.

Survival of the blue-phase is favored during the hunting season, too. Hunters prefer the "big white bird" to the darker one. Both types may make nonstop flights from Hudson Bay to Louisiana, but white snows tend to interrupt their migra-

Concentration of snow geese and other waterfowl at Tule Lake National Wildlife Refuge, California.

*A lone blue goose looks askance at plane
and photographer over the Canadian prairie.*

tions more often than the blues do
and there is more time to hunt them.

LESSER SNOW GEESE, including the
blue phase, nest in 14 major concentrations between Baffin Island and
Siberia, with a large gap in Alaska.
The breeding distribution of greater
snow geese partly overlaps that of
the smaller forms and includes parts
of the Canadian Islands of Baffin,
Bylot, Devon, Ellesmere, and Somerset and western Greenland.

During spring and autumn migration, greater snow geese rest 8 to 10
weeks at Cap Tourmente, on the St.
Lawrence River. The birds from all
nesting areas concentrate in winter,
in the Chesapeake Bay-Currituck
Sound area of Maryland, Virginia,
and North Carolina.

Lesser snows (including the blue
phase) are more widespread in win-

ter. They segregate, more or less, by
breeding populations along the coast
of the Gulf of Mexico from Plaque-
mines Parish in Louisiana to Veracruz, Mexico, along the delta of the
Colorado, the Central Valley of California, and in Puget Sound. Geese
that nest around Hudson Bay generally winter in coastal Louisiana
and Texas. Nesters in the central
Canadian Arctic may winter in Mexico. Those that nest in the western
Canadian Arctic go primarily to
California. Birds that breed in Siberia spend the winter near Puget
Sound and the Fraser Delta of British Columbia and in the Central
Valley of California.

UNLIKE THE GREATER SNOW GEESE,
lesser snows, blue and white, use
many stopping places. Some flocks
apparently have different migration
routes. The spring flight from the
Gulf coast is in slow, easy stages up
the Mississippi-Missouri and then by
a direct flight from the Dakotas to
James Bay. Autumn migration in
the eastern part of their range is
sometimes a spectacular flight of a
thousand miles from James Bay directly to the Gulf coast. In recent
years, however, the birds stop over
in the Dakotas quite regularly. Migrations of the far-western lesser
snow populations also vary seasonally. Spring migration through Canada is close to the Rocky Mountains,
but in autumn the southward-mov-
ing geese spread out across Saskatchewan and Alberta. Many migrants
fly at 6 thousand feet or more.

For breeding, greater snow geese
on Bylot Island favor the valley
banks where streams have eroded

the interior plateau. They tend to breed in small numbers in any one locality, except perhaps on Bylot Island and some sections of Ellesmere Island. Many nest in small, isolated colonies at the heads of deep fiords.

Major colonies of lesser snow geese show similar preferences for climate, vegetation, and land types. White and blue phases nest close to the sea on open, flat tundra. Nesting areas are limestone basins, islands in river deltas, and plains, usually drained by relatively large rivers that open early in the season. Most of the birds nest within 5 miles of salt water (except at Egg River, Banks Island and Wrangel Island, Siberia) but not between the tidal wrack and the sea. Snow goose habitat is somewhat like shortgrass prairie. The tundra grasses and sedges grow to about 6 inches, and miles of perennial flowers bloom just as the goslings hatch. Plants and insect larvae provide most of the food for young goslings.

Snow geese like to be close to each other. I know of nesting concentrations of 1,200 pairs to the square mile. The largest known concentration of geese in the world extends for 350 miles along the shore of Foxe Basin and inland on Baffin Island for 5 to 20 miles. In mid-July there are usually at least a million geese of three species in that area. Other smaller colonies numbered about 35 thousand adults each, except for a group at Egg River, Banks Island, which in some years may contain 100 thousand birds, and one on Wrangel Island, which may contain 300 thousand birds. The colonies on Baffin, Banks, and Wrangel Islands are so large that their success in breeding largely de-

LESSER SNOW GOOSE
Breeding Grounds ●●●
Wintering Grounds ○ ○

GREATER SNOW GOOSE
Breeding Grounds ▲▲
Wintering Grounds △ △

termines fall populations in the Mid-western States and along the Pacific Flyway.

THE SEASONAL ACTIVITY of lesser snow geese is much the same at the different colonies. In the East, the birds arrive about June 1 and begin to nest within 2 weeks. In the western Arctic, nesting generally begins a week earlier, during the last week of May. Egg laying ceases 11 days after the first has been laid. Incubation takes 22 or 23 days. In mid-August, 42 days later, young birds make their first flights. Nonbreeding adults and subadults leave the breeding ground about that time. Adults, with young, follow during the first week of September.

Bad weather may delay nesting for as much as 2 weeks. If conditions are not better by then, the birds do not nest. At the start of nesting, 80 to 95 percent of the land is still covered with snow or water; temperatures rarely rise above 45° F. at midday and fall to 25° at night. It is an early season if 20 percent of the habitat is clear of snow and water when the birds arrive. As little as 5 percent of the habitat may be available in late seasons.

REPRODUCTION is affected by seasonal conditions, density of population, age of the birds, and habitat conditions. The average number of eggs is 4.4 in an early season and 3.8 in a late season. T. W. Barry discovered that a change in the female's organs causes a reduction in the size of the clutch and so compensates for the late season and the corresponding decrease in time available (no more than 110 days) to lay eggs, incubate them, and rear the young. A delay of less than a week in nesting can reduce the average basic clutch from 4.4 to 4.1. Some white-phase geese tend to nest earlier than blue-phase birds, and so are more sensitive to delays in the start of the nesting season

LOSSES TO PREDATORS also are linked with the season. In early seasons, when places to nest are easy to find, the geese stake out their claims to nesting sites in favorable places, and the loss to enemies is low. But when habitat is restricted or when the number of pairs exceeds the carrying capacity of the habitat, the system of selecting places breaks down. Then random laying occurs, and the birds are forced into marginal habitat where predators exert the maximum effect. Mr. Barry reported that 49 percent of the eggs of black brant and snow geese which were laid in poor habitat at Anderson River, Northwest Territories, were destroyed by parasitic jaegers during the 1959 season.

Most geese arrive at the breeding grounds within a week in early seasons. Their arrival may be spread over 2 or 3 weeks in late seasons. A certain threshold in numbers that seems necessary to trigger nesting usually is not reached until at least one-third of the group is present. The start of nesting also awaits the thawing of the frozen ground to a depth of about an inch.

The amount of habitat and time available for nesting are restricted and lead to competition for nesting space. The competition gets keener each day nesting is delayed. When late seasons follow a year or two of large broods, many birds, usually 3-year-olds that have just attained sexual maturity, are kept from nesting by older, more experienced pairs, which normally nest first.

That happened in the 1961 season. Of 530 thousand blue-phase geese that went north, only 110 thousand—20 percent—were 3 years old or older. Because of restricted habitat and pressure of predators, reproduction was the lowest since 1954. Production in 1962, however, was greater than in 1961, despite a lower population. The reason seems to be that the 1962 populations included nearly twice as many breeders 3 years of age or older.

The breeding colonies of snow geese in 1962 could not support populations larger than those of the peak years. In very early seasons, the habitat may be underutilized, but a greater annual carryover would worsen the situation in years when the season is late and habitat is restricted.

The only way to enlarge the numbers is to colonize new areas. That happened at Cape Henrietta Maria, Ontario, in 1947, 1954, and in 1957, when several hundred birds stopped their flight and nested. The birds have returned there every year since, and the colony had grown to at least 15 thousand birds in 10 years. A colony near Eskimo Point, Keewatin, probably began in the same way. I have heard that geese recently have extended their breeding range westward in Siberia toward the Taymyr Peninsula.

Large sections of seemingly good habitat have no breeding populations, nor is it likely that they will have any soon, because they lie north of present colonies or off the

A pair of lesser snow geese, which are intermediate in size between the Ross' goose and greater snow goose.

main spring migration routes. We doubt whether efforts to transplant breeding pairs there would succeed; the places are so isolated that it would be almost impossible to maintain a captive flock the year around, as has been done with Canada geese.

THE BREEDING AREAS of lesser snow geese may suffer some day because of their small size and heavy use by the birds. So far people have not unduly disturbed them. But the possible development of oil and mineral deposits in the Canadian Arctic and military installations may some day harm them. As a safeguard, nine Federal migratory bird sanctuaries were established by the Canadian Government between 1957 and 1961. These cover all of the major known colonies of lesser snow geese in Canada. Some of the sanctuaries are large—22,240 square miles at Queen Maud Gulf. They total 36,903 square miles. In addition the Province of Ontario has set aside the Henrietta Maria colony as a Provincial sanctuary. The breeding grounds of the greater snow goose are unprotected as of 1964, but the need is not so urgent because breeding grounds are dispersed and isolated and the number of birds at one location is small.

In the East, southern Hudson Bay and James Bay are autumn concentration points; young geese, having little fear of man, are most vulnerable there. To protect these, three Federal and two Provincial sanctuaries have been established. In other localities, people living more than 25 miles from the sparsely inhabited coast are forbidden to hunt. Limited accommodations restrict the number of tourist hunters in open areas, and their kill is controlled by a season limit.

In the West, the flocks are scattered widely in autumn, and the need for refuges to safeguard birds in passage is not yet urgent.

SNOW GEESE, like other arctic species, nest mainly in unspoiled, primitive areas. Colonies in Siberia, on the mainland and on Wrangel Island, have been exploited, so that birds that formerly wintered off the coast of Japan have disappeared. The North American breeding grounds and the Siberian colonies that supply birds to the west coast of North America have been practically untouched, however, and fall flights continue in good numbers.

But we should not be complacent. One interesting development arouses fears and some hope. Geese need wintering grounds as well as points of refuge in passage. State and Federal refuges along the Atlantic, Pacific, and Gulf coasts are ample for present populations. In Texas, California, and Louisiana, the birds are moving out of wilderness areas to new winter quarters in fallow ricefields, irrigated lands, and improved pastures. That is quite a change, because some of the geese have moved to cultivated lands apparently of their own will, for the natural haunts they abandoned are in good condition.

The change brings birds into closer contact with the growing human population. The geese on farmland are becoming more available to hunters, and the take certainly will be greater. It can be expected, too, that geese will damage more pastures and growing crops; as fast as one such problem is solved, another seems to spring up. At the same time many farmers find that geese can help them weed their ricefields.

Regardless of what happens, these colorful birds should continue to prosper if we treat them with the respect they merit. They have every-thing else it takes to do well, whether at the high seventies of North Latitude or on the lower forty of the old plantation.

—F. G. Cooch.

In God's wildness lies the hope of the world—the great fresh, unblighted, unredeemed wilderness. The galling harness of civilization drops off, and the wounds heal ere we are aware. —John Muir.

WHITE-FRONTED GEESE

White-Fronts

THE WHITE-FRONTED goose, a true Westerner, likes open spaces—the trackless Arctic prairies in summer and a few remaining vistas in Texas, California, and Mexico in winter. Even on his northward or southward flights through Washington, Oregon, Saskatchewan, the Dakotas, and Nebraska, he chooses an area with elbowroom for resting and feeding. He is primarily a grazer, but at opportune times he will fill his gizzard with barley, wheat, rice, or corn.

Whether you know him as specklebelly, tiger brant, or grey wavey, the white-fronted goose is a delight on the table. The Canada goose may rate as a trophy bird, but the white-front is an eating bird, relished alike by the Danish housewife in Greenland, who fattens up a young white-front for Christmas, the Eskimo in Alaska, the Indian of the Mackenzie Valley, the wheat farmer of Saskatchewan and the Dakotas, the Cajun of Louisiana, and city folk in San Francisco, Mexico City, and Houston. To nature lovers, in early fall, the white-front signals the coming of winter as he scurries south before the first hard frosts. He gladdens the hearts of many as he swoops down, calling *klōw, lyōw,* and shows

135

the beauty of his white forehead, dark belly bars, bright orange feet, and handsome plumage.

IN DISTRIBUTION, white-fronts are almost circumpolar. They nest between 60° and 75° latitudes in Asia and North America. There are four distinct types.

The European subspecies breeds from the Kanin Peninsula on the Arctic coast of Russia and east along the Siberian coast to the Kolyma River. It winters in England, the Netherlands, Germany, Hungary, Yugoslavia, Greece, Egypt, Iraq, Iran, the Black and Caspian Sea coasts, and India. It has a somewhat shorter neck, is generally lighter colored, and is smaller than its American cousin, the Pacific white-fronted goose.

The Pacific white-front breeds from the Kolyma River eastward to the Anadyr Basin and across Bering Strait into North America. On our continent it breeds on the tundra from Alaska east to the eastern Canadian Arctic on King William Island. Wintering grounds of the Siberian birds are the coastal marshes of Japan and China. The American breeders winter mainly on the inland refuges of California and the coastal marshes of Mexico, Texas, and Louisiana.

The Greenland form is slightly larger and darker than the European or the Pacific. It has an orange bill; the others have pinkish bills. It breeds on the western coast of Greenland between latitudes 64° and 72° and winters in Ireland, England, and Wales. A few make their way westward in autumn down the east coast to Quebec and as far south as the Carolinas.

The fourth subspecies is something of a puzzle. The Tule white-fronted goose is a large North American form of the white-front. It reaches 8 pounds, compared to 5 to 7 pounds of the other three. The color of the back and neck is darker and browner than the smaller subspecies. Its breeding grounds are unknown. The Mackenzie River Delta, one of the Canadian arctic islands, or even Alaska are possibilities. The birds migrate in limited numbers through southern Oregon. The wintering grounds are chiefly in Butte, Colusa, and Sutter Counties of California. Some have been taken on the western coast of Mexico. We fear this subspecies is on the verge of extinction, as fewer reports about it come in each year. It is less wary and more easily taken with a gun than the smaller forms.

A much smaller cousin, the lesser white-fronted goose, nests across northern Siberia into Lapland, somewhat further inland than the white-front. It winters over Europe, Asia Minor, coastal China, and Japan. North American specimens are rare.

THE BREEDING GROUNDS of the white-fronted goose are dispersed over 2,500 miles of the Alaskan and the Canadian Arctic. All are generally uninhabited, strewn with lakes and streams, and infested with mosquitoes. The vegetation is short and grassy or brushy. Winters are cold and long. Summers are warm and short. But this land of the midnight sun has long days, and birds can feed many hours of the 24. The white-front, like other arctic-breeding geese, rarely stays longer than 120 days—a short time for nest building, egg laying, incubation, and rearing of young.

Once on site, the female scratches a bowl in the ground and lines it with dried grasses, sticks, and down. The male protects his "staked-out" territory around his mate. He calls loudly, hisses, and flies at other white-fronts that come too close to the nest. The first eggs are laid about May 25, and the starting of new nests continues for about three weeks. Each female lays 4 to 7 eggs, usually one every day or two. The female does the incubating for 23 to 28 days, while the gander stands guard.

The first goslings appear about June 25. The parents lead the young through the wet tundra. Young birds grow fast on grasses, sedges, and insects. In 6 or 7 weeks they can fly. Adult white-fronts moult their flight feathers when their goslings are 2 to 3 weeks old and remain flightless about 3 weeks. Nonbreeding and yearling birds moult earlier and regain their flight earlier. By August 10–25, most white-fronts can fly again.

The European, North American, and Greenland white-fronts generally are associated with middle and low arctic tundras. Vegetation there is short. Permafrost occurs 1 to 2 feet below the surface and the little soil available to plants is fairly sterile. Nesting pairs utilize the open wet tundra, borders of shallow marshes and lakes, river banks and islands, deltas, dry knolls, and hillocks near rivers and ponds. Nests are seldom far from water. The chief plants of the breeding habitat are sedges, horsetails, cottongrasses, bluegrass, fescue, and arctagrostis. Sphagnum moss is found in depressions. Reindeer-moss and cetraria grow on the drier sites. Dwarf birch, several kinds

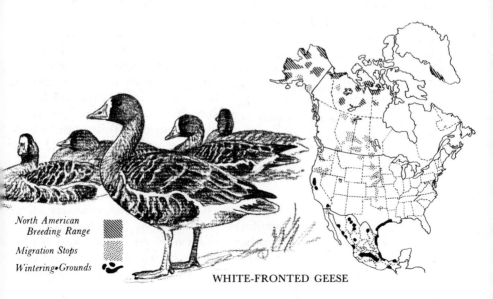

North American
   Breeding Range

Migration Stops

Wintering•Grounds

WHITE-FRONTED GEESE

of willow, and low shrubs like bilberries, crowberries, labrador-tea, cassiope, raspberries, and dryas grow there, too.

IN ALASKA, white-fronts breed in loose colonies along the Yukon River, where they lay their eggs in hollows scraped out of the sand. Alfred Bailey, of the Denver Museum, noted east of Point Barrow that small, loose colonies of 15 to 20 pairs inhabited an area of one-fourth square mile. They are generally not colonial nesters, although pairs tend to gather in the few favored locations. On the Yukon-Kuskokwim Delta, they nest chiefly on higher ground 12 to 15 miles from the coast. Their nests, therefore, are less vulnerable to flooding by high tides than are those of brant or cackling geese, which nest closer to the sea.

Henry Hansen of the Bureau of Sport Fisheries and Wildlife finds that some of the best white-front habitat in central Alaska is willow- and shrub-fringed streams and ponds. Fires, caused mostly by lightning, regularly destroy and replace goose breeding habitat by removing the thin layers of undecayed vegetation on the tundra. It is replaced by willows and later by grasses, which geese use for pasture. Even on the Arctic coasts, white-fronts favor prostrate willow and other upland vegetation more than other geese do.

IN THE WESTERN Canadian Arctic, two types of tundra breeding ground occur between Mackenzie and Anderson Rivers of Northwest Territories. Coastal tundra, which is low and flat, has uncounted shallow lakes and ponds. Tidal action limits vegetative growth near the sea. Land-locked ponds have a narrow fringe of sedge. Upland tundra has gently rolling uplands 50 to 700 feet above sea level and lakes and ponds in all depressions. Westward, the 2 thousand square miles of inland habitat of Old Crow Flats in Yukon Territory lie in an elevated basin surrounded by mountains. Here spruce and willow are present, but much of the wet, barren lands resembles the upland tundra of the Arctic coast. Eastward, the white-front breeding places in the Queen Maud Gulf region of Northwest Territories are broadly similar to coastal and upland tundra types. Further inland, along the upper Thelon River of Northwest Territories, low willows cover some habitat the pairs and broods use.

Figures on the extent of habitat are meaningless because of low densities and fluctuations in numbers on the breeding grounds. Pairs use only small percentages of the Arctic tracts available to them. We estimate, though, that about 40 thousand square miles of habitat in the Yukon-Kuskokwim and Bristol Bay districts of Alaska are available to nearly 200 thousand white-fronts, which winter in the Pacific Flyway.

Wintering birds of the Central Flyway, which number more than 70 thousand, utilize nearly all of the remaining 84 thousand square miles of rivers, deltas, and coastal plains spotted northward and eastward from the Yukon-Kuskokwim

Delta. Another 35 thousand square miles of localized breeding places are dispersed through the Canadian Arctic from the Alaskan border east to Boothia Peninsula and south to tree line. Some Central Flyway geese breed here, but these lowlands are also summer homes for a large portion of the 25 thousand white-fronts which winter in Louisiana.

Most white-fronts do not mature until their second or even third summer, and fewer than half the 250 to 300 thousand birds counted on wintering grounds will nest the following spring. Accordingly, densities of nesters over the 159 thousand square miles of breeding grounds are slim, indeed.

NESTING DENSITIES for 800 square miles of the best habitat in the Yukon-Kuskokwim Delta average six to seven white-fronts to the square mile. In a nearby area of 20 thousand square miles, they average one to the square mile. Densities of one bird to 3 to 16 square miles have been noted for various blocks of habitat in the western Canadian Arctic. Old Crow Flats, which held no white-fronts in 1948, showed a population of 2.2 to a square mile in 1949. Such fluctuations may be due partly to inadequate census coverage, but mostly they reflect yearly ups-and-downs of white-front populations in the North.

White-fronts on both sides of the Rocky Mountains have their own breeding, migration, and wintering areas. Those wintering in California breed mainly on the Yukon-Kuskokwim Delta and Bristol Bay areas, although a small area of overlap between Pacific and Central Flyways' birds is noted in the Innoko River. Others wintering in Texas and Mexico migrate northward and southward through the Great Plains. They nest in central and northern Alaska, and eastward into arctic Canada. Small numbers of white-fronts are taken west of the Mississippi River in Louisiana, an indication of a degree of interchange of birds between the Central and Mississippi Flyways.

WEATHER IN THE ARCTIC affects breeding more than any other factor. Nesting sites are not available in a late, cold spring because of snow cover; then pairs quarrel and fight over the few bare patches. Food may be scant, and many birds do not attempt to nest. Among those that do, clutches and resultant broods are smaller. Goslings grow slowly, and some may not be able to fly before hard frosts come in mid-August. It all adds up to low production; in 1961–1962, the number of young in fall flocks migrating through Saskatchewan was only 25 percent. Furthermore, the few young that move southward in such years are in poor condition, covered with pin feathers, and easily taken by hunters.

The hatching rate of white-fronts is high, usually more than 80 percent in warm springs. And a good thing it is, because poor years occur regularly in the Far North, and a bumper crop of goslings now and again is necessary if the species is to survive. The short summer allows too little time for geese that lose their eggs or young to nest a second time. The white-front endures mainly because of its widespread breeding range. In any one spring, the weather seldom is bad all the way from Alaska to the eastern Arctic—a saving feature.

BREEDING HABITAT of white-fronts is not being destroyed nor is it in immediate jeopardy, because of its inaccessibility and the foresight of the United States and Canadian Governments. In December 1960, 2,200 square miles of the best white-fronted goose habitat in Alaska were withdrawn by the United States Department of the Interior from public domain lands to establish the Kuskokwim National Wildlife Range. It is an area of low-lying tundra in southwestern Alaska along the coast of the Bering Sea. It is a land with myriad small lakes, ponds, and sloughs and is ideal as a waterfowl breeding area. In January 1961, the Range was renamed the Clarence Rhode National Wildlife Range in honor of the late Regional Director of the Bureau of Sport Fisheries and Wildlife for Alaska. Clarence Rhode was an authority on Alaska's wildlife resources, an outstanding leader, and an expert pilot. He lost his life in October 1958 while on a mission for the Bureau.

The Canadian Government in 1962 set aside 24,240 square miles as the Queen Maud Gulf Bird Sanctuary primarily to safeguard breeding habitat for the rare Ross' goose but also to provide for the small Canada and white-fronted goose. The Anderson River Delta Bird Sanctuary, of 418 square miles, was also created then. Both supply white-fronts to the Central and Mississippi Flyways. The sanctuaries were established to effect some measure of control over exploratory and development work of mining interests.

At least two extensive breeding areas may be in jeopardy. The proposed Rampart Dam on the upper Yukon River, Alaska, would flood several thousand square miles of white-front habitat along the flats below Fort Yukon. In the Old Crow Flats of the Canadian Yukon, intensive oil exploration and production, unless controlled, could impair this habitat.

COLONIZATION of new breeding areas has been taking place in the North, possibly because of increased numbers in the past 50 years. The large group of breeding white-fronts on the Thelon River may be a new development, since Dr. C. H. D. Clarke found no breeding birds in the area in 1937. The Danish scientist, Finn Salomonsen, in 1948 reported a northward spread of the Greenland white-front along the northernmost points of its breeding range. This spread seems due to an increase in temperatures over the first 50 years of the present century and the availability of more suitable habitat. A similar moderation of climate in North America may extend the breeding limits to other Arctic islands.

As for the increased numbers of white-fronts over the past half century, several explanations are possible. A system of refuges, especially in wintering areas of the United States, has provided the bird with safe resting and feeding grounds; hunting has been better controlled; and breeding areas in the Arctic have been extended.

AUTUMN IN THE FAR NORTH comes early, and white-fronts are among the first geese to move south, well ahead of the first severe frosts. Family groups and nonbreeders gather into flocks about August 15. By the second week of September, Pacific Flyway birds have crossed the Alaskan Peninsula, moved down the coast of British Columbia, and are again on the Oregon coast.

The last leave Alaska by the end of September. They tarry on the coast for several weeks. Then they move inland, dawdling and feeding about the Tule-Klamath Basin. November finds the birds in the Central Valley wintering grounds of California. A few thousand move south through Imperial Valley and winter on the west coast of Mexico.

In the Central and Mississippi Flyways, the first nonbreeders return by August 20 to staging or rallying areas around Brackett Lake, Northwest Territories, Hay-Zama lakes in Northwest Alberta, and The Pas-Cumberland Marshes of Manitoba. A week later, flocks wind their way southward to grainfields of west-central Saskatchewan.

The white-fronted goose is a bird of the West. It rarely occurs east of the Mississippi River.

Family groups start to arrive there by September 5. The first wanderers are reported on the Gulf coast wintering areas of Texas and Louisiana by the last week of September. By October 15, few white-fronts are left in Canada, their lonely cry unheard until the following spring. Several thousand birds stop off in North Dakota and Nebraska for short periods. Up to 15 thousand white-fronts continue further south and bask in the winter sun along Mexico's east coast and the interior highland lakes.

THERE IS A TENDENCY (reported also in Europe and Asia) for this species to change suddenly its fall and spring flight patterns. The white-front was generally unknown to goose hunters of western Saskatchewan and eastern Alberta as late as 1935. Now, more than 50 thousand birds pass through the area in autumn. At the same time, populations moving through the Last Mountain Lake-Quill Lakes areas of eastern Saskatchewan, some 250 miles to the east, have been reduced markedly during the period 1940–1960. Droughts, floods, changes in land use, or lack of food may shift the migration route.

The life history and biology of the white-front are not well known. Its nesting densities are sparse; up to 1955, only a handful had been banded. Only recently has some understanding been gained of its distribution from breeding to wintering grounds. An accurate count of wintering white-fronts is nearly impossible to obtain, especially in the Central Flyway, where small flocks disperse throughout Texas and Mexico.

White-fronts are not subjected to heavy hunting by Eskimos. Limited hunting is done by natives in Alaska and the Canadian Arctic on a few areas where moulting birds congregate. To these hardy people, a goose, even if taken in summer, is a welcome change from the daily fare of fish, seal meat, and blubber. But the kill in North America by Eskimos and Indians is negligible compared to the yearly kill by sportsmen in the United States and southern Canada, which is estimated at between 90 thousand and 120 thousand.

Predators on the breeding grounds include the gull-like jaegers, which steal unprotected eggs, and glaucous gulls, which swallow live young less than a week old. Arctic foxes, red foxes, and an occasional tundra wolf take a few scattered nests and goslings. Eagles and snowy owls take an insignificant number of young on the breeding grounds. Barren ground grizzlies now and then destroy a few nests in their travels along the coast. Polar bears are not regular visitors to mainland coasts in summer and therefore do not affect nesting white-fronts.

WHAT DOES THE FUTURE HOLD for the white-front? Things ahead look reasonably promising. Its main breeding grounds in the frozen Arctic appear to be secure, and out of reach to those who might drain, mine, farm, or flood. Water and food conditions are fairly stable in the remote North, but spring weather will continue to plague the white-front and cause some pairs to return south each year without young. Wintering grounds are adequate to hold and feed the present flocks, and more. Expanding agriculture and industry, with their effects on habitat, are sure to make inroads on wintering areas. But this species has demonstrated a remarkable ability to adapt; it is not likely to feel the pinch for some time because of changes at its southern terminus.

Although there may be no immediate shortage of breeding and wintering habitat for the bird's welfare, the problem does not end here. During the shooting season disturbance by hunters makes many areas unavailable that would be suitable otherwise. As intermediate stopping points along migration routes are eliminated the birds make longer flights; not only to the detriment of the birds but also to the hunters along the way who then have little opportunity to share in the harvest. There is need, therefore, to acquire migration habitat — places safe from disturbance where the birds may delay, then move on. But time moves on, too. And each passing year sees more land preempted for domestic needs. Tomorrow may be too late. We should act now with a vigorous program of land acquisition to secure not only the land needed for the future of these and other waterfowl but also the areas required to distribute the resource and make it available for recreational purposes.

—ALEX DZUBIN,
HARVEY W. MILLER,
and GEORGE V. SCHILDMAN.

EMPEROR GEESE
ALASKAN BROWN BEAR

Brant, Ross' Goose, and Emperor Goose

THE FAST, agile, white-bellied brant once were popular sporting birds along the Atlantic coast. In the early 1930's they became almost extinct because eelgrass, their chief food in winter, suddenly died off due to a disease caused by a mycetozoan, *Labyrinthula*. The surviving birds changed foods and the number of Atlantic brant slowly rose again. Then another untoward event happened. They lost prestige as a game bird because sea-lettuce, the chief item of their new diet, taints their flesh. Now eelgrass is slowly recovering, and brant once more feed on it. We hope their meat in time will become more palatable.

Another remarkable thing: As Atlantic brant changed their diet, they also changed their migration routes. By the midthirties, about two-thirds of them, no longer dependent on coastal eelgrass beds, were using overland routes in spring flights north, instead of following the seacoast. Most of our 150 thousand to 200 thousand Atlantic brant today are their descendants; they fly directly to James, Hudson, and Ungava Bays before spreading out to their nesting grounds.

Because eelgrass on the Pacific coast was little affected by the die-off, the black brant suffered less, and they still provide excellent sport and tasty game. They continue their regular migration along the coast and follow the shores of Gulf of Alaska to Cold Bay before heading to the breeding grounds. Pacific brant number 100 thousand to 175 thousand.

Both Atlantic and Pacific brant are truly sea geese. Their well-developed salt glands enable them to drink sea water and eat coastal plants. But during the 3-month breeding season, they are land grazers and use fresh water, although they are never far from the ocean. They live then in all parts of the Arctic, concentrating in their favorite nesting grounds close to the sea shore.

Atlantic brant nest on the eastern Arctic coast and islands. Pacific brant nest in the Yukon-Kuskokwim Delta and coasts of Siberia and western Arctic Canada. They both nest in Queen Maud Gulf and on Prince Patrick and Melville Islands, but they seldom interbreed because they choose mates during long association in fall, winter, and spring while the two forms are on opposite sides of the continent.

MAJOR NESTING GROUNDS for brant are Foxe Basin (Koukdjuak River and Bowman Bay, on the coasts of Baffin Island, and Prince Charles Island), Southampton Island (Bay of God's Mercy, East Bay, Ell Bay,

and Bear Cove), Central and Western Arctic (southern coast of Queen Maud Gulf, Erebus Bay on King William Island, Albert Edward Bay and Wellington Bay on Victoria Island, western coast and inland lakes of Banks Island, Anderson River Delta, Dalhousie Peninsula and Liverpool Bay, Mackenzie River Delta, Colville River Delta, and Yukon-Kuskokwim Delta), High Arctic (southeastern coast of Prince Patrick Island, Melville Island, Ellef Ringnes and Amund Ringnes Islands, suitable country of Axel Heiberg and Ellesmere Islands and of Greenland to the northern extremity of land) and Siberia.

BRANT NEST BARELY A FOOT above the high tide line on flats, islets, river deltas, and raised beaches or occasionally on the rocks and points of inland lakes. Usually they simply form a hollow in the turf, adding down until a thick pillow is formed. Sometimes they use grass, old feathers, leaves, seaweeds, and driftwood chips. At the beginning of the season, the nest rests on permafrost, which slowly recedes during the summer. Only the down insulates the eggs from ground chill.

Because they are so close to water, you may think brant nests would be destroyed by floods and storm tides. But in 8 seasons, I have never seen more than 3 percent of nests destroyed by floods. One reason is that in most locations brant nest after the spring floods are over. Another is that if the sea is covered with ice, winds cannot push up storm tides. The sea ice in most places usually breaks up late in July, after the hatch. At Yukon-Kuskokwim Delta, sea ice moves offshore in late May, and there is a chance that storm tides may damage nests. This occurred in 1963 when a storm tide wiped out many of the nests in this area. In some instances when a nest has been flooded, parent birds can successfully continue incubation after the tide has receded a few hours later, if the nest is intact and if incubation was not far along before it was flooded.

Brant are among the last birds to arrive on the breeding grounds each year, probably because their habitat clears of snow and water later than higher terrain. The dates—late May to early June—are nearly the same every year in each locality, but they vary across their range.

Brant are well adapted to the short nesting season in several ways. Selecting their mates while they are farther south, they do not spend time in prenuptial display on the nesting grounds. The females are ready to lay eggs within a few days after arrival. Their arrival at about the same date each year is timed to take advantage of the normal thaw of the nesting locality.

The birds stay in breeding condition for only about 10 days after their arrival. If snow and water delay nesting, the females begin to resorb the maturing eggs. The later the snow clears, therefore, the fewer eggs they can lay. In very late seasons, few females lay the normal clutch of four or five eggs, and many resorb all their eggs. When large tracts of nesting habitat are ready for use too late, few young hatch.

The fact that earliness of the spring thaw influences the number of young is an advantage to the species. A delayed season would not allow time for the young to gain flight and for the adults to complete their molt before freezeup. No doubt late nesters and renesters were "frozen out" of the brant population long ago.

Brant that fail to nest bypass the 24-day incubation period and begin

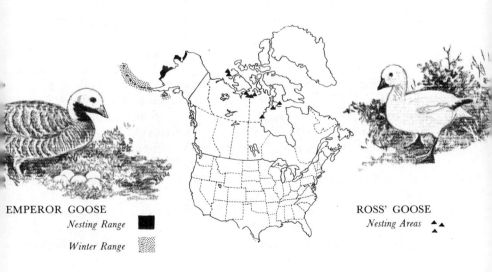

EMPEROR GOOSE
Nesting Range ■

Winter Range ▨

ROSS' GOOSE
Nesting Areas ▲▲
                  ▲

Ross' goose at Malheur National Wildlife Refuge, Oregon.

molting a month early. They are strong on the wing by early August, long before freezeup. By skipping a late season that would result in considerable loss of young, the parents are better able to survive until the next season. Geese are long lived, and the adults will breed in later years; they can make up for a poor nesting season.

PREDATORS are on hand from the moment brant arrive in the Arctic until they leave. Birds of prey sometimes take adults and young. A snowy owl stayed all summer on the goose nesting grounds at Anderson River Delta one year, probably because lemmings were absent that year. It lived by capturing female brant on their nests and averaged two birds every 5 days. But losses to hawks, owls, and eagles are neg-

ligible compared to losses to jaeger and gulls.

Parasitic jaegers, piratical wanderers of the open seas, are a relentless threat during the egg laying period. Brant lay an egg a day. They are inclined to wander off in the meantime and leave their nests untended. Then the jaegers move in, peck holes in the eggs, and sometimes tear the nest to pieces.

Once incubating, brant are more diligent in driving off enemies, but in the late season of 1959, brant on Anderson River Delta seemed less protective than usual. It happened that many jaegers did not nest that year and so were not confined to territories of their own. Those free ranging jaegers concentrated at the goose colony in greater numbers than ever, and on one large island jaegers took nearly half the brant eggs

Jaegers often hunt in teams. I have seen such a pair dive repeatedly at an incubating brant while her mate stood guard, trying to fend off the attacks and keep her on the nest.

During a 3-year study on Southampton Island, I found that herring gulls destroyed as many as 14 percent of the brant eggs. They took young up to 2 weeks old. In the central and western Arctic, glaucous gulls, largest of Arctic gulls, feed heavily on young brant, swallowing them whole. Bigger young, some up to two and one-half pounds, are pecked to death.

Wolves prowl the shores of Anderson River, but only once in 5 years of observation did one swim out to the nesting islands. There it destroyed 10 brant and goose nests and 20 gull nests. Of the 23 polar bears I have seen on nesting grounds, none bothered brant or their young, nor were brant afraid of the bears, although they passed within a few feet of incubating females. But barren ground grizzly bears in Anderson and Mackenzie Deltas are a different matter; brant panicked as the bears approached. Grizzlies range widely, and because they have appeared only twice in 6 years at Anderson River Delta, it seems pure chance when they stumble into a goose colony. But when they did show up in 1958, two of them ate eggs and young from the nests of 135 brant and 160 snow geese in 6 days.

THE ARCTIC FOX is by far the most destructive predator on brant, which are too small to scare them off. The larger snow geese usually can drive them away. Several times I have watched a pair of foxes work together to rob a brant nest. The birds put up an almost suicidal defense, but the foxes were not intimidated and carried off the eggs one by one. One nest cleaned out, the pair moved on to the next. Foxes on Anderson River Delta destroyed 112

BLACK BRANT
Nesting Areas

ATLANTIC BRANT
Nesting Areas

The emperor goose is chiefly an Alaskan species. Most hunters have never seen one, because it does not frequent the flyways with the better-known species of geese.

nests in this way in 7 days; they ate about 10 percent of the eggs and cached the rest.

Eskimos tell me foxes do not like to get wet, and I have watched a fox walk nearly half a mile around a lake to get to a brant nest it could have reached by 20 feet of wading. For that reason, foxes rarely bother nests on small islets unless food is exceptionally scarce, and it may be that brant have evolved their preference for such nest sites as a consequence.

Arctic foxes and lemmings on Banks Island reached a high density before the numbers of lemming fell sharply in the late winter of 1961. The foxes managed to survive until the geese arrived. The thaw was early that spring, and weather was

exceptionally good for goose reproduction. Foxes ate eggs and young birds all summer as a substitute for lemmings. The result was that the crop of brant and snow geese was reduced by half. Foxes disappeared shortly after the geese went south. Probably they died out in the absence of a food supply. Weather in 1962 again was ideal for nesting and the brant reproduced well because the foxes were gone.

As soon as they are dry, young brant are led away to small pools or tide flats to feed on insects, larvae, small shoots of grass, and blossoms. In the Anderson River, Mackenzie, and Yukon-Kuskokwim Deltas, the families flock to beds of pondweed at low tide. The young grow rapidly and can fly in 45 to 50 days. Adults can still fly, although they seldom do, until about 14 days after the hatch. Then they molt their flight feathers and are able to fly again when the young take wing.

As their wings strengthen, families abandon nesting and molting grounds. They congregate in large flocks along the coast near tide flats and lagoons rank with food plants. By early September, when the first heavy snow and freezeup can be expected, the flocks move south—over Hudson Bay in the east and along the Arctic coast to the Bering Sea in the west. The main groups of Pacific brant fly directly from Cold Bay to northern California. Most of the Atlantic brant migrate overland from Hudson and James Bays to the Atlantic coast in the vicinity of New Jersey. In poor years, when they are less well developed because of a late nesting season or an early freezeup, they may stop oftener to rest.

THE ROSS' GOOSE is too small to cope with most predators, especially arctic foxes. That fact may control its peculiar distribution in the Arctic. I surveyed all the streams and rivers flowing into Queen Maud Gulf between Kent Peninsula and Sherman Inlet in 1960 and tabulated at least 9 thousand Ross' geese. Most of them were around a large unnamed lake and river flowing into Mc-Laughlin Bay 100 miles east of Perry River, where the Ross' goose was first discovered nesting. Actually, there may have been twice that number, because confusion with the snow geese, which also nest there, made a precise count impossible.

This region, with thousands of lakes, sloughs, and streams, may prove to be the main breeding grounds of Ross' geese. Elsewhere, a few have been found in other con centrations of snow geese on Banks Island, the McConnell River region south of Eskimo Point on Hudson's Bay, and at Boas River and East Bay on Southampton Island. It would not be surprising to find they are nesting also in goose colonies of the Foxe Basin shore of Baffin Island.

The common feature of nearly all nesting places is a remote island-studded lake or delta, 8 to 40 miles inland, where surrounding country is somewhat dry. They nest less often along river and lake shores. Their island nesting sites undoubtedly give them protection from foxes, and their inland location relieves them somewhat from depredations by gulls

and jaegers, which abound along the coast. Their choice of habitat also explains why their breeding grounds remained a mystery until 1938. Arctic travelers, using the coasts and rivers as highways, were not likely to penetrate Ross' goose country except in winter.

Almost the entire winter population of Ross' geese, which was as high as 30 thousand in 1962–1963, is in the interior valleys of California. The few seen on coasts in Louisiana and Texas in company with snow and blue geese may be migrants from McConnel River and South-ampton Island.

These small, white geese begin moving north by easy stages in early March. They pass through eastern Oregon in early April and continue into northwestern Montana and along the Alberta-Saskatchewan border. They are among the later goose migrants to Athabaska Delta and Great Slave Lake, where they arrive in mid-May. In 1963 the Ross' arrived at Perry River June 5 to 7. Eskimos report the usual arrival date is the last week of May. Birds seen in the Northwest Territories, west of this route, probably nest on Banks Island with snow geese from California.

DEPENDING ON WEATHER and snow cover, nesting begins June 6 to 15. The nest, like the nest of a snow goose but smaller, is a scrape mounded up with twigs of creeping willow, ground birch, grass, moss tufts, and lichen. It has a sparse lining of down. The female develops the brood patch typical of arctic waterfowl. They are inclined to be colonial nesters; in 1963 the 6 small islands of Arlone Lake near Perry River had 769 Ross' goose nests.

The clutch is four or five eggs, although at Perry River in 1963 John P. Ryder found the average of 769 nests to be 3.7. In 1949 H. L. Hanson, P. Queneau, and P. Scott found the average to be 3.0. They surmised that low temperatures that spring, and hence a late thaw, accounted for small clutches and failure to nest. From what is known about the influence of late seasons on brant and other arctic geese, we can guess that Ross' geese are affected similarly.

Incubation is 21 days; after hatching, the birds form flocks of family groups and the adults begin molting. They gather in large, marsh-edged lakes or move downstream toward the coast. Many molting flocks use grassy marshes near the mouth of Perry River. The leisurely downstream journey from nesting sites allows the young to feed on insects and tender shoots of aquatic grasses and sedges.

Young and adults are flying by late August and are enroute south by September. Except for white-fronted geese, they are the earliest to leave the Arctic. In very mild years, such as 1962, they may linger until early November at the Athabaska Delta and in the Prairie Provinces, where they feed on waste grain in harvested fields. Most years they are bound for Tule Lake in California by mid-October. Ross' geese are uncommon compared to other geese and in the past have been protected from hunting in Canada and the United States. Even so, because they are easily mistaken for snow geese, 500 to 1,200 a year were killed by mistake in Saskatchewan, Alberta, and California. Due to the ineffectiveness of the closed season and recent increases in the Ross' goose population, a bag limit of one bird was established in the Central and Pacific Flyways in 1963. In Canada the closed season on Ross' geese was removed in 1963 but in the areas where this bird is frequently killed the season opening date for white geese was set back to October 7. It was discovered that by this date most of the Ross' have migrated south and are safe from shooting.

EMPEROR GEESE may number as many as 200 thousand but they are less familiar to sportsmen and naturalists than most other North American geese. The winter and summer range is confined to sparsely settled and uninhabited lands bordering the Bering Sea. It stays far from centers of human population even in migration.

The emperor is almost as much a sea goose as the brant. It frequents rocks and reefs and shoals of salt and brackish lagoons. It forages over sandy beaches and mudflats for seaweeds and shellfish, which sometimes affect its flavor. It becomes a land bird in the breeding season, grazing in marshy stretches above tideflats and even invading the drier tundra for crowberries.

The outer Aleutians are the primary North American wintering grounds of the emperor. It becomes gradually less common east to the Alaska Peninsula. A few occur on Shumagin Islands and southern

The male black brant weighs only about 3 pounds, but he is fearless in defense of his offspring.

Kodiak Island. We have records of its occasional appearance all along the coast to California. On the Siberian side, they winter at Commander Island and possibly along the coast of Kamchatka Peninsula.

The North American emperors leave the winter range in late April. The main breeding ground is Yukon-Kuskokwim Delta, although others are common along northern Seward Peninsula from Cape Prince of Wales to Cape Espenberg. Occasional pairs nest on the north shore of Kotzebue Sound. A few may nest as far north as Point Barrow as well as on the southeast coast of St. Lawrence Island, a region also used by molting subadults. Siberian breeding grounds are on Chukotski Peninsula from the mouth of Anadyr River around to Kolyuchin Bay on the north coast.

EMPERORS ARRIVE at breeding grounds between May 15 and June 1, when river channels and sea are still frozen and snow still covers much of the tundra. They favor ponds and marshes in low, rolling

A clutch of black brant eggs just hatching in a nest along the lower Kashunuk River, Alaska. For the next few days the chief enemy of the young will be the glaucous gull.

hills, inland from the flats bordering brant country. Often they choose the driftwood debris of the line of high tide. There the female can hide in camouflage, as brant do in like terrain.

Most geese in Yukon-Kuskokwim Delta nest in zones delineated by the terrain and food plants preferred by each species. Brant are most abundant close to shore. Proceeding inland are cackling geese, then emperor geese, and finally whitefronts. The zones of emperors, cackling geese, and brant overlap somewhat.

The birds are mated on arrival. Most clutches are complete by the second week in June, although dates vary with local climate and weather at the start of the season. Five or six eggs are laid in a scrape lined with down, grass, and leaves. Incubation lasts 24 days. The young feed on aquatic insects and marsh grass at first and later move upland with the flocks to graze and feed on berries. Adults molt 2 or 3 weeks after the hatch. They and the young are flying again in early August.

Subadult, nonbreeding emperors molt sooner and show up as early as August 20 at stopping points en route to wintering grounds. Migration of families begins the first week in September, but some may not leave until freeze-up, as late as November 1.

ENEMIES OF THE EMPEROR GOOSE are those of all arctic geese. Parasitic jaegers prey on eggs. Glaucous gulls take young. Arctic foxes, when they are abundant, take both. But most foxes in such low, wet country as the Yukon-Kuskokwim Delta are restricted to territories in which they can maintain dry dens. Most such sites are known to Eskimos and are heavily trapped.

SPORTSMEN SOMETIMES COMPLAIN that Eskimos and northern Indians kill too many geese and "egg out" colonies. The complaint is not justified, and is less and less valid as the native economy continues to change. Migrating birds in the spring offer Eskimos a welcome change from a steady diet of seal all winter but the total take is small. In most of the Arctic where spring geese are shot, the earlier arriving snow, blue, and white-fronted geese are shot most frequently.

Today's Eskimos spend more time in villages, especially after winter trapping is over. The season of waterfowl migration and nesting is the most difficult time to travel, and hunting for caribou and seal is more productive.

All told, brant are faring well. Barring such disasters as the sudden and mysterious disappearance of eelgrass, they should continue to prosper in the arctic vastness where they breed. They have their troubles now and again, as do their associates, the Ross' and emperor geese. Arctic weather being what it is, years of nesting failure must be expected. And predators, a chronic drain on the geese, sometimes multiply their numbers and efforts and sharply lower production of the birds. But the Arctic is like that, and these geese are adapted to it. They can survive the bad years and make the most of the good ones.

—THOMAS W. BARRY.

TRUMPETER SWANS
BARROW'S GOLDENEYES

Our Native Swans

SWANS ARE PART and parcel of our history and culture, but they are, alas, hardly a part of our lives any more. For a period of 200 years, from 1700 to 1900, our native swans suffered extreme losses by the hand of man. Only a pitiful remnant of the once great swan flocks remain today.

Time was when they were as American as anything in the American scene, as in 1714, when a surveyor-naturalist, John Lawson wrote in his book, *History of North Carolina:* "Of the swans we have two sorts: the one we call Trompeters because of a sort of Trompeting noise they make. These are the largest sort we have. The sort of Swan called the Hoopers, are the least."

Swan skins and quills were valuable items of trade during the late 18th and early 19th centuries. The Hudson's Bay Company sold some 108 thousand skins in London between 1823 and 1880. The trumpeter, because it nested in the Canadian fur country south to the permanent water areas of Minnesota and Iowa, was more vulnerable to exploitation by the early westward-

155

ing fur traders and settlers than the whistling swan. Trumpeter swans had been reduced nearly to extinction by the end of the 19th century.

John Lawson's "trompeter" and "hooper" swans were the same birds we now know as the trumpeter swan and the whistling swan. Both species resemble each other closely. Adults are all white and have black bills and feet. The cygnets—the young ones—are gray. Whistling swans are usually smaller than trumpeters, and most whistlers have a yellow spot on the bill in front of each eye. Unless the yellow spot is present, however, it is almost impossible to tell them apart unless one hears the voice. The deep, resonant, hornlike call of the trumpeter distinguishes it from the high-pitched, bark-whistle of the whistling swan. Any male swan commonly is called a cob. The female is known as a pen.

The long necks, short legs, and large webbed feet of swans fit them well to live in shallow water. They rarely go ashore to feed but prefer to remain in the water, where they consume large quantities of leaves, stems, seeds, and tubers of plants. Swans can reach foods in several feet of water with little effort. Their powerful legs and large feet enable them to dig deep for roots and tubers in soft mud.

THE TRUMPETER SWAN once ranged as a breeding bird throughout the north, west, and central parts of North America, from Alaska and Arctic Canada south to Iowa and Missouri and east to Indiana. Vast numbers of trumpeters wintered on the estuaries of the Central Atlantic States, in the Ohio and Mississippi River Valleys, in the freshwater estuaries along the Gulf of Mexico and in the lakes and sloughs of the lower Columbia River.

The only trumpeters we have now are descendants of those that escaped hunting or that moved only short distances between protected grounds and favorable winter quarters.

Trumpeter swans made a remarkable comeback in the Yellowstone Park Region after the United States Fish and Wildlife Service established the Red Rock Lakes National Wildlife Refuge in 1935. Under the strict protection afforded by the Park and Refuge this population of trumpeters increased from fewer than 100 in the early thirties to more than 600 by 1954. More will be told about this successful program later.

The trumpeters that breed near Grande Prairie, in the Peace River District of Alberta, have numbered about 100 over the years. Here further growth of the population seems to be restricted by a shortage of proper habitat and the large space required by a breeding pair. The nesting places available near Grande Prairie will apparently support no more than about 35 breeding pairs. All but two of the nesting territories are on lakes of no more than 800 acres—and one lake, of some 1,500 acres, accommodates only two pairs. It is plain that the loss of even one nesting territory will jeopardize still more the survival of this small group.

Some extension of the range has occurred in Canada since 1950 or so. One or two pairs have nested each year in the Cypress Hills region of southwestern Saskatchewan. Two or three pairs have had young on prairie sloughs in southeastern Alberta. Their origin is not known, but they may have come from the Grande Prairie flock, which winters in the Yellowstone region with the swans from Red Rock lakes.

A trumpeter swan nest was found in Alaska in 1869, but little was written about this species for the next 50 years to clarify the status of populations there or along the coast of British Columbia, where trumpeters from Alaska winter. A few trumpeters were reported in southeastern Alaska in 1951, and several investigations of nesting and wintering grounds have been made since then. A population of about 200 trumpeters was discovered in 1957 on Kenai Peninsula. Wintering estimates and breeding surveys indicate that Alaska and western Canada support at least a thousand trumpeter swans.

WHISTLING SWANS nest in the remote Arctic regions of Alaska and Canada, but nevertheless they, too, have suffered at the hands of man, particularly during migration and on the wintering grounds. Vast numbers of whistling swans once graced the Texas Gulf Coast during the winter, but they have long since been forgotten, and the tremendous numbers reported by Lewis and Clark in the extensive wapato marshes of the lower Columbia River are today but a phantom flock. About half of the 70 thousand to 90 thousand whistlers in North America winter on the estuaries of Chesapeake Bay and Currituck Sound of the Atlantic coast. The others spend their winters in coastal States of the Pacific Flyway, chiefly in the Central Valley of California.

THE BREEDING CYCLES of our native swans are fairly well known. Swans pair for life, but if one of a

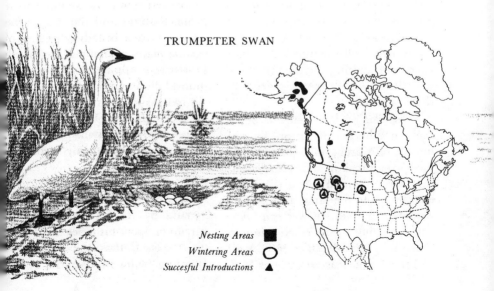

TRUMPETER SWAN

Nesting Areas ■
Wintering Areas ○
Succesful Introductions ▲

A cruising pair of trumpeter swans—the ultimate of gracefulness in motion.

pair dies, the survivor may take another mate. During observations of captive trumpeters on the Malheur National Wildlife Refuge, it was noted that pairing did not occur until the birds were 3 years old. Other observations of known-age pairs released to the wild are that initial nesting does not occur until the fourth and sometimes the sixth year. The pairing characteristics of whistling swans probably are like those of trumpeters.

Whistling swans usually begin their northerly migration by the middle of March, immediately after the spring breakup. Whistling swans that winter on the Atlantic coast migrate about the same time as their western relatives. In western Canada, whistling swans reach southern Canada by late March or early April and the Arctic coast as early as May

4 in some years although they usually do not arrive until mid-May.

Whistling swans nest over a wide area in the Arctic, from Alaska Peninsula east to Ungava Peninsula. But most of the continental population breeds in Alaska, mainly on the Yukon-Kuskokwim Delta and in the marshy valleys that border Bristol Bay. A small number also nest along the wet tundra margins of Kotzebue Sound. With the exception of concentrations on the Mackenzie and Anderson River Deltas in Arctic Canada, breeding whistling swans scatter widely and thinly across the north country.

EXTENSIVE AIR SURVEYS in Arctic Canada by Robert Smith, of the Bureau of Sport Fisheries and Wildlife, disclosed that the density of whistling swans in Canada, about one pair to the square mile, was heaviest along the coastal strip from the west side of Mackenzie Delta to the east side of Anderson Delta. Nesting densities become sparser in inland nesting habitats particularly south of the tree line. Swans generally do not frequent the rugged, rock-ribbed Precambrian areas in central and eastern Arctic Canada but may be found thinly scattered wherever tundra replaces rocky barrens. They nest regularly in the southern part of Banks Island and sometimes south of Prince of Wales Island. A few nest near the Thelon River in the northern Canadian barrens but that seems to be the southern limit of their breeding range.

Whistlers choose a variety of nesting sites, from the water's edge to the top of low hills half a mile from water. They seem to prefer small islands in shallow tundra ponds. Their nests are usually mounds of moss, dried grass, or sedge 1 or 2 feet high.

They begin to lay eggs soon after their arrival on the breeding grounds in late May or early June. A clutch of four eggs is usual, but as many as seven are laid on occasion. The average incubation period probably is about 32 days. Cygnets hatch in late June or early July. On Adelaide Peninsula in Arctic Canada, a later clutch once was seen pipping on July 14.

ON NESTING GROUNDS farther south, trumpeter swans use muskrat houses almost exclusively for their nesting sites. Nest mounds resembling haycocks are sometimes built up by a pair of swans before egg laying begins, but it is more usual for the pen simply to scrape a nest out of the top of a muskrat house and start laying. Nesting swans are jealous of their territories and claim relatively large areas for nesting and raising their young. Swans usually tolerate ducks in their nesting ter-

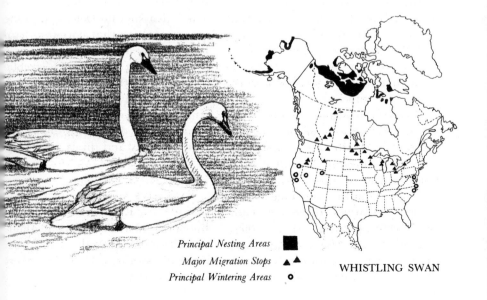

Principal Nesting Areas ■
Major Migration Stops ▲ ▲
Principal Wintering Areas o

WHISTLING SWAN

ritories but drive off larger trespassers such as geese and other swans.

Trumpeters start to nest soon after they arrive on their territories in late April or early May, sometimes before the ice is out. They lay an egg every other day until the clutch is complete. The average clutch at Red Rock Lakes and in Alberta was five or six eggs, although as many as nine may be laid. As the sex of swans in the field cannot be definitely determined, we do not know for sure whether the cob shares the duties of incubation, but we believe those duties are carried out by the pen. After the last egg is laid, incubation begins. Hatching takes place 32 or 33 days later.

AS MANY AS HALF OF THE EGGS fail to hatch in some years. Success varied from 51 to 66 percent during 3 years of studies that were carried out at Red Rock Lakes. That was lower than the 55 to 92 percent recorded during 6 years at Grande Prairie. Infertility and the death of immature embryos are the main causes of failure.

The first week of life is most hazardous for the trumpeter cygnet, as it is for most other birds. Their clumsy parents may trample some cygnets. Others, on their first feeding ventures from the nest, become entangled in nearby plants and drown. Some cygnets fall prey to leeches and to parasites which infect internal organs. Weak birds may succumb from these causes.

Adult trumpeters molt their flight feathers in summer and are grounded for a month or more. The pen usually starts to lose her feathers about the time her cygnets hatch and is flightless with them for their first month or so. Whistling swans molt somewhat later with the pen becoming flightless about 2 weeks after the young hatch. The cob becomes flightless about the time the pen regains her flight, so that one or the other of the parents usually has the power of flight during the brood period. On the average, only two or three cygnets in a clutch survive to fly in autumn.

Young trumpeters usually start flying about the end of September. Young whistlers in the Far North probably become airborne a week or two earlier. Occasionally, when spring occurs late and winter sets in early, cygnets of both species may be still flightless at freezeup. Sometimes they find enough food to survive to flight stage, only to die of malnutrition and exhaustion in migration. Some never gain flight and perish on the breeding grounds.

THE SOUTHWARD FALL MIGRATION of whistling swans usually takes place more leisurely than the northward movement in the spring and is therefore less spectacular. Whistlers usually start to leave northern breeding grounds about the middle of September. Some from northern Alaska apparently head east and cross the Rocky Mountains in the Arctic to join the Canadian population in their southerly migration through the interior of Canada. The Mackenzie River drainage then becomes a boulevard, and large flocks rest and feed in small lakes east of the river.

The first main assemblies along the Mackenzie take place on Lake Claire and Richardson Lake in northeastern Alberta, where concentrations build up about the beginning of October. During surveys from the air, Tom Barry, of the Canadian Wildlife Service, has seen as many as 25 thousand swans on those lakes, located at the delta of Lake Athabasca. From there populations separate, those with different destinations splitting off to travel traditional flyways over the prairies of Canada and the Northern States. Atlantic-bound birds head southeasterly. Western groups head southwesterly.

The first whistling swans usually arrive at Bear River Delta, in northern Utah, during the second week of October and reach peak numbers of 10 thousand to 20 thousand during the latter part of November. If the weather is not too severe, some swans remain to winter on State and Federal waterfowl refuges there.

Trumpeters that nest in Alberta apparently move south with the last of the whistlers and join some of the Red Rock Lakes population which winter on the upper reaches of Henry's Fork of the Snake River in Fremont County in Idaho. Trumpeters that nest in Alaska move out to coastal lakes and rivers of southeastern Alaska and British Columbia as winter approaches. During severe winters, trumpeters may be found in the southernmost parts of Vancouver Island.

SWANS are listed as game birds by the Migratory Bird Treaties but the Treaty with Great Britain closed the season on swans for the period 1916 through 1926. This closure was continued until 1962 when an experimental season on whistlers was established in Utah with a thousand 1-bird permits being issued. The same season was continued in 1963. The reported bag was 320 for the 1962 season and 392 in 1963. There is an annual loss of both whistlers and trumpeters due to unscrupulous or uninformed hunters each year. Because of their low numbers, it is particularly unfortunate when trumpeters are killed.

Trumpeter swan country. This vast terrain on the Dall River is important as a breeding area for trumpeters in Alaska.

The whistling swan is the common swan of most of North America. It is slightly smaller than the trumpeter but is is not always possible to distinguish the two species by sight.

THE MIGRATORY BIRD TREATY of 1916, which prohibited the shooting of swans in the United States and Canada, was a significant step. More has been done since to secure their future. The Bureau of Sport Fisheries and Wildlife has established refuges for the protection of both species. A major breeding grounds of whistling swans on the Yukon-Kuskokwin Delta, Alaska, was preserved when far-sighted conservationists established the Clarence Rhode National Wildlife Range in 1960. Important populations of trumpeter swans have been protected for years on the Kenai National Moose Range, Alaska, and the Red Rock Lakes National Wildlife Refuge, Montana.

The preservation and increase of the trumpeters on the Red Rock Lakes Refuge is a famous conservation story—one of the few victories in modern times of saving a wild population from extinction. In the early thirties, when the Refuge was established, less than 100 trumpeters existed on widely scattered lakes in Yellowstone Park and the surrounding country. Losses from illegal gunning and disturbance on their nesting grounds outside Yellowstone Park subtracted as many or more swans from the total population as were raised each year. This deteriorating situation was stopped by establishment of the Refuge in 1935.

Many of the early practices carried out on the Refuge were time-proven wildlife restoration measures. Harmful disturbance by man during the critical nesting period was eliminated, illegal shooting was reduced, winter feeding was practiced, and cygnets were taken to other favorable locations to start new colonies. As a result of the latter program, small but increasing populations of trumpeters are now to be found on the National Elk Refuge, Jackson,

Wyoming; Malheur National Wildlife Refuge, Burns, Oregon; Ruby Lake National Wildlife Refuge, Wells, Nevada; and Lacreek National Wildlife Refuge, Martin, South Dakota. Efforts to reestablish breeding populations of trumpeters elsewhere in the Midwest, where they were formerly abundant, will be difficult since they are so vulnerable to shooting during migration. Only in a few locations within their breeding range does the presence of open water during the winter make long, hazardous migrations unnecessary.

In the Yellowstone region, the trumpeter population increased at a steady rate of 10 percent annually for a period of about 20 years after refuge management measures were started in 1935. The wide ranging population of 97 swans counted in 1934 grew to 279 by 1944. By 1954, their numbers had increased to 642; 380 of these were counted on the Refuge. From 1955 to 1963, their numbers leveled out and then declined slightly—the habitat was "full." During this latter period, a balance was struck whereby an increase in breeding pairs resulted in fewer cygnets raised and annual gains only compensated for the losses.

In 1955, six trumpeters were moved from the Red Rock Lakes flock to the Delta Waterfowl Research Station in Manitoba, Canada. That transfer resulted in the first successful breeding of captive trumpeters in North America in recent times. Trumpeter broods were produced at Delta each year between 1959 and 1962.

Two sanctuaries were established by Canadian Wildlife authorities in British Columbia in the twenties to protect trumpeter swans on their wintering grounds. One proved to be of little value and was discontinued. The other, Vaseaux Lake Sanctuary, was used by a flock of trumpeters until most of the birds were poisoned by eating lead shot in

The biologist at Red Rock Lakes National Wildlife Refuge is out to feed the trumpeter swans. Warm springs maintain open water for them on the Refuge. They remain there throughout the severe winter.

1925. Trumpeters have only rarely been seen there since then.

Part-time wardens on swan wintering areas on Queen Charlotte Islands and Lonesome Lake, British Columbia, and on breeding grounds at Grande Prairie, Alberta, have protected the small groups there. A winter feeding program at Lonesome Lake also has helped to sustain that population.

As we mentioned, there has been some extension of the range of trumpeter swans in southeastern Alberta and southwestern Saskatchewan. We believe that if illegal shooting can be reduced, further extensions of breeding range can be accomplished by the release of birds in suitable habitat across the prairies. To that end, the Canadian Wildlife Service has begun a project to establish several captive breeding flocks in order to produce more swans for use in transplanting. Facilities for the purpose are at Swan Lake near Vernon, British Columbia, the Delta Waterfowl Station, the Calgary Zoo, the Saskatchewan Natural History Museum in Regina, and the Stanley Park Zoo in Vancouver. Swans raised at Delta and wounded birds from the wild provide the basic stock. Experimental releases of the progeny are planned. In the United States, the successful establishment of a trumpeter swan population on the Lacreek National Wildlife Refuge in South Dakota shows what can be done.

EXPLORATION AND DEVELOPMENT in northern regions have been expanding rapidly. Although little effect on breeding grounds of whis-

tling swans has been noted, action has been taken by United States and Canadian wildlife agencies to protect some of that habitat. Besides the large Clarence Rhode National Wildlife Range established by the United States in the Yukon-Kuskokwim Delta, Alaska, 12 sanctuaries have been established in important waterfowl nesting areas in the Canadian North.

Continued vigilance and the determination of an informed public to save the swans are also needed to prevent unnecessary and unwise disturbance or destruction of breeding habitat.

Many marshes and shallow lakes once used by swans for nesting have been ditched, drained, and plowed. Much more habitat may be drained in the future. If the program of transplanting is to succeed, former breeding marshes must be saved from the dragline and the plow.

The value of our swans cannot be measured in dollars and cents, but their beauty and grace have influenced and inspired mankind's folklore, history, literature, drama, art, and music through the ages. We shall be remiss in our responsibilities to future generations if we fail in our efforts to perpetuate these noble birds.—WINSTON E. BANKO and
R. H. MACKAY.

We may read indignantly of the Great Auk and the Passenger Pigeon and say complacently that such a thing could not happen nowadays, but only by the narrowest margin is the Trumpeter Swan of North America, the largest of all waterfowl, still included in the avifauna of the world.—PETER SCOTT.

CANADA GEESE

Down the Flyways

BRANT

Atlantic Flyway

ONE COLD SEPTEMBER day a family of Canada geese lifted from the windswept tundra of Baffin Island and headed south. Their journey would be a long one and urgent. Lengthening nights, freezing temperatures, and snow squalls already had brought winter to their summer home in the Arctic.

No one saw them leave or noticed them as they battled the winds of Hudson Strait and the rigors of Ungava Peninsula. Off the mouth of the Povungnituk, a sharp-eyed Es-

kimo boy, standing quietly in the dusk, watched the family descend on motionless wings, talked down by hundreds of their kind. A brief rest, then off again, driven by instinct or habit they could not deny. The next few weeks, the family moved with the clan as it worked its way south along the shores of Hudson Bay and James Bay. There, hundreds of thousands of similar missions joined them. And there, too, a parting of the ways.

The destination of some was to be

the Eastern Shore of Maryland or the James River of Virginia. Some would tumble out at Lake Mattamuskeet or Gaddy's Pond in North Carolina. Our family from Baffin Island and a few thousand more will find a winter home at St. Mark's National Wildlife Refuge in northern Florida. But whatever the terminus, most of them are bound for the Atlantic Flyway along our eastern seaboard, the traditional winter home of honkers out of eastern Canada and many other kinds of geese, ducks, swans, and coots from other parts of the North American Continent.

New England, New York, Pennsylvania, West Virginia, and the coastal States south to Florida, 17 in all, make up the Stateside part of the Atlantic Flyway. It covers 446 thousand square miles, about one-seventh the area of 48 States. It has a coastline of more than 7 thousand miles. From the top of Maine to the tip of Florida, the flyway is about 1,800 miles long. The greatest width is about 500 miles; the average, about 300. More than 70 million people live there, well over a third of the population of the United States. About two-thirds live in and between Boston and Washington, a coastal strip that is becoming a continuous metropolis.

Climate and vegetation differ north to south and west to east. The North has warm summers and cold, snowy winters. The southern end is hot and humid. Snow and rain total 40 to 60 inches. North of upper New Jersey fresh and slightly brackish waters usually remain frozen most winters. Spruce-fir and hardwood forests of the North give way to mangrove swamps and the Everglades of southern Florida.

The Appalachian Mountains extend through much of the flyway on the west. Waters flowing east from the mountains pass through pine and southern hardwood forests of the rolling Piedmont Region. The flat Coastal Plain begins at the Fall Line; longleaf, loblolly, and slash pine forests and cypress, tupelo, and sweetgum swamps are common there. Within a few hundred miles, from the crest of the Alleghenies in the Carolinas to the river swamps and marine habitats of the coast, habitats of animal life and climate are widely diverse.

THE IRREGULAR COASTLINE has hundreds of islands, bays, sounds, river estuaries, and low-lying swamps and marshes. Southward from the rocky coast of Maine, the surf shoreline becomes wide, sandy beach. Sand is replaced in southern Florida by finely ground marl, derived from the ground-up shells of coral, clams and other marine shellfish. Also, farther south, tidal bays and estuaries become larger, and the expanse of marsh and swamp greater. Coastal habitats of the middle and southern parts of the flyway attract the bulk of migrant and wintering waterfowl.

Although the Atlantic Flyway is populous and has more than 600 thousand miles of rural roads, it also has a surprising amount of unoccupied land. More than half is wooded; the area for hunting and fishing is considerable. Cropland occupies about 14 percent. Corn and other grains, fruit, vegetables, cotton, tobacco, soybeans, and hay are the main crops. Grazing is important. Fewer than one-fourth of the farms of the United States are here; they average about 113 acres, less than half the national average.

THIS FLYWAY has more than 32 million acres of wetland habitat, 96 percent of it from Maryland south. That is more than one-third of the wetlands of the United States, but only 4 million acres, or 12 percent, is of moderate to high value for waterfowl. The figures indicate that the Atlantic Flyway is long on wetlands but short on wetland habitat for waterfowl.

About 29 million acres are inland fresh-water areas and about 3.5 million acres are coastal, fresh, and saline areas. About 14 million acres of marsh, 12 million acres of swamp, and 3 million acres of bog make up the inland fresh waters. Coastal habitats have about one-half million acres of fresh marshes and 2.5 million acres of salt marshes. One-half million acres of mangrove occur in Florida.

Roughly 10 million acres of permanent, shallow, open waters are of value to ducks and geese. Included are lakes, reservoirs, large rivers and streams, bays, sounds, estuaries, and tidal flats. Not included are thousands of farm ponds, small wooded streams and other natural areas of a few acres, some of which waterfowl use at various times.

Most of the wetland habitat has low value for waterfowl. Millions of acres are dark-water acid bog types, and sterile lakes and ponds. Saw-grass, needlerush, phragmites, cattails, and cordgrasses cover large tracts. Productive habitats are widely scattered and are associated usually with alkaline and brackish waters, which generally produce pondweeds, bulrushes, wildrice, and other preferred duck foods in abundance. Many wetlands adjacent to upland and open-water feeding areas receive greater use by waterfowl. Having a major share of the wetlands does not assure us a major share of the waterfowl: The Atlantic Flyway harbors scarcely 15 percent of the ducks, only 20 percent of all geese (not counting brant), and a quarter of the coot.

The story of the discovery and settlement of the Country portrays the history of the Atlantic Flyway. It is a story of pioneers determined to conquer and exploit a fertile land and its rich flora and fauna. The eastern strip was the beachhead from which battles raged between the pioneer and the land and its waters, between the pioneer and the virgin forests, the pioneer and wildlife, and native Indian tribes.

By the middle of the 18th century, most of the larger rivers supported towns and cities, and settlements sprang up in the interior. Natural waterways for a long time were the only satisfactory means of travel and communication. They provided fish, shellfish, and bird and other animal life. It was natural therefore that centers of population would build up along major watercourses. Many locations chosen for settlement were also areas of prime waterfowl habitat—but there was no need to think of that then.

The need grew for deeper channels and canals to connect watercourses, and many were built. Until railroads came, they made easier the exploitation of mineral resources, the development of industrial power, and communication generally. But they also caused major changes in the landscape. Dredging operations destroyed some habitat directly, but more important was the change that came in quality of water and the increased human activity that followed. The changes often destroyed permanently extensive beds of aquatics. In 1925, for example, Manasquan Inlet and Bay Canal were opened as part of the Inland Waterway, and the once famous Barnegat Bay and its marshes were changed from a predominantly brackish area, where duck foods abounded, to a saline environment in which little food for ducks could grow. Barnegat Bay no longer attracts the thousands of canvasbacks, redheads, and other species it once did.

With rapid growth of industry, development of agriculture, mushrooming of populations, and building of great cities, major changes continued in waterfowl habitat of the flyway. In the rush of expansion, hundreds of thousands of acres of habitat disappeared. No piece of any importance has gone unscathed.

The cutting of forests and tillage and grazing of slopes, with little care to prevent erosion, caused tremendous losses of soil and ruined rivers, lakes, and estuaries that once were attractive to waterfowl. Much effort has been put forward in recent years to protect watersheds, yet pollution from soil erosion remains serious today.

To provide for the need of a growing population and expanding industry for ever greater amounts of power and water and for flood control and navigation, hundreds of reservoirs, covering more than a million acres, have been built. Sometimes reservoirs help ducks. Often they do not. By impounding water, they reduce flow downstream and sometimes cause increases in salinity, to the detriment of some aquatic habitats. Upstream reservoirs and the diversion of waters of the Santee River in South Carolina, for example, put an end to rice farming and eliminated thousands of acres of prime waterfowl habitat in the Lower Santee and nearby coastal areas.

OTHER EXAMPLES are at hand of how manipulation of waterflow has changed the environment. The productive capacity for waterfowl of the Back Bay-Currituck area was once jeopardized by the Albemarle-Chesapeake Canal. Before locks were installed the canal let in too much salinity. When the barrier dunes, however, were built up they prevented occasional flooding by salt water. The periodic introduction of sea water into fresh-water habitats has helped to maintain the brackish conditions needed for maximum production of duck food.

Major marsh and swamp-drainage projects have altered the Montezuma marshes in New York, Lake

Canada geese finding refuge and rest in a pond in North Carolina.

Mattamuskeet in North Carolina, and parts of the Everglades areas in Florida. Less spectacular has been the disappearance of many smaller interior swamps and marshes.

THE MARSHES of the Atlantic coast have been infested with mosquitoes, the worst being the saltmarsh mosquito. At first, oil applied to standing waters effectively controlled some, but not the saltmarsh variety. Consequently, in the early thirties, the Civilian Conservation Corps, at the request of cities and resorts, began to ditch marshes. Close to one-half million acres of coastal marsh from southern New England to Maryland were ditched and drained. Many extensive marshes in the Middle Atlantic region were made nearly useless for waterfowl.

The coastal marshes are important not only to waterfowl; they support a sizable fur resource and are important nursery grounds for some species of marine animal life. But they have been badly abused. Probably more than half of the original high-quality marsh habitat has disappeared or has been so modified as to be of low value for wildlife.

Also of great importance are the open water habitats, such as streams, rivers, lakes, bays, sounds, and estuaries. They are used heavily by migrant and wintering diving ducks and many species of puddle ducks and geese.

On Chincoteague National Wildlife Refuge in Virginia, and elsewhere in the Atlantic Flyway, the marsh is protected from the ocean by a sand barrier. Hurricanes sometimes destroy or damage the barriers. Here a bulldozer is being used to repair damage.

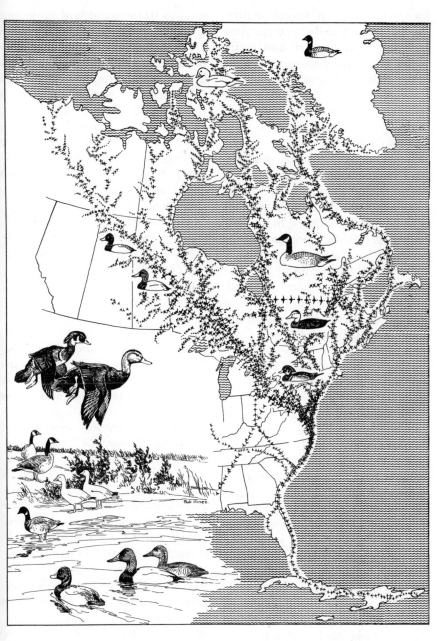

Bob Hines.

Hardly a waterway exists that has not been changed by dredging, filling, channeling, dams, canals, and diversion of waters. But perhaps the most serious man-caused problem for waterfowl is pollution.

As populations increase and congestion develops, the disposal of wastes becomes an urgent matter. We have not handled the problem well, for the most part, and many of the great watercourses are little better than open sewers.

Nearly every conceivable type of pollutant material is discharged into the waters of the Atlantic Flyway. Untreated domestic sewage is the most prevalent. The rivers of southern New England, the Middle Atlantic States, and Florida are most seriously affected. Many tidal bottoms in those States are closed to the harvesting of shellfish because of the possibility of infection.

Untreated wastes of industry can cause great damage and loss to fish and wildlife. Thousands of tons of organic and inorganic materials are discharged daily into the water systems of the flyway. High on the offending list are discharges from pulp and paper mills, which ruin hundreds of miles of stream habitats from Maine to Florida. Washings from mining operations ruin many downstream habitats. In the coal region of Pennsylvania and West Virginia, leakage of mine acids destroys plant and animal life along many miles of stream. Although direct kills of fish and waterfowl sometimes occur, the chief effect is to destroy habitat on which fish and waterfowl depend.

Oil pollution also has become serious. The annual loss of waterfowl by oil pollution could well exceed 100 thousand birds. Critical areas are Delaware Bay, northern New Jersey, New York, southern New England, the St. Lawrence River, and the ocean. Spectacular spillages have occurred, and losses of 5 thousand to 10 thousand birds from one spillage have not been unusual. Even greater losses may be due to unspectacular but continuing unlawful release of oil by ships.

The effect of pesticides is a growing cause for alarm. Tremendous amounts of highly toxic insecticides have been used. Much has been used unwisely, carelessly, and unnecessarily. Some organisms that are not killed outright by the poisons may carry them in their body tissues. Birds that feed on them have suffered high mortality. The possible effect of the poisons on the reproductive capacity of waterfowl that have ingested sublethal amounts remains to be determined.

Lead shot kills many thousands of waterfowl each year, and the accumulation of spent shot in heavily-hunted marshes is a worrisome problem here, as elsewhere. Most species of ducks, geese, and swans are affected.

Plant pests are still another hazard in the flyway. It is saddled with four introduced species that succeeded too well—water-hyacinth, waterchestnut, alligatorweed, and Eurasian watermilfoil. The first two are floating plants and may completely cover the water surface, kill submerged plants, and hamper boat travel. Alligatorweed grows on moist soils as well as over water. It is aggressive and persistent. Thousands of acres of fresh waters from the Carolinas south are choked with it and water-hyacinth. Eurasian watermilfoil grows submerged and is so prolific as to crowd out all native aquatics.

A blanket of waterchestnut once

eliminated all food plants from a 40-mile stretch of the Potomac River. Even boats had difficulty getting through. It took 20 years and several hundred thousand dollars to get rid of the plant. Sizable infestations occur in New York State, Vermont, and Massachusetts.

Thousands of acres of waterfowl habitats are infested with watermilfoil in New York, New Jersey, Maryland, Virginia, and Pea Island, North Carolina. The total elimination of these invaders may not be practical, but ways are being found to reduce them locally.

Add to the factors that destroy and impair habitat still others, such as harassment by boaters and fishermen and losses to a thriving number of predators, and one gets a discouraged outlook for waterfowl of the Atlantic Flyway. The situation is not all bad, even so. Some plus factors hold out promise.

Much of the best natural habitat has been lost, it is true, but part of what remains is basically good. Losses of natural habitat are made up somewhat by local upland feeding areas on private and public lands in New York, Pennsylvania, Maryland, and States south to Florida. Well-developed State and Federal management areas in many places provide improved habitat, although they can take care of only some of the fowl, primarily Canada geese and puddle ducks. Little has been done for diving ducks.

In the midfifties nearly twice as many ducks wintered in the flyway as were present during the early sixties. We conclude that the habitat can still sustain about the same size of waterfowl population as it did in the midfifties. But that does not imply that Atlantic Flyway habitats are as big and good as they should be. More good places throughout the flyway are desirable because some localities vary year to year in the amount and kinds of foods they produce. Work to that end has been started.

FEDERAL AND STATE wildlife agencies have purchased 750 thousand acres for waterfowl management and have that many additional acres under long-term lease. On these areas living conditions for waterfowl have been improved. Long range plans of the Bureau of Sport Fisheries and Wildlife and the State Fish and Game Departments include acquisitions that would nearly double the acreage held in 1962. A growing public interest in preserving and developing recreational areas has encouraged the Federal Government and many States to plan to acquire hundreds of thousands of acres for the enjoyment of all citizens. Such recreational projects will include side benefits for waterfowl.

We take note, also, that new habitat is being created in programs of land and water management agencies not primarily concerned with wildlife. Many reservoirs have been built and planned. Those in farming regions will benefit waterfowl if nearby lands and waters are managed well. The agencies and services doing such work cooperate closely.

Many ponds, impoundments, and streambank improvements have been made under programs of the Department of Agriculture. Many of

Robert E. Stewart, Bureau of Sport Fisheries and Wildlife biologists, collects samples of waterfowl food from Susquehanna Flats, Maryland, one of the most famous canvasback concentration areas of the Atlantic Flyway.

them have value to waterfowl, regardless of their chief purpose. Likewise, State Fish and Game Departments foster cooperative projects to devote p r i v a t e tracts to small marshes. Furthermore, the flooding of salt marshes in place of ditching and draining them is a new way to control mosquitoes that could return many acres to the use of waterfowl.

All this points up again the close relationship between the welfare of people and the existence of waterfowl. Both need water, land, space, and a place to live, rest, and rear families. But this we should bear in mind: Much of what we do not use—water, land, space—tends to be wasted. Not so if we put it to good use for the living things that also need to share our good earth. In so doing, we will find that the environment that is best for people is quite acceptable to waterfowl as well.

The two major groups of ducks, dabblers and divers, occur in about equal numbers in the Atlantic Flyway. The dabblers have furnished about 80 percent of the total harvest. Three-fourths of this take has been sustained by five species of dabblers— black duck, wood duck, mallard, green-winged teal, and widgeon.

THE BLACK DUCK is the ranking bird by numbers and preference in the hunter's bag. It is shy, wary, swift and strong in flight, and larger than most ducks. You can count it a good day when you bring a brace of these fine birds to bag. A quarter of a million or more are taken annually. The status of the species spells success of the season in the northern part of the flyway.

Blacks nest from North Carolina to tree line in eastern Canada and into Ontario and the Lake States. Nests may be over water or hundreds of yards from it in all sorts of situations. For instance, they may be found in tree cavities and old duck blinds. Nesting usually is scattered, but there are local concentrations. Around Lake Champlain in Vermont and Eastern Bay in Maryland, we have counted up to 21 nests an acre on some islands where predators do not bother them.

Blacks from the north filter into the flyway in September. Southward migration is at a peak in early November. New England gunners are often greeted in December by late flights of big blacks coming out of the Maritimes. They are mostly adult males, commonly referred to as northern or Canadian redlegs.

Blacks are strongly attached to specific wintering places. Many remain as far north as open water permits. Some always winter on the New England coast and move southward only if December is unusually cold. If severe weather holds off until mid-January, most blacks remain in the north, but some of them may starve.

Tidal a r e a s and fresh-water swamps and marshes from New Jersey to South Carolina are their pref-

erences for wintering. A few appear in northern Florida; some remain in Newfoundland. Black ducks are the only puddle ducks occurring in numbers during the winter in New England and the Maritime Provinces. They use all types of fresh-water and saltmarsh habitats. They feed on both animal and plant foods and commonly in u p l a n d grainfields. Black ducks and mallards often are seen together, and they have similar voices.

MALLARDS are important from New York south to northern Florida. Some breed in the flyway, but most are migrants from the forested country of the Lake States, Ontario, and Manitoba. The prairie potholes of Manitoba and Saskatchewan are important contributors during years of plentiful water. Birds from the pothole habitats winter in the southern end of the flyway.

More than half of the mallards winter in w o o d e d bottomlands, marshes, and management impoundments of South Carolina. Marshes and grainfields of the Delmarva Peninsula farther north are particularly attractive. The mallard takes readily to grainfields. The widespread use of mechanical cornpickers, which leave more kernels and standing stubble, has improved greatly the quality and extent of habitat for mallards. Many farms are managed with an eye to the hunting season.

In an effort to establish local breeding flocks and to supply more birds for hunting, large numbers of hand-reared mallards have been released in past decades. New York has propagated ducks for nearly 30 years, and several thousand mallards a year have been released throughout the State as 5- to 6-week ducklings. The Pennsylvania Game Commission releases up to 10 thousand mallards a year. Releases have also been made in Connecticut, Maryland, and other States. Even private agencies and individuals have introduced hand-reared birds into the flyway. For many years, under the ownership of Glenn L. Martin and now Remington Arms Company, Remington Farms has released 10 thousand to 20 thousand mallards a year. Perhaps as many as 40 thousand propagated mallards have been released each year in the Atlantic Flyway since 1940.

WOOD DUCKS nest in every State in the flyway and are by far the most abundant ducks during the summer. Most birds shot in the flyway are produced in the flyway. The woodies need tree holes for nesting A shortage of suitable sites may have cut their numbers in years past. A severe hurricane in the Northeast in 1938 felled many trees that had cavities large enough for the ducks Widespread timber cutting in the East also reduced the number o nesting sites. To help overcome the shortage, Fish and Game Departments, sportsmen's clubs, and other have erected thousands of nesting boxes.

The woody leaves the Northern States during September and Octo

Salt marshes along the Atlantic coast like this one near Southport, North Carolina, are useful to wintering migratory waterfowl.

ber. Although migration begins before seasons open in some Northern
States, the hunters' harvest of woodies ranks second or third for the
flyway. Heavy kills often are made
of birds going to roosts in the evening. The main wintering areas are
fresh-water swamps and marshes of
Florida, Georgia, and South Carolina. They feed primarily on plant
foods during the fall and winter.

THE GREEN-WINGED TEAL is abundant in this flyway and is fourth in
the hunters' bags. The wooded areas
of eastern Canada, as far west as
Manitoba, supply most of the green-
wings. The birds move into the
Northern States in early fall. Georgia, South Carolina, and North
Carolina winter most of them. Some
remain in the North, even in Nova
Scotia and Newfoundland, in mild
winters. Green-wings are birds of
fresh and brackish marsh areas.
Sometimes they feed in grainfields
and wooded bottomlands.

THE AMERICAN WIDGEON, OR BALD-
PATE, is another puddle duck important to hunters in this flyway. Most
of them come from prairie Canada,
and to the north. Those bound for
the Middle Atlantic States cross
New York and Pennsylvania. The
Montezuma National Wildlife Refuge in central New York State is a
favorite stopping place. Early in fall,
the widgeon often is the dominant
species on the Susquehanna Flats. It
winters on fresh and brackish
marshes from Long Island south,
especially in Maryland, South Carolina, and Florida. Although a few
thousand may winter in southern

New England, the widgeon is not ordinarily seen or shot by the New
England hunter.

OTHER SPECIES of puddle ducks in
the flyway are the Florida duck,
blue-winged teal, gadwall, pintail,
and shoveler. These are locally important, particularly to the hunter
in the southern part of the flyway.
The Florida variety of black duck is
restricted to the State and is eagerly
sought by the Florida gunner. The
gadwall winters mainly in South
Carolina. Local breeding colonies
occur along the coast from eastern
North Carolina to Long Island. The
shoveler, or spoonbill, is comparatively rare and winters mostly in
South Carolina.

TWO SPECIES OF SCAUP—or maybe
you call them broadbill, bluebill, or
blackhead—occur in this flyway.
They are less popular with hunters
than the black, mallard, canvasback,
and other species. The bag ranks
about sixth.

Greater scaup breed across northern Canada and into Alaska. The
Atlantic Flyway draws birds from all
sections. Most of those produced in
Alaska, from the Seward Peninsula
north and east across the top of the
State, winter in southern New England and the Middle Atlantic States.
Migration is southeast over the interior chain of lakes (Great Slave,
Athabasca, Winnipeg) to the Great
Lakes and then eastward into the
flyway.

The lesser moves southward
through Canada and down parts of
the Mississippi Flyway before crossing into the Atlantic Flyway. The

eastern part of the Prairie Provinces, the Northwest Territories, and central and western Alaska contribute to the Atlantic Flyway.

Most scaup wintering from Newfoundland to northern New Jersey are the greater scaup. They occur farther south in lesser numbers, except in severe winters, when they appear in Chesapeake Bay and points south of there. The lesser scaup is the dominant species in the southern part of the flyway; the large concentrations in Florida comprise the smaller species almost entirely.

The two species often frequent the same waters, but the greater commonly uses broad coastal bays, sounds, and tidal estuaries and larger lakes and rivers. The lesser is widely dispersed inland on fresh waters, but primary concentrations are on brackish coastal areas. Both feed on a variety of plant and animal foods, but plant foods predominate in the diet of the lesser.

THE RING-NECKED DUCK, or ringbill, is not particularly abundant in the flyway, but it is a favorite of hunters. It flies swiftly, decoys well, is good to eat, and contributes much to hunting recreation, particularly in the southern sections. It usually ranks fifth in the flyway kill.

Ringnecks prefer floating marsh, bog, or muskeg habitat on both wintering and breeding grounds. The leading breeding range is the wooded country of Canada westward from Ontario. The species became established as a breeding bird in Maine and the Maritime Provinces about 1930. This small eastern population has been steadily growing and spreading to neighboring States.

Most wintering ringnecks arrive in South Carolina, Georgia, and Florida through the Mississippi Flyway. Smaller groups of a few thousand birds occur as far north as Chesapeake Bay. The eastern fringe of the main continental migration passes through the Lake States, Ontario, and then into this area. Preferred wintering habitats are fresh and slightly brackish water. Concentrations of several thousand birds are not uncommon, but the species is generally widely dispersed on marshes, lakes, ponds, and reservoirs throughout the South.

THE CANVASBACK, a popular duck, winters mainly in this flyway. Some of them arrive from Alaska and the Northwest Territories, but most are produced in the pothole country of the Prairie Provinces. Drought there in recent years has temporarily eliminated most of the prime nesting habitat, and populations of canvasbacks have fallen sharply. In 1960 it became unlawful to hunt them.

Canvasbacks travel southeast across southern Ontario, northern Minnesota, Wisconsin, and Michigan and enter the Atlantic Flyway through New York and Pennsylvania. The Finger Lakes of New York and the Susquehanna Flats at the head of Chesapeake Bay may be concentration points early in the fall. Most of the birds are on Susquehanna Flats generally by mid November, before moving southward into the main wintering areas of southern Maryland, Virginia, and the Carolinas.

Some concentration and shooting areas, such as Susquehanna Flats, the Finger Lakes, Chester and Potomac Rivers in Maryland, and locations farther south, are alkaline or slightly brackish waters, where wildcelery and pondweeds thrive. Therefore, the "can" restricts its winter movements largely to those special habitats.

OTHER DIVING DUCKS in the flyway include the redhead, common goldeneye, bufflehead, ruddy, harlequin, three kinds of fish ducks, or mergansers, three kinds of eiders, three kinds of scoters, and the old squaw.

Seasons permitting, the redhead supplies local shooting in the Finger Lakes, the eastern shore of Maryland, eastern North Carolina, and the west coast of Florida. Goldeneyes and bufflehead provide good shooting late in the season in the middle and northern part of the flyway. The ruddy is locally important, primarily in Maryland and Virginia. The harlequin is uncommon. The total kill of all these species has scarcely equaled that of the green-winged teal.

The total of mergansers, eiders, scoters, and old squaws probably exceeds a million birds, but the take is of minor consequence. The little hooded and the larger red-breasted merganser are shot throughout the flyway, although they are not ordinarily sought after by hunters. Eiders, scoters, and old squaws are taken primarily along the New England coast, where a special early season on sea coots is permitted. The term "sea coot" refers to scoters, although eiders are sometimes called

coots. Confusing though it may be, the American coot is also called mudhen, chickenbill, ivory bill, and bluepeter, but actually it belongs to the rail family.

CANADA GEESE of the Atlantic Flyway are produced mainly in eastern Canada. Several thousand have been raised under captive and wild conditions in the Northern States of the flyway as far south as Virginia. Many of them are the progeny of live decoys released years ago when the use of live decoys for hunting was outlawed. Landowners and State and Federal management agencies have done a great deal on their own lands to protect and encourage these small flocks.

More than 75 percent of the wintering population occurs on or near tidewater from Kent County in Delaware to Hyde County in North Carolina. Concentrations of up to 10 thousand or more are at various inland points, such as in northwest Florida, the Santee Refuge of South Carolina, and the Gaddy's Pond area in North Carolina. Since 1950, Canadas have averaged about 400 thousand during the winter. Peak numbers have exceeded 500 thousand. The harvest in some years has been more than 100 thousand.

Canada geese generally are well dispersed in the flyway. Efforts have been started to establish new wintering flocks in the Piedmont and upper Coastal Plain regions. Plans have been made for management areas in the Northern States in order to delay southward flights so that northern hunters may share in the harvest.

Efforts to control the distribution and movements of Canada geese carry risks as well as rewards. Careful planning is especially important in northern localities where an ample acreage of grain crops could delay migration and hold many geese through the fall and even into winter. Improper management of goose areas in States, such as New York and Pennsylvania, could nullify the management program for the whole flyway. Such problems are not likely to be serious in New England, where grain farming is limited.

EELGRASS is the primary food of American brant. Resembling wildcelery, it was once abundant in salt and brackish tidal waters from North Carolina to Hudson Bay. Fishermen and boaters cursed this "seaweed" because it fouled the propeller and fishing equipment. Its importance in the ecology of tidewater was not recognized until the plant suddenly disappeared in 1931 and 1932.

Eelgrass often made solid stands covering hundreds or thousands of acres in bays and sounds. Many forms of animal life, such as amphipods, crabs, worms, fish, and mollusks, flourished in it. It was protective cover for the commercially important bay scallop. Its roots, leaves, and seeds were eaten by many species of waterfowl, which also fed on the animal life. Eelgrass was 90 percent of the food of brant during fall and winter.

When the eelgrass went, startling things happened. Bay bottoms, which were bound by the eelgrass, washed and eroded and so underwent changes in configuration and productivity. Bay scallops all but disappeared. Vast reaches became less attractive to waterfowl.

BRANT DECLINED DRASTICALLY after 1931 when the eelgrass disappeared. The lack of an adequate diet while on the wintering areas may have caused losses of birds and contributed to low productivity on the breeding grounds. The winter population fell to about 60 thousand in 1948 but reached a peak of about 265 thousand in 1961.

Many former eelgrass areas developed abundant growths of an alga, called sea-lettuce. Other bottoms, particularly some of those that eroded badly, supported no plant life for many years. At some locations small patches of eelgrass would appear only to be killed back by the disease, the causative organism of which was an amoebalike mycetozoan, *Labyrinthula*. In time, however, the plant began to make headway, and by the middle forties colonies of various sizes were established in hundreds of places along the coast. Since 1950, many areas—but not all—have had eelgrass comparable to its former abundance.

With their main food item lacking, brant turned to feeding extensively on sea-lettuce and other aquatics. They were observed feeding or grazing on the upland, a practice unheard of in former years. At Atlantic City, brant have been a nuisance on an athletic field and a hazard to aircraft at an airport where they graze by the hundreds.

Brant, which breed on far northern Arctic Islands, winter along the coast from Cape Cod to North

Carolina—mostly in the Barnegat Bay area of New Jersey. In the fall, they usually arrive in New Jersey about the middle of October. Most of the flight is completed by November 1.

THE GREATER SNOW GOOSE and the whistling swan are the show birds of the flyway. There has been a closed season on both species for many years, although the snow goose is hunted in eastern Canada. The population of each has fluctuated between 40 thousand and 60 thousand. They breed above the Arctic Circle and winter on tidal bays and marshes from New Jersey to North Carolina. The lesser snow goose, both white and blue phases, is also present in the flyway but in very small numbers. Although they are not native, a few hundred mute swan breed in southern New England to northern New Jersey.

THE AMERICAN COOT breeds mostly in the pothole country of the prairie States and Provinces. Only a few broods are raised in the flyway. During migration, only the Middle and South Atlantic States receive significant numbers. It is not generally considered a table delicacy, but in the southern part of the flyway it enjoys a good status as a game bird.

NOT ALL PARTS of this flyway have a rich assortment of ducks. Some lack the right habitat to attract birds and New England and the Maritime Provinces of Canada are bypassed by the bulk of the ducks entering the flyway. The breeding grounds of most of our ducks are in Canada west of James and Hudson Bays, and most of them come out of the Northwest and enter the flyway from New York south.

Black ducks, wood ducks, green-winged teal, and Canada geese which are produced in the Northeast contribute to populations in the lower part of the flyway. South of New York, however, ducks produced in the Lake States and western Canada are a greater percentage of the total. Also, the numbers of migrants received from the Mississippi Flyway increases towards the South. Limited bandings suggest that wintering populations in Georgia and Florida may include more birds from the Mississippi Flyway than the Atlantic.

Over the full length of the Atlan-

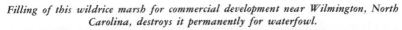

Filling of this wildrice marsh for commercial development near Wilmington, North Carolina, destroys it permanently for waterfowl.

184

tic Flyway there is considerable variation in the composition and origin of the populations. The New England gunner is concerned with black ducks, wood ducks, green-winged teal, goldeneye, bufflehead, scaup, and a few mallards and Canada geese. He enjoys also the traditional off-shore shooting of sea-coots. But most of the birds available to hunters in New England are raised locally or come from northern and eastern Canada. The prairie potholes contribute very little.

The Middle Atlantic States have a greater diversity of species. The Northeastern States and northern and eastern Canada contribute importantly to these populations but at this point there are substantial additions from the prairies of the Midwest. The most common species are black ducks, mallards, widgeon, canvasback, ruddy, scaup, green-winged teal, wood duck, pintail, brant, coot, and Canada geese. The South Carolina-Florida area is the end of the line; nearly all Atlantic Flyway species are represented. By the time many of them arrive at this terminus, they have already contributed substantially to the harvest in southern Canada and the Mississippi Flyway.

IN COLONIAL AMERICA, waterfowl and other wildlife made possible the survival of settlers by providing food and other needs for living. Later, commercial hunting became a major business, and markets of big coastal cities were well stocked with wild ducks and geese. Then followed development of sport hunting, and a number of sites in the flyway became well known.

Names like Merrymeeting Bay, the Cape, Great South Bay, Barnegat Bay, Susquehanna Flats, Back Bay, Chesapeake Bay, and Currituck became synonymous with the ultimate in waterfowling in minds of duck hunters everywhere. In days long ago, they rivaled the best in the world. Some are still among the best locally, but duck hunting in the Atlantic Flyway is not what it used to be.

It seems unlikely that even the best of technical skills can restore this flyway to its past richness. Seventy million persons and all they need for existence cannot live in a limited area without changing it. We cannot return to the primitive old days, and not many of us want to.

But we cannot be entirely pessimistic. Some breeding grounds in this flyway are still wild and remote and send forth their fall flights. Besides, the flyway may even be less subject to exploitation than others; it seems to be approaching a point of stability, and stability is important to waterfowl. People who live here, furthermore, have a growing awareness that ducks don't just happen. They want to understand and provide for the needs of waterfowl. It is not too much to expect then, that conservationists and other citizens will join efforts to manage things wisely enough to offset the impact of still more people and so attain a stability of the kind that will insure a valuable resource for generations to come.

—C. EDWARD ADDY.

MALLARDS

Mississippi Flyway

MISSISSIPPI meant big river to the Ojibway Indians and "big" is the word we can use for the waterfowl flyway that bears its name. Besides having the grandaddy of all rivers, three of the five largest lakes of the world, and the number one inland waterway, this Flyway also has other "king-size" features suited to the needs of waterfowl and people.

The Mississippi Flyway States are Minnesota, Wisconsin, Michigan, Ohio, Indiana, Illinois, Iowa, Missouri, Kentucky, Tennessee, Arkansas, Louisiana, Mississippi, and Alabama. They embrace 742 thou-sand square miles, one-fourth the area of the 48 adjoining States.

These 14 States contain more than half the acreage of wetlands classified as having significant value to waterfowl in the 48 contiguous States. Their residents buy 40 percent of the duck stamps sold and kill nearly 40 percent of the total ducks taken in the United States.

The Mississippi Flyway draws from breeding grounds that reach northward to the Mackenzie River Delta and Alaska in the west and to Hudson Bay and Baffin Island in the east. It includes most of the

185

productive prairie pothole region. Birds funnel from these breeding grounds into the flyway States from the northwest or the northeast without encountering any high ridge. Because water and feed along the way are ample, long hops are unnecessary, although some species seem to prefer nonstop flights. Each year some 8 million ducks, geese, swans, and coots winter here. Many others use it as a migration route on their way to nearby flyways or Latin America.

We boast 11.5 million acres of wetlands of high or moderate value and 20 million acres of lesser importance. Grainfields provide additional waterfowl range. This flyway in 1960 included the four leading soybean producing States, three of the four top rice producers, and one of the four top barley producers. Two-thirds of the Nation's corn crop is grown here. In short, the flyway is big in the things that count for the birds and for people who enjoy having them around.

SOME 70 OR 80 CENTURIES AGO the departing ice age left countless lakes, marshes, and potholes. Small ponds marked the tall-grass prairies of the northern half of the flyway. They provided top-quality breeding grounds for ducks. Larger lakes, many filled with sago pondweed, wild celery, and other choice duck foods, were steppingstones for birds migrating through the midcontinent. Of this, Frederick Lincoln wrote in 1935: "This route is followed by such vast numbers of ducks, geese, (and other birds) that observers stationed at favorable points in the Mississippi Valley during the height of migration can see a greater number of species and individuals than can be noted anywhere else in the world."

Halfway down the flyway, the bottomland lakes of the Illinois Valley were a paradise, especially for mallards. Extending 650 miles from Cape Girardeau, Missouri, to the Gulf of Mexico, the flood plain of the Mississippi River leads to the coastal prairies and marshes of Louisiana. Together these were the principal wintering grounds. They still are.

Much remains of this legacy of production, migration, and wintering habitat. But in less than a century, man, with his technical skills and machines, has wrought great changes. Before 1900, for example, Iowa had an estimated 6 million acres of prairie, profusely dotted with small wetlands. For ducks it was an ideal breeding range. Now, a few dozen marshes, most of them saved through a State acquisition program, are all that remain.

Similar habitat once existed in Illinois and Indiana, but little of it remains. Only Minnesota, in this flyway, retains a sizable block of prairie breeding range, and that is disappearing despite a desperate effort by State and Federal conservation agencies to save the remainder. Among the famous large breeding marshes, the Kankakee in Indiana exemplified one almost completely claimed by agriculture. Horicon Marsh in Wisconsin provides a happier case history; it has been reclaimed for wildlife after a drainage project failed.

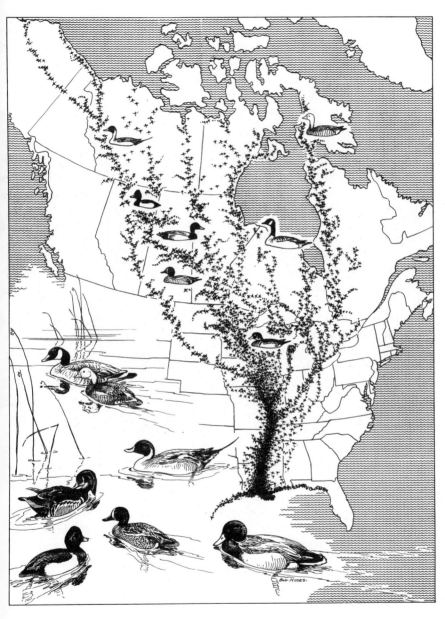

But the situation is not hopeless. Minnesota is still a land of 10 thousand lakes, many of which provide excellent migrational habitat. Minnesota also has the finest breeding grounds remaining and an active program aimed at preserving them. Also in Minnesota, Agassiz National Wildlife Refuge and Roseau River Refuge, a State management area, demonstrate that lands too wet for agriculture but too dry for waterfowl can be converted into highly productive breeding marshes. A big acreage of the Lake States region has similar possibilities. Famous among the larger natural lakes and bays of this region are Lake Christina and Heron Lake in Minnesota; Poygan, Butte des Morts, and Winnebago in Wisconsin; Saginaw Bay and Lake St. Clair in Michigan, and the Lake Erie Marshes of Michigan and Ohio.

Except for wood ducks, the midlands of the flyway lost most of their production potential for waterfowl when they gained the title of the Nation's breadbasket. Some of these crops, notably corn, are staple foods for several kinds of ducks and geese. In fact, with extensive grainfields, manmade reservoirs, and refuges, we now have features attractive to some waterfowl that originally were lacking. Canada goose populations apparently have responded to these changes to the extent that they may now be at an alltime high level.

Developments in the South have compensated to some degree for destructive forces I have mentioned and for additional hazards, such as pollution. Drainage and clearing of bottomlands were most harmful to wood ducks. Mallards also like bottomland habitat, but—more versatile than wood ducks—they took immediate advantage of rice culture as it spread across the prairies of Arkansas and Louisiana. Small reservoirs built to flood ricefields and larger ones for flood control proved to be ideal for many displaced mallards. And the supply of waste rice and associated weed seeds was far more dependable than the intermittent mast crops of bottomlands. Mallards, pintails, and some geese have accepted agricultural lands in apparent preference to natural habitat. But hunters who lost their hunting grounds with the destruction of bottomlands have had more difficulty adjusting. A limited number follow the birds to the ricefields, but others have had to quit hunting or accept poorer sport.

Vast marshlands of the Gulf coast have experienced human disturbances, but damages to this habitat have not crippled their usefulness. Great fluctuations in their value to waterfowl have marked these marshes from the beginning. In recent years they have demonstrated an exceptionally high carrying capacity by holding more than two-thirds of the total wintering population.

Looking back, one has to conclude that advancing civilization has ruined a large segment of the waterfowl habitat. Even so, except in years of adversity on the principal breeding grounds, large numbers of birds have returned each fall and winter to provide thousands of persons with recreation.

WETLANDS ARE VITAL to waterfowl and people, and despite many losses to drainage and other causes, the Mississippi Flyway still contains more than half the total, so classified, in the 48 contiguous States. The Mississippi Flyway Council determined in 1958 that 3.2 million acres of these wetlands were being managed by Federal, State, and private organizations (other than duck clubs) for the benefit of waterfowl or hunters. About half was closed to hunting. Hunting clubs and individuals who had posted their property against public trespass controlled about 6.8 million acres, or more than double that controlled by various agencies. Another 5 million acres were not posted or could be hunted by obtaining permission. Of approximately 10 million controlled or semicontrolled acres, about three-quarters were privately owned.

More than 3.5 million acres in more than 700 different locations were under State or Federal management by the end of 1961. It was a sizable increase in a short time. Included were 35 major Federal refuges (1.2 million acres) and 670 State areas (2.3 million acres), mostly of smaller size. About 1,548,-000 acres, or 44 percent, of this total were considered to be usable by waterfowl, including feed fields, planted specifically for the birds, as well as wetlands. Prime waterfowl real estate thus is considerably less than gross figures sometimes indicate.

The ratio between sanctuary and public hunting grounds on State and Federally managed areas is about 2 to 3. About 625 thousand acres are officially in sanctuary. Not included are other types of sanctuaries such as large, open-water areas that, in some States, cannot be hunted legally or, in others, may not be feasible to hunt. Further reductions of acreage open

to hunting result from rest grounds on duck clubs, closed areas of metropolitan districts (sometimes involving whole counties), and private lands and estates closed to hunting.

About 400 thousand acres were in public hunting grounds in 1950. By 1963 the figure more than doubled—to 923 thousand acres. This would provide about an acre for each buyer of a duck stamp, based on average stamp sales during the midfifties. This is not much elbowroom, but all hunters do not hunt at the same time, and not all use public hunting grounds. For every acre controlled for public shooting, 3 or 4 acres on private holdings help distribute hunting pressure.

Public areas generally receive greater use per acre of habitat than private areas. Most of the choicest hunting spots still are controlled by private clubs or wealthy individuals, but many are being brought under public ownership. Unless that is done, the average hunter of the future will be unable to find a place to hunt. Many of these wetlands will be diverted to uses other than waterfowl. Public ownership, up to a point, is in the public interest, but the ultimate goal is a good balance between publicly and privately controlled lands.

BREEDING GROUNDS beyond the present reach of agriculture serve as an "ever-normal granary" for waterfowl populations, a reservoir that cannot be drained entirely of its breeding stock. Even when the prairies were wet in the midfifties, a third or more of the duck population and most of the geese bred in the Far North. When drought hit the prairies, the portion increased to over half the ducks. But the displaced birds did not find suitable nesting conditions. They added few offspring to the flocks and their populations dwindled. Even so, complete disaster was averted thanks largely to this extensive hinterland area and other breeding grounds which were drought-proof. They can be counted on to safeguard most kinds of waterfowl from extirpation. They cannot assure adequate duck populations for good hunting, however. That is the job of the prairie pothole region.

Until recently, we considered the far northern breeding grounds safe from man's interference. We were wrong. Before this is printed, a dam across the Saskatchewan River at Grand Rapids, Manitoba, will commence backing up water over the famous Saskatchewan Delta, until it destroys most of one of the continent's best duck hatcheries. Alertness by the Manitoba Game Branch will save a portion of it. An even greater hatchery would be lost if the proposed Rampart Dam were constructed. This project would destroy the Yukon flats in Alaska. Evidently, our "ever-normal granary" has sprung a leak which must be patched before it becomes a gaping hole.

Hunting such as we knew it in the midfifties requires the help of some 7.5 million acres of prairie pothole habitat, most of which is outside the boundaries of this flyway. Federal and State agencies have plans to acquire by purchase or lease over 2 million acres of this kind of habitat in the Dakotas and Minnesota. The remainder of this prime breeding ground is in Canada where no comparable acquisition program exists. But Canadian officials are aware of the problem and are considering ways to solve it.

Because scattered water areas are an asset to ranchers in that they help distribute livestock, the grassland part of the pothole country is less likely to be disturbed than the croplands. Similar areas in cropland are a nuisance. Furthermore, some species of ducks, notably mallards and pintails, feed extensively on grain crops; they are unpopular therefore among grain farmers, who are unsympathetic about saving wetland nesting grounds. Solving this depredation problem and getting prairie farmers to view wetlands as an asset, rather than as a liability, may well be the key to the future of duck hunting.

Several species of waterfowl breed in significant numbers in the Flyway, but the wood duck alone nests in all 14 States, using bottomlands, beaver flowages, and other wooded wetland areas. Other habitat types used for nesting include the Gulf coast marshes, home of mottled and fulvous tree ducks; bogs and lakes of the north woods, used by ring-necked ducks, black ducks, mallards, and goldeneyes; rock outcrop lakes and streams, used primarily by mergansers; and prairie marshes and potholes used by dabbling and diving ducks. The raising of Canada geese, all from introduced stock, occurs on several National wildlife refuges, notably Seney in Michigan, and on several State managed or private areas, especially Lake St. Mary's in Ohio.

MIGRATION HABITAT at present seems ample to carry all the waterfowl likely to be produced. Major public works programs have meant that some States have more surface water than they had in the past. Still more areas have been proposed. Wisconsin is well along in an outdoor recreation program, which will be a major contribution to wetlands for waterfowl. Some will produce ducks and furnish resting areas and places to hunt. Minnesota has a similar plan under consideration and for several years has earmarked one dollar from every small game license sold for the purchase of wetlands.

Missouri has added 139 thousand farm ponds to its surface water acreage since 1940. In the aggregate, the ponds are larger than Lake of the Ozarks, one of Missouri's major impoundments. Other Flyway States have farm pond programs that total 2 million surface acres, with prospects for an increase of 25 percent in acreage by 1976. Much of this will have low or negligible value to waterfowl, but some of it is a major addition to the habitat.

Federal programs under Public Law 85–624 (Fish and Wildlife Coordination Act), Public Law 87–703 (Food and Agriculture Act of 1962), and the administrative order that created the Bureau of Outdoor Recreation all carry provisions that should result in additional waterfowl habitat, some useful for pro-production and wintering, but mostly valuable for migrational or recreational uses. The Federal Government, using funds borrowed from anticipated duck stamp revenue, and State conservation departments, leaning heavily on funds from the Federal Aid to Wildlife Restoration Act, are working toward a goal of nearly 2 million acres to be acquired for management purposes in this Flyway. Some of this acreage will be useful primarily as public hunting grounds or refuges during the migration period.

On the debit side, considerable habitat is likely to be lost through large-scale public works programs, such as those underway in the lower part of the Mississippi Valley. Urbanization, drainage, highway building, and other developments, will remove more. Grain-harvesting methods are becoming more and more efficient and may become a matter of concern for the welfare of mallards, pintails, and Canada geese, species that have adapted themselves more than others to field feeding. Migration habitat generally is of no immediate concern.

WINTERING HABITAT, like migration habitat, seems to be in no immediate danger. Nature recently tested the adequacy of the winter range for waterfowl on a scale that could not be duplicated experimentally. During the midfifties waterfowl populations built up to the highest levels of recent times, perhaps higher than will occur again. At the same time, the main wintering area was experiencing a drastic reduction of bottomlands through drainage, drought, and the end-products of an unfavorable stage of plant succession. The waterfowl simply bypassed unsuitable areas, and they seemed not to have suffered as a result.

More recently, severe storms reversed plant succession over broad areas of the Gulf coast marshes to a stage more favorable for duck food production. Habitat that had been dry became usable. Intensified management practices, such as those in Rockefeller Refuge in Louisiana, increased the carrying capacity of some parts of the winter range to a point seldom, if ever, experienced in the past. This high carrying capacity has continued in southwestern Louisiana for several years.

Obviously, we cannot count on these lush conditions to prevail indefinitely. Again in the future, a greater portion of the population may find it necessary to continue its flight into Latin America, to spread out more widely within the flyway, or perhaps to concentrate in greater numbers on the growing number of managed areas. Waterfowl are highly mobile creatures, able to adjust promptly to conditions, good or bad. In fact, an important problem of recent years has been that more than half of the mallard population has wintered north of the Ohio River, presumably because the combination of large reservoirs and adjacent crop fields made it unnecessary for them to migrate south. Some years, up to a million mallards have ended their migration along the Missouri River in South Dakota before even reaching this flyway.

There are several possibilities for expanding or improving winter range. Under existing acreage restrictions and cropping practices, more than half of the rice-belt lands used by waterfowl are fallow rather than in a rice crop. These fallow ricefields, as well as those that have produced a crop, have a high potential for waterfowl management. Assuming continued deterioration and some destruction of Dixieland marshes and swamps, management of ricefields and fallow fields could more than make up for this loss of wintering habitat. Expansion of "green-tree" management of reservoirs holds promise for obtaining greater use of bottomland types normally too dry for waterfowl.

All told, the number of waterfowl in the future will be determined largely by the condition of the breeding grounds and not by any foreseeable changes along flight lanes or on the wintering grounds. Prospects for holding the line seem brighter for migration and wintering habitat than they do for production habitat.

PLACES FOR RECREATION and space for elbowroom are important parts of the waterfowl picture. There is little justification for maintaining waterfowl unless people have the opportunity to enjoy them. Fun is yours in various ways. Some enjoy watching the birds; others in studying their habits; and untold miles of film have been exposed recording the colorful traits of these fowl. But these forms of recreation require little space compared with hunting. For many people nothing compares with duck and goose shooting; and preserving this sport becomes increasingly difficult as space for the purpose becomes less and less.

Two basic challenges are posed: One, to improve distribution of the birds, so that more people can enjoy them; the other, to uphold reasonable sporting standards despite a growing demand for greater recreational opportunity.

Food abundance and waterfowl distribution go hand in hand. Before and during the nesting period, protein demands of the hen are especially high. They continue to be high for ducklings and for moulting adults. Because so much energy is burned at all stages of the duck's life, a great abundance of high-quality food must be readily available at all times. The low densities of waterfowl in the infertile parts of their range are no mere accident.

The food requirements of many species are met in different ways in various parts of their range. Ducklings depend heavily on various animal foods, but as fall migration approaches plant foods become an increasing part of their diet. Mallards and pintails respond immediately to grain harvest on the prairies by field feeding. This habit becomes so prevalent at times that serious farm losses occur. Canvasbacks congregate where sago pondweed offers an abundant food supply. Ring-

A mallard banded on Shiawassee National Wildlife Refuge in Michigan is once again— as free as a bird.

necked ducks and most other species take advantage of a good wildrice crop or one of the other important foods of breeding grounds and staging areas. Geese, which are grazers and grubbers, seek out coastal flats where sedges, grasses, and some berries offer abundant food.

In some Northern States, residues of small grain remain important until covered by fall plowing. Indians, encouraged by high prices, remove as much of the wildrice crop as they can, but enough is lost in this primitive harvest to meet the needs of great numbers of waterfowl as they pass through Minnesota.

One study revealed that nearly half the food in stomachs of ducks taken on several Minnesota lakes was wild-rice.

As grain-eating species proceed south, corn replaces small grain. It composed nearly half the contents of 3 thousand stomachs of mallards examined in Illinois. Canada geese, also, are fond of corn and, with it, buckwheat, winter wheat, rye and ryegrass, and ladino clover. Sometimes they spend considerable time on stubble fields, or even plowed stubble, eating both grain and new grass sprouts.

Farther south, rice replaces corn as the staple of field-feeding species. And high on the list are smartweeds, wild millet, cyperuses, pondweeds, bulrushes, spikerushes, and naiads. In some places, coontail and rice cutgrass are among the top 10 wild food plants. In the South, sawgrass and paspalum seeds rank high, and, when mast crops are good, mallards and wood ducks forsake all other foods to gorge on acorns. Snails and mussels are relished by some diving ducks, and minnows are used even by mallards under certain conditions.

Blue and snow geese sometimes "grub" so heavily on rhizomes of common and Olney threesquares or rootstocks of cattail as to cause an "eat-out." Openings so created by overgrubbing, usually are beneficial to ducks but objectionable to muskrat trappers and cattlemen. Extensive feeding by geese also occurs in ricefields, cattle pastures, cornfields, stubble, and in newly planted grainfields during spring migration.

Are the waterfowl of this flyway getting enough to eat? I know of no evidence to the contrary. More than half of our waterfowl feed to a large extent on agricultural crops, more bountiful now than ever before. Increased efficiency of harvesting and prompt plowing of crop residues are reducing the amount of food left for the birds. But waterfowl seem well able to seek out places where food supplies are adequate.

Some waterfowl, particularly most of the divers, do not utilize agricultural crops to any extent. These include the scaup, which prefers animal foods, and judging from its present status the "bluebill" seems to be doing well. This species and others that feed almost entirely in natural wetlands, are finding the best food conditions of recent times in the coastal marshes of Louisiana. Eventually natural succession will cause this situation to deteriorate, but species now concentrating there are all great travelers with a winter range extending into the Southern Hemisphere. It is not likely therefore that a food shortage will trouble this group.

CLIMATE AND WEATHER have a tremendous influence on the well-being and distribution of waterfowl. Some years, blue and snow geese, nesting in colonies on the braided deltas of arctic rivers, produce practically nothing because of a delayed spring or flooding, which destroys the nests. If first efforts fail, time does not permit renesting in this severe climate. When this happened in 1961, Louisiana hunters noted that almost all the blue geese had the characteristic white heads of adult birds—meaning there were no young.

Canada geese that year had poor success, too, presumably because the extreme conditions that caused the northern breeders to fail also affected the climatic zone farther south where most honkers breed. In the same year, prairie ducks also had an unproductive year, but for an entirely different reason—drought. But ringnecks and scaup have a broad breeding range between the prairies and the Far North. They enjoyed fair success. Wood ducks had outstanding hatches in the swamplands of the flyway's interior, and mottled ducks along the coastal area also produced a bumper crop. Thus the dispersal of waterfowl through the full spectrum of climatic conditions has both advantages and disadvantages. It is unusual when conditions are favorable throughout most of the breeding grounds, but, by the same token, it is rare when everything is on the bad side.

By some standards, it is unfortunate that the bulk of our sporting duck population originates in the land of boom or bust, the prairie pothole region. This area, important to duck hunters everywhere, can produce enormous duck crops, as evidenced by those of the mid-fifties. It can also produce practically nothing as evidenced in 1959 and 1961. Normally the Great Plains Region, which contains the best of the pothole country, is semi-arid, but history shows that the climate of this area may vary from almost humid, as in 1905 and 1956, to almost arid, as in 1910, 1945, and 1961. This succession of dry and wet periods is likely to continue.

CLIMATE AFFECTS LANDSCAPES, and landscapes affect migration. Waterfowl follow well-defined landmarks, such as streams, lakes, and mountains for navigation. The close relationships between flight lanes and the physical features of this flyway are obvious. The Missouri River, with its new manmade reservoirs, leads birds in from the Northwest. The Mississippi Valley, with its older manmade pools, forms a north-south highway. The Great Lakes usher birds from the Northeast while guiding others in an opposite direction to the Atlantic coast. Iowa streams form conspicuous landmarks for prairie birds headed for the Illinois Valley, but, once there, the flight must dogleg back if the destination is the ricefields of Arkansas or the Gulf coast. More easterly flights find the Tennessee Valley Authority reservoirs pointed toward their wintering grounds.

As winter approaches, waterfowl move southward to wetter, warmer conditions. Within the flyway, annual precipitation ranges from 20 inches in northwestern Minnesota to 65 inches at Mobile Bay in Alabama. The northern half of the flyway averages less than 40 inches, whereas the southern half exceeds 40 inches. Average annual snowfall has a bearing on where birds spend the winter. It varies from 100 inches in northern Michigan to zero in the Gulf States. In the north half of the flyway, an inch or more of snow normally covers waterfowl areas for at least 40 days. South of Kentucky and Missouri, the average annual snowfall is less than 10 inches.

Below-freezing temperatures in combination with snow have a considerable effect on the distribution and well-being of wintering waterfowl. By December 1 the "freeze line" (normal mean temperature of 32°) has reached as far south as Davenport and Des Moines, the Wisconsin-Illinois border, and Lansing, Mich. A month later it passes through the southern parts of Indiana, Illinois, and Missouri.

Some waterfowl ignore temperatures and winter in the North as long as feed is available. And sometimes they get in trouble. A cold snap or blizzard may suddenly seal the food supply, and malnutri-

tion or even starvation sometimes results. Other kinds of waterfowl are not tempted to gamble on open northern winters. Until recently, for example, most blue-winged teal scorned even the Gulf coast area as a wintering resort. They much preferred Latin America, and still do. Several years ago, however, a quarter of a million bluewings discovered fine feeding in southwestern Louisiana. Similar numbers have wintered there ever since.

Fulvous tree ducks are perhaps least tolerant of chilling weather. They seldom get north of the Gulf coast plain, even in summer; when fall comes they depart for even warmer climes. But always, of course, there are exceptions, and individuals will sometimes wander as far north as Michigan, Minnesota, and Ontario.

This pair of Canada geese at Seney National Wildlife Refuge, Michigan, wanted a big family. They got one by borrowing some goslings from another brood.

Severe hail storms can have disastrous effects on waterfowl. Even swans have been felled by hailstones. Nests may be mashed into the ground and young birds and even adults destroyed in large numbers. Fortunately, such storms usually are quite restricted. Blizzards and cold waves can be extremely hard on ducks, and it is poor policy to encourage birds to winter in the North. Wintering ground developments, therefore, are limited to below the "freeze line," roughly marked by the Ohio River.

AND, NOW, having looked at the habitat, what about the birds that use it?

More than two dozen kinds of waterfowl consistently use this flyway. A few others, such as Atlantic brant and European widgeon, visit only occasionally. To the novice, the variety of water birds to be seen during a day on the marsh is confusing. Hunters especially are concerned with identification because of the increased emphasis on species management. It is illegal to shoot some kinds; at the same time a bonus is declared on others. Actually, though, only a dozen species are bagged in this flyway with any regularity, and a mere 10 species make up 95 percent of the total duck bag.

Here, by species, are our common waterfowl—where they come from, where they go, and what they do along the way.

CANADA GEESE are produced in Canada (mostly in Ontario), except one fairly large nesting group at Seney National Wildlife Refuge in Michigan and a few smaller colonies scattered elsewhere through the flyway. A few appear in early September. Peak populations reach Northern States by late October or early November. They reach midflyway States by late November where most of them spend the winter.

These geese, more than any other waterfowl, respond readily to management of habitat. Horicon National Wildlife Refuge, for example, started from scratch and built up a fall population exceeding 100 thousand in less than 20 years. Other developments, notably Union County and Horseshoe Lake State Refuges and Crab Orchard National Wildlife Refuge in southern Illinois, and Swan Lake National Wildlife Refuge in Missouri, gained sharply in numbers at the same time that Southern States were reporting a drastic decline. The implication was that the birds were shortstopped by attractive habitat developments.

Three more or less separate populations of Canadas use this flyway. The largest is the Mississippi Valley population which originates west of James Bay, migrates south through Ontario, the Lake States, western Ohio, Indiana, Illinois, and eastern Iowa to its major wintering area in southern Illinois. The next largest, the eastern prairie population, breeds in Ontario and Manitoba, migrates through the eastern Dakotas, western Minnesota, and Iowa and winters in greatest numbers in central Missouri. A few thousand continue into Louisiana

and Texas. The smallest group, a segment of the southeast population, breeds south of James Bay and passes through Ohio, Kentucky, and Tennessee and into Alabama (Wheeler National Wildlife Refuge). Some units stop to winter in each of those States.

The 1962–1963 midwinter count of Canada geese was more than 400 thousand, the highest on record. Distribution and harvest of the birds, however, leave much to be desired. Most are shot in a few places, notably Allegan County in Michigan, Horicon area in Wisconsin, Willow Slough in Indiana, three places in southern Illinois, Swan Lake area in Missouri, and the Lacassine area in Louisiana. Improving distribution and harvest of the birds is currently one of management's biggest challenges.

Even the experts have not reached full agreement on the different races of Canada geese that use this flyway, except that there are several ranging all the way from giants to pygmies. The largest may exceed 12 pounds, the smallest is about 4. Most are of intermediate size.

WHITE-FRONTED GEESE occur only as stragglers, except in one small part of Louisiana near the Lacassine Refuge. They are arctic nesters, which migrate early in the fall and reach their wintering area by November 1. Although they are highly prized by hunters and gunned heavily in Canada and in parts of the Central Flyway, the segment wintering in Louisiana has been increasing. This may be another example of the drawing power of habitat improvements rather than a reflection of improved status of the birds.

LESSER SNOW GEESE nest in colonies near the mouths of streams entering Hudson Bay and on Baffin Island. Early in fall they collect on concentration areas, the largest of which is at the south end of James Bay. Shortly after mid-October they leave this staging area in a spectacular mass migration to the coastal marshes of Louisiana, always arriving between October 22 and November 1. For most of the population, this flight is nonstop, but occasionally, when there are many young birds or adverse weather is encountered, large numbers stop in unexpected places and hunters are quick to take advantage of these brief bonanzas. Along major flight lanes, wildlife managers have had some success in stopping the birds for brief periods. In a few places, such as Squaw Creek in Missouri and near the mouth of the Illinois River, wintering flocks have become established. About 90 percent of the wintering population is the blue phase.

These geese are important to the James Bay Indian population as a staple food item and as a source of revenue in exchange for services as guides to white hunters. Between James Bay and the Louisiana marshes, the take of these birds

Mallards are the "bread and butter" duck of the Mississippi Flyway. White River National Wildlife Refuge in Arkansas is the site of this scene.

usually is light. Periodic nesting failures caused by a severe and variable arctic climate appear mainly responsible for the ups and downs of the snows.

MALLARDS make up about half of the total duck bag. In winter they usually outnumber all other ducks. Mallards nest both in prairie and wooded habitat of the northern part of the flyway, especially in Minnesota, but the bulk of the fall flight originates in Canada and the Dakotas. Bumper crops occur only when the prairie pothole duck factory is at or near its full potential.

About mid-October their numbers build up rapidly to a peak featured by the grand passage. This major movement usually occurs the first week of November. It is the most spectacular event of the entire fall migration because of the large number of birds that pass a given point in a short period. The mass movement reflects the mallards' reluctance to leave good feeding grounds in the North until a sudden cold snap drives them southward.

Various parts of the Flyway vie for the title of mallard capitol, but two general areas with the strongest tradition in their favor are the Illinois River Valley and the Grand Prairie of Arkansas. Both are famous nationwide for their great concentrations and excellent shooting.

BLACK DUCKS are of greatest importance to the eastern half of the flyway. They breed commonly in Michigan, northern Ohio, and westward into Minnesota, but a more important breeding area is in Ontario. The majority winter north of the Ohio River, notably in Ohio or Indiana. About 85 percent winter from Tennessee northward; their migration therefore is short compared to that of most other ducks. The ratio of mallards to black ducks in the flyway is about 20 to 1. Even so, the black is a popular duck and contributes significantly to the harvest. In Louisiana, native mottled ducks are difficult to distinguish from blacks unless you have them in your hand.

GADWALLS breed almost entirely outside the Mississippi Flyway and use mainly the western half during migration although some are taken by hunters in Ohio. Few arrive before mid-October, yet within a month they reach peak numbers on wintering grounds in Louisiana. Depending on habitat conditions, a variable portion of the population remains for the winter. The rest continue into Texas and Latin America. This is the duck that most hunters find difficult to identify because at first glance it looks like a mallard.

AMERICAN WIDGEONS nest in limited numbers in Minnesota. Most are produced on breeding grounds in Canada. Vanguards of the fall flight are adult drakes, which gang up in September on large marshes, such as Horicon and those along Lake Erie. Peak numbers in late October, or early November, are several times greater than wintering numbers, indicating that many more pass through than remain to winter. Practically all that remain spend the winter in Louisiana. Hunters usually take considerably more widgeons than gadwalls because of their better distribution in the flyway, but neither species ranks among the top five.

PINTAILS breed in small numbers in the flyway, especially in Minnesota, but most of them are hatched in the grasslands to the west and north. These birds are prolific when conditions are right, and decidedly desultory when they are wrong. They like open country dotted with innumerable ponds. Last year's grain stubble is about as attractive as grassland for nesting cover when nearby surface water conditions are right. Unlike the mallard, the pintail will use arctic tundra as a nesting grounds but will not use forested country.

The earliness of the fall flight of pintails rivals that of the blue-winged teal. Some pass through by late August or early September. The peak, however, does not occur until late November or December. By that time many pintails have continued on into Latin America, but in recent years great crops of wild millet and other natural foods have induced an unusually large part of the population to remain in Louisiana. In numbers shot, this species ranks about midway among the top ten.

GREEN-WINGED TEAL breed almost entirely outside the flyway in an extensive range, including the prairies and beyond to the Arctic. Traveling across their vast breeding grounds, one gets the impression of scarcity, since big gaps occur between pairs or broods seen. During migration they seldom are found in major concentrations, but they are well distributed and rank near the top in numbers taken by hunters. They also rank near the top as a wintering bird of the flyway. Louisiana is the principal wintering area.

Fall migration spans a long period from late in August until final freezeup in the North. The main flights occur late in October or early in November. The western half of the flyway carries the heaviest traffic of this pint-sized duck.

BLUE-WINGED TEAL are second in numbers to the wood duck as a breeding duck within the flyway. A few even nest in the coastal marshes of Louisiana. From Iowa northward they use a wide variety of wetland habitat, but they have strong preference for small, prairie-type ponds and marshes. They often use stockponds and dugouts and sometimes marshy lakes of wooded country. Iowa, before it was drained of its potholes, was a great blue-wing producer. Missouri has attempted to establish this bird as a breeder on the thousands of farm ponds in that State. The Lake States still produce substantial numbers of blue-wings, but larger numbers come from the Dakotas and Canada.

These teal are fair-weather ducks; they leave their summer homes long before either cold weather or a food shortage dictates. The most spectacular blue-wing movement I ever saw took place on September 1, 1939, Labor Day evening. Between sunset and dark, an estimated 15 thousand of these birds passed the Sante Fe railroad bridge over the Illinois River near Chillicothe. By that date and earlier, substantial numbers already have reached the coast, ready for the long hop across the Gulf of Mexico to Latin America. Blue-wings used to be uncommon as a wintering bird in the flyway, but this situation was changed by Hurricane Audrey. Following that storm in 1957, foods attractive to these birds became so abundant in the Louisiana marshes that large numbers changed their habits and remained over winter. Similar concentrations have occurred in that area every winter since.

SHOVELERS are primarily birds of the western part of the flyway and even there are quite spotty in distribution. Thus they are relatively minor in the kill, except in a few localities. They nest to a limited extent in the prairie portions of the flyway but largely in the more extensive grasslands farther west and north. An early migrant, they reach peak numbers before November. Large but variable numbers spend the winter in Louisiana; major increases have occurred after 1957.

WOOD DUCKS, more than any other species, are truly birds of this flyway. They breed in all 14 States. The greater part of this widespread population also winters within its boundaries. They respond well to management. In the right surround-

ings, the woodie is not averse to using a hollow tree or nesting box located in one's backyard. Such nestings, even though within a stone's throw of your living room window, often go unseen unless you know something about their interesting habits. If you do, you find many hours of exciting entertainment.

Woodies are associated with trees throughout their lifetime. They nest in trees, they rest and hide in swampy places, and they depend heavily on acorns for food. Trees must have suitable hollows, or they are worthless as nest sites. Where cavities are scarce, artificial boxes may be substituted to improve their range. These, however, should be so built, or so placed, that raccoons and other predators cannot enter them. Otherwise, you may be enticing the bird to a death trap instead of giving it a helping hand.

Late in summer, woodies gather for the night on roosts, which sometimes build up to several hundred birds. This habit, which continues throughout the winter, may offer a means for a census of the birds and a means for their capture and banding. Recoveries from such banded birds help to define migration routes and wintering grounds, and yield information on harvest rates, longevity of the birds, and other facts needed for their management.

Wood ducks leave Northern States by November 1, and Central States by mid-November for their sojourn in the South. Some, which live in the South in summer, may not migrate at all. They rank with the leaders in the flyway kill.

DIVING DUCKS, including mergansers, about equal the dabbling ducks in number of species but not in numbers of individuals counted during the annual January survey. During a 10-year period, 1953–1962, they collectively composed about 13 percent of the wintering population, but in 1961–1962 this proportion had more than doubled. They still make up less than a fifth of the duck bag, despite the fact that a large part of the Atlantic Flyway's wintering population passes through this flyway during migration. Divers are of greatest importance to the Northern States, since the main flight lanes cross the Lake States.

REDHEADS breed to a limited extent within the flyway but less often now than formerly. Most of their preferred habitat, the prairie marsh, has gone down the drain. The small remaining brood stock does well to survive, because of the extremely heavy hunting pressure, which sometimes occurs before the broods of these late nesters have time to disperse. Furthermore, the bird is its own worst enemy, for it often lays its eggs in the nests of other ducks. No other North American duck is so wasteful of its own eggs or such a nuisance to other ducks which nest in the same marshes.

Redheads are widely distributed as they pass through Minnesota during the fall flight, perhaps because this State is on the crossroads of two major flight lanes. One points toward Chesapeake Bay, the other toward Laguna Madre

on the Gulf of Mexico. Lakes of the Fox River chain in Wisconsin and Saginaw Bay and Lake St. Clair in Michigan are stopping places along the eastern route. The other route has two forks. One is almost directly southward to the Laguna where most redheads spend the winter. The other is via the Mississippi and Illinois Valleys toward a small wintering area off the Chandeleur Islands south of Mississippi, or, perhaps beyond to a wintering area on the Gulf side of the Florida coast. They migrate early, reaching a peak during the latter part of October. Few remain to winter. There was no open season on this bird during 1961–1962.

RING-NECKED DUCKS, during the breeding season, are usually linked with sedge-meadow marshes and bogs, a type of habitat limited to the Lake States in this Flyway. In western Minnesota where bogs and prairie potholes converge, the ring-neck nests in fair abundance in the land of the prairie ducks. Overall, however, this contribution to the total ring-neck population is small—most come from north of the prairies in western Canada. This species has disinguished itself since 1930 by expanding its breeding range into the Northeastern States and Canada. It is not a species likely to be eliminated by drainage ditches, because it thrives best in country submarginal for agriculture.

Many hunters call both ring-necks and scaup "bluebills," but for management reasons this confusion is unfortunate. The scaup is an abundant species; the ringneck is considerably less numerous. One reason for the scaup's abundance may be its liking for large bodies of water where it is comparatively safe from hunters. Ringnecks, however, are aptly called marsh bluebills, because during migration they frequent areas that are readily accessible to hunters and suffer heavy gunning losses as a result.

Their fall distribution within the flyway is better than that of the other divers, but some places are widely known as major concentration points. In that connection, Reelfoot Lake in Tennessee is the most famous. Surveys indicate that about November 1, when peak numbers are reached, the birds are almost equally divided among Northern, Central, and Southern States. Tennessee and Louisiana have the highest wintering populations, but most ringnecks spend the winter either in the Atlantic Flyway or in Mexico.

CANVASBACKS have been crowded by civilization into one last corner of the flyway, northwestern Minnesota. The best of that remnant is in Mahnomen County. Each year sees less of the right kind of habitat. Great flights have not been seen the last few years which, as recently as the midfifties, left Delta Marsh, Manitoba, in mid-October. They regathered first on Lake Christina in Minnesota, next on Lake Poygan in Wisconsin, then St. Clair Flats in Michigan, and finally on to wintering grounds in Chesapeake Bay. The reproductive success of canvasbacks is tied closely to an abundance of small pot-holes, rimmed with cattail or bulrush. Such situations have been scarce during drought years.

Besides the major flight lane in the Lake States, a lesser route led via the Illinois and Mississippi River Valleys to a wintering area on Mobile Bay in Alabama and freshwater lakes in Louisiana. The other important wintering area in the flyway is along the Detroit River. The canvasback exemplifies an orderly by-the-calendar and steppingstone type of migration, in contrast to species that filter undetected through an area or others that stay wherever the feed is abundant until severe weather drives them out. A comparison of peak numbers with those wintering indicates that about two-thirds of the fall population leaves the flyway.

LESSER SCAUP occupy a breeding range almost entirely north of the border. They are the most abundant diving duck of the flyway. Among all ducks, they are second in numbers only to the mallard. Bluebills have not been cropped as intensively as they could be, although special hunting regulations have been tried in an effort to increase the take.

Like some of the other divers, they use two main routes during migration. One crosses the Lake States and terminates along the Atlantic coast. Another flight heads for the Gulf coast by way of the Illinois and Mississippi Valleys. More than a million scaup winter within a few miles of New Orleans on Lake Borgne, Lake Pontchartrain, and other nearby lakes. Many more range along the shoal waters of the Gulf, west of the Texas line. A few thousand annually accept the rigors of a northern winter near Detroit.

COOTS are not waterfowl by the book, but their habits bring them in close association, if not in direct competition, with ducks. Many hunters do not consider them worthy of their marksmanship, but in a few areas this member of the rail family is a prime target. Some even claim they eat better than ducks. The fact remains that the harvest of coots exceeds that of most ducks.

Coots nest in the northern part of the Mississippi Flyway, but far greater numbers come from the prairie potholes and marshes of the Dakotas and Canada. So aggressive are they about protecting their eggs that their hatching success far surpasses that of ducks nesting on the same marshes. During migration they travel at night and are seldom seen. Between September 15 and October 1 a noticeable increase occurs in the flyway. Numbers reach a peak during the second half of October. The onset of winter pushes stragglers out of the North and to warmer climates. Only Louisiana holds sizable numbers over winter.

WHAT ABOUT THE FUTURE of waterfowl in the Mississippi Flyway?

Two blue-winged teal rest and stretch in the sun on Agassiz National Wildlife Refuge in Minnesota, preparing for a long winter trip south.

People interested in the out-of-doors—and they include just about everyone—agree that *all* species should be preserved at *all* cost. But hunters especially have interests that go far beyond the preservation of some of each kind. They want large numbers preserved for sporting and other recreational use. And so we arrive at the key questions: How many birds do we need? How many hunters can be provided sport of reasonable quality? What are our chances of meeting the objectives?

An International Migratory Bird Committee in 1962 stated a specific goal, which was widely endorsed: "To maintain waterfowl population levels within the bracket of high and low populations present during the period 1950 through 1956." This objective recognizes—the best of management to the contrary—that waterfowl fluctuate widely in response to weather conditions. Realistic, too, is acceptance of the fact that we cannot hope to restore duck numbers to peaks attained in the good old days. The human population explosion and irreversible land developments have changed all that. The best we can hope for is to hold the line.

Regaining population levels of the early fifties is not hopeless as some may think. True, waterfowl were in the doldrums in 1963. Restrictions have been severe for several years. Sales of duck stamps were at the lowest point since the late thirties—evidence that many hunters had given up. But is this loss of interest justified by the facts? Need it be permanent? I think not.

The future revolves around populations of waterfowl and people. As for waterfowl, their numbers can be maintained if we supply them with adequate habitat of the right kind and do not deplete basic breeding stocks. Demographers tell us that by the turn of the century there will be twice as many people in this country as there are today. What this will mean in terms of competition for space is anybody's guess.

Supplying adequate food for this pyramiding population apparently is not an immediate problem. According to the United States Department of Agriculture, "Our potential for agricultural production is likely to outrun prospective demand for farm products over the next 10 or 20 years, even with augmented food aid programs at home and abroad. By 1980 we will need an estimated 51 million acres less cropland than . . . we had in 1959."

Thus it appears it will be at least a couple of decades before agricultural interests will take a covetous look at acreage now devoted to wildlife purposes. This should provide time for wildlife managers to develop ways for maintaining sporting numbers of waterfowl on a gradually declining acreage. Agricultural technicians have accomplished miracles in line with their responsibilities; so can wildlife technicians, given adequate public and financial support.

The Mississippi Flyway Council has agreed it is desirable and necessary to plan quantitatively on the number of birds needed and hunters to be accommodated, while at the same time not overlooking certain goals of quality. The guiding slogan of this Flyway is *more fun per gun* rather than *more birds per hunter*. Is there any point in preserving wildfowling as a sport if it becomes so unsuccessful and so regimented that it is no longer any fun? The consensus among waterfowl experts of this Flyway is an emphatic no.

But how can reasonable standards of quality be upheld when space is becoming an increasing problem and there is real doubt that bird populations can be maintained at desirable levels? The only answer is to find ways to make better and fuller use of what we have through bird- and habitat-stretching devices. In this field waterfowl technicians can make their greatest contribution.

Some bird-stretching devices may be at hand. Improved sportsmanship and stricter enforcement can help to reduce crippling, wanton waste, and illegal practices that serve as wasteful drains on waterfowl. Pollution is everyone's business, and restored waterways could add much productive habitat without adding acreage. Lead poisoning of waterfowl, through ingestion of spent shot, is becoming serious. A lead-substitute in shot shells would reduce those losses.

Finding a way to increase the relative take of the species of waterfowl that are harvested at lower rates than others while reducing the harvest of those being shot too heavily is an aspect of species management—another way of making better use of what we have.

Habitat-stretching devices include improving breeding habitat so that its output per unit of area is doubled or tripled. Good possibilities appear to exist, too, for bringing new areas into production through suitable habitat improvements. The development of new strains of waterfowl or conditioned individuals to establish nesting colonies in new areas offers considerable promise. Habitat may be stretched, also, by examining areas controlled by public agencies to ascertain whether some now inviolate sanctuary could be opened to public hunting without endangering the resource.

We should reexamine some regulations, such as a statewide ban on open-water shooting, to determine if zoning or controlled boat travel would permit hunting without forcing birds to abandon the area or cause excessive harvest. We should consider incentives for farmers to maintain and improve marshes and to provide places to hunt.

Is it an idle dream to hope that your grandchildren will enjoy wildfowling much as you have known it? Not if you and your fellow conservationists make it a point to learn about the problems and insist on having them solved. It then enters the realm of the technical—and technical people have a way of getting the job done when the chips are down.—ARTHUR S. HAWKINS.

GADWALLS
YELLOW-HEADED BLACKBIRD

Central Flyway

THE CENTRAL FLYWAY is the go-for-broke flyway. In the spirit of the Old West, nothing here is done by half measures, whether grain crops, cattle herds, or mallards-on-the-marsh. The middle road is humdrum; we seldom travel it for long. An "average" year for ducks is something we see fleetingly while rocketing to the peak. We live with it again regularly, but momentarily, while plummeting to the bottom. In the Big Prairie country things are that way. It all relates to water.

The plains country slopes eastward from the foothills of the Rockies and runs as a rich vein from Texas to the Prairie Provinces of Canada. The upper end of this cornucopia is pothole country, the Dakotas, Alberta, Saskatchewan, and Manitoba, the nursery for the bulk of our birds. The bulk is large when water fills the prairie hollows. In drought years, which come periodically, the northern prairies can be desolate. Then all along the line we read the result in empty ponds, dry sloughs, and uninhabited coastal marshes.

The Central Flyway is roomy. It measures 1,115,000 square miles, more than one-third of the area of

209

all the flyways put together. Less than one-sixth of this total would qualify as waterfowl habitat, but that is enough to support bumper crops when they occur. For regulatory purposes, the flyway takes in all or parts of Montana, North Dakota, South Dakota, Wyoming, Colorado, Nebraska, Kansas, Oklahoma, New Mexico, and Texas. Of many geographic features, we can list four major types.

MOST OF THE GREAT PLAINS receive less than 20 inches of rainfall annually, so it is a region of short grasses, livestock, dryfarming, and giant irrigation projects. The gently rolling northern part has glacially-produced potholes and sloughs. Badlands cover parts of Wyoming and the Dakotas. Northwestern Nebraska is a land of sand hills, among which are tucked lakes, marshes, and now and then a stream. The southern part of the Great Plains is an expanse of level grassland, so rich in its primitive state that the bison herds it supported were measured by miles-in-width and days-to-pass-a-given-point.

THE ROCKY MOUNTAINS are the western boundary, a rugged rampart that reaches as high as 14 thousand feet above sea level. Between the mountain ranges are basinlike areas, called parks. They have plenty of water, and are high in waterfowl value. Broods of ducks live on beaver ponds and marshes of these mountain meadows. Reservoirs on lowland rivers harbor migrating waterfowl.

THE CENTRAL LOWLANDS on the eastern side of the Great Plains include the eastern parts of North and South Dakota, Nebraska, Kansas, and Oklahoma, and part of Texas. The line between the Central Lowlands and the Great Plains is marked in the Dakotas by the Missouri Coteau. The northern part is mantled with rocks left by glacial drift and with potholes scoured by glaciers. South of the glacier line, the lower, eastfacing escarpments indicate the line. The absence of glacial features in Kansas, Oklahoma, and Texas marks the southern part of the Central Lowlands from the northern. The Central Lowlands, which gets more than 20 inches of rain a year, is a region of tall grasses and woodlands and includes a major corn-producing region and the spring wheat sections of the Dakotas.

THE GULF COASTAL PLAIN borders the Central Lowlands and the Great Plains on the south. It extends from the Gulf of Mexico to an irregular zone a few miles west of Fort Worth, San Antonio, and Austin and then along an escarpment to the Rio Grande. Lagoons and coastal marshes border the Gulf. Woodlands, rivers, lakes, and reservoirs occur inland. The eastern part has 40 to 80 inches of rain and the western part 20 to 40 inches. Nearly level, the Coastal Plain is mostly agricultural. Its value for waterfowl is high.

THE MEN who came here saw a bountiful land. First were the Spanish Conquistadores in the

Southwest, the traders who ascended the Missouri and its tributaries before the Lewis and Clark Expedition of 1804, and the mountain men and fur traders who ascended the Platte, the Missouri, and their tributaries. Then came the Mormons, cattlemen, and farmers. From the swamps, lakes, marshes, rivers, and potholes they took the meat that kept them alive.

Their journals tell of their wonder and gratitude. Robert Stuart traveled from what is now Astoria in Oregon to St. Louis in 1812 and 1813—a trek which led to the discovery of the Oregon Trail. He wrote, on March 27, 1813, that the section of the Platte River in Nebraska, which is now covered by Lake McConaughy, was "an extensive swamp, the resort of innumerable numbers of Geese, Brant, a few Swans, and an endless variety of Ducks; during the latter part of this day's march, we found several similar places, all well stocked with wildfowl."

George Frederick Ruxton, a 19th century soldier of fortune, enroute from Vera Cruz, Mexico, to New Mexico and Colorado in 1846, reported large numbers of geese and grullas (cranes) in flooded flat country near Durango, Mexico. Nearing Chihuahua, he observed more cranes "whose meat is excellent." He shot geese in the spring of 1847 on the "Arkansa" near the present-day city of Pueblo, Colorado.

BEGINNING with the sodbusters, men have done many things to change the country and its life. To get water for livestock, agriculture, and communities in a semiarid land, many of the larger rivers were dammed—the Missouri, North Platte, Platte, Arkansas, Red, Rio Grande. Some needed deepening and channeling for navigation. Some prone to flood needed disciplining. When that was done, the streamside marshes used by waterfowl for breeding, feeding, and resting no longer got the floodwaters that made them marshes. But irrigated meadows and croplands have replaced some of this natural habitat, and many reservoirs have become way stations of migrating birds.

Many potholes have been drained for cultivation in the Central Lowlands. Somebody may have gained, but not the ducks that once bred there. Converting marshland in the Gulf Coastal Plain for growing rice benefited some waterfowl, but the dredging, filling, and draining of marshes, bays, and lagoons for industrial and municipal developments reduced the amount and quality of aquatic habitat. Pollution and siltation, which seem always to attend the growth of cities and industry, spoiled the homes of birds and animals, just as they befoul man's environs.

Go-for-broke it has been, and broke applies now to some—not all—of the Central Flyway. Parts of it the fur trader, explorer, and pioneer farmer of a century ago would not recognize and surely would not rhapsodize about in his journals and letters home. Yet much remains unchanged. Autumn skies still echo the calls of waterfowl. Farms have taken places where waterfowl nested, but the birds still

*Duck hunters being towed out to blinds in the bay near Rockport, Texas,
for a day of hunting.*

have places for wintering. Waterfowl, specialists and slaves of habit
though they are, have risen to new
situations, and in so doing they have
prospered where less adaptable forms
of wildlife have disappeared.

THE MALLARD, here as elsewhere,
is a choice species and commonest
of all the dabblers. It ranges all over
the flyway. It is the prize in the
hunter's bag. Tabulations of information on legbands returned to us
tell us that Alberta, Saskatchewan,
and Manitoba contribute a substantial portion of the Central Flyway

mallards. More than a million have
been recorded on Fort Randall Reservoir in South Dakota in late
December and early January. Many
of them do not reach wintering area
farther south until subfreezing temperatures and snowdrifts cover their
food supplies and force them to move
on.

Mallards en route to winter quarters in the Mississippi Flyway also
use habitat within the northern and
midflyway States. Many greenheads
that concentrate on refuges, reservoirs, lakes, and potholes in North
Dakota and South Dakota in the fall

eventually migrate southeastward to Arkansas and Louisiana but not until ice and snow force them to. Their tendency to winter as far north in the flyway as food and water conditions permit has bearing on the management and the future of mallards. The agricultural economy of the Central Flyway has created new situations the mallards seem to like.

PINTAILS, graceful, fast, agile birds, prefer the short-grass prairie for nesting, but some breed in Alaska, the Yukon, and the Northwest Territories. About half of those that breed in the prairies and their offspring belong in the Pacific Flyway. Some of them have a roundrobin migration—down the Pacific Flyway in the fall, into and across Mexico to the Gulf coast in late winter, and up the Central Flyway in the spring. Pintails and mallards total about half to two-thirds of all the ducks harvested in the Central Flyway.

Pintails of the Central Flyway migrate directly to their winter resorts on the Texas coast. Some of the Mississippi Flyway pintails pass through the northern part of the Central Flyway. Pintails generally do not tolerate the low temperatures and snow and ice of the Northern States, but seek warmer climates for the winter. During years of peak pintail numbers, 80 percent of the Central Flyway pintails winter on the coast of Texas and eastern Mexico. The Laguna Madre is a favored area, but shifts of greater numbers to the upper coast—West Bay, Galveston County, and the coastal marshes of Jefferson and Chambers Counties—have been noted during years of high rainfall.

GREEN-WINGED AND BLUE-WINGED TEAL together rank next to mallards and pintails in the flyway in numbers and harvest. They are the smallest of the dabbling ducks and provide the most elusive targets. In the kill, the green-wing outnumbers the blue-wing.

Blue-winged teal may be the most numerous breeding duck in the States of the flyway. Their arrival on the prairies in late spring usually signals the start of the breeding season. They migrate in early fall. Drakes generally leave before the young birds and hens. One of the longest fall flights recorded for a duck, more than 4 thousand miles, was made by a blue-winged teal. Often their flights exceed 2,500 miles. One flew 3,800 miles from the place it was banded to the point of recovery in a month, averaging 125 miles a day.

Locally-raised blue-wings are a sizable part of the hunter's reward during the first days of the season in the Dakotas and Nebraska. Not so farther south in the flyway; most of these birds are in Mexico, Central America, South America, and the West Indies when the hunting season opens in this region.

The hardy green-winged teal, also a prairie nester, prefers wooded potholes and streams more than the blue-wing. Its fall migration, usually in large, swift, well-ordered flocks, occurs with the first cold weather. The migrating birds like to linger wherever they find attractive feeding grounds. Many green-wings

winter in the marshes of the upper Texas coast.

THE CINNAMON TEAL, a close relative of the blue-wing, is rare east of the Rockies. Once in a while it nests in parts of Texas, Montana, Wyoming, Colorado, and New Mexico. It seems to like alkali marshes. Wintering populations are small, and the colorful, unusually silent cinnamon teals are unimportant in the hunting harvest.

THE SHOVELER, or spoonbill, closely resembles the blue-winged teal in habits. It migrates in late spring and early fall and nests throughout the prairies. It prefers the warmer sections of the flyway for wintering and often associates with blue-winged teal in the fall migration. Fresh and brackish marshes of the western Gulf coast are its main winter home. Unwary and easily mistaken for a mallard, the shoveler often shows up in the bag of the novice hunter.

THE AMERICAN WIDGEON breeds in all parts of the prairies, the Far North, and Alaska. It is a late spring migrant, nesting well into June. It is not a major breeder in the United States' part of the Central Flyway. More commonly it nests in the aspen parklands of Canada and the tundra of the Northwest Territories. In the fall, it migrates usually in fast, compact flocks, later than teal and pintails but earlier than mallards. Often it winters near mallards and pintails, but it has a greater liking for green foods, natural and cultivated. In some localities, widgeon feed on truck crops, especially lettuce and spinach.

THE GADWALL, although somewhat smaller than a mallard, is often mistaken for a hen mallard. It prefers to nest in grassland and commonly is associated with alkali marshes. A midseason migrant, gadwall seek the warmer climates in winter. A sizable number of the gadwall in this flyway winters on the Texas coast and in Mexico.

THE MOTTLED DUCK and the Mexican duck are close relatives of the mallard, but they lack the mallard's distinctive color differences between sexes. The Gulf race of the mottled duck is a year-round resident of the coastal prairies and marshes of Texas. On the upper Texas coast it is common in the hunter's bag during the early part of the season. The northern Mexican duck, now nearly extinct, is a resident of the Rio Grande Valley of southern New Mexico. Wildlife managers are attempting to increase its numbers by releasing young birds in suitable habitat.

THE WOOD DUCK, a tree-cavity nester, is limited in range in the flyway primarily to the Southern States. Here it is found along wooded stream bottoms and in "green-tree" ponds. It is relatively unimportant to hunters, because it does not frequent areas used by other ducks.

A concentration of bluebills (lesser scaup) in an arroyo near Aransas Pass, Texas.

DIVING DUCKS, the second of the two major groups of ducks, occupy large lakes and reservoirs and coastal marshes and bays. They seldom feed in uplands. Their main foods are aquatic forms, for which they commonly dive to depths of 15 feet. Canvasbacks have been observed to descend to 25 feet and old squaws to 200 feet to obtain choice food items. The tendency of diving ducks to form compact flocks with members of their own kind or with other divers leads some hunters to call them raft ducks. Large paddle feet, well back on the body, make all of them excellent divers. They can travel far under water to escape danger—goldeneyes pursued by a falcon were observed to drop to the water, pass out of sight, and rise nearly 100 yards away, flying low over the water. The diver group is 10 to 20 percent of the total duck population that winters in the Central Flyway.

REDHEADS are first among diving ducks in total numbers and in hunters' bags, when it is legal to take them. They nest in the deeper marshes of the northern Plains States and the southern parts of the Prairie Provinces. They are primarily over-water nesters, using phragmites, bulrushes, and cattails to make their nests. Drought on the Canadian prairies has reduced nesting cover and curtailed their numbers. Hunting redheads became illegal in the 1960-1961 season.

The redhead's fall migration is well underway in October. Birds raised on the prairies and in the Plains States disperse widely to the Pacific and Texas coasts and east to Chesapeake Bay. A female redhead and her brood were banded in southern Saskatchewan in 1954. During the hunting season that fall, one of her young was recovered on the lower Texas coast, but she was taken at the eastern end of Lake Ontario, presumably en route to wintering grounds on the east coast.

Redheads from the Bear River marshes in Utah also contribute to the Central Flyway population. Migrating flocks utilize lakes, larger sloughs, and potholes of the Plain States. The end of the line for as much as 80 percent of the total continental population is the Laguna Madre of Texas and Mexico. This extensive, shallow-water bay, rich in animal life and lush beds of shoalgrass and widgeongrass (preferred redhead foods), has long been a choice winter haven for this duck. Large rafts, numbering more than 100 thousand birds, are common.

THE CANVASBACK is another overwater nester and breeds in marshes, sloughs, and potholes of the prairies. Unlike the redhead, its breeding range extends northward into the forests of Canada and central Alaska, and birds entering the Central Flyway originate in the western part of that range. They frequent many of the areas used by migrating redheads. The center of the flyway's wintering population is the Texas coast and east coast of Mexico.

THE LESSER SCAUP outranks the canvasback numerically, but the

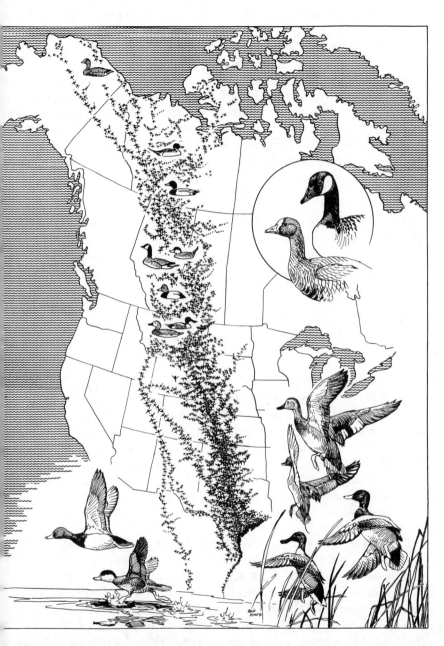

flyway harvest of the bluebill has been small until recently. Its breeding range extends from the prairies northward into the Northwest Ter-

ritories and Alaska, where drought does not affect its status very much. The birds are late nesters. The young are among the last to leave the breeding grounds. Fall migration is leisurely and just ahead of winter. The flyway population utilizes larger, deep-water marshes, lakes, and reservoirs en route to southern wintering areas. Most of them winter on the bays and estuaries of the upper Texas coast and in the Tamaulipas and Tamiahua lagoons of the east coast of Mexico.

THE RING-NECKED DUCK, which looks much like the scaup, is not nearly so abundant or important in the harvest. It breeds sparsely throughout the prairies and northward to forested northern Canada. Fall migration begins ahead of the scaup, and wintering blackjack prefer the deeper fresh-water marshes, open lakes, reservoirs, and coastal bays.

THE COMMON GOLDENEYE nests in tree cavities. It breeds over a wide range of forested Canada and Alaska. It is hardy and winters in the northern part of the flyway, primarily along open streams and spring-fed ponds of Montana and Wyoming. The whistler is not an important species in this flyway.

THE BUFFLEHEAD is also a tree-cavity nester. Its breeding range is the wooded region north and west of the prairies. It, too, is a hardy bird and does not migrate until driven south by approaching winter. The butterball frequents the larger, deeper lakes and reservoirs. It is relatively unimportant in numbers.

THE HARLEQUIN DUCK, a colorful bird, winters in small numbers on the open streams and rivers o Montana and Wyoming. It is o little importance as a game bird.

MERGANSERS are a breed apart We do not classify them with eithe the dabbling or diving groups. Bot hooded and common mergansers winter in New Mexico, Oklahoma and Texas. Hunters do not go ou of their way to get them.

THE RUDDY DUCK breeds in th prairie sloughs of the Plains State and Provinces wherever it can find bulrushes, phragmites, and cattail for nesting cover and material. Fal migration usually occurs in Septem ber. They winter in the shallowe and more protected bays and estu aries along the Texas coast. It is not important in this flyway.

THE FULVOUS TREE DUCKS and the black-bellied tree ducks occu in the Central Flyway only along the Texas coast and in Mexico They are not hunted but are said to be more palatable than the ruddy and bufflehead, because the feed on grain, seeds, and othe plant materials. The fulvous tre duck, or squealer, sometimes dam ages newly-planted ricefields along the Texas coast.

CANADA GEESE, prized game bird over most of the continent, at som time of the year are found in ever Territory and Province of Canada every State of the flyway, and ir northern Mexico. A complex group they come from far northern breed ing grounds and to a limited exten from the Canadian prairies and

Montana, Wyoming, Colorado, North Dakota, and South Dakota. The western Canada goose is the predominant breeder in the States of the Central Flyway, although the rare giant Canada goose has been found in the Dakotas. Breeding colonies have been established in New Mexico, Nebraska, Colorado, Kansas, Wyoming, Montana, Oklahoma, and the Dakotas.

All races have distinct breeding grounds, but they intermingle on migrating and wintering grounds. The small Canadas nest along the Arctic Coast from Alaska eastward to Baffin Island, the relative size of these birds becomes progressively larger north to south. Medium to large Canadas nest throughout the forest tundra and rock barrens east to the west shore of Hudson Bay. The largest of all nest in the prairies and Plains States.

Hanson and Smith describe the fall migration of Canada geese as ". . . a segment of the concentric waves produced by an object striking the surface of a body of water; the earliest flocks or migratory waves travel the greatest distances in the shortest periods of time and reach their wintering grounds in the far south before many other flocks have left the north country." *Canada Geese of the Mississippi Flyway,* Vol. 25, Art. 3, Illinois Natural History Survey, 1950.) In this flyway, the small Canadas nest farther north, migrate earlier, and winter farther south than the large birds.

Migrations follow two routes, which are connected with the tallgrass and shortgrass prairies. Many concentrate at well-defined gathering points or staging areas during fall migration. One of the first such staging areas for birds moving down the more western shortgrass route is the Hay Lakes district of northwestern Alberta. The next area, near Hanna, Alberta, and Kindersley, Saskatchewan, is a way station for geese from a wider region of the breeding range. Canada geese moving down the more eastern tallgrass route gather in the Interlake District in Manitoba and remain for a time before continuing southward.

Migration from the Canadian staging areas takes place in mid-September or early October. The first arrivals of small Canada geese at refuges in North Dakota and South Dakota and other points occur about the third week of September and a week or more before the first arrivals of larger birds. Arrivals at refuges in Nebraska, Kansas, and Oklahoma occur a week or two later. First arrivals reach the Texas coast the second week of October. The first to come are primarily small birds. The flocks wintering on the northerly refuges contain a higher proportion of large Canadas.

The western Canada goose breeds in the western prairie section of Canada, the Flathead Valley, and north central Montana; the Green, Snake, Bear, North Platte, and Wind Rivers in Wyoming; the Yampa and Green Rivers, the San Luis Valley, and reservoirs in the Fort Collins area of Colorado. Those breeding in the eastern section of the Canadian prairies,

220

WATERFOWL TOMORROW

North Dakota, South Dakota, and Nebraska are now thought to have a connection with the giant Canada goose, which winters in part of its breeding area. A part of the western colony winters on the lower Colorado River and Roosevelt Lake in Arizona. Other segments winter in the Rio Grande Valley in New Mexico; northern Mexico; on the Platte River in western Nebraska; and at Cheyenne Bottoms in Kansas.

WHITE-FRONTED GEESE enter the Central Flyway from the Yukon Delta, Innoko River, Selawik River, and Minto Lakes in Alaska, and the rivers, marshes, and lakes of the tundra in northern Canada. The first flights reach the Hanna-Kindersley staging area in late August or early September. Another segment of the white-front group reaches Lower Souris Refuge in North Dakota about a week later. A third and smaller flight passes through the Saskatchewan River delta area and Oak Lake in Manitoba the first week of September.

Migrating "specklebellies" use many refuges and management areas en route south. Year after year, the first arrivals rarely vary more than a few days at Lower Souris, Lac Aux Mortes, Tewaukon, and Long Lake Refuges in North Dakota; Sand Lake and La Creek Refuges in South Dakota; Kirwin and Quivira Refuges and Cheyenne Bottoms in Kansas; and Salt Plains and Tishomingo Refuges in Oklahoma. The first flights reach the Lissie Prairie in Colorado and Wharton Counties in Texas the first week of October. Most of the white-fronts are on wintering grounds in Louisiana, Texas, and the east coast and central plateau of Mexico by late October.

SNOW GEESE move from nesting grounds to the Texas coast in a short period and by direct flight. Flocks of strong-flying snows of both blue and white phases sometimes make a spectacular journey, traveling from Canada to the Texas gulf coast, a distance of 2 thousand miles, in 2 days. At other times they move in flocks of 3 thousand to 5 thousand in shorter hops and stop at traditional resting and feeding spots along the way, such as the Devils Lake area in North Dakota; Sand Lake Refuge in South Dakota; and the Missouri River from Yankton to Omaha. They often remain loyal to favorite stop over areas long after changes in land use have removed the original attraction. An example: Forney's Lake in southwestern Iowa now is cornfields, but snows and blues visit it in numbers spring and fall. Both phases travel together, but the earlier flocks often are 90 percent blues and 10 percent snows. The flock composition gradually changes until the latest stragglers are composed largely of the white-phase birds.

THE ROSS' GOOSE, a small species resembling the snow goose, sometimes is found with flocks of snows wintering on the Texas coast. It breeds in the Perry River region in Canada.

Some snow and Ross' geese pass through the Alberta-Saskatchewan staging area, but most snows in the Central Flyway move south through its eastern part. Freezeout Lake in Teton County in Montana often is a stopover for large numbers of snow geese, although we regard them as Pacific Flyway birds.

ALL GEESE respond to management techniques that assure food and freedom from human disturbance and hunting. Examples of State and Federal habitat-management projects and refuges are those at Freezeout Lake in Montana; Lower Souris and Tewaukon Refuges in North Dakota; Sand Lake Refuge and the State-controlled Hecla and Brule Bottoms units in South Dakota; De Soto Refuge and Plattsmouth in Nebraska; Two Buttes Reservoir in Colorado; Cheyenne Bottoms in Kansas; Tishomingo and Salt Plains Refuges in Oklahoma; Bosque del Apache Refuge and La Cueva in New Mexico; and Buffalo Lake, Hagerman, Aransas, and Laguna Atascosa Refuges in Texas.

These projects serve the birds as migration or wintering areas. They also make available greater numbers of geese for people to hunt and enjoy. Most of the goose harvest occurs on or near these concentration points.

TRUMPETER SWANS, once abundant and widespread on the continent, were killed by explorers and pioneer farmers for food and plumage. Commercial hunting for the plumage trade later brought the trumpeter to the verge of extinction. Efforts to preserve the

bird in the United States were initiated in 1935, when Red Rock Lakes Migratory Waterfowl Refuge in Montana was acquired for the purpose of protecting the remnant flock. This refuge now represents the trumpeter's principal breeding and wintering area south of Alaska and British Columbia.

WHISTLING SWANS are uncommon wintering birds in the Central Flyway, although a sizable flock that winters annually in the Pacific Flyway passes through Freezeout Lake in Montana. Aggregations of fewer than a hundred have been seen on lakes and reservoirs of the Wind River Indian Reservation and the Big Horn Basin in Wyoming. Smaller flocks and family groups pass through the northeastern Dakotas enroute to eastern wintering areas each fall. Their diet is largely vegetable, and sometimes they are accused of destroying large amounts of aquatic duck foods.

AMERICAN COOTS nest throughout the Canadian prairies and the Great Plains States. Like several of the diving ducks, they nest over water. They are early fall migrants, and most of their flying is in loose aggregations in the evening and at night. Lakes, brackish waters, lagoons, and estuaries are favored as wintering habitat. Most of the coot population in the Central Flyway winters on the Texas coast and east coast of Mexico.

THE NUMBER of ducks and geese that wing down the flyway each fall depends largely on the amount and quality of the places where they breed. More than that, birds need good habitat to sustain them during the part of each year that they spend in migration and on the wintering grounds. How extensive and how adequate is the habitat used by ducks and geese in the Central Flyway? Where is it? Is it stable? Does it satisfy the requirements of the different species?

ANCESTRAL wintering grounds were swamps, flooded river bottoms, lakes, and coastal marshes where waterfowl could find such foods as pondweeds, sedges, wild millet, smartweed, chufa, bulrushes, wild-celery, and arrowheads. Then, as now, the quality and amount of much of this habitat depended on rainfall, flooding, and other aspects of weather. Human activities have changed greatly in these lands and waters.

We have said much about the loss of habitat through drainage, urbanization, industrialization, and channelization, activities that certainly have destroyed or impaired many areas. Outside of the production areas in the northern tier of prairie States, however, losses in the Central Flyway have not reached critical dimensions. Some 6.5 million acres of wetlands and permanent water were listed in 1964 as of high value. The States and the Federal Government manage about 925 thousand acres of water, wetland, and croplands for use by waterfowl. Some of it is natural habitat that has been improved by various management practices to increase its carrying capacity. Much was created in connection with water-development programs of the States and the Bureau of Sport Fisheries and Wildlife and construction programs of other agencies.

Conservation and watershed-protection programs of the United States Department of Agriculture have led to the making of about 750 thousand acres of farm ponds, stock ponds, runoff-detention reservoirs, and irrigation storage reservoirs in the Central Flyway. Besides, many landowners have improved extensive acreages without Federal assistance. Not all are suitable waterfowl habitat, but on an acreage basis stock ponds in South Dakota have been found to be just as valuable for breeding ducks as the best natural areas. In western Oklahoma, ducks are common on runoff-detention reservoirs from late November to early January. Irrigation reservoirs in the rice-growing section of the Texas coast also furnish habitat for wintering waterfowl.

Habitat created by construction programs of the Bureau of Reclamation, Corps of Engineers, and private irrigation companies is used by waterfowl for nesting, resting, and feeding. At least 4 million surface acres of reservoirs existed in the Central Flyway in 1956; much more has been added since. Many reservoirs have little or no value for waterfowl, but others close to grainfields are heavily used by migrating or wintering birds. Moreover, the values to waterfowl of some reservoirs are being enhanced through the efforts of the Bureau of Sport Fisheries and Wildlife and the State game and fish departments.

AT THE SOUTHERN END of the flyway, the coastal waters of the Gulf of Mexico, and the coastal marshes of Texas and adjacent ricelands accommodate up to 45 percent of the wintering ducks and about 90 percent of the geese. The area encompasses 5 million acres of land and water where the annual rainfall varies from 52 inches on the upper coast to 24 inches in the lower reaches. The region supports a diversified agriculture, including rice, cotton, corn, sorghum, citrus, and vegetable crops. Three major habitat types are recognized.

The deep-marsh rice belt, east of Galveston Bay, is an extension of the deep marshes of Louisiana. This region, of about 520 thousand acres, is subject to almost year-round flooding by fresh or salt water. The fresh and brackish marshes afford a much greater abundance of waterfowl food plants (saltgrass, bulrushes, spikerushes, and widgeongrass) than does the saline marsh of some 11 thousand acres. The marshes are heavily used by waterfowl, especially snow geese. Total ducks and geese may number 750 thousand in late December and January. Ducks are attracted mainly to adjacent ricefields, the acreage of which exceeds that of marsh. Rice irrigation systems provide such duck foods as smartweeds, wild millet, pondweeds, and waste rice.

The shallow-marsh rice belt is transitional habitat of some 300 thousand acres located between fresh and tidal marshes. Shallow flooding by fall and spring rains makes the water fresh to slightly brackish. The area extends from Galveston Bay through Matagorda Bay and Calhoun County. Plants common to the shallow marsh are similar to those found in the deep marsh. Some 2 million acres of surrounding area are in rice production, and rice is a big part of the waterfowl diet. Tidal marshes in this region are in low areas adjacent to bays and on the bay side of Matagorda Peninsula. Offshore islands here do not create the shallow bays that waterfowl like.

THE TIDAL MARSH extends from Matagorda Bay to the Rio Grande and is essentially a narrow, saline marsh, flooded by tidal action. It covers about 500 thousand acres and supports heavy growth of saltgrass, saltflat-grass, and cordgrass. More than 750 thousand acres of shallow bays produce shoalgrass and widgeongrass, besides snails and bivalves, all of which redheads and scaups like.

The offshore islands of Galveston, Matagorda, St. Joseph, Mustang, and Padre are leading waterfowl resting areas. Three hundred thousand acres of offshore islands form one side of the shallow bays, which are rich in submerged plant and animal foods. Most of the land adjacent to the shallow bays of the lower Texas coast is brushland pasture. During years of average or above average rainfall, numerous small freshwater ponds and potholes provide wintering habitat and supply an abundance of waterfowl food plants, such as waterlilies, pondweeds, and smartweeds.

THE RICE BELT, the nearby coastal marshes, and the shallow bays of the lower Texas coast winter more than 2 million ducks and geese. Mallards use the deep marsh and rice belt. Redheads and scaup prefer the shallow bays of the lower coast. Wintering pintails prefer marshes of the upper coast and the mouth of Arroyo Colorado in Laguna Madre. Marshes of Jefferson and Chambers Counties winter large numbers of blue and snow geese. Ricefields of Colorado and Wharton Counties are the chief wintering grounds of the whitefronted goose. Canada geese are most abundant in the mid and lower sections of the coast. The Texas coast is a mixing pot for all the subspecies in the flyway, except possibly the western Canadas.

Ricefields, irrigation systems for rice, and the shallow bays are the most stable of coastal wintering habitat. The value of the marshes deteriorates with time, and only when this trend is reversed by some disturbance, such as hurricanes or fire, do they become attractive again for waterfowl.

THE ECONOMIC development of the Texas coast has been spectacular—and devastating to habitat. Industrialization, urbanization, channelization, pollution, drainage, and water control projects have destroyed or impaired large acreages. Channelization of stream courses has eliminated winter flooding of hardwood bottomlands, to

the detriment of puddle ducks. Millions of gallons of industrial waste and millions of gallons of sewage are discharged daily into coastal waters. Large amounts of silt, carried by streams into the shallow bays, have harmed aquatic vegetation. Drainage of ricefields, necessary during periods of heavy rainfall, pours excessive amounts of fresh water into coastal marshes, upsets the balance of brackish and fresh water, and so eliminates aquatic plants attractive to waterfowl. Drains through the lower water levels of marshes convert marsh to wet meadow, and waterfowl move on.

Texans look longingly toward the offshore islands as places for recreation. They want causeways to link offshore islands and the mainland— causeways that will reduce the exchange of waters, increase their salinity, cause further loss of aquatic plants and animals, and reduce waterfowl carrying capacity. Many large reservoirs have been built and planned to meet domestic, industrial, and agricultural needs, provide flood protection, and reduce soil erosion. Reservoirs reduce the flow of fresh water into the marshes which gradually change from brackish to saline. When they do, preferred vegetation disappears. Reservoirs cannot replace the coastal marshes and bays as homes for waterfowl.

The Bureau of Sport Fisheries and Wildlife and the Texas Game and Fish Commission manage about 110 thousand acres on the Texas coast. Plans have been announced to add 100 thousand acres. This intensively managed habitat, plus marshes not yet altered, will help provide for wintering needs of waterfowl on the Texas coast—but the distribution of birds will be affected, and that is important to people, if not to ducks.

PLAYA LAKES, artificial lakes, and stock ponds of the Texas Panhandle are the second leading winter habitat of the Central Flyway. The playas, shallow depressions a few hundred feet to a mile in diameter, provide about 230 thousand acres of unstable but important habitat. The Soil Conservation Service has constructed many artificial lakes and stock ponds. They and reservoirs for domestic water supplies contribute an additional 6,500 acres of habitat, doubly important because they are havens when the playas dry up.

The Panhandle is devoted to winter wheat, sorghums, cotton, and grazing. Water areas contain spikerushes, smartweeds, pondweeds, and wild millet. Food for waterfowl therefore is ample, and large numbers of ducks and Canada geese winter here. In 1956, a year of good populations, more than a million ducks, three-fourths of them mallards, were here. Canada geese number 5 to 10 thousand, and most of them are usually on Buffalo Lake and Muleshoe National Wildlife Refuges.

EAST OF THE PANHANDLE, stock ponds and winter wheat of the Waggoner Ranch, Wilbarger County, provide wintering habitat for 10 to 70 thousand Canada geese. Hager-

man National Wildlife Refuge winters 10 to 15 thousand Canadas. The lakes and water areas of central and east Texas winter fewer waterfowl.

Texas winters about half of the waterfowl of the flyway on 2,265,000 acres of prime wetlands and permanent water, 91,760 acres of which are in State and Federal management. Public hunting is permitted on 51 thousand acres of this managed area. About 20 percent of the hunters in the flyway are Texans. They harvest 25 percent of the ducks and 30 percent of the geese, mostly mallards, pintails, greenwinged teal, and snow geese.

IN NEW MEXICO, wintering habitat is limited to the middle Rio Grande Valley, the Pecos Valley, and lakes and reservoirs of the northeastern section of the State. Channelization of the Rio Grande has eliminated most of the flooded bottomlands formerly used by ducks and geese. Wintering habitat is now represented by the State-managed areas at Belen and LaJoya, Bosque del Apache National Wildlife Refuge, and Elephant Butte and Caballo reservoirs. Wintering populations in the Rio Grande Valley number about 65 thousand ducks and 5 thousand geese. Mallards and pintails are the most common ducks; the geese are predominantly western Canadas. The Pecos River Valley winters fewer ducks and geese. Most of the ducks are found on Bitter Lake National Wildlife Refuge, Lake McMillan, and Avalon Reservoir. Lakes and reservoirs of the northeastern New Mexico plains are more important as migration habitat than wintering habitat. Peak fall and spring populations exceed 40 thousand ducks, but snow and ice reduce numbers in winter to 5 thousand to 8 thousand birds. An average of about 2,500 Canada geese winter in this section of New Mexico.

New Mexico has about 60 thousand acres of good wetlands and permanent water, of which 24,500 acres are in management areas under State and Federal control. Public hunting is permitted on 4,160 acres of the managed units. New Mexico has the lowest number of waterfowl hunters of all the flyway States. Its hunters bag only 2 percent of the total duck kill and less than 1 percent of the geese, mostly Canadas. The mallard is the principal duck in the bag.

OKLAHOMA winters slightly more than 100 thousand ducks and 18 thousand Canada geese, but waterfowl in the State occur in greatest numbers during migration. Reservoirs, farm ponds, and lakes of less than 10 acres provide about 350 thousand acres of habitat. Natural lakes, of 10 acres or more, provide an additional 72,317 acres. The Watershed Protection and Flood Prevention Program of the Soil Conservation Service has made more than 7 thousand acres of small reservoir-type habitat.

On a per-acre basis, watershed detention reservoirs, small lakes, and farm ponds are of greater importance for wintering ducks than are large lakes and reservoirs in Oklahoma. Many smaller areas contain desir-

able food plants, such as smartweed and pondweeds, and provide better shelter from rough weather. Large reservoirs are useful, however, and construction programs of the Corps of Engineers and the Bureau of Reclamation may provide at least 150 thousand additional surface acres of this type.

The value of large reservoirs a waterfowl habitat is increased when State or Federal wildlife agencies in tensively manage all or parts of the reservoir and adjoining lands. The Oklahoma Department of Wildlife Conservation maintains waterfow management areas on Fort Gibson Hulah, and Wister Reservoirs. The Bureau of Sport Fisheries and Wildlife maintains national wildlife ref uges (Salt Plains, Tishomingo, and Washita) on Great Salt Plains Reservoir, Lake Texoma, and Fos Reservoir. Additional State or Fed eral managed areas are planned fo reservoirs being built or planned in 1964.

Oklahoma has nearly 400 thousand acres of high value wetland and permanent water. About 25 thousand acres are in managed units. Waterfowl hunting is permitted on 3,600 acres of State- and Federal-controlled areas. About 10 percent of the hunters of the flyway reside in Oklahoma. They harvest 5 percent of the ducks and 8 per cent of the geese. The mallard ac counts for half of the duck harvest Mallards and green-winged and blue-winged teal make up more than 75 percent of the bag. Canada geese comprise about half of the harvest of geese; the rest are blues and snows.

COLORADO waterfowl wintering habitat is centered in the San Luis Valley, the Arkansas River Valley, the South Platte River Valley, the foothills north of Denver, and the Gunnison and Uncompahgre River Valleys of the western slope. Most of the 300 thousand or more wintering ducks are mallards. Some 30 thousand to 40 thousand Canada geese that pass through the Hanna-Kindersley staging area of Canada winter on Two Buttes Reservoir and lakes and reservoirs of the Arkansas Valley—Eads, Blue, Meredith, Henry, John Martin, and Horsecreek. Approximately 3 thousand Canadas winter on lakes and reservoirs in the foothills north of Denver. These are western Canada geese from locally-established nesting colonies and the Bowdoin National Wildlife Refuge in Montana.

San Luis Valley in south-central Colorado is important for nesting and migrating ducks but affords little wintering habitat, since only the artesian wells, springs, and the larger streams are ice-free in winter. Most mallards wintering in the valley rest on the Monte Vista National Wildlife Refuge, where they feed on barley, field peas, and aquatic plants or forage in harvested grainfields off the refuge.

Many lakes and reservoirs in the Arkansas Valley become ice-covered also, but the river normally winters about 50 thousand ducks and some Canada geese, which feed in harvested grainfields. The offstream reservoirs of Latham, Prewitt, Jackson, and Jumbo and the South Platte River of northeastern Colorado provide resting space for most of the State's wintering duck population. Many of these birds forage in nearby cornfields or in grain stubble of the Nebraska Panhandle. When the reservoirs freeze, the birds move into the South Platte River bottoms.

Breeding, migrating, and wintering waterfowl in Colorado utilize about 185 thousand acres of good-quality wetlands and permanent water for these purposes. A total of 41,200 acres, of which 35,800 acres are open to public hunting, is managed by the State or the Bureau. Colorado hunters represent about 8 percent of the flyway total, and harvest slightly more than 5 percent of the ducks and fewer than 10 percent of the geese. The mallard and Canada goose are the principal species brought to bag.

KANSAS winters about the same number of ducks as Colorado and is more important as a migration area. A little nesting occurs. The chief wintering districts include the Arkansas and Cimarron Rivers, Lake McKinney, and Cedar Bluff Reservoir in western Kansas; Kanopolis Reservoir, Kirwin and Quivira National Wildlife Refuges, and the State-managed Cheyenne Bottoms unit in the central part of the State; and Fall River Reservoir and State units of Neosho and Marais des Cygnes in southeastern Kansas. Some 6 thousand Canada geese, mostly of the larger races, winter in Kansas.

Sorghums and other grain crops are grown on State and Federal units for migrating and wintering birds. Birds that winter on lakes, rivers, and reservoirs feed on aquatic plants or in wheat and sorghum stubblefields. The Kansas River Valley and winter wheatfields of eastern Kansas are visited in spring by migrating flocks of snow geese.

Kansas, like Oklahoma, is increasing its reservoir-type habitat, and reservoirs that offer potential for intensive waterfowl management are or will be managed for this purpose by the Kansas Forestry, Fish and Game Commission or the Bureau of Sport Fisheries and Wildlife. Tuttle Creek and John Redmond Reservoirs are of this type.

Kansas hunters benefit from about 183 thousand acres of high-value wetlands and permanent water used by waterfowl. State and Federal agencies manage about 71 thousand acres of this habitat, of which nearly 47 thousand acres are open to public hunting. In addition, 62 thousand farm ponds provide for a wide variety of hunting opportunity.

About 15 percent of the hunters of the flyway reside in Kansas, although habitat conditions and availability of birds cause radical fluctuations in the number of resident hunters. They harvest approximately 10 percent of the ducks and 10 percent of the geese. Almost one-third of the ducks bagged are mallards; another third are teal. Nearly half of the goose harvest is Canadas. Snow geese account for about one-third of the total number of geese taken by hunters.

NEBRASKA has more than 523 thousand acres of high-value wetlands and permanent water available for breeding, migrating, and wintering waterfowl. Migrating and wintering birds concentrate on the Platte River and its tributaries, State and Federal management areas, and the larger reservoirs, such as Harlan County, Enders, and Lake McConaughy. Aquatic plants and waste grain provide ample food for wintering birds.

The Platte River is visited by spring flights of white-fronted geese en route to the breeding grounds. Concentrations of 60 thousand to 70 thousand geese are common in late March and early April. Lakes, marshes, and sloughs of the sandhills, the rainwater basin of south-central Nebraska, and Crescent Lake and Valentine National Wildlife Refuges are important breeding and migration areas.

About 81 thousand acres of the important habitat are under government control, and 56 thousand acres of this are open to public hunting. About 15 percent of the flyway duck harvest is made by Nebraska hunters, who are fewer than 15 percent of the hunters of the flyway. More than half of the ducks bagged are mallards. Teal represent another 25 percent. Canada geese account for nearly half of the goose kill; they and snows constitute 90 percent of the total harvest of geese.

SOUTH DAKOTA waterfowl habitat amounts to nearly 855 thousand acres of good-quality wetlands and permanent water. Potholes, sloughs, stock ponds, lakes, rivers, and State and National wildlife refuges are important as nesting and migration habitat. But only large water areas and small spring-fed streams remain as wintering habitat after freezeup closes smaller waters. The State and the Bureau of Sport Fisheries and Wildlife manage about 85 thousand acres of high-value habitat. About 73,500 acres are open to public hunting.

Wintering waterfowl concentrate on Fort Randall and Gavins Point Reservoirs, Lake Andes, the Little Bend and Big Bend sections of the Missouri River, and on streams and spring-fed lakes of the northern Black Hills. The number of ducks that winter in the State is related directly to the severity of the weather. During mild, open winters, a million or more mallards trade between Fort Randall Reservoir, Lake Andes, and adjacent cornfields. When heavy snow and ice force them to seek other haven, they move into the flooded oak bottoms and ricefields of Arkansas and Louisiana. The Missouri River downstream from Big Bend winters some 15 thousand to 20 thousand Canada geese.

Slightly more than 10 percent of the hunters of the flyway reside in South Dakota. About 10 percent of the duck harvest occurs there. The total goose harvest is second only to the harvest in Texas. Some two-thirds of all ducks bagged are mallards. Teal represent 10 percent. The pintail ranks third. The kill of snow geese, including both blue and

This female gadwall on Lower Souris National Wildlife Refuge in North Dakota rests in a luxurious bed of down—her own.

white phases, often exceeds that of Canadas; the two species form about 95 percent of the total bag of geese.

WYOMING has 285 thousand acres of high-value wetlands and permanent water. The State and Federal governments manage about 11,500 acres, of which 5,900 acres are open to public hunting. The principal managed areas include the Ocean Lake and Springer units and Hutton Lake and Pathfinder National Wildlife Refuges.

In Wyoming breeding ducks find suitable nesting habitat in lakes, marshes, and streams of the Laramie Plains, in Big Horn Basin, Jackson Hole, Star Valley, in 13 thousand stock ponds, and in the streamside marshes and oxbows of the Bear, Green, Snake, and Wind Rivers. Wind River also provides nesting habitat for western Canada geese. Canada geese have nested on the Green River for a century or more since Powell's party, in its first exploration of the Colorado River, ". . . shot geese in May 1869 on the Green between the Black's Fork and the Henry's Fork, after a chase on the water." Many geese that nest on the Bear and Green Rivers winter along the Colorado River in southern Arizona and California. The reservoirs and harvested grainfields of southeastern Wyoming are used by Canada geese en route from Bowdoin National Wildlife Refuge in Montana, to wintering areas in the Rio Grande Valley in New Mexico.

Wyoming winters about 100 thousand ducks, primarily mallards, and 2 thousand Canada geese. Its hunters bag less than 3 percent of the total duck harvest and less than 1 percent of the goose harvest. The mallard accounts for about 70 percent of all ducks bagged.

MONTANA hunters benefit from more than 825 thousand acres of good-quality habitat, of which 315 thousand acres are publicly managed and nearly 44 thousand acres are open to public hunting. Hunters in the State comprise about 7 percent of all hunters in the flyway. They harvest approximately 8 percent of the ducks, primarily mallards, and 4 percent of the geese. The State winters about 100 thousand ducks and 5 thousand Canada geese, and its habitat is important to breeding and migrating birds. Breeding ducks concentrate in the potholes and marshes of the glaciated portion of the northeast section.

Western Canada geese nest in north-central Montana and in Flathead Valley. Bowdoin National Wildlife Refuge is the focal point for the north-central breeding population that extends into the lakes and marshes of the Cypress Hills in southwestern Saskatchewan. The Flathead Valley population is mostly resident; it leaves the valley about one in every four or five winters, at which time these birds winter on the Snake River in Idaho. The State has established a breeding colony of Canada geese at its Freezeout Lake Management Area, which is also used by substantial numbers of migrating ducks and snow geese.

NORTH DAKOTA is one of the best waterfowl-producing States, although it rarely winters 10 thousand ducks on its nearly 1 million acres of high-value wetlands and permanent water. Habitat in the State is utilized by many ducks and geese during migration to wintering areas mostly in the Central and Mississippi Flyways. There are 29 thousand acres open to public hunting on 180 thousand acres under government control. Normally, North Dakota hunters enjoy the highest average duck kill of all States.

BREEDING DUCKS concentrate on lakes, marshes, and potholes of the northern and eastern sections of the State and on the stock ponds in the southwestern quadrant. Ducks and geese in migration congregate on water areas of Arrowwood, Chase Lake, Des Lacs, Lake Ilo, Long Lake, Lostwood, Lower Souris, and Snake Creek and Tewaukon and Upper Souris National Wildlife Refuges. Use of State-managed areas by migrating birds is also moderate to high.

North Dakota accounts for about 10 percent of the flyway hunters. They bag less than 15 percent of the total duck harvest despite their high individual success. Species composition of the goose kill, which is approximately 10 percent of the total for the flyway, depends largely upon the fall migration of both blue- and white-phase snows. When these birds stop, they frequently constitute half or more of the total take. When they do not, Canada geese make up nearly three-fourths of the take. About 10 percent of the geese harvested are white-fronts. They are hunted primarily in the vicinity of

Lower Souris National Wildlife Refuge.

THE STORY OF WATERFOWL is the story of water, and what happens to ducks and geese in the years ahead will reflect as a mirror what happens to water. Over the past few decades, we have handled this life-giving commodity with abandon. Drainage and siltation have leveled the land and drawn the water from vast areas. And what has not been hurried to the seas has been polluted recklessly. The effects on waterfowl are apparent enough.

To a considerable extent, water areas of the Central Flyway are small, of variable volume, and as scattered as puddles in a country road. By comparison with what has happened elsewhere, this has proved to be of some advantage. But that is not to say that our ponds, lakes, and marshes are secure. In the northern end of the flyway, potholes have gotten in the way of agriculture. They have been drained by the tens of thousands. Along the important Gulf coast, the problems of habitat loss have paralleled those of coastal areas elsewhere.

But, on the other hand, thousands of manmade ponds have byproduct values for waterfowl. Large reservoirs, particularly where their management includes consideration of waterfowl welfare, have added substantial amounts of habitat. State and Federal conservation agencies have created many useful areas, although hardly in an amount to offset other losses. And, waterfowl, too, have adjusted to the times. Some species are finding domestic crops a

fair substitute for the marsh environments that were displaced in the
conversion.

What will happen next? Competition for land and water surely will
grow as our human numbers grow.
That means that our present area
of habitat—or less—will have to be
managed intensively to accommodate the desired populations of
ducks and geese. A fair challenge,

and one that professional people face
with confidence.

—RAYMOND J. BULLER.

*We must realize that in America we
have no more land frontiers, that we must
do with what we have, and that the continued welfare of this generation, and every
succeeding one, depends first upon how
wisely we shall use the land which is
ours.*—EDWARD H. GRAHAM.

PINTAILS

Pacific Flyway

BETWEEN THE CREST of the Rockies and the Pacific and between the borders of Canada and Mexico is the Pacific Flyway, an area of about 825 thousand square miles or 25 percent of the continental United States.

Less than 1 percent of the land west of the Rockies is classed as good waterfowl habitat — some 6,200 square miles where waterfowl seek food, shelter, and water during their winter stay.

Each project, each visit, each development since the time of the Spanish explorers—trappers, military and railroad companies, gold seekers,

pioneers of the westward movement of the 1800's, farmers, builders of cities—has modified land, water, and geography so that the flyway now is far different from what it was 10 years ago, 100 years ago, 200 years ago. The Pacific Flyway has five major units.

In Nevada and adjoining parts of California, Oregon, and Utah is the Great Basin, a high intermountain plateau. It has no rivers that flow to sea level. It has low rainfall, cold winters, and low humidity. Runoff, when it occurs, goes into shallow lakes or sumps. That water has a high content of mineral salts. Be-

233

cause the sumps have no outlet, they become saltier as the water evaporates. Salt concentrations in Great Salt Lake are greater than in the ocean.

While dissected with small mountain ranges, this area is set on a relatively level base. Streams and rivers meander through valleys to accumulate in shallow saline lakes. The country is largely arid, but where water exists it is extremely productive in spring and summer. Winter weather, however, is severe, and except in the southern fringes of this unit early freezeup makes much of it uninhabitable from late November to mid-February for all but the hardiest waterfowl.

The second segment is a series of coastal bays and river valleys of the Pacific from Vancouver Island to Baja California, Mexico. Best known are Puget Sound, Grays Harbor, and Willapa in Washington, Tillamook and Coos Bays along the Oregon coast; and Humboldt, San Francisco, Morro, and San Diego Bays in California.

THE COLORADO BASIN, with its tributary streams rising along the western slope of the Rockies, covers the Pacific Southwest. Streams leaving forested slopes of the mountains drop rapidly into desert canyons. In the West, fast-water and pine-clad slopes offer little attraction for ducks, although small numbers find summer homes in meadows and along streams at higher elevations. As the river system comes to more level gradients in the lower reaches, accumulated silt is piled up, and shifting channels

form sloughs and oxbows. Aquatic vegetation becomes more abundant and available for waterfowl in winter. Historically, the lower Colorado River was high-quality waterfowl habitat and was also valuable as a north-south waterway en route to Mexico.

COASTAL BAYS AND RIVER VALLEYS at or near tide level occur at intervals from the Canadian to the Mexican border. In the high rainfall belt northward from San Francisco Bay, these areas are bordered by a heavy cover of coniferous forest. South of San Francisco, spruce, redwood, and Douglas-fir were replaced by more open types of brush or grassland. Waterfowl found here a series of wintering areas and a travel lane to more southern climates. Eelgrass and shellfish in brackish bays supply food for diving ducks and black brant.

The other three units are the land areas drained by the major river systems of the West—the Columbia, the Colorado, and the Sacramento-San Joaquin.

The drainage basin of the Columbia River system encompasses most of the land area of Washington, Oregon, and Idaho and parts of Montana, Utah, and Nevada. Contributing rivers to the Columbia include the Willamette, Yakima, Okanogan, Kootenai, Flathead, Snake, Boise, and Owyhee.

THE COLUMBIA RIVER system begins along the northern portions of the Continental Divide. Tributary streams at their source encounter steep slopes and pass through heavily

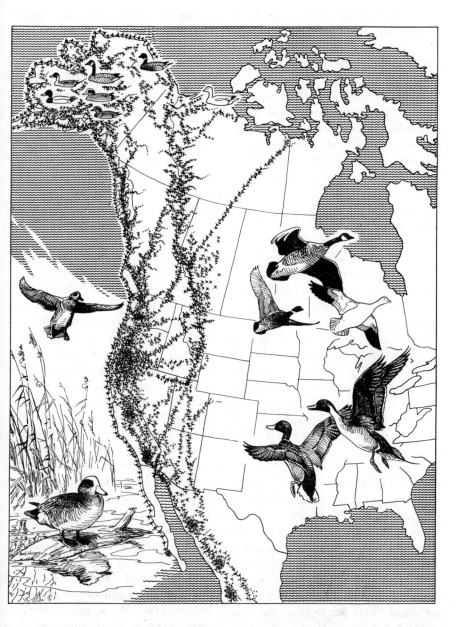

forested areas. On reaching lower elevations they enter the arid lava-plateau area or rolling, open hills of eastern Washington, Oregon, and southern Idaho.

Except for slow-moving sections of this river system, there is no great abundance of food and habitat for waterfowl. Islands in the broader river channels produce Canada geese and ducks in fair numbers. Winter in most of the basin is severe. In its original condition, the habitat could not support great concentrations of waterfowl.

Ranking first in area but perhaps last in waterfowl values, is the basin of the Colorado River. Most of Utah, southern Nevada, all of Arizona, and the western parts of Wyoming, Colorado, and New Mexico are drained by the muddy Colorado. Tributaries include the Green, Yampa, Little Colorado, and Gila which flow through arid country that has been eroded by wind and flash floods.

Smallest in size, but certainly not in waterfowl importance, is the Sacramento-San Joaquin River drainage basin in California. It collects the bulk of its drainage from sources along the western slope of the Sierra Nevada. The valley formed by the Sacramento-San Joaquin Rivers between the Coast Range and the Sierras is the winter quarters for a large share of the ducks and geese in the flyway.

THE SACRAMENTO-SAN JOAQUIN river system is the largest watered flatland in the Pacific Flyway. Numerous short tributaries fall rapidly from the Sierra Nevada slopes into the Central Valley of California. Fall rains and melting snows in the high country provide an abundance of water. This water flows through meandering channels, and frequent overflows each winter cover extensive marshes and wet grasslands. Mild winters help make this habitat a center for wintering waterfowl.

This simplified slicing of the Pacific Flyway into five segments is chiefly for geographic orientation. The Salton Sea in southern California and Klamath Basin in northeastern California and south-central Oregon do not fit into the pattern, yet they are areas of importance to waterfowl. Salton Sea was formed in the early 1900's by accidental "reverse" drainage of the Colorado River into what was a desert basin some 250 feet below sea level. The Klamath Basin is a high, volcanic plateau drained by the Klamath River, which cuts through the mountains of the Coast Range.

Settlement of the West has brought marked changes to the flyway since the middle 1800's.

In the dry southwestern or Colorado Basin segment, major influences have been livestock, agriculture, and hydroelectric power. Water is critical here. Throughout the upper reaches of the Colorado Basin, water has been used wherever possible to grow irrigated crops or to produce hay. Surface runoff has been developed in some places to extend livestock ranges. The lower reaches of the Colorado have been extensively dammed for power storage and water supply, and channelization has been necessary to control deposition of the heavy load of silt. Flooding along the lower reaches of the river is essentially a thing of the past.

Water diversion to the Imperial Valley, lower delta, and upstream points has been so extensive that this once mighty river now fails to reach the Gulf of California. Below the United States border, it fans out into a series of canals, and what little is left disappears into the sandy soil of its own flood plain.

Going next to the Great Basin, we find highly altered conditions resulting from man's activities. Here, again, water is critical. Livestock and farming operations utilize essentially all available water supplies. Inland saline lakes, which have high values for waterfowl, continue to shrink as a result of consumptive use in a moisture-deficient region. Construction of reservoirs and projects to store water has not been entirely detrimental to waterfowl, however. Small-grain farming in conjunction with stored water supplies has proved beneficial in this section of the flyway by creating new food sources and resting areas.

Since Lewis and Clark traversed the Columbia Basin to reach the Pacific Ocean, much has happened to modify waterfowl habitat in this area. Almost all of the tributary rivers have been harnessed for power development, flood control, and irrigation. The main stem of the Columbia for almost its entire length is a series of pools behind manmade dams. Much of the Columbia River watershed receives enough moisture to produce dryland grain crops of wheat or other small grains. Supplemental water from reclamation and irrigation projects has enabled agricultural development of additional lands. Interspersion of storage reservoirs with small-grain farming has resulted in the creation of a type of habitat highly suited to use by waterfowl.

The Sacramento-San Joaquin Valley in California has experienced the

Migrating waterfowl stop to rest at Tule Lake National Wildlife Refuge, California, on their way to the breeding grounds. Mt. Shasta is in the background.

greatest change from its original condition. Marshes were drained. Flooding was controlled. An agricultural economy has developed rapidly and intensively. The climate is suited to the growing of truck crops, small grains, hay, and fruit. Land was rich, markets for crops became available, and people prospered. In less than 100 years, some 6 thousand square miles of this Central Valley changed from grassland and marsh into high-value farmland, town sites, and paths of communication. Nearly all available surface runoff is used for agricultural and domestic purposes. Water diversions or transfer from the better watered northern Sacramento Valley to deficient areas in the San Joaquin Valley have been insufficient to supply demands. Subsurface water supplies are overtaxed and seriously depleted. The last big parcel of waterfowl habitat lost in recent years was in the southern end of the San Joaquin Valley. Flood-control and water-storage dams diverted water from Tulare and Buena Vista Lake marshlands shortly after the Second World War.

Coastal bays and river valleys have been changed by dredging, filling, and industrial development. They have cut the size and quality of the habitat used by waterfowl. The use of shoreline for shipping and boating facilities, homesites, and urban developments also has lowered their value for waterfowl. Pollution and siltation, likewise have been adverse factors.

Thus, has the Pacific Flyway undergone radical change under man's influence. More changes are due. Many are in progress. So

much for habitat. What about the waterfowl themselves?

THE MALLARD is the most widely distributed duck of the Pacific Flyway. Mallards nest and raise their young in all the flyway States under many conditions—lakes, marshes, ponds, rivers, streams, and irrigation ditches.

The true stronghold of mallard production in summer lies in the prairies and parklands of Canada. For Pacific Flyway mallards this means Alberta; others come from British Columbia and western Saskatchewan. In Canada, north of agricultural lands, the density of breeding mallards fades rapidly.

Mallards are hardy and migrate southward late. They can stand adverse weather in winter. Few mallards go south of a line between Los Angeles and Phoenix. Western Mexico rarely sees a mallard. No reason has been advanced for this migration habit, but it has considerable management significance in that the future status of this species will be determined by influences in southern Canada and the United States. The fall migration of mallards into the flyway may be gradual or sudden, depending on weather conditions farther north. Locally produced birds begin to collect in small flocks as breeding areas of late spring and summer dry up. Fall freezeup at higher elevations or farther north forces additional birds to more suitable — more southerly — winter quarters.

Once its course is set, the mallard moves as directly as possible to its chosen winter quarters and stays there until spring. Mallards banded before the hunting season in such areas as Puget Sound, Willamette Valley, or eastern Washington are already settled on their wintering grounds. These areas are the terminus of the migration. And knowing this, provides a basis for management on an area or flock basis.

The mallard, being adaptable, hardy, and able to forage widely, has prospered with the development of new croplands. An example is the mid-Columbia and Snake River Basins of Washington, Oregon, and Idaho. Dryfarming and irrigated crops there provide food supplementing well that of rivers and reservoirs. The Columbia Basin Project of the Bureau of Reclamation developed about 500 thousand acres of farmland in east-central Washington between 1950 and 1960. The whole project is to include more than a million acres of irrigated cropland. One result: Between 1950 and 1961, fall and winter populations of mallards climbed from 200 thousand to more than 700 thousand.

Within the Columbia and Snake River drainages of Washington, Oregon, and Idaho, mallard populations increased from 500 thousand in 1950 to almost 2 million in 1961. Very likely these are new birds in the flyway—not birds attracted from elsewhere, in this flyway or other flyways. Added agricultural lands, well interspersed with water, portend well for mallards in the two drainages.

THE PINTAIL, or sprig, is a close second to the mallard in total harvest and is superior in numbers over the entire continental Pacific Flyway. The pintail prefers open spaces for nesting, migrating, and wintering. Unlike the mallard, the pintail avoids trees, brush, and dense marshes. It likes shallow water, shortgrass cover, and open feeding places. Its breeding range is extensive. It is no longer one of the most common nesters in the flyway but does occur with fair frequency.

Early records indicate it was an abundant nesting species as far south as lower San Joaquin Valley, in the grasslands, at Tulare Lake, and Buena Vista Lake. Habitat changes there and in the Sacramento Valley and the Great Basin have reduced sharply these southern breeding places.

North of the flyway in the open prairie of southern Canada, the pintail becomes the predominant nesting duck. Northward from there, pintails decline as woody parkland vegetation increases. Skipping over the parkland and coniferous bush country into the Yukon, Northwest Territories, and Alaska, the pintail again encounters suitable habitat and breeds over a broad area.

The pintail ignores the international dateline. Continuing westward across Alaska, it ventures into Siberia, where it finds summer nesting quarters in extensive marshes. Pintails banded at various localities in Alaska and other parts of the United States and Canada have been recovered in spring, summer, and early fall from the Anadyr, Kolyma, and Lena River drainages in the Soviet Union—sometimes more than 2 thousand miles from the North American Continent. We do not know how many pintails fly in the fall from Siberia to the Pacific Flyway.

The fall migration of most pintails from their far-flung nesting range begins early. Small flights are noted in the Sacramento and San Joaquin Valleys in early August. By September 15 as many as a million migrants may be present. On comparable dates, peak numbers of the same size are in the marshes of Great Salt Lake. A survey of the western coast of Mexico in mid-September 1962— a low year for pintails over the entire flyway—revealed about 100 thousand pintails already present on established wintering areas.

California is the winter home for more than 75 percent of the pintails in the flyway. Mexico has about 15 percent. The rest are scattered in other States where winters are mild. Spring migration is most spectacular in the eastern States of the flyway. Many pintails counted in California in January appear to move into Mexico, thence northward in spring through the Central Flyway.

The pintail has taken to upland or dryland feed. Wheat, barley, rice, and millet form a substantial part of its diet during migration and wintering periods. This liking for grain, particularly barley and rice, at times becomes a serious problem to farmers.

THE AMERICAN WIDGEON, or baldpate, is third among the flyway ducks in numbers and bag. Green feed—grass or submerged parts of water plants—is its main feed.

The widgeon rarely nests in the flyway. In prairie Canada, however, it finds suitable breeding areas, which extend through Alberta and Saskatchewan into the Yukon and then through central Alaska to the Bering Sea. Parkland potholes and heavily wooded areas avoided by pintails furnish suitable summer quarters for nesting widgeon. The widgeon, among the puddle ducks, is a relatively late nester, produces larger broods than the mallard or pintail, and cares for the young ducklings in good and noisy fashion. In areas of heavy cover, you almost always hear the protesting females before you see them.

The widgeon is a middle migrant, neither early nor late in autumn. In their travels they seek out grass, pastures, and green feed. Some use parks, golf courses, and lawns in urban areas. This grazing habit means that widgeon require higher rainfall or irrigated winter habitat where green grass or pasture is available. It is the second most numerous duck wintering in Oregon and Washington, and is third behind the pintail and mallard in California.

The widgeon is a strong coastal migrant, and good numbers occur on coastal bays and rivers from Puget Sound to Willamette Valley and south to Humboldt Bay in inland valleys with heavy soils, truck crops, and pastures or wet-meadows. They resemble mallards in their tendency to return to the same wintering localities each year. Flock or area management with this species may be a distinct possibility, since there is little evidence of interchange between wintering flocks.

Man's activities along coastal bays and rivers of the Pacific Northwest and in Imperial Valley of California have encouraged many widgeon

Opening day at the Public Shooting Grounds of the Bear River National Wildlife Refuge, Utah, brings a rush of hunters.

Clearing and development of pastures and truck farming in northern coastal areas have provided new habitat. Fields of lettuce and alfalfa in Imperial Valley attract the birds.

Widgeon frequently associate with black brant and coots in coastal bays and lagoons. Here the widgeon utilize floating eelgrass and other once-submerged aquatics pulled or clipped by brant and coot feeding in deeper water.

THE GADWALL is another large puddle duck of the flyway. From the standpoint of hunter recognition, either in flight or in the bag, this species is not well known.

The gadwall, even more than the mallard, is a southern nester. It nests in suitable areas in all States of the flyway, although it is not common in Arizona, which has relatively few nesting ducks. Along with the mallard and cinnamon teal, the gadwall nests commonly throughout the Great Basin section of the flyway and in the Sacramento-San Joaquin Valley.

Like the pintail in the southern Canadian prairies, it prefers open grassland and shallow ponds for nesting and feeding. Unlike the pintail, however, it does not nest north of the Canadian prairies but fades out sharply in the parkland areas and does not venture into the bush or northern tundra. The gadwall is a mid-seasonal fall migrant through the intermountain section. During mid-winter it seeks mild climates in the San Joaquin Valley. The main winter concentrations are in coastal marshes of western Mexico.

THREE SPECIES OF TEAL occur in the Pacific Flyway, but only the green-wing is abundant. It nests in northern flyway States and through Canada and southern Alaska. It is secretive, sparsely distributed, and prefers more heavily wooded pothole habitat.

GREEN-WINGED TEAL use coastal and inland migration routes in fall and winter. Fall migration occurs relatively early, closely following that of the pintail. Wintering flocks are scattered in milder areas throughout the flyway, but most winter in California and Mexico, in coastal and inland marshes.

THE CINNAMON TEAL nests in all States of the flyway. The major part of the nesting range lies south of the Canadian border and west of the Rockies. It is characteristically a southern duck. Though it commonly breeds in the central highlands of Mexico, the Great Basin is the center of its summer distribution. Fall migration occurs early. By late October or early November most birds have migrated to winter habitat in Mexico. Small numbers may winter in the San Joaquin and Imperial Valleys and along the lower Colorado River. Cinnamon teal are relatively unimportant to hunters, but they are interesting and colorful during the summer nesting season.

BLUE-WINGED TEAL, a cousin of the cinnamon, is not common in the flyway. It nests in small numbers in eastern Washington, eastern Oregon, Idaho, and northeastern California. It is a very early migrant, leaving the flyway for Mexico and extreme southern wintering areas generally before our hunting seasons begin.

THE SHOVELER, or spoonbill, nests in the northern half of the flyway, primarily in the Great Basin, and northward into Canada and central Alaska. Uplands near shallow, weedy ponds are typical nesting spots. Their ducklings hatch in midsummer. Migration southward occurs relatively early.

On wintering areas, the shoveler prefers mild weather and accordingly spends this period in the southern end of the flyway. It uses coastal and inland migration routes, and is a frequent associate of the green-winged teal and pintail on their travels up and down the flyway. Numerically, the shoveler ranks fourth in the flyway and, being unwary, is often taken by hunters.

THE WOOD DUCK occupies a restricted nesting range in the flyway. Wooded streams, lakes or ponds in the Pacific Northwest and British Columbia provide summer homesites. Its habit of nesting in tree-cavities is unique among puddle ducks.

Migration usually begins early in the fall and proceeds only for a short distance to north-coast streams and the Sacramento Valley. The wood duck is of little importance to hunters, partly because it frequents places unused by most other ducks and duck hunters. Restricted bag limits over the years have helped the species to maintain normal numbers. Wood ducks readily accept artificial nest sites or nest boxes, even those placed many miles from what would appear to be suitable localities.

DIVING DUCKS make up less than 10 percent of the total duck population and the duck bags of the flyway. They frequent coastal bays and deep water marshes mostly.

THE GREATER SCAUP is of primary importance in the coastal bays and sounds of the flyway from San Francisco Bay northward. It breeds chiefly on the Bering Sea and arctic coasts of Alaska and Canada.

THE LESSER SCAUP is our most important diving duck. It nests principally in the Canadian prairies, northern Canada, and eastern Alaska. Scaup of both species are late-nesting birds and move south in advance of approaching winter in the north country. Most lesser scaup probably move south via interior routes and stop off in the larger interior marshes to feed. They winter chiefly in open salt-water habitat of the coastal bays. Some remain inland along larger rivers and deeper fresh-water areas, but more than half continue south to winter in the western coastal lagoons of Mexico.

THE RING-NECKED DUCK, which resembles the lesser scaup, is of minor importance to sportsmen in this flyway. Breeding largely north of the Canadian prairie, they migrate south in midfall, and winter sparsely throughout the flyway on deeper fresh-water ponds and rivers.

CANVASBACKS nest mainly in the southern Canadian prairies and managed marshes in the Great Basin. Fall concentrations occur sporadically in Klamath Basin, Malheur Lake, and Stillwater near Fallon, Nevada. The center of the wintering canvasback population in the Pacific Flyway is on San Francisco Bay, where during hunting seasons it is a prized bird. Elsewhere in the flyway it is usually taken incidental to other duck hunting.

REDHEADS in this flyway nest principally in the Great Basin. Larger deep-water marshes, such as Bear River, Ogden Bay, Malheur, Klamath, and Stillwater, are focal points. Others nest in marshes and potholes of the southern Canadian prairies. Following nesting, redheads usually migrate south of our border by late October. More than two-thirds of them winter in the coastal lagoons of western Mexico. During the early part of the hunting season, redheads are heavily shot on western production marshes as they fly in tight flocks along watercourses or between deep-water marsh units.

COMMON GOLDENEYES, like wood ducks, nest in tree holes over a broad range in wooded sections of Canada and Alaska. They are hardy birds and winter well north in the flyway, notably on lakes and rivers in the Pacific Northwest, where subsurface animal food is available.

CLOSELY RELATED is the Barrow's goldeneye, which also nests in tree cavities, in the mountains of the Pacific Northwest, and the northern

Rockies. Fall migration is a short hop to coastal areas of Oregon, Washington, and northern California.

THE BUFFLEHEAD, likewise a cavity nester, breeds north and west of the Canadian prairies in wooded areas. It is small, hardy, adventuresome, and relatively late in migration. Single birds or small flocks may be found in salt and fresh water. Its activity, distribution, and striking black and white feathers make the bufflehead an obvious target for hunters. Nowhere is it abundant, but often it ranks disproportionately high among diving ducks in total harvest.

THE RUDDY DUCK is another leader among the diving ducks in the Pacific Flyway. It nests in deep-water marshes of the Great Basin and in prairie Canada. The ruddy seems to be a good judge of the permanency of potholes. Ponds selected by ruddies for spring nesting rarely, if ever, dry up during the summer. During migration and on winter areas, mainly California and Mexico, the ruddy uses both salt and fresh water places.

THE PACIFIC FLYWAY also is home to three species of mergansers, commonly called fish ducks. Three species of scoters or "sea coots" winter mainly in coastal bays and along the open seacoast. The fulvous tree duck, primarily a Mexican species, extends northward into Imperial Valley and southern San Joaquin Valley. The oldsquaw and harlequin ducks occur in small numbers in north coastal bays. Occa-

Migrating waterfowl almost blacken the sky over Sacramento National Wildlife Refuge in California.

sionally these birds are shot, but (except the fulvous tree ducks) their diet of fish or shellfish gives their meat an off-flavor.

THE SNOW GOOSE and Ross' goose are the two white geese that use the Pacific Flyway. The snow is the more abundant. It nests in colonies along shores and islands of the Arctic Ocean off northern Canada and eastern Siberia. An early fall migrant, it arrives at spots in the flyway in late September and early October. Migrating birds from northern nesting areas use both inland and coastal routes.

Stopping points on the way to winter abodes in the Sacramento-San Joaquin Valley include lakes in southern Saskatchewan and Alberta; Freezeout Lake in Montana; Skagit Flats on Puget Sound in Washington; Malheur, Summer Lake, and Warner Valley in Oregon; Stillwater in Nevada; and the Klamath Basin and Goose Lake on the Oregon-California border. Small numbers stop at other points, but Summer Lake in Oregon and the Klamath-Tule Lake district of northern California are the mother lode for snows and their hunters.

Freezeup in this high plateau country comes in mid-November or early December. Then the snows move southward into Central Valley. Harvested rice fields and wet grasslands there provide winter homes until spring migration, when they reverse their journey to return to nesting grounds.

THE ROSS' GOOSE resembles the snow goose but is smaller. It breeds in arctic Canada near Perry River. Its migration southward parallels the inland routes of the snow goose. Stopover points also may coincide.

The main wintering grounds are valleys of the Sacramento and San Joaquin Rivers in California. Their co-association with flocks of cackling geese in winter habitat may be a key to distinguishing the Ross' from snows.

THE WHITE-FRONTED GOOSE breeds in scattered numbers over much of western arctic Canada and the northern half of Alaska. A coastal migration route brings birds into the flyway. In late September they appear along the Washington coast, turn inland up the Columbia River, and then cross the Cascades. They build up spectacularly in early fall in the Klamath Basin. Smaller flocks extend inland at suitable spots in the western Great Basin section, such as Summer Lake, Warner Valley, and Goose Lake. With approaching winter, most of them move into Central Valley. Small flocks may move southward to the east of the Sierra Nevadas and down the lower Colorado into Mexico. A subspecies, the Tule white-fronted goose, is much like the Pacific white-front, the common subspecies, but is larger. It is the rarest of the North American geese and shares this status in the flyway with the Aleutian Canada goose.

CANADA GEESE are split by geography into numerous subgroups or races. Collectively they are the most numerous and widely distributed of the geese in all four flyways. Indi-

246

WATERFOWL TOMORROW

vidual subspecies or races, however, may be localized in both breeding and wintering places. Graduated large to small, we have the western Canada goose, dusky, and cackling Canada goose as examples of the Canada groups in the Pacific Flyway.

The western Canada nests mostly within the flyway in the Great Basin and Columbia Basin. Some flocks extend into southern Alberta, Saskatchewan, Montana, Wyoming, and western Colorado. Wintering areas include many of its own nesting areas (except in extremely severe winters) and the Sacramento, San Joaquin, and Imperial Valleys of California. Southern Nevada, Utah, Arizona, and the lower Colorado River are the winter habitat for some groups.

The dusky Canada goose is a local flock that breeds around Prince William Sound and Cooke Inlet in Alaska and winters chiefly in the central Willamette Valley.

Taverner's Canada goose, slightly smaller than the dusky Canada, breeds in northwestern Canada and northern and western Alaska. It winters mainly along the Columbia River in eastern Washington and eastern Oregon. Small numbers also winter in Central Valley.

The smallest member of the Canada group is the cackling Canada goose. From its restricted breeding ground in the Yukon-Kuskokwim Delta of Alaska, the cackler utilizes a coastal migration route in a pattern like that of the white-front. The diminutive cackler is a hardy bird and endures a fair amount of rough fall weather before moving into the Central Valley to winter.

THE BLACK BRANT is restricted to Pacific coastal waters. Breeding areas include arctic tundra in western Canada and northern Alaska and the Yukon-Kuskokwim Delta of western Alaska. With the pintail and snow goose, black brant also nest along the coast of northeastern Siberia.

Black brant are late fall migrants. Their winter habitat stretches from Puget Sound south to Baja California. Some winter in mainland coastal lagoons of western Mexico. Brant rarely fly over land and are found primarily on larger coastal bays, where eelgrass beds furnish the main food supply.

SWANS are the largest of our waterfowl. The whistling swan winters in all States in the flyway and is familiar to most hunters. They breed only in the remote tundra of northern Canada and Alaska. Among waterfowl, they are the latest to arrive in the fall and among the earliest to return north in the spring. Fall concentrations appear in large marshes of the Great Basin and Klamath Basin. The center of their wintering habitat is around the Sacramento-San Joaquin Delta.

THE TRUMPETER SWAN, largest of all our native waterfowl, now occupies much reduced breeding ranges in Alaska, Alberta, and along the Continental Divide near Yellowstone Park and Red Rock Lakes in Montana. Completely protected from hunting for many years, the trumpeter winters on or near its nesting areas. This, in effect, means the uppermost tributaries of the Snake and Missouri Rivers on each side of the Continental Divide.

THE AMERICAN COOT is a close associate of all waterfowl in the flyway. Despite its low rating among hunters as a game species, the coot must be rated a huge success biologically. It is an efficient feeder, a competitive and successful breeder, and no stickler for special winter conditions. Coots breed on all of the deep, fresh-water marshes throughout the flyway and on most of the permanent potholes and lakes in southern Canada. During the breeding season, the presence of coots on a pond is a good indicator that the water will persist.

In winter, the coot is equally at home on waters, shallow or deep, fresh or brackish. Submerged aquatic plants, upland green feed, and dry grain are its food. Coots winter in almost any habitat suitable for ducks in all of the flyway States but are most abundant as wintering birds in the Central Valley and coastal lagoons and marshes of Mexico.

Most waterfowl shooters hunt in their own backyard, the State in which they live or hunt other types of game.

WASHINGTON hunters benefit from about 450 thousand acres of good-quality wetland and permanent water used by waterfowl. This is just over 10 percent of the flyway total. In 1952–1961, an average of about 740 thousand ducks and 70 thousand geese wintered in the State. There are 150 thousand acres of open territory available for public hunting on State and Federal waterfowl management areas.

Leading hunting sections in Washington are principally in the Columbia Basin of eastern Washington and the tidelands of Puget Sound, especially Skagit Flats. Minor areas include coastal bays of Grays Harbor and Willapa. Most rewarding are the wheatlands of eastern Washington for geese; the Columbia River islands for Canada geese; Skagit Flats for snow geese; and Puget Sound and Willapa Bays for late-season brant shooting. Washington hunters take about 15 percent of the ducks and 8 percent of the geese bagged in the flyway. American widgeon, green-winged teal, pintails, and mallards predominate in the bag along the coast. The mallard dominates in eastern Washington, especially from mid-November to the close of the hunting season.

OREGON has some 600 thousand acres of wetland and permanent water commonly used by waterfowl—15 percent of the flyway total. Wintering duck populations have averaged 550 thousand. Goose populations have averaged 60 thousand birds. Both figures amount to 9 percent of the stateside flyway total.

Public hunting is available on 30 thousand acres of State or Federally managed lands. Important hunting areas include agricultural lands along the Snake and Columbia Rivers, Willamette Valley, and various southeastern Oregon lakes and marshes, such as Summer Lake, Goose Lake, Malheur Lake, Warner Valley, and the extensive Klamath Basin lakes and marshes.

The harvest of ducks varies, but mallards and pintails predominate. Widgeon, teal, and shovelers occur with fair frequency. Goose hunting is fair to good in almost all popular Oregon hunting areas. Summer Lake especially can be outstanding for snow geese in early fall. Oregon hunters shoot about 10 percent of the ducks and 15 percent of the geese taken in the flyway.

IDAHO waterfowl habitat aggregates about 520 thousand acres of wetlands and permanent water of high or moderate value. During the 1952–1961 period, wintering duck populations in Idaho averaged 450 thousand. Geese, almost exclusively the large western Canadas, have averaged about 10 thousand.

There were 17 thousand acres for public hunting on State and Federally operated waterfowl areas in 1962. Principal waterfowl hunting in Idaho is in the Snake and Boise River valleys. This includes most of the irrigated croplands of southern Idaho and nearby lakes and reservoirs. The mallard is the dominant species in the hunter's bag. Small numbers of pintails, teal, and widgeon are included in early fall. About 10 percent of the flyway ducks are taken by Idaho gunners. Canada goose hunting is good to excellent for the more skillful hunters over much of the same area; generally the birds are available throughout the season.

UTAH has more than 900 thousand acres of wetlands and permanent water, mostly around Great Salt Lake. Hunting is chiefly in managed marshes along the eastern shore of Great Salt Lake close to cities. Duck hunting reaches a peak during the early fall and tends to decline as winter forces the ducks to migrate southward. Hunting early in the season is mostly for pintail, teal, and gadwall. Mallards, shovelers, and locally produced redheads at times add their share to the bag.

Goose hunting is restricted almost entirely to local and migrant Canada geese, but it can be among the best anywhere. Almost 80 thousand acres of public hunting space was available to hunters on State and Federally managed lands in 1962. Utah hunters take less than 10 percent of the ducks shot in the flyway. Wintering ducks averaged 85 thousand during 1952–1961. An average of 5 thousand Canada geese also winter in Utah. Severe weather, rather than inadequate habitat, is the prime factor in determining numbers of waterfowl in winter.

NEVADA has about 320 thousand acres of wetland and permanent water used by waterfowl. Because of the few hunters, Nevada has the greatest number of acres of waterfowl habitat per hunter of all the States of the flyway. Wintering waterfowl populations fluctuate markedly with weather and drought conditions but have averaged 55 thousand ducks and 10 thousand geese during the 10 years to 1962.

The most important hunting area is the extensive Stillwater Marsh near Fallon. The best hunting is during early- and midseason before the late fall freezeup, usually by early December. Pintails, green-winged teal, gadwalls, mallards, and redheads are commonest in hunter bags. Canada and snow goose shooting is good at times.

Almost 40 percent of the Nevada marshes are under State or Federal control. More than 300 thousand acres of these lands are open to public hunting by the 10 thousand duck hunters in the State. Thus, the region is among the lowest in the flyway in hunter pressure and highest in space per hunter. Even so, the duck and goose kill in Nevada amounts to only about 2 percent of the flyway total.

ARIZONA, of all the flyway States, has the lowest rating as a waterfowl paradise—fewer than 55 thousand acres of good-quality waterfowl habitat. That is less than 2 percent of the flyway total. Wintering ducks averaged 30 thousand during the past decade. Geese averaged 5 thousand. Both amounted to less than 1 percent of the flyway total.

Principal waterfowl hunting areas of Arizona lie along the Colorado River and its tributaries, where mixed bags of pintails, teal, and widgeon are taken. The east-central plateau provides some mallard and pintail shooting. Roosevelt Lake and the lower Colorado River provide good Canada goose hunting during the latter part of the season. Most of Arizona's waterfowl habitat is in public ownership. Almost 25 thousand acres of State or Federal waterfowl lands were open to public shooting in 1962.

IN CALIFORNIA wintering duck populations during the past decade have averaged 4.1 million birds, or 68 percent of the total recorded. Geese numbered 740 thousand or 83 percent of the flyway total. California has more than 1.1 million acres of wetlands and permanent water areas, which receive intensive waterfowl use. This is 28 percent of the total to be found in the flyway.

State and Federal ownership of California waterfowl habitat amounts to about 10 percent of the total. Public hunting on managed waterfowl areas was permitted on 44 thousand acres in 1962. These public hunting areas are under tremendous pressure. With the exception of places in the Klamath Basin, all California-operated public hunting areas are subject to advance registration. Minimum fees are charged to cover administration costs of this operation.

California offers a wide variety of hunting conditions throughout the season. Important areas include Klamath Basin, the entire Central Valley, San Francisco and Suisun Bays, and Imperial Valley. Additional places are inland and along the coast.

California is home to more than 40 percent of the duck hunters in the entire flyway. Ducks and geese are present in the State in large numbers throughout the hunting season. California hunters account for about 55 percent of the total flyway duck kill and almost 70 percent of the total goose kill.

Nearly all waterfowl in the flyway may be shot by California hunters, but most commonly bagged are pintail, mallard, green-winged

teal, American widgeon, and shoveler. All species of geese are taken in California. The marshes and farmlands in the northeastern part of the State provide excellent goose hunting during early fall.

On their wintering areas in the Central Valley, geese group into large flocks and utilize either refuge areas or larger blocks of private land, and in so doing, become less accessible to hunters. Generally, hunters using private duck club lands concentrate on duck shooting and spend minimal effort in attempting to bag geese. California goose kill is quite equally divided among the principal species: Canada (including the several races), snow, and white-fronted. But most hunters rank the white-front as most desirable; the big Canadas are a close second.

San Francisco Bay is first for diving ducks in the flyway. Canvasback, lesser scaup, and ruddy are the principal species hunted. The best hunting is usually during December, when peak populations of these birds arrive to winter here.

WATERFOWL HAVE PROBLEMS which relate mainly to environmental affairs and man-caused influences. Environmental or natural problems refer principally to weather and climate. Severe drought can reduce habitat and its carrying capacity for waterfowl, sometimes for extended periods. This can happen and is equally disastrous both on breeding and wintering areas.

Within limits, waterfowl can adapt themselves to such situations by leaving dry areas and going elsewhere to seek living space.

Extreme cold, ice, and snow-covered feeding areas on winter habitat also cause hardships. Losses of ducks in winter have occurred at various times and places in the flyway. Mallards, because of their habit of wintering in colder localities, are most frequently involved. Birds exposed to such conditions in midwinter are either unwilling or unable to migrate to warmer climates. Instead, they take conditions as they are, sometimes with dire consequences.

Problems arising directly and indirectly from man's activities exercise even more extreme and more severe effects on our waterfowl resource. Permanent drainage or conversion of marsh and water areas has been a major factor affecting duck populations. Obviously waterfowl must be produced to be maintained; they need areas suitable for nesting and rearing young. They also require suitable habitat at other times and places. And losses to waterfowl can and do occur through pollution, lead poisoning, and harassment. Such factors may act either as direct causes of mortality or they may make otherwise good habitat unsuitable for occupancy.

An important conflict develops when waterfowl consume agricultural crops. Crop depredations have created critical situations in many

Sandhill cranes share with migrating waterfowl the outstanding Malheur National Wildlife Refuge in Oregon.

localities. Solutions to this problem usually lie in removing waterfowl from threatened croplands or providing alternate food supplies.

A final problem: access to hunting areas. It is basically a problem in human relations, not of biology. Increasing human demands for waterfowl have passed the point where the supply can meet demands. Neither the consumer nor the custodian can take waterfowl abundance for granted. The future for ducks and geese in the Pacific Flyway, however, holds much promise. It is our task to fulfill that promise.—JOHN E. CHATTIN.

The continent has given us much and will give us more, if we work with her. But if we continue our neglect and contempt for her land and waters, she will exact a calamitous penalty, and all the laboratories, all the machines, all the banks, will not offset it.

—STUART CHASE.

BLACK-BELLIED TREE DUCKS

South of the Border

I REMEMBER tropical Mexico as a land of verdant marshes and swamps festooned with clusters of white egrets, flocks of brilliant flamingos against dark mangrove, gaudy macaws scolding over emerald jungle, white pelicans soaring above blue waters, rivers and lagoons churning with fish, great scatterings of herons, and neat lines of roseate spoonbills hurrying to roost in the fading light. And along the offshore Pacific—colonies of sea birds in unbelievable numbers. Some small rocky islands loom on the horizon like icebergs in the blue ocean—they are that covered with white guano. Huge mantas swim,

birdlike, in the foaming sea off rocky headlands; gray whales surface and dive like bobbing ships in a heaving sea. And, overhead, soaring, always soaring on tropical winds, are the graceful man-o'-wars, or frigate birds. After 15 seasons there as a biologist, I remember Mexico also as a haven for waterfowl, a snug harbor for the bulk of the ducks and geese that winter south of the United States. The waterfowl flourish in the bays, lagoons, lakes, and marshes of the long, narrow Gulf and Pacific coastal plains, which are backed by the two great Sierras and the high plateaus beyond.

The Pacific coast has eight main

253

waterfowl wintering grounds. The Gulf coast has seven. The interior plateaus have more than a dozen.

The wintering grounds differ in topography, climate, drainage, and rainfall. They are open coastal bays; marshes; fertile river-delta lagoons; lush, tropical, rain-forest swamps and marshes; and the temperate-zone lakes and marshes of the highlands.

Saline and brackish coastal bays and lagoons attract the largest concentrations of waterfowl, chiefly pintails and scaup. Freshwater lagoons and marshes of the rich river deltas, however, have more species because of a greater. variety of habitats and food.

Freshwater lagoons in northern Mexico include open basins, with arid surroundings and lagoons whose shores are carpeted by marsh plants, and have a wooded background of mesquite or thorn forest. Widgeongrass and muskgrass grow in some. The food in others is chiefly coontail or southern naiad. The marsh fringe may be of southern bulrush and cattail, but on highly alkaline soil there may be nothing but saltgrass and saltflat-grass.

Farther south in the tropics, rainfall is greater and the vegetation more luxuriant. Lagoons often are bordered by tall southern bulrush, sawgrass, cattail, and phragmites. The variety of submerged aquatics and waterlilies is greater there.

In the humid tropics of Tabasco, rainfall reaches 150 inches a year. The freshwater lagoons are full of vegetation. Some have an abundance of food, but others are blanketed with such pest plants as water-hyacinth, waterlettuce, and salvinia.

Coastal bays show less variation in aquatic flora and fauna than the lagoons. Aquatic plants are mostly shoalgrass or widgeongrass. Animal foods for diving ducks include tiny crustaceans and many species of small mollusks.

On the Pacific coastal plain of Sonora and Sinaloa, large irrigation reservoirs water thousands of acres of grain on land previously covered with thorn forest, cacti, and desert shrubs. Deltas of the Rio Yaqui near Ciudad Obregon in Sonora and of the Rio Culiacan in Sinaloa are examples of such changes since 1930. The stubble fields attract great flights of pintails and smaller numbers of other dabblers and geese. But the drying of many marshes because of controlled river flow has reduced local flights of such marsh feeders as teal and widgeon.

No comparable grain-producing areas exist on the Gulf coast. The grain sorghum district near Matamoros in Tamaulipas is much smaller and is unirrigated, but it attracts many geese. The lakes in the highlands of the Central Plateau are like some in our Southwest. They are broad, open, usually shallow, and alkaline.

In the volcanic zone to the south of the Plateau, in the States of Michoacan, Jalisco, Guanajuato, and eastward, are the most important waterfowl lakes of the highlands. The largest are Chapala, Patzcuaro, Cuitzeo, and Yuriria. All were excellent wintering grounds once, but by 1962 only Patzcuaro retained its bountiful supply of aquatic food for dabblers and divers. Lake Chapala, more than 40 miles long, formerly was the most spectacular wintering ground in the highlands. Its eastern end and the nearby delta of the Lerma River had an abundance of food and attracted tremendous numbers of waterfowl through the twenties.

TIMES HAVE CHANGED. Most of the delta marsh has been diked and drained. Diversions upstream have reduced greatly the flow of the Lerma River. Water-hyacinth has taken over much of the lake and has shaded out most submerged food plants. Photographs of Lake Chapala in 1896 showed some water-hyacinths, still in 1948 the amount on the lake was not critical, probably because of periodic winter freezes. Since then it has spread tremendously, to the great disadvantage of waterfowl, fishermen, and hunters. In a survey I made in 1948, I saw 163 thousand ducks and 200 geese; in 1962, 15,600 ducks and 90 geese were noted. Croplands in the delta provide food for pintails and other field feeders, but little is available to waterfowl on the lake.

To the southeast in this volcanic zone lies the Valley of Mexico. Its Lake Texcoco, now encroached by Mexico City, was an outstanding waterfowl haven for centuries. It continued so until increased drainage over many years changed it to a series of salty pools in an alkaline dustbowl. Ducks still go there and to nearby Lake Zumpango, but they are a small remnant of once great flights. Some good, small lakes are in the States of Hidalgo, Mexico,

and Puebla, but they too have declined in size and value to waterfowl.

In the highlands, the lack of permanent streams, low annual rainfall, density of the human population, and an urgent need for more farmlands have increased the impounding of water in reservoirs for irrigation and municipal use. The reservoirs have limited value for waterfowl and serve chiefly as safe resting places. Of the many impoundments, those in grain and vegetable districts attract more birds, especially field-feeding ducks and coots and some geese.

In many parts of Mexico, much deforestation, stream erosion, silting of lagoons and marshes, and the spread of weed plants has occurred, especially during the past three decades. They have had profound effects on the wintering grounds and the distribution of waterfowl. Carrying capacity has been cut seriously in many localities, but in spite of these losses, much more water, food, and cover are available than there are birds to use them.

OF THE PONDWEEDS, bulrushes, smartweeds, widgeongrass, and muskgrass, which usually are rated among the top natural waterfowl foods, only widgeongrass, bulrushes and muskgrass occur abundantly in many localities of Mexico, although pondweeds abound in several of the temperate-zone lakes of the highlands.

Bulrushes are valuable, but only one species, southern bulrush, is common in many of the coastal marshes. Alkali bulrush grows in some of the brackish Pacific coastal waters and usually seeds heavily. Smartweeds grow in places, especially in marshes of river deltas and of some highland lakes.

Widgeongrass, the best duck food in Mexico, grows in most of the coastal bays, lagoons, and deltas, and in the highland lakes. It thrives under a wide range of conditions of salinity and temperature and comes back quickly in lagoons and lakes that suffer seasonally from drought.

Muskgrasses, widespread in alkaline and brackish waters, especially in coastal lagoons of Yucatan, can withstand seasonal drying and great variations in salinity.

Shoalgrass is a valuable food on the Gulf coast, especially for red-heads and pintails. It flourishes in sea water but grows also in situations of almost twice that salinity and survives in brackish bays where the water for a time may be only one-tenth as salty as the sea.

Eelgrass, a mainstay of black brant in many places, very likely does not grow as far south as Baja California. In its place, surfgrass may be the main food of black brant in lagoons of southern Baja California. Also of note in coastal lagoons and marshes are wild millet, other grasses, coontail, sawgrass, spikerushes, duckweeds, southern naiad, floatingheart, banana water-lily, sedges, saltwort, and more. Among the plants considered unim-

A small part of Mexico's vast "Marismas Nacionales" (tidal lagoons). This wintering area contains food resources for many times the migratory ducks that use it.

Tarascan Indians at Lake Patzcuaro, Mexico, hunting waterfowl with spears.

portant to ducks in the United States, but locally valuable as waterfowl food in Mexico are sea-blite, waterstargrass, and thalia.

Plankton is taken greedily by several kinds of ducks, notably the shoveler. The tropical climate and year-round growing season make some lagoons great bowls of duck soup, where shovelers and teal contentedly guzzle their meals. Plankton is highly nutritious and draws tens of thousands of shovelers to Pacific coastal lagoons from Sinaloa to Chiapas. Some of the plankton contains an abundance of animal life, from microscopic protozoans to shrimplike crustaceans one-sixteenth inch long. In some coastal waters countless numbers of insect larvae, tiny shrimp, and small mollusks attract diving ducks, among them lesser scaup, ruddies, canvasbacks, and redheads.

On the Pacific coast, cultivated grain, grasses, glasswort, saltwort, and other succulent green plants of fields and coastal flats form the chief fare of geese. On the Gulf coast, geese feed in fields of grain sorghum southwest of Matamoros, on the Rio Grande flats and low ridges, grassy flats and hills west of Laguna Madre, lagoon margins west of Tampico, and wet meadows of the upper Papaloapan Delta. Snow geese are especially fond of the roots of saltwort.

SPORTSMEN prize waterfowl above other migratory game birds in Mexico. Twenty-six kinds of migratory ducks, and the coot, winter here, but only 13 are common game species. The pintail, lesser scaup, and shoveler are most plentiful.

Blue-winged teal bound for South America make the long journey by way of Mexico and Central America or via the West Indies. On the vast marshes and lagoons of Venezuela and Colombia they are well fed and contented all winter. A few green-wings, widgeon, pintails, and shovelers, as well as native species share the marshes with them. Smaller numbers of teal, pintails, widgeon, gadwalls, shovelers, and lesser scaup winter on coastal bays, lagoons, marshes, and inland lakes of Central America and the West Indies.

To name the principal waterfowl for each important wintering ground would be too long a list; but the relative abundance of the principal species of waterfowl in Mexico according to zones—Pacific, Interior, and Gulf—is shown in the accompanying tabulation.

The black duck, familiar to many in the eastern United States and Canada, does not occur in Mexico. Two related resident species, the Mexican duck of the highlands and the mottled duck of northeastern Mexico, often are mistaken for the black.

Mallards formerly were more common winter residents in the highlands of Mexico, but large acreages of wheat, rice, sorghum, and other grains in the West and Midwest induced mallards to stay in the United States. For years they were rare in Mexico and only since the forties have their numbers risen very much south of the border. Croplands of the Colorado River Delta, rice and wheat fields of Sonora and Sinaloa, and wheat and corn fields in Chihuahua now attract flights of a few thousand.

Geese are fewer and farther between in the Republic than ducks. One encounters five species, mostly in northern Mexico. The whitefront is commonest. Lesser snow geese, in-

cluding a few blues, the black brant, and several races of Canada geese visit the country. Tule white-fronted geese and Ross' geese are rare visitors. A few whistling swans have been spotted on several air surveys. Once they were more frequent winter residents in northern Mexico.

Waterfowl that go to Mexico and other Latin American countries each winter total several million or more. Most of them are believed to follow inherited patterns of migration and to go to Latin America regardless of the availability of habitat in the United States. Bad weather, a shortage of favorite foods, or excessive shooting pressure in the Southwestern States may cause additional birds to cross the border. Coots are widely distributed, especially on the Gulf coast, where the average yearly number is almost as large as the total of all ducks noted in surveys from the air.

Six resident species are the fulvous tree duck, black-bellied tree duck, muscovy duck, mottled duck, Mexican duck, and masked duck. There are a few local breeding records for the mallard, cinnamon teal, blue-winged teal, and ruddy duck.

The first reconnaissance of Mexican wintering grounds from airplanes was made in January 1938. Comprehensive air surveys have been flown by the Fish and Wildlife Service in the Republic each January since 1947, except 1957, to obtain information on waterfowl.

Some Mexican wintering grounds are so vast that it is feasible to make aerial surveys of only a small part of them; but the surveys made are believed to indicate trends at

AVERAGE ABUNDANCE AND DISTRIBUTION OF WINTERING MIGRATORY WATERFOWL AND COOTS OBSERVED IN MEXICO [1]

Pacific Coast		Gulf Coast		Mexican Highlands	
Pintail	457,300	Lesser Scaup	226,900	Pintail	257,400
Shoveler	240,300	Pintail	186,600	Shoveler	80,500
Lesser Scaup	175,800	Blue-winged Teal	135,300	Green-winged Teal	68,200
Green-winged Teal	123,800	Widgeon	104,900	Widgeon	46,300
Gadwall	58,200	Redhead	84,900	Blue-winged Teal	43,600
Blue-winged Teal	53,700	Gadwall	55,600	Gadwall	26,200
Widgeon	50,700	Green-winged Teal	18,500	Canvasback	16,600
Ruddy	38,400	Shoveler	16,400	Lesser Scaup	6,700
Redhead	23,100	Ring-necked Duck	8,600	Ruddy	2,100
Ring-necked Duck	700	Canvasback	8,000	Redhead	1,600
Total ducks, including other species	1,201,700		937,900		566,000
Total Black Brant	74,200		-----		-----
Total Other Geese	10,800		10,600		19,600
Total Waterfowl	1,286,700		948,500		585,600
Total Coots	115,200		842,800		42,800
Grand Total	1,401,900		1,791,300		628,400

[1] Only the top ten ducks are listed for each region. The figures are an average of estimates made by the Fish and Wildlife Service on the January aerial survey, as follows: Pacific Coast, 1948–1962; Gulf Coast, 1948–1962; Interior Highlands, 1951–1961. These are not total counts as the wintering grounds are not covered completely, but they do indicate relative abundance.

least in the principal species. Tables from these reports show the relative abundance of ducks, geese, and coots on the Gulf coast, Pacific coast, and in the interior highlands. Ground surveys since 1937 also have yielded data on wintering places, waterfowl populations, their food, and hunting pressure.

WHICH FLYWAYS supply waterfowl to Mexico? The largest numbers probably are from the Pacific Flyway, and most of them follow the Coastal Plain to the attractive bays and lagoons that extend from the Yaqui Delta of Sonora to Culiacan, Mazatlan, and Acapulco. Others journey to the coastal waters of Oaxaca and Chiapas or beyond.

Their distribution varies with species and food preferences. Most remain in coastal waters. Others leave the lowlands and fly up the larger valleys to lakes in the highlands. Some, especially pintails, continue eastward to the Gulf coast. Some banded on the Pacific coast of the United States in autumn are taken on the Gulf coast in late winter and in spring migration. Pintails banded in Kansas during spring migration and reported from the Pacific coast of the United States and Mexico in autumn and winter give further proof of this roundabout route.

Waterfowl of the Central Flyway probably are second in importance in Mexico. They have two chief migration routes—one southward over the interior highlands and the other along the Gulf coastal plain.

Before the decline of the big lakes of Chihuahua, Coahuila, and Durango, most of the waterfowl of the Central Flyway that came to Mexico may have wintered in the interior highlands. As recently as the 1880's those lakes, according to old-time residents, were more extensive and had many more waterfowl. Some vast basins had their tributary streams shunted for irrigation and parts of them became blowing dustbowls.

Widespread drainage, water diversion and periodic drought elsewhere in the highlands have shrunk most of the remaining natural lakes and marshes. This reduction in the carrying capacity of the interior has shifted, more and more of the wintering birds from this area to the Gulf coast and possibly to the Pacific coast.

From the Mississippi Flyway come flights of blue-winged teal, shovelers, pintails, and lesser scaup, which pass along the Gulf coast from Louisiana to Texas and into Mexico and beyond. Some widgeon, ringnecks, and others also follow that route to their wintering grounds. Flights of those ducks also cross the Gulf directly south from the coast of Louisiana to the northern shore of Yucatan. They often wait for a tail wind to aid them on the southbound trip, and southerly trade winds help many on the northbound flights.

Some Mississippi Flyway waterfowl swing inland from the Texas coast to the Central Plateau and reach the highland lakes that are used chiefly by Central Flyway birds.

Few ducks of the Atlantic Flyway winter in or pass through Mexico. Small flights of bluewings, pintails, lesser scaup, widgeon, and ringnecks follow a route from southern Florida to Cuba and then across to the Yucatan Peninsula.

AMONG MY MOST vivid impressions of waterfowl haunts in Mexico is the great isolation of many of the finest wintering places, I scouted lagoons and marshes for weeks during ground surveys. In many localities I saw tens of thousands of ducks but no hunters, and I did not hear a shot. Hundreds of square miles of some wintering grounds have no access roads for ordinary cars—even an amphibious vehicle would have its troubles. Many migratory birds seek these natural refuges.

Some misunderstanding has arisen regarding hunting in Mexico. It stems partly from a failure to appreciate the size of the Latin American wintering grounds and the lack of hunting pressure on most of them. Allegations that great numbers of waterfowl are slaughtered in Mexico are baseless or exaggerated. Some hunters, chiefly Americans, shoot too many birds, but the total kill in any large district is a small percentage of the waterfowl present. Some commercial shooting and marketing of waterfowl has occurred, but has been reduced greatly through enforcement of regulations by Mexican authorities.

In the United States there are hundreds of sport shooters for every hunter who needs the fowl to feed his family. The reverse is true among Mexicans. Most of the Mexicans who hunt do so because of economic necessity. Therefore the deer hunters far outnumber the duck hunters in

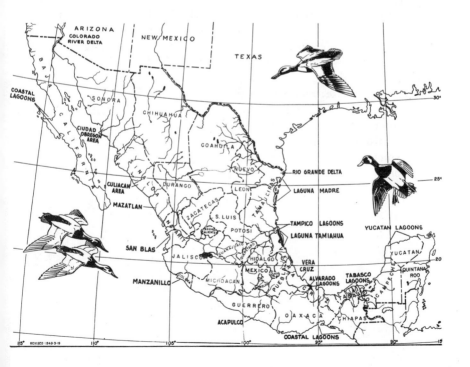

Mexico, because deer provide much more meat and useful hides. Most Mexicans prefer chicken, goat, beef, lamb, venison, wild hog, and fish to duck. Guns and ammunition, furthermore, cost much more in Mexico than in the United States and Canada; many Mexicans cannot afford to buy them. Permits to possess and carry guns are difficult to obtain in many localities.

Waterfowl haunts near cities and towns have more hunting as one would expect, but even there it is a small fraction of the pressure in places of comparable population in the United States. The number of resident duck hunters in Mexico is lower than we have in Delaware, for example, and the total bag is so light that stringent regulations like ours are not needed. Much of the small harvest of waterfowl is made by or for visiting Americans. In localities near the United States border, the number of nonresident hunters has gone up steadily. Were it not for the lack of satisfactory accommodations in many places, the delays in obtaining hunting licenses and arms and ammunition permits, the discomfort of dysentery and insect pests, and complications of language, many more Americans would shoot ducks in Mexico.

ALL TOLD, the waterfowl that winter in Mexico find the additional flight worthwhile. Choice marshes greet them and feed them and give them isolation in a balmy climate. Such conditions are likely to prevail for a long time, especially in the remote places.

But the mark of human exploitation is appearing on the land that is Mexico, too. Roadways, agriculture, drainage, siltation, and other accompaniments of growth and development are biting into wintering habitat. The attrition is slow—more rapid in the highlands, much slower in coastal marshes and swamps, yet so nominal in terms of the whole, as to appear innocuous. Therein lies the hazard. What happens in any one year on any single marsh seems unimportant. What happens in a decade to hundreds of square miles of habitat may be appalling. And we in the United States stand in testimony of what can happen. May planning and foresight be more timely south of the border!

—GEORGE B. SAUNDERS.

Men and nature must work hand in hand. The throwing out of balance the resources of nature throws out of balance also the lives of men.

—FRANKLIN D. ROOSEVELT.

MALLARD

Nature at Work

MALLARDS

Mammoths and Mallards

A FEW MINUTES AGO, as we mark the history of men and mallards, the land that some of us now call the duck factory lay under a thick sheet of ice. Nothing could stop this plowing, grinding mass as it inched along like a gigantic snail. All it touched it changed. It leveled mountains and made prairies. It gouged out deep lakes, carved swamps and holes, and made watercourses. All this the icy mass did as easily as a school child wipes clean his slate, and the final effect was as thorough. When the ice finally melted, all living things that could live in the land the glacier had re-made had to invade it again and begin anew.

Even then, 15 thousand years ago, people elsewhere had begun to enrich their lives with arts and crafts and in parts of Asia and Africa were advancing from food gathering to primitive farming. When the last ice had melted from the far northern nesting grounds about 6 thousand years ago (in some places much later), men in other lands had started to build cities.

On our continent, mastodons and mammoths roamed. They were well suited to browse the flora, and the woolly mammoth to endure an

265

arctic climate. A thin skin, though, underlay its warm, thick, hairy coat, and any kind of spear could pierce it. To the early ancestors of our Indians, these big elephants must have seemed too good to be true— tons of excellent meat and a great, warm hide, all in one kill, dangerous as it must have been to attack them with stones and sharpened sticks.

The remains of those beasts have been found alongside the remains of crude weapons. Modern science has given us ways to determine how long ago any bone ceased to be part of a living body. An element in animal bodies is carbon, originating from living plants. As a result of cosmic radiation, a portion of the carbon bound into any tissue is the radioactive isotope, Carbon 14. From the moment of death no more is added, and what is there loses its radioactivity at a constant rate. With these facts at hand, scientists can compute with good accuracy the age of many fossil remains. Thus we conclude that these big mammals disappeared first in Alaska and the dry Southwest. They remained longer in the Great Plains.

Speculation is tempting. The time of glacial retreat, when thick dustbowl soils were laid down, must have been tough on big herbivores, but pockets of them seemed to have lived until the period 6000 to 4000 B.C. There is even a shaky dating of between 2000 B.C. and less than 100 B.C. for Florida. There were no closed seasons and no national refuges; man may have pushed them over the brink.

Man has always had difficulty in forming a realistic concept of time. He has gazed into the galaxies. He has been told that the light he sees from the North Star started from there 49 years ago and that mountains have been raised upon the earth and worn down again numerous times. Nevertheless, it is difficult for him to accept the fact that his short life span is but "as a flicker of light in the darkness of eternity." This he must do, however, if he is to understand the workings of our earth, which we call geology.

HILLS AND MOUNTAINS are normally formed by a heaving up of the earth's crust by tremendous pressures beneath. As soon as upheaval is begun, natural forces go to work to level the land again. The particles of earth, loosened and removed by temperature changes and wind, are carried from high points to low points on the earth's surface by water and wind. The steeper the gradient, the faster the water flows and the more debris it carries.

So, eventually hills are worn down, and the valleys are filled with the fertile debris. We never notice, however, for it takes millions of years, and in the process we may end up being part of the debris in this eternal process of upheaval and change.

THE GEOLOGICAL RECORD SHOWS that some periods have been more unstable than others; then mountain ranges were shoved up, twisted, and bent. These periods lasted millions of years, but the results are so impressive that the geologists call them revolutions.

When upheavals are going on,

molten rock from inside the earth comes welling up. Where heat and pressure involve the beds of sand, ooze, and mud that have formed rock, these get changed. But these beds may also be heaved up unchanged—in their original form. Often this type of rock contains remains of animals and plants, called fossils, sometimes few, occasionally very many. When identified and classified, the fossils have provided geologists with a basis for establishing geological intervals of time.

OF SEVERAL GREAT GEOLOGIC ERAS, the oldest is called the Precambrian. These are the earth's oldest rocks, and they are practically without fossils or other evidences of life. Then came the early Paleozoic, when only simple plants and animals living in the water were present. But near the end of the period, land plants, fishes, and the earliest reptiles made their appearance. A later era (Mesozoic) saw the rise and fall of dinosaurs. It was the age of reptiles, and along with them and related to them came the birds. The most recent era (Cenozoic) is called the age of mammals, because mammals, and finally man, came to dominate. A great variety of animal and plant types were evolved in this last era, and many of these are still with us. But many more, by far, have passed into the darkness of extinction.

This passing of geologic time involved many millions of years, and the Ice Age, ancient though it may seem, is but seconds away by comparison. You might even say it is an event of the day, because half

the ice (Greenland and Antarctica) is still present. And men and mallards were around throughout its last southward thrust.

THE ICE AGE planted its mark boldly on the northern half of our continent. The results of its being are plain to see. As for what was before we can only guess. For a glimpse into the preglacial past we can judge probable appearances by looking at parts of our own continent that have never been glaciated. Rivers are mature with wide valleys and flood plains, which provide most of the duck marshes. Not many lakes, large or small, are to be found. There are, however, deltas of all sizes where rivers go to the sea. There are hardwood forests, coniferous forests, and grasslands.

This probably was the picture everywhere before the ice came. Over much of the great horseshoe around Hudson Bay there must have been beds of Paleozoic rock, because they still cover areas southwest of the Bay. In the days before the ice, this land was higher, richer, and also well drained. There was no Hudson Bay.

BUT GLACIATION CHANGED THINGS over the top one-third of the globe—as well you might expect. Imagine a sheet of ice, 2 miles thick in places, advancing over the landscape—a scraping, griding, bulldozing mass that leveled hills here and deposited others there. A monster created by climate, it in turn altered climate. And, above all, a builder and tiller of soils, a maker of immense lakes and millions of ponds, potholes, and sloughs. These things of times past shaped the world of waterfowl today. How did it all come about? And what has it all meant, for mallards—and mammoths?

A glacier is a river of ice granules. If snow lasts all summer and then more snow comes and lasts, eventually the deep layers consolidate. The mass is plastic, and forms clear ice only on margins. Ice of this consistency can flow and does creep inexorably outward, following gradients where there are such. But glaciers can flow uphill, too, because of the great pressure at the center.

WHY DID THE snow pile up? It happens whenever more snow falls than can melt in summer. Now it is known that the climate may have been little different from the present if the Arctic seas were open, as they seem to have been.

To understand the effect this can have, look at a rainfall map of the continent. The tundra area of the north has a very low precipitation and gets very little snow. Cold as it is, a few bright summer days suffice to melt the snow. Prevailing winter winds off the Arctic and Hudson Bay carry little moisture, because both are ice covered. If these waters were open in the winter, the same thing could happen as happens near the Great Lakes. In cold weather the land is colder than the water, and winds passing over the water pick up moisture, which is shed when they blow over the colder land. Thus snow belts are formed in the lee of each lake.

SEVENTY YEARS AGO the Norwegian explorer Nansen built an ice-resistant ship, the *Fram,* and froze her in the Arctic ice. There he made ice measurements. Today the ice is less than half as thick as it was then. A little more of the same trend, and the Arctic sea could flush out. Then, in its lee, there could be a snow belt to end all snow belts, right in the middle of the Canadian "barren ground," where it would have a poor chance of melting in summer. Could the icecap then come back? The prospect is enough to set a man to wondering.

Once the pileup starts, the outward flow begins. And when the ice mass is large enough, it makes its own climate and influences climate in other areas. Mountain glaciation increases everywhere. In time the rate of buildup slows down. Ice fills the Arctic seas. The glacier stands relatively still for a long time, and to break its hold may take a more drastic climatic change than the one that started it.

There are signs of a tremendous drought coinciding with the retreat. Huge duststorms deposited unleached glacial clay (called loess) over large areas of the Midwest and in the process gave it some of its best soils. Dry-country animals have eastern and western races that were separated by continental glaciation and are now meeting again. Whatever happened, once the ice really started to melt it vanished fairly fast.

THE ICE NOW IS GONE, except in Greenland. But let us not forget that this has happened before. The ice appeared, then vanished, four times in the Northern States. Two of the inbetween periods were long. One of them certainly was longer and milder than the one we are in now.

With each period of glaciation, more rock flour was ground off the Precambrian Shield, leaving it more barren and adding to lands to the south, making them more fertile. But we are mainly concerned only with the last, or Wisconsin, glaciation. When that ice melted, nature again had a clean slate.

The ice ground hills, and, when it flowed along valleys, it enlarged, rounded, and deepened them. When it melted, it left dumps of ground-up material everywhere. Rarely was a natural watercourse left unplugged. For example, the river system that used to drain the watershed where the Great Lakes now are located was completely destroyed.

This sort of thing went on, in one form or another, at a million places in the glaciated area. Sometimes, as the ice retreated in the big melt, the water dammed up behind it. Of course, even a big ice mass is a poor dam, but it often lasted long enough to deposit mud on lands previously scraped bare. The result was fertile soil.

CLAY AND STONES pushed ahead by moving ice, then abandoned in retreat, make moraines. They are good water seals and may hold forever (or almost), like the by-passed clay plug in the Niagara whirlpool. A moraine once blocked the Nelson River and backed up prehistoric Lake Agassiz, one of the biggest lakes ever known. At an earlier stage when the lake was even bigger, it was dammed up by ice. It covered most of what is now southern Manitoba, parts of Saskatchewan and Ontario, and even a great chunk of Minnesota. It spilled over the height of land into the Minnesota River and thence into the Mississippi. It must have been a great lake for ducks, because it was huge, shallow, and fertile.

But the moraine dam really was not very big, and the lake was doomed. All the creeks east of the barrier drained to Hudson Bay. Eventually, one of those creeks ate its way back to capture a creek running into Lake Agassiz. The new, enlarged creek repeated the performance until the time came when it tapped the lake, and glacial Lake Agassiz began to die. The stages in the shrinkage of Lake Agassiz are spelled out in a series of old sand beaches from its original shore. During this shrinking process, great expanses of fertile mud flats were laid bare to the sun. One is led to wonder if this might not have been the golden age of shore birds and other waders.

The smallest lakes formed by glacial plugs may be only a few square rods and are called sloughs. Another source of small lakes was the soil-covered chunks of ice (ice lenses) left behind in the glacial clay. When they finaly melted they left dimples below the soil water table.

There are more small lakes than large, and Nature is always trying to fill them with debris; in the forest she makes pretty good headway. In the grassland it takes a long time and here most of them are still left. We call these prairie sloughs, potholes, or lakes, depending on size and depth. They are an important part of the duck factory. It is hard to say whether glacial dams or melted ice lenses were most important in their formation. Glaciers had a way of retreating down a valley, and the debris they left on the gentler slopes often dammed springs fed by deep ground water. Such sloughs, on what is called a perched water table, are watered in the driest years. At these times, they are oases to waterfowl seeking places to nest and rear young. Whether or not other potholes, especially those from ice lenses, dry up in bad years depends also on their relation to the water table.

HERDS OF BUFFALO could enlarge a slough, and often did. As a boy I sat at the feet of an old missionary, who had gone into Alberta in the 1860's, and heard him tell how he saw a herd of buffalo descend on a lake of several acres, suck it dry, and then wallow in it and carry tons of mud away on their hides. They can also create a slough, because one will roll where another has rolled, and both carry away dust when it is dry and mud when it is wet. In a millenium, you get a slough. I recall seeing a first-class slough with a large, beautifully polished glacial boulder standing in the middle. However, buffalo wallows usually make the kind of slough that is available to ducks only in the "good" wet years.

ANOTHER MAMMAL, the beaver, makes ponds in the forest for the ducks. The jumbled-up drainage system left by the glaciers makes a beaver paradise. In the mature drainage of unglaciated areas, such as Siberia, nearly all the beaver are bank beaver. Dams are rare, because there are few places to make them.

ANOTHER IMPORTANT EVENT that affected waterfowl was the postglacial flooding of seashore areas in the north. Ten thousand feet of ice perched on a platform as unstable as the earth's crust requires that something give. The crust was depressed, and the extra water running into the sea caused the coasts to be flooded. Because the earth's crust is elastic, it has gradually bounced back. The upper Great Lakes, previously joined, have been separated and made to run out over Niagara Falls, instead of partly down the Ottawa. A salt water sea has drained out of the Ottawa-St. Lawrence Valley, and Hudson Bay has shrunk to its present size—half what it once was. This, we are told, happened within the last 5 thousand years.

The present bottoms of Hudson Bay and the Gulf of St. Lawrence can be looked upon as unredeemed land, pushed down by the ice, not yet sprung back in place, and apt to do so most any millenium. On the other hand, if the Greenland and Antarctic ice were to melt, the sea could rise more than 2 hundred feet, enough to wash out such places as Manhattan and Washington, D.C. It may even be a good thing for the ducks.

THE COMING AND MELTING of the great glaciers affected the numbers of waterfowl and their migrations. The earliest ice retreat was probably best for the ducks. It must have left as many prairie potholes as we have now. New and succeeding ice sheets scraped the northland a little barer and left it a little poorer than it was before, without improving the prairie. When the last advance came, the ducks surely lost their best nesting grounds. Be that as it may, we must live with what we have.

In front of the glacial margin a narrow strip of barren ground tundra occurred. South of this was a belt of coniferous forest. In the Southwest there was grassland and dry country. In the East there was hardwood forest. In the unglaciated areas drainage was then as it is now—mature and settled, with places for wildfowl in the flood plains. Presumably ducks from the north flew south, and what are now northern species, such as snow geese, were in small numbers on the tundra fringes.

Probably the first break for waterfowl came when the first meltwater lakes were formed as the icecap retreated. They were able to raise more young in expanded nesting areas. As glacial retreat went on, new areas were exposed and occupied, but the birds still congregated at the original ground on their way south. For snow geese of the interior there is now a great wintering ground on the Gulf Coast. On their way south they stop on the south shore of Hudson Bay, where there is still a strong tendency to nest, and then take off for the gulf. Returning, the birds stop in an old ice margin and Lake Agassiz shore area where they might well have nested once. This is probably the reason for the otherwise illogical migration pattern. Then they fly north. There is a strong probability that the Gulf has always been their winter home.

PART OF ALASKA was free of ice throughout the Ice Age, and must have been stocked with birds, then as now. Out of this we get two flight patterns. Black brant, eiders, and yellow-billed loons, even those from far to the east, fly northwest along the coast to the Bering Sea, then south. Geese and cranes, on the other hand, including some nesting in Siberia, fly inland along what was once an unglaciated Rocky Mountain corridor.

Tradition is a reasonable explanation of a flight that is perverse by any other standard. Parts of Greenland were and are ice free. Barnacle geese and pink-footed geese nesting there fly to Europe. Now, in summer, they are close to greater snow geese, which fly south to the lower St. Lawrence and the Atlantic coast.

FOR THE DUCKS, the great ice sheet created a wonderful breeding ground. Successive advances took it away, but each retreat gave it back. If natural processes go unhindered, the prairie sloughs will, in time, choke with vegetation and become dry land. The now barren Precambrian lakes will, in slight compensation, become richer and more marshy as nutrients are gradually added to them.

In time the drainage will become mature again, as it was before the slate was cleaned. Then the ice age will be seen for what it really was— a speeding up of natural erosion of the hills around Hudson Bay. One day the material laid down in the sea may be heaved up into new mountains. The normal expectation of evolution would be that by that time man and the mallard will be only fossils, either replaced by improved descendants, or joined to the list of types that dropped out during the age when mammals dominated the earth.

WHAT IS ON THIS EARTH TODAY is the result of natural forces through time down to the present. The drives and actions of our own species must be included among these forces. In our concern over the direction in which human impulses are driving us, we can look at the past—at events long gone—then read the result. It may well help us to understand both men and mallards better and to project a better future for both.—C. H. D. CLARKE.

Conservation is a state of harmony between men and land.—ALDO LEOPOLD

SHARP-TAILED GROUSE
SHOVELER AND BROOD

Water

WATER COMES to the land in the form of rain, snow, and dew. It is lost through evaporation, plant transpiration, and runoff. The amount of precipitation varies greatly from one part of the continent to another; so does the rate of loss. In areas with high temperature and low humidity, moisture loss will be much greater than where it is cool and the humidity is higher. Wind increases the rate of loss.

The balance between water received and water lost has much to do with the character of the land and its use by waterfowl. Where the potential for water loss greatly exceeds the amount received, a desert condition prevails and streams are few and far between. Where the reverse is true, vegetation grows luxuriantly and drainage systems are frequent and well developed.

Surprisingly, most ducks in North America are raised in areas where there is a potential net deficiency of 4 to 10 inches between average precipitation and the water loss through evaporation and transpiration. The chief production area in this category is the pothole breeding range in prairies and parklands in the southern portion of Alberta, Saskatchewan, and Manitoba; in

North and South Dakota north and east of the Missouri River; western Minnesota, and northern Montana. A secondary area of production lies along the MacKenzie River drainage in the western portion of the Northwest Territory.

It is the southern prairies, the grasslands and aspen parklands, that provide the preferred duck breeding habitat. Here in the mid 1950's the breeding population of prairie ducks averaged 30 pairs to the square mile and reached 150 to 200 pairs in the potholes of old glacial moraines. The importance of this area to breeding waterfowl is emphasized by the fact that the continental waterfowl population fluctuates with water conditions on the prairies. In drought years waterfowl populations decline regardless of the fact that abundant water is available in the North. There is more to waterfowl habitat than water!

TOPOGRAPHICALLY the last glacier, as it receded from the northern plains some 10 thousand years ago, left behind the basis of waterfowl habitat. The landscape was remolded from something probably akin to badlands into an undulating plain, interrupted by low hills of morainic origin and typical poorly drained knob-and-kettle terrain. The flat plains of southern Manitoba, North Dakota, and southern Saskatchewan came from sedimentation in the large lakes that formed at the base of the melting ice.

During the 10 thousand years since the last glacier, there has been a precarious balance between mois-

ture received and moisture lost in this area. At no time has precipitation greatly exceeded the amount lost due to transpiration and evaporation. Had this not been so, the millions of depressions would have filled to overflowing, gullies would have formed, and the areas would have drained. On the other hand, there must have been sufficient rainfall to preserve a vegetative cover and prevent wind and water erosion from filling the potholes.

In an average year, spring runoff water from melting snow collects in the multitude of small depressions. From surveys by the U.S. Fish and Wildlife Service from 1953 to 1961, J. Bernard Gollop, of the Canadian Wildlife Service, calculated the number of ponds on the Canadian prairies in May of each year. The average during the 9 years was 3,985,000. In the wettest year, 1954 there were 6,760,000 ponds; even in the driest, 1961, there were 1,702,000. The density of potholes varies from just a few to as many as 200 per square mile. The potholes differ greatly in shape and size but average between 1 and 2 acres. It is the multitude of small wetland areas in a variety of sizes and arrangements which contribute one of the essential elements which make up duck breeding habitat.

But water by itself is only the basic physical requirement of waterfowl habitat. Like a factory, the output is dependent upon the quality of the machinery once the basic building is established. Here the complicated chemical processes in water, expressed in the term fertility, are the machinery of production. Vegetation, climate, and the soils of the watershed, together with the chemical processes in the ponds and bottom muds, are the determining factors of fertility.

Till—the load of soil, crumbling rocks, and stones carried by the moving glacier—had its origin in the Pre-Cambrian and Paleozoic rocks near the center of glaciation. Glaciation stirred up the material lying at the pre-glacial surface and incorporated into it this fresh mineral material, containing a good supply of potash and phosphorus from Pre-Cambrian rocks and lime from Paleozoic limestone. Left be-

hind, as the ice receded, were the elements of a productive soil, on which the soil-forming agencies, climatic, vegetative, and biological, began to act.

Some authorities suggest that as the ice retreated vegetative zones developed southward from the ice front in the familiar sequence of today of tundra, coniferous forests, deciduous forests, and grassland. Others believe this did not happen, at least not in Manitoba. Except for the immediate ice face, the climate was not too severe, they believe, and a marsh-grassland developed on the denuded soil. Further west a drier type of grassland may have ap-

More dry potholes show up in this photograph than filled ones.   The site is typical pothole country in Saskatchewan, Canada, in a dry year.

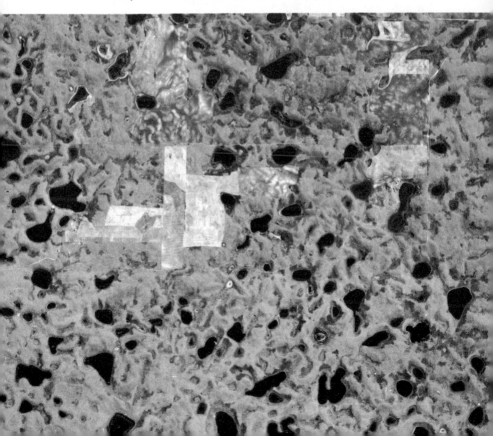

peared. Spruce could not gain an early foothold, because the nearest source of seed was the Rocky Mountains. Spruce appeared later along drainages from the West, where a spruce parkland developed. The rich, unleached soils of the present prairies confirmed that, if covered by forests, it must have been of short duration.

The warming period immediately following glaciation is believed to have culminated in a temperature maximum in the interval between 6 thousand and 2 thousand years ago. This period probably saw the greatest northward extension of the prairies. During the last 2 thousand years the climate has been cooler and more variable, and spruce forest has expanded southward. In turn, the deciduous forest has been pressing into the prairies from the north and east. This advance has been rapid in the past 100 years since buffalo were eliminated from the prairies and grass fires were controlled. Conspicuous changes have occurred within the memory of people still living.

Grasslands develop and persist in a climate that in the long run approaches semi-aridity. Annual variability, in western Canada at least, is characteristic. It is cold in January and warm in July. But who knows how cold or how warm it will be. So, too, as to rain and snow. Long-time averages mean little; variability may be extreme. Thus in southern Alberta, although average precipitation is 13.3 inches, the range is between 25.3 and 6.7 inches. In southern Saskatchewan, the average is 14.9, and the range 24.0 to 8.3

inches. Attempting to forecast precipitation in a coming year keeps prairie farmers and ranchers awake at night and makes waterfowl men old before their time! Annual prairie precipitation tends to be cyclic, however, and the best guess is that next year will be much like the last. But often a wet year comes in the middle of a dry cycle, and vice-versa.

RICH PRAIRIE SOILS are a result of semi-arid climate. The process has two parts. First, low average precipitation and high evaporation mean that a minimum of water moves through the soil. The more soluble minerals are moved from upper to lower levels but not too deep for plant roots to reach them. The store of minerals the glacier left is thus conserved; where much water moves in the soil, the more soluble minerals are leached out and flow in the water to the streams. Secondly, prairie vegetation develops a deep humus, rich in nitrogen and phosphorus. Water flowing over and through such soil brings a rich load of minerals and plant nutrients to a prairie pond.

Quite the opposite is true in areas where precipitation exceeds the amount lost through transpiration and evaporation. In most areas with excess moisture a forest is the climax-type vegetation. Forests have developed to the north of the breeding area of prairie and parkland potholes. One reason is that lower temperatures and evaporation make rainfall more effective, even though the annual amount is almost the same as on the prairies. With an excess of rainfall in rela-

Potholes knee-deep to a cow will not last out the summer in this prairie country of relatively low rainfall but they provide good nesting sites for waterfowl.   Light grazing like this is compatible with good waterfowl management.

tion to loss through evaporation and transpiration, more water is available for runoff. Consequently, leaching of the more soluble minerals from the soil is more active. The organic residue of coniferous forests and associated plants is acid in reaction and imparts this characteristic to the percolating waters, which raises their solvent powers. Soils that have supported coniferous forests for any length of time tend to be leached and acid in reaction. Water percolating through and over such soils carries little mineral matter or plant nutrients to a forest pond.

NATURE IS DYNAMIC. All water areas, large and small, proceed through sedimentation and accumulation of organic debris to dry land, their ultimate destiny. Filling is rapid in cold, acidic forest ponds because decomposition is slow, and

peat and other organic residue accumulate faster than they can be broken down. In the northern half of the Northern Great Plains, most ponds which must have dotted the immediate post-glacial landscape and persisted through the period of maximum grassland, have long since become bog and spruce forests.

But the alkaline waters and high temperatures of the prairies promote rapid decomposition. Organic material is soon broken down and mineralized to a form usable by plants. Drought helps this process, for decomposition proceeds quickly when pond bottoms are exposed and aerated. Pond fertility is thus greater when reflooded, and the rate of filling is slowed down. In the long range view drought, paradoxically, helps keep a pond a pond! Minnesota, while not in the zone we are discussing, has the same transition northeast to southwest from coniferous forest to prairie. A 10-inch excess of water is available for runoff in the northeastern part of the State. A 10-inch deficit exists in the southwest. John B. Moyle found a general increase in the common chemical constituents (carbonates, sulphates, and chlorides) from northeast to southwest. Fertility, as shown by the amounts of nitrogen and phosphorus, was related to the concentration of dissolved salts. The distribution of nitrogen and phosphorus coincided with the plant geography of the State. The least fertile waters were in the coniferous forest area. Those of moderate fertility were in the hardwood forest. Those of highest fertility were in the prairies.

A similar zonation exists in Saskatchewan. Lakes of the northern coniferous region with continuous outflow contain fewer than 200 parts per million (p.p.m.) total solids. Southward, lakes of the aspen parklands and prairies with seasonal outflow or none at all usually have dissolved solids of at least 1,000 p.p.m.—often several times this amount.

My point is that the most valuable waterfowl food plants grow best in waters with good amounts of dissolved minerals and are absent from the typical soft-water lakes of the coniferous forest. These plants do not begin to appear until total alkalinity is in the range of 90–250 p.p.m. and the sulphate ion at least 50 p.p.m. The important pondweeds range from this level into very high concentrations. At the Bear River Refuge in Utah, sago pondweed, a first-rate food plant,

grows best when the water contains 4,200 to 7,000 p.p.m. of dissolved salts. Growth is checked above 12,000 p.p.m., but widgeongrass, another good food plant, flourishes at higher concentrations.

The prairie lakes of Saskatchewan and Alberta are mostly quite saline. Widgeongrass grows in Redberry Lake, where the total dissolved salts are 14,200 p.p.m. Sago pondweed grows in Little Quill, where total dissolved salts are 20,000 p.p.m. Prairie ponds, too, are rich in dissolved salts. In the Minnedosa potholes of southwestern Manitoba, one of the best breeding areas, Nolan Perret found total dissolved solids ranged from 13,000 to 3,042 p.p.m. Nitrogen levels were high, and the water productive. Salts, however, particularly those with a stronge alkaline reaction, may accumulate in some prairie waters to the point where all plant and animal life is excluded. Alkali sloughs, white with salt, are common on the prairie in dry years.

Increasing amounts of bottom fauna reflect increasing fertility of water, as indicated by carbonate hardness and total dissolved solids. According to Moyle, typical soft-water lakes usually produce less than 20 pounds of bottom organisms to the acre. Lakes of the Minnesota prairie region, which have large quantities of dissolved minerals, may have 200 pounds an acre. Furthermore, the invertebrates increase with the amount of aquatic plants. Fine-leafed plants, such as sago pondweed, northern watermilfoil, and muskgrass, characteristic of hard prairie waters and excellent food plants in themselves, support

larger numbers of aquatic invertebrates than the large-leafed species
of soft-water lakes.

A high-protein diet is needed by
laying females and young ducklings. This cannot be supplied by
aquatic plants and here the aquatic invertebrates are very important.
Nolan Perret found that male and
female mallards in Manitoba differ
markedly in their food habits.
Females consumed 63.5 percent
animal food; males, only 45 percent—evidence perhaps of the high-
protein requirement of laying hens.
It is possible, however, that the
difference may be due partly to the
lower activity of hens at laying time.

Prairie ponds thus are highly
fertile, and plants and animals
waterfowl need most thrive in them.
That is not true of the lakes of the
coniferous forest. We lack chemical
analyses of water in the smaller
ponds, but from the air they are
brown-stained waters filled with
yellow waterlily, which we may
take as an indication of a small
amount of dissolved minerals. At
any rate, they are of little value to
waterfowl, giving rise to the expression that generally "ducks and
water lilies don't go together."

FURTHER to the north and west,
generally within the MacKenzie
River drainage in the western portion of the Northwest Territory, is
a region in which the water areas
superficially appear similar to those
in the coniferous forests further
south. Yet it is much more productive of ducks. Here, in many years,
population densities of breeding
ducks, only slightly below that of
the prairie further south, have been

found. No intensive studies have
been conducted in this area, and
little is known concerning the specific characteristics of the water
areas. However, some understanding was gained from a study of *The
Climates of Canada According to the
New Thornthwaite Classification.* This
publication by Marie Sanderson
compares average precipitation and
water loss through transpiration
and evaporation. Reference to this
work revealed a surprising correla-
tion between the distribution and
density of breeding ducks, and the
area along the MacKenzie River
with a net deficiency in water of
from 4 to 6 inches. Since there
would obviously be much less leaching of nutrient material in an area
with a net deficiency in rainfall, it
seems likely that the ponds in this
area may be correspondingly richer
than ponds in higher rainfall areas
and are thus more favorable for
waterfowl production.

Another interesting exception is
found in lakes associated with the
deltas of the great northern rivers,
the Saskatchewan, Athabasca, and
MacKenzie. Fertility here is much
higher than in coniferous forest
lakes not so associated. A number
of lakes of above average fertility
also occur on the southern edge of
the coniferous forest. These are
used by thousands of male diving
ducks during their moult in summer and fall. The excrement of the
many thousands of ducks involved
may be a factor in maintaining the
fertility of these waters.

Furthermore not only do the
prairies provide an abundance of
highly fertile water areas for nesting waterfowl in years of adequate

runoff, but the long prairie summer improves the chances of successful renesting if the first nest is destroyed. The combination of favorable habitat and a long time to exploit it explains the "booms" in waterfowl populations when habitat conditions are good on the prairies. The "boom" is spectacular, but so is the "bust" which occurs on the prairies in drought years, regardless of the northern habitat.

Only on the prairies and only during wet years do enough acceptable water areas exist to provide adequate space for breeding pairs. And only on the prairies are these ponds fertile enough to produce the abundance and quality of food required during a successful breeding season. A firm, open shore, nesting cover of prairie plants, and a landscape open to a distant horizon may also be im-

portant. The difference between those conditions and the floating, spruce-crowded, wet sedge rim of a forest pond is clear.

It may be that only a small part of the potential duck breeding population is stimulated to nest during a drought year.

In dry 1959, for instance, loose flocks, apparently non-breeding mallards and pintails, were seen on the prairies through spring and early summer. Similar flocks of what seemed to be displaced prairie birds have been noted in the Arctic during prairie drought years. John P. Rogers showed that nesting of lesser scaup was inhibited by adverse habitat conditions in 1959 in the Minnedosa potholes of southwestern Manitoba. The proportion of resident pairs that nested dropped from 64 percent in 1958 to 8 percent in 1959. In 1960,

Lake Nebraska in Saskatchewan had a history of going dry when ducks needed it most. Ducks Unlimited built a dike and a water control structure to conserve the water when it was plentiful.

when water levels were about the same as 1958, the proportion of resident pairs that nested was 60 percent. Mudflats separated the water from the shoreline growth in 1959. It was suggested that the presence of the mudflats may have had a psychological effect which discouraged nesting and inhibited development of ovaries. As lesser scaup often walk to the nest site from the water's edge and nest within 10 feet of it, the mudflat between water and nesting cover may have constituted a psychological barrier since it prevented easy access to shoreline cover, and thus hindered the selection of nest sites.

H. J. Frith reported a close relationship between water conditions and breeding activity of Australian ducks, some of which are closely related to North American forms. The gray teal may move over the entire continent at all seasons in search of suitable living conditions. It breeds wherever and whenever acceptable conditions occur but not when the habitat is unsuitable. Dr. Frith reported: "The Australian black duck tends to have a regular breeding season but apparently individuals differ greatly in the sensitivity of their response to the proximate factors initiating breeding. In unfavorable seasons, those with low rainfall and shrinking water levels, very few birds breed. In seasons with normal rainfall, all

the local birds breed and when floods occur the local birds are reinforced by newcomers who occupy and breed in the new habitat created."

THE ASSERTION that a sizable number of prairie ducks may not breed in drought years seems entirely possible if we consider their biological characteristics. Physiologically ducks are hardy and long lived. They mature at 1 year, renest persistently under favorable conditions, and lay large clutches. These are adaptations to prairie habitat. They can thus survive long drought and increase quickly when favorable conditions return.

The prairie ponds are the key to the future of waterfowling. Without them no harvestable surplus can be produced. Destruction by draining, filling, and agricultural encroachment means permanent drought in terms of waterfowl production, and relegates the population permanently to drought levels. For without the prairie ponds the population can never "boom" and the "bust" is not enough.—WILLIAM G. LEITCH.

To sum up, wildlife once fed us and shaped our culture. It still yields us pleasure for leisure hours, but we try to reap that pleasure by modern machinery and thus destroy part of its value. Reaping it by modern mentality would yield not only pleasure, but wisdom as well.
—ALDO LEOPOLD.

BLACK BRANT

Weather

THOSE DARK and stormy days that are "fit only for ducks" can be fine for hunting, and may in some remarkable ways be beneficial for waterfowl. But ducks and geese do not enjoy inclement weather. Wildfowl that seem unusually active at the approach of a winter storm are probably anticipating trouble, not fun. In their excited comings and goings, they are seeking a sheltered spot where they can ride out the imminent unpleasantness in safety and comparative comfort.

They show something akin to prescience in their adroit avoidance of bad weather. This faculty may be associated with the "barometric" capabilities of their body air sacs—or possibly they have evolved other systems, yet unknown to science. Whatever the innate ability, it seems to work well enough to have qualified waterfowl as homespun weather prophets long before the science of meteorology was born.

At one time of year, however, waterfowl cannot back away from the weather. When winter wanes, the numbers of ducks and geese reach low ebb. Birds lost during the past year must be replaced if species are to endure. The losses can

283

be made good only during nesting seasons to come. Each spring, therefore, waterfowl undertake the journey north to nesting grounds. En route they must have enough food, sunlight, warmth, and other things that make them physiologically ready to mate and nest. At their destination, early-nesting species, such as pintails and mallards, must find nesting territories ready for immediate occupancy. Environmental conditions must remain favorable during the weeks they need to incubate eggs and rear the young.

Weather is a vital factor at every stage. It often decides the outcome of a season's nesting. Waterfowl have great reproductive potential, and given exceptional weather one nesting season, they can bring off a spectacular hatch. More often nest-

ing weather will be only moderately favorable, but so long as annual hatches compensate for annual losses, waterfowl can meet their biological goal, which is survival rather than perpetual abundance. Now and then very adverse nesting weather intervenes, in which case some species face a grim battle with the elements.

THE EARTH'S ATMOSPHERE, to waterfowl, is a restless ocean of air. Atmospheric tides and airstreams influence their movements, welfare, and very survival. Most ducks and geese flee southward each fall ahead of cold polar and arctic airmasses that then dominate the upper half of North America. The winter ebb and flow of the polar airtides bring us the bluebird days and the duck weather of the hunt-

A breeding pair of mallards arrives on nesting territory while king winter still reigns—a trait common to the species.

ing season. As winter wanes, the cold airtides lose their force and begin to recede northward. Pushing against this retreating cold air come currents of warm, spring air that well up from tropical regions.

For waterfowl, the most important of the tropical airstreams is one we may call the atmospheric Gulf stream. It is a current of warm, moist air that originates in the Caribbean and flows northward up the Mississippi Valley before it swings east toward the Atlantic coast. Occasionally it drifts farther west and spills into the Great Plains. At other times, it may flow far east of its normal spring track, depending on the location of the Bermuda High. The gulf airstream is vital to the waterfowl of North America, just as the famous oceanic Gulf stream is important to the rich marine life of the cold North Atlantic.

When spring arrives, the gulf airstream surges northward with ever-increasing strength. Migrant ducks and geese are borne along on its boisterous current. Its warm winds melt away the snow and ice. Travel-weary waterfowl find open waters where they can rest and feed. Aquatic insects, crustaceans, and other organisms become active as water temperatures rise. Many ducks seek out these burgeoning sources of animal proteins, to be in peak condition for egg laying.

But the atmosphere in spring can be turbulent. If the cold airmasses of winter were to retreat smoothly and steadily northward each spring, tropical airstreams could move up and replace them without meeting opposition. Then summer would come placidly to the nesting grounds—but then, too, there might not be very many waterfowl in North America.

The transition from winter to summer is seldom sedate and often is tumultuous. The gulf airstream, instead of flowing serenely all spring, sometimes becomes a raging atmospheric torrent that is impelled northward by backwash from the Bermuda High and by strong low-pressure systems in the southern Great Plains of the United States. The polar airmasses may be stubborn some years about retreating northward. Often they surge back south with great power during the spring months. When these dissimilar airmasses meet, they clash. Since both cannot occupy the same space, the warm gulf air may ride up on top of the cold air, or the cold air may thrust a cold wedge under the warm airmasses.

That is the battleground that meteorologists call a weather front. It spawns tornadoes, hailstorms, freezing rain, and general aerological uproar. Spring storms can be a real danger to migrant birds. Yet out of the clash comes precipitation, and waterfowl are benefited by it—except when it comes in hard, cold chunks.

MANY DUCKS NEST in the northern Great Plains and in the Prairie Provinces of Saskatchewan, Alberta, and Manitoba, a region that was bulldozed and graded by glaciers long ago in a way that left potholes, ponds, sloughs, and other depressions, small and large, that can hold water when they get water.

But this duck factory is semiarid. The total yearly rainfall averages less than 20 inches. Some droughty places may get only 5 inches. The region is drained by rivers and man's ditches. There also is evaporation of surface water and soil water into the atmosphere—an atmosphere so dry that the winter blanket of snow will sometimes evaporate directly into the air without first melting.

THE DUCK FACTORY DEPENDS entirely on the atmosphere for replenishment of surface and soil water. Giant airstreams from the Pacific Ocean periodically flow in from the west, but this air, warm and moist when it left its oceanic source, drops most of its load of water as it climbs the west slopes of the Rocky Mountains. It is dry by the time it gets to the east slopes of the

Continental Divide, where the plains and prairies begin. Spring and summer circulation from the north represents polar air too cool to carry much moisture. As this air moves south, it becomes progressively warmer and therefore more thirsty. Polar airmasses do not in themselves contribute much water to the region, although under some circumstances they can serve as the bung-start to tap the water supply of other airmasses.

The gulf airstream flows into this region from the south by way of a route not blocked by mountains. This tropical air can bring abundant moisture to the summer skies of the plains and prairies. In a normal summer, when polar air has withdrawn to the Far North, intruding gulf air will settle over the prairie region and simmer. Finally, hot summer weather triggers thermal buildup in the atmosphere. By this lifting process, moist air is

Canada geese in a snowstorm at Seney National Wildlife Refuge, Michigan. Weather such as this usually stimulates birds to move south in search of less hostile conditions.

mushroomed to high altitude, where it is cooled into churning cumulonimbus clouds and forced to unload its moisture. Summer is usually the wet season in this region; it gets one-third of its average annual water supply from thunderstorms in June and July.

But this water arrives late in a nesting season which, for pintails and mallards, should start by mid-April and be in full swing in May. Furthermore, the greatest seasonal loss of surface water takes place during hot midsummer, when evaporation and plant transpiration are at a peak. A mallard, exploring the prairie skies during this period, may see towering cumulus clouds festooned with long drapes of rain. If it flies beneath such a cloud at an altitude of 5 thousand feet, it will be pelted by raindrops. Yet down at 1 thousand feet, it may stay perfectly dry, because the raindrops, falling through dry air, will have evaporated to minute droplets that never reach the ground.

Spring and fall rainfall ordinarily is not great in the prairie region. Yet snow or rain during either period can sometimes be heavy and general and may set the stage for spectacular waterfowl production. This change-of-season precipitation takes place when cool polar air that overlies the plains and prairies defiantly refuses to retreat in the face of inrushing gulf air.

The annual spring inflow of the moist gulf airstream slammed into and overran polar air that had not yet begun its northward retreat in 1953 and again in 1954. The resultant prairiewide precipitation set the stage in prairie Canada for the waterfowl explosion of the midfifties. In the fall of 1959, accelerated southward surging of winter polar air caught the moist summer airmasses before the latter had started their annual withdrawal from the prairies and plains. This gave dwindling moisture reserves a needed boost in time for nesting in 1960.

THE IDEAL PRECIPITATION PATTERN for nesting waterfowl would call for heavy and general rain during late summer and fall. It will saturate soil to the point that a good frost seal develops when cold weather sets in. In spring, the winter snow melts and runs off the frozen ground into potholes. A backlog of moisture of this type makes for a highly successful nesting season.

This ideal pattern of precipitation, however, produces not only water. It also produces waterfowl problems. If fall rains interfere with normal wheat harvest, much grain remains in the field to be destroyed by migrant waterfowl. Furthermore, such precipitation often stems from violent frontal thunder squalls, that may produce vicious hailstorms, which are rough on ducks.

Unusually heavy snow or rain in April and May can interrupt nesting. If their first nests are lost, many ducks may try a second nesting. They seem to be almost clairvoyant in this regard. If the water in the potholes is abundant at the time and is likely to be maintained by midsummer rains, ducks will try again. Ducklings from late hatches help perpetuate the species, but second nestings are never so productive as good first-nesting attempts.

Given two or more wet summers in a row, late-season nesting may add materially to waterfowl abundance. Apparently the young produced one summer by late nesting—actually renesting—will not mature until the latter part of the following summer. For them, a late-season nesting is an enthusiastic first nesting, rather than a half-hearted second try. The young from this late hatch may become late-season breeders the following sumer. If so, late-season nesting will continue through subsequent summers as long as weather permits, and the breeding schedule of the mallard and other northern-nesting ducks will then temporarily resemble the leisurely (and advantageous) 6- to 9-month annual reproductive period of some southern-nesting waterfowl. But one dry summer can end this happy arrangement abruptly; if no late-hatched ducklings appear that season, there will be no late-maturing breeders the following year.

Occasionally the northern plains and prairies have too much water. If heavy rains continue, especially in spring, floods may occur. Areas most subject to general flooding, however, are valleys, glacial lake-beds, and other flatlands below the thousand-foot contour, where relatively few important nesting habitats exist. The most dependable waterfowl-producing regions of the prairies and plains are in the undulating and rolling pothole country at elevations greater than 1 thousand feet. Flooding there is seldom a serious problem to nesting waterfowl. Water is in such great demand in this semi arid region that it is welcome no matter when or how it arrives, or in what quantities. If it celebrates its coming by forcing ducks off their nests, some persistent mothers, encouraged by abundant water, will probably nest again that summer. Excess water that carries over into the following season will eventually produce nesting benefits that far outweigh any immediate damage.

MOST GEESE and some ducks nest in arctic or subarctic regions north of the limits of agriculture. Water deficiency is not the problem here that it is on the plains and prairies, although waterfowl that nest in the river deltas of the Far North sometimes are plagued by too much water. But an abundance of water does not make for a carefree life. At best, nesters in the Arctic trade problems of drought for problems of cold.

Those nesting grounds lie close to or within the strongholds of polar airmasses. Whether warm weather will arrive in time for geese and ducks to get an early nesting start in a notoriously short summer is always a problem. Whether it will stay warm until goslings and ducklings take wing and get out is still another problem. Adding to these whethers is permafrost, the permanently frozen subsoil, found generally in Arctic North America above the isotherm that denotes a 23° F. mean annual temperature. Any bird that nests on the ground in this region may find that its

Recording devices of many kinds are used by waterfowl biologists to determine what makes the marsh "tick." Here John M. Anderson notes water temperature changes in studies on vegetation at Winous Point Club in Ohio.

eggs are mere inches above permafrost, and insulated from it only by a thin layer of mosses, lichens, and down.

In spring, arctic regions are warmed by solar heat, warm airmasses, and in localities by northward flowing rivers. When warm airmasses dominate the Far North, skies are clear or partly cloudy. Direct sunlight can thus reach the ground. Some heat loss is due to radiation on cloudless nights, but that is compensated so long as the influx of warm air continues. When this combination prevails, snow cover quickly disappears, and the moss layer atop the permafrost thaws and dries. Once dry to a depth of 5 inches or more, this surface layer seals off ground chill. During such periods, weather in the Far North is balmy.

But restless polar airmasses always lurk ominously close. They may gather strength and push southward at intervals during the late winter. Then spring breakup is delayed so that waterfowl cannot start nesting until too late to be successful. At worst, they may not nest at all. At other times, the airmasses may recede northward on schedule and allow a false spring to develop, only to return with great violence after a season's nesting has already gotten off to a promising start. If waterfowl lose their first nests in the Far North, there is little time for a second try.

Deceptively mild but insidious weather may develop when polar air slowly drifts in from the north or northeast. Coming from a region of partly frozen arctic seas, cold rocks, and thawing ice and snow, this intruding air is cool and moist to the point of saturation. When it flows over a range of hills, it may produce dense clouds. Greater disturbance is apt to produce a solid overcast down to the treetops. Because of a general stagnation of circulation, such dark spring weather takes a long time to clear. There is no heating of an airmass during such periods, and there can be no solar heating of the ground as long as heavy overcast blocks out sunlight. The long, soaking drizzle that usually accompanies such weather wets surface mosses and peats and robs them of their insulative capacity, so that thawing permafrost will then contribute to the general chill. A 3- to 5-day spell of this raw weather seems to discourage all ground-nesting birds.

Fortunately, geese and many diving ducks that are traditional arctic nesters are relatively long-lived birds and do not need the high replacement demanded by the short-lived dabbling ducks. An occasional nesting failure therefore is less than critical, and the birds are seldom faced with two bad summers in a row.

It's PLAIN THAT WEATHER can be ideal for the day-to-day requirements of waterfowl, given a happy combination of atmospheric conditions. Yet for every favorable combination, many acutely unhappy combinations are equally possible. The whole subject of meteorology for ducks and geese seems to be an account of weather that can be salubrious but seldom is.

Climate and weather were not designed for the exclusive benefit of waterfowl; rather, waterfowl evolved in response to the opportunities and challenges presented by weather. Ducks and geese, by virtue of great reproductive capacity, are quick to take advantage of environmental opportunities. When bad weather

thwarts their nesting or otherwise disrupts their normal pattern of living, they show great resourcefulness in coping with adversity. For them, the inconvenience may be only temporary, the improvement lasting—as the road signs advise us when our highways are closed for renovations.

When high altitude Westerlies so decree, the annual surface battles between the gulf airstream and the polar airmasses take place not over the plains and prairies, but far to the east or southeast. Being thus denied the benefit of frontal rains, the prairie duck factory begins to go dry. As water reserves decline, waterfowl reproductive success also declines. Late-season nesting is usually the first to suffer. Eventually, early nesting is also curtailed. Predation may increase because of the concentration of carnivores and other waterfowl enemies around the dwindling water areas. Diseases, such as botulism, usually become more prevalent with low water.

THESE MOISTURE DEFICIENCIES eventually may attain the proportions of serious drought, and waterfowl production on the plains and prairies then comes almost to a halt. This apparent disaster to birds in the long run can be accompanied by a remarkable renovation of waterfowl habitats. In the aquatic environments of this cool climate, floating bog tends to develop. Any small pond that stays wet long enough may gradually lose its rich flora of submerged and emergent plants and its invertebrate fauna, and become covered by relatively lifeless muskeg. Drought rudely halts this process, thus preventing pintail and mallard ponds from degenerating into habitats for grebes, loons, and owls. Drying also allows aquatic plant residues and other organic accumulations to oxidize, thus increasing the fertility of pond bottoms.

Once a drying trend starts in the prairie habitat, some advantage may accrue if a real drought develops. Radical drying speeds soil oxidation, reduces many enemies and diseases of waterfowl, and may reverse the slow process of pond filling. It is remarkable that potholes of the plains and prairies have survived at all, especially since most of them are now surrounded by freshly plowed grainfields. Light prairie soils become airborne during dry weather and drift across the potholes. If the potholes are full of water or even merely moist, they become dust traps that catch the drift. But once they go completely dry, trapped soils may be blown out again by eddies and whorls of strong surface winds that usually accompany drought.

The process of renovation by severe weather can be seen in many environments used by waterfowl. In fact, it appears that the best wetlands for waterfowl are those so productive (of all living things as well as waterfowl) that they play out after a time. A rest, or fallow period, or vigorous cultivation and fertilization are necessary for such wetlands, even though the birds that frequent them suffer considerable hardship in the meantime. Thus occasional floods benefit the rich deltas of the Far North. High water may thwart one season's nesting, but without it the rich alluvial habitats of northern deltas may eventually become sterile bogs.

THE SAME DESTRUCTIVE PROCESS of renovation may be seen on the wintering grounds. Given favorable weather one growing season, these winter habitats will be blessed with ample foods when ducks and geese arrive in the fall. But Nature can be profligate, and sometimes excellent growing weather occurs several summers in a row. Then winter habitats, especially those of the Deep South

Waterfowl can have too much water! Canada goose nest on Malheur National Wildlife Refuge in Oregon, flooded out and abandoned.

where plant growth is lush, begin to deteriorate. Rank perennial vegetation tends to crowd out more desirable food plants and eventually encroaches upon and obliterates marsh ponds. Having brought on this ecological excess, weather then provides a purge for overgrown habitats.

The most heroic curative measures may be seen on the seacoasts. Ever so often ocean storms may sweep these coastal waterfowl habitats. The physical destruction and salt water flooding that accompany tropical hurricanes may be severe. But the ecologist sees the physical disturbance to these environments as a form of natural cultivation of wetlands, and the salt intrusion as an application of herbicide and fertilizer. Sea water, when it first invades these habitats, has such a high content of salt that it will kill much vegetation, including many plants that are undesirable for waterfowl. But it is also rich in nutrient elements vital to plant and animal growth. Once the salt concentration is diluted below toxic levels by rainwater, the nutrients hasten the recovery of the more desirable plants.

WEATHER also cultivates the marshes of inland regions that winter waterfowl. Heavy rains may bring floods that devastate (but at the same time clean out) the more static marshes that periodically need a vigorous flushing. Too little rain during a growing season allows some marshes to dry out, a development that may seem tragic at the time but ultimately can firm up pond bottoms, clear turbidity, remove undesirable plants and coarse fish, and vastly

improve habitats for waterfowl. If the rainfall deficit is only moderate in summer, wild millet and other annual plants may develop on exposed pond bottoms and produce a bonanza for seed-eating ducks. When drought is severe and long, marsh fires sweep through and open up vast tracts of rank vegetation and may even burn out new ponds in peaty marsh soils. Since the fires are often touched off by lightning during thunderstorms, weather can be credited with accumulating the fuel, laying the fire, and applying the match.

SO, THEN, WEATHER is seldom simply good or bad for waterfowl. It may bring them great opportunity, or incredible hardship. Either circumstance represents challenge to the resilient biotic potential of these remarkable birds, and is a stimulus to their environments. When weather is salubrious, most ducks and geese can parlay this opportunity into a gratifying abundance of their kind, yet their environments may become distressingly "overripe" if the period of prosperity is greatly prolonged. Inevitably the good times are followed by periods of adversity, when unfavorable weather will curtail nesting success and may in its more violent moments destroy adult birds. Yet this hardship for birds is often accompanied by renovation of their habitats, so today's inclement weather may signal greater opportunity for waterfowl tomorrow. It is an ill wind indeed that does not blow some good, for some duck, somewhere along the line.

—JOHN J. LYNCH.

SHOVELERS

Plants on Parade

A GREEN PARADE takes place each year in fields, woods, meadows, and marshes across the land. Plants put on the show silently, without trumpets, and without fanfare. The procession is ever changing. Its precise makeup varies from marsh to field and from woods to quiet lakeshore. Basically, though, the plant parade in each of these localities has the same beginning, changes in a similar way, and proceeds finally to a terminal status or climax.

It begins wherever a spot is newly flooded or is partly or completely denuded of vegetation—on bare granite, abandoned farmland, or cutover forest. First to appear are the plant pioneers. They are unassuming, rugged plants, requiring open sunlight and few other special conditions to survive. Among them are annual weeds, lichens, mosses, and simple water plants. This vanguard is followed in succeeding years by new waves of vegetation, each usually larger in growth form and more complex in requirements than the preceding.

The new participants in the parade modify the site by building soil, retaining moisture, creating shade, and slowly causing definite, subtle changes that escape discern-

293

ment by all but the plants themselves. As each stage of plant life develops, it sows the seeds of its own destruction until the final and most permanent stage is reached. By merely living, prevailing plants of developmental stages create conditions unfavorable to themselves but suitable for other groups to follow.

You can see this plant parade in an abandoned field. Here the pioneers are quick to appear on denuded ground once it is no longer cultivated. These are annual weeds—ragweed, creeping jenny, pigweed, and purslane, the common antagonists in your home garden. Undisturbed, they persist for a few years. Then they are replaced by perennial herbs and grasses. Brush eventually may enter the scene, then scrub trees, and finally, perhaps, forest. The stages remain for different lengths of time; in this case, occupancy and replacement take longer with each successive group.

The final act or stage—the climax vegetation—is similar over wide zones. We commonly recognize four major regions—tundra, desert, grassland, and forest. This ultimate type of plant life is determined by and large by climate, and a natural balance is established between climate and plants. The climax vegetation remains indefinitely, if undisturbed.

Tundra prevails in North America between the ice of the Arctic and the coniferous forests of Canada.

Deserts, which have a unique vegetation of bushes, shrubs, and trees especially adapted to tolerate hot, dry weather, are prominent in southwestern United States.

Expansive grasslands exist in the western prairies, where moisture is too limited for tree growth.

Forests cover large parts of North America. The particular types of trees in an area are influenced largely by soil characteristics and seasonal temperatures and moisture conditions.

Regardless of origin, whether bare rock, open water, or fertile mineral soil, all sites within each great climatic region are destined for similar climax vegetation. The time required to reach this final stage varies with the kind of site. And, as always with Nature, minor exceptions occur. Yet the pattern, the sequence, is so fixed as to be completely predictable. A knowing observer, anywhere in a great climatic region, will recognize the developmental stage of plant life where he stands. He can tell the stages that have gone before and predict those that are to follow.

BIOLOGISTS KNOW this plant parade as plant succession. It moves ever forward, if undisturbed, until the most efficient type of vegetation prevails. It is Nature's way of healing open sores of the land and bringing about uniform stands of vegetation. Working as a team over eons of time, natural erosion and plant succession slowly modify the earth's surface by eroding hills and filling depressions. In this way, growing conditions become similar within climatic regions, and the vegetation is simplified.

But even before the white man came, this uniformity of plant life within climatic regions never was achieved. Why? One answer lies in the varying rates of succession. Plant

*On Delta Natonal Wildlife Refuge in Louisiana the spikes of common threesquare contain
seeds which ducks like.   Rootstocks of this plant are relished by geese.*

development obviously cannot proceed as rapidly on bare rock or in
open water as on finely ground
mineral deposits. More important:
Fire, flood, drought, wind, activities
of animals, and other natural disturbances interrupt, halt, or set back
the successional parade. To these
natural forces man has added plow,
axe, livestock, and chemical sprayer.

The degree of interruption of successional progress depends on the
severity of the disturbance. A pine
forest leveled by a tornado may be
replaced by aspen, a stage one or
two steps removed from the climax.
But a hot fire in a wooded dune may
be followed only by pioneer weeds

able to cope with the altered environment. They begin anew the
long and orderly parade back to the
tree stage. Before the scorched site is
again wooded, many years will go by
and many plants will appear, but
only in passing. For each, in turn, is
destined to be replaced by new
troops in the parade.

All animal life ultimately depends
on plants for food and shelter. So
succession's passing parade is one of
animals, too. Geologically speaking,
succession can mean that yesterday's
lake is today's pond or marsh, tomorrow's sedge meadow, and a forest
of the day after. Uninterrupted, undisturbed, the parade of plants can

bring deer trails—or the plow—where canvasbacks once swam.

The realm of waterfowl extends from coast to coast and from the Arctic to the Tropics. Over two continents are many millions of ponds, potholes, rivers, lakes, bays, and sloughs. Some contribute substantially to the food and cover needs of waterfowl. Others are unproductive and are used mainly for shelter and rest. But whatever their present status, change can be expected—given enough time. Some aquatic areas will become more favorable to waterfowl, others less. Each wetland site is a living, dynamic entity—never static, always changing. This is the will of Nature. This is the great natural force with which biologists must contend, working sometimes with it, sometimes against it, to better the lot of waterfowl.

The potential of plant succession in influencing food and cover conditions for waterfowl is tremendous. Where penetration of sunlight is adequate, submerged plants are the first to colonize open water. Seeds or plant fragments are often brought in on the feet, bills, feathers, or in droppings of waterfowl. Typical aquatic stages that eventually follow each other can be seen in capsule form around many ponds. In the center there is open water. Extending outwards to the periphery are the aquatics: First an area of submerged plants, then floating-leaved, and finally emergent. The pond margin includes sedges and grasses; depending on climate, higher ground may have a zone of shrubs and trees.

By encouraging the deposition of waterborne and windborne sediments, to which they add their own remains, each stage of aquatics contributes to the filling of depressions. Through these means, water plants encourage their own replacement. As water depth is reduced, the innermost of the concentric zones of vegetation is succeeded in time by more outward bordering plants. Dryland vegetation eventually occupies the site. This may occur in decades or centuries, or it may require eons. Nature is the judge of time.

Of the zones of aquatic vegetation, emergents are the vital ones for waterfowl. Their patterns largely determine the degree to which waterfowl will use fertile breeding ponds and marshes. Clumps of emergents well interspersed with open water offer excellent nesting cover for overwater nesters, such as redheads, ruddy ducks, canvasbacks, and coots. Such habitat also serves as fine escape cover for many species of waterfowl. In contrast, shorelines supporting dense stands of emergents, such as cattail, exclude open edges preferred by ducks for loafing and shallow-water feeding.

In the absence of disturbance, Nature's drive is to encourage development of these compact stands of emergents. Their presence signifies that waterfowl habitat has reached old age. Waterfowl managers seek to interrupt the formation of this normal successional stage. Their aim is to maintain interspersion of emergents, open water, and preferred plants attractive to waterfowl. Interrupting and retarding plant succession are means to waterfowl management.

But Nature works in devious ways,

and what one hand gives the other takes away. And so it is that natural forces are constantly bucking successional trends in millions of aquatic areas. Factors working toward this good end include fire, fluctuating water levels, hurricanes, and ice action. Varied patterns of aquatic and marsh plants are produced by these disturbances. Sometimes changes are abrupt. Sometimes they are so gradual as to be scarcely noticeable. But whatever the speed of accomplishment, these natural forces and others of lesser importance cause a periodic rejuvenation of waterfowl habitat. If this were not so, many of our best aquatic habitats, and waterfowl with them, would have yielded long since to the plant parade. In their place would stand cornfields and cottontails or woodlands and whitetails.

SEASONAL FLUCTUATIONS of water levels have a marked influence on the succession of aquatic plants, sometimes to the benefit and at other times to the detriment of waterfowl. Spectacular vegetative changes commonly occur in the landlocked prairie potholes, the best duck-producing areas in North America. The changes in plant life result from fluctuations in water levels that range from complete drying of the basins in drought years to flooding in years of high precipitation. Populations of prairie-nesting waterfowl fluctuate widely in response to the changes.

Water levels normally recede in many potholes during June, July, and August, when losses of water from evaporation, transpiration, and seepage exceed gains from rain and runoff. In places where moisture and salt conditions are favorable, exposed bottom soils are taken over by annual, moist-soil plants that produce heavy crops of seeds. Vegetative reproduction of aggressive emergents, such as cattails and bulrushes, is retarded, but germination of their seeds is enhanced where soil moisture and salts are favorable and competition from other plants is not excessive. A patchwork of developing emergents often results. Fruiting of submerged aquatics is stimulated in remaining pools by the gradual recession of water levels.

When water levels remain higher than normal during the growing season, established moist-soil plants are lost, and new growths are prevented from developing. Submerged aquatics thrive in deep zones where penetration of sunlight is adequate, but seed production usually is curtailed. Some or all of the emergent aquatics break loose from the bottom, float, and often collect in clumps on the shore. This breaking up of uniform stands of emergents frequently encourages a desirable patchwork of cover plants. Such interspersion of open water and emergent vegetation temporarily provides excellent food, cover, and water conditions for waterfowl.

If, however, high water continues for several growing seasons, emergent aquatics may disintegrate. Then the pothole can become a body of open water of little or no value for breeding waterfowl. Open water more than 18 to 24 inches deep is used primarily for resting by waterfowl and secondarily for feeding by diving ducks.

The other extreme occurs when most of the shallow basins in the

Hardstem bulrush provides both food and cover for waterfowl.   New growth produces choice food and old growth forms mats which are used as nesting sites.

prairie become completely dry during drought years. Aquatic plants become sparse and disappear completely if the dry period is prolonged. Then large numbers of plants unimportant to waterfowl invade the dry soils where natural salts are not excessive. Their occupancy is brief—until water again fills the depressions.

Alternating water levels affect pothole basins as well as plant development. Exposure of the moist bottom to air accelerates decay. Organic matter is consumed faster than it is produced. Simultaneously, chemical nutrients are converted to forms available for plant growth. Fertility of potholes is sustained by these processes. In exposed salt-encrusted basins devoid of vegetation, wind may remove dry salts and soils and help maintain basin depth. By these means, filling of potholes is delayed and sometimes may be prevented indefinitely. Likewise, the clock of plant succession is reset.

While periodic droughts temporarily eliminate duck production over the prairies, they contribute to the lifespan of the depressions by reducing the rate at which organic matter accumulates and fills the basins. Whether viewed from the short-term beneficial effects on vegetation or the long-term favorable effects on the depressions, periodic droughts of short duration are beneficial. They maintain over eons of time aquatic vegetation in potholes in a form attractive for breeding waterfowl.

This sequence of natural events has been altered in many grassland areas thru cultivation. Before the prairie sod was broken for cultivation, more than 100 years ago, prairie grasses held upland soils in place, and windborne and waterborne silt accumulated slowly in potholes. Now, soils exposed by intensive cultivation and highway construction are eroded by wind and water and often accumulate in pothole basins. The result is not reversible, since no natural means exist for removing the layers of accumulated silt. Upland soils can best be kept where they lie by maintaining a vegetative cover on the land. By so limiting upland erosion, the lifespan of the millions of natural pothole basins can be prolonged.

HURRICANES on coastal wintering grounds are a major force in reversing plant succession. An example occurred in late June of 1957 when hurricane Audrey placed 9 feet of water over southwestern Louisiana marshes choked with emergent plants of little value to waterfowl. Much of the vegetation floated and was redistributed over a broad area by violent winds. With return of normal water levels, lush stands of moist-soil plants developed on the scoured and exposed soils. Submerged waterfowl food plants subsequently thrived in shallow depressions that held surface water of proper salt concentration.

In killing out advanced stages of vegetation, the hurricane permitted a spectacular growth of seed-yielding pioneer plants, such as millets and smartweeds. Water levels, at the time waterfowl are present, determine the availability of these choice seeds. In most winters since this major renovation of Louisiana marshes, rainfall has been sufficient to provide full availability of the abundant food supply. Waterfowl, as if drawn by a magnet, have flocked to this bounty from far and wide. The result has been a sweeping redistribution of wintering waterfowl. How long the lush coastal marshes will remain so attractive is hard to say. Winter populations in 1963–64 continued at a high level. In time, choked stands of emergents will again develop to limit food production and discourage use by waterfowl. The time is uncertain; the final result is not. It's that way with the parade of plants.

ICE ACTION alters numerous shallow lakes and marshes in forested regions between prairie breeding grounds and coastal wintering areas. Basins equipped with active inlets and outlets, or only outlets, are affected most. Where ice forms to the basin floor, masses of plants and bottom soils may be uplifted, resulting in a dramatic setback of plant succession. Jacking action of ice, caused by alternate expansion and contraction, can be as effective as a bulldozer in clearing plants from shores. Losses of emergent vegetation in interior parts of a basin can occur in a few years, even though the water level remains relatively constant during succeeding growing seasons. Such changes may appear baffling until close inspection reveals the cause.

When spring runoff floods the basin, the buoyancy of submerged ice and air spaces in leaves and stems of emergent plants is enough to uproot blocks of marsh. Winds and waves pound these large floating blocks, splitting small chunks off the edges. These clumps often float down the outlet stream or become lodged in spots where such plants never grew before.

Following disruption of marsh vegetation in spring, the water level returns to the established outlet level in summer. According to the outlet reading, the water level is the same as that of former years. But for plants in the basin, the distance from water surface to submerged soil is considerably deeper in places where vegetation and soil were uplifted and floated away. The greater depth fosters open water or floating-leaved aquatics, such as waterlilies, where emergents had formerly grown. Succession has reverted to earlier stages.

CONSTANT WATER LEVEL during the growing season slows advancement of plant succession in open water to a snail's pace. Peat and muck soils are often unstable and finely divided and provide a poor base for underwater plants. Without exposure to air, nutrients remain bound in bottom soils in a form largely unusable by pioneering plants. Unless there is a gradual lowering of the water level by changes at the outlet or a slow upbuilding of the basin bottom by sediments, water depth delays succession for long periods.

This creeping advance of plant life is in progress at deeper lakes throughout North America. Shallow shorelines, bays, and coves, especially those sheltered from winds and waves, may be in any of the more advanced successional stages, except climax forest. But lake basins are still in the open water stage more than 10 thousand years after glaciers formed the depressions. Though constantly heading towards the climax, Nature rarely, if ever, has reached it on deepwater lakes.

THE ABUNDANCE AND VARIETY of waterfowl differ widely on aquatic habitats in the broad North American vegetative regions of grasslands and forests. Over a 10-year period, including years of no production when depressions are dry, prairie potholes will average 3 to 7 ducklings an acre. A duckling to the acre on ponds in forested regions is about all that can be expected, except during the first few favorable years on new impoundments.

Freshly flooded ground and newly disturbed land attract and support a large variety and abundance of wildlife. The animals respond to the release of stored fertility and the lush crops of pioneering plants. These first-year plants include many of top food value. This phenomenon explains why fish do best during the first few years after ponds and reservoirs are flooded, why pheasants are found regularly around fallow fields and truck gardens, and why duck production on new woodland impoundments with constant water levels may approach that of prairie ponds for the first 2 to 4 years.

The type and quality of food produced on impoundments depend largely on basin development and plant succession. Extremes in successional stages are obvious in northern watersheds covered with evergreen trees. Both initial and advanced stages of basin development now prevail.

Where the glacier cleaned out soils and left lake basins of rock, as in much of Ontario, aquatics still grow sparsely. A hundred centuries have been too short a time for succession to advance very far. Emergents are restricted largely to small, isolated, sparse stands on limited silt beds deposited at the mouths of inflowing streams. At this continuing early stage of development of lake basins, food and cover

A vigorous stand of softstem bulrush on Hutton Lake National Wildlife Refuge, Wyoming. This photograph was taken the second year after impoundment. The plant is important to waterfowl.

are scarce. Most waterfowl seek more favorable habitat. Rock lakes are useful mainly to fish-eating ducks.

The conversion of bare rock to soil involves a process measured not in decades but in centuries. And, so, after a few more thousands of years, additional parts of certain existing rocky lakes will be converted to marshes. Conversion will be fastest where streams bring in rich silt from distant sources. Delta soils and nutrients yield top-quality waterfowl plants. Then, in a few eons, these habitats will support more waterfowl than the relatively few using such water now. But rocky lakes, except for those few with fertile deltas, will never become major centers of waterfowl abundance. Broken-down granite rock is poor in nutrients needed for plant growth. Though the date is distant, most existing, youthful rock lakes will form bog lakes at maturity.

BOG LAKES in advanced aquatic successional stages are common in glaciated areas and forecast characteristics that youthful rock lakes will ultimately possess. They differ in many respects from other freshwater lakes. Their acid and stained waters restrict penetration of life-generating sunlight. Soils are soft, mucky, and poor in nutrients needed by plants. This poor environment permits only scanty crops of aquatic plants and small creatures of value to waterfowl.

Even the limited food in a bog lake is made largely unavailable to most wildfowl by other plant growth. A sedge, *Carex lasiocarpa*, often forms a floating mat, ever striving to advance toward the center of the lake. This mat eliminates shallow waters preferred by waterfowl for resting and required by dabbling ducks for feeding. Only divers, such as the ring-necked duck, can utilize the limited foods.

As is true of all wetland sites, dry land will eventually prevail as the amphibious sedge eliminates open water. Many stands of tamarack and black spruce are found in bog depressions that formerly contained open water, sparse crops of aquatic foods, and meager seasonal waterfowl populations.

SOME MAMMALS are manipulators of plant succession. The beaver especially makes a noteworthy contribution to waterfowl by constructing suitable impoundments on small woodland streams. Accomplishment of an individual may involve a small acreage, but the combined area over the country includes hundreds of thousands of acres. As natural processes go, the beaver is a fast worker and converts flowing water to waterfowl habitat in weeks, months, or a few years. Its temporary wooden dams flood small basins, permitting aquatic plants to thrive on nutrients previously prepared for them by the air. These fertile pools, in otherwise poor duck habitat, become well known to ducks and hunters.

Water levels in beaver impoundments are held constant for some time by well-maintained dams. Attractiveness for waterfowl declines as woody vegetation deteriorates under continuous submergence

Ten years is generally considered a useful lifespan of a beaver impoundment. Without exposure of bottom soils, most emergents fail to germinate and replace the decomposing woody cover. Replacement depends on a few emergents, such as burreed and pickerelweed, which can develop under water, and others that may spread vegetatively from stands present before flooding. But even plants capable of becoming established may fail to do so. Sometimes they are eaten by beavers before they have a chance to spread.

Replenishment of waterfowl food and cover in beaver ponds depends on new floodings, not rejuvenation of old impoundments. Beaver are forced to move to new locations as they cut preferred food trees faster than they are replaced by growth. Movements occur when the distance to desired trees becomes too great. Following abandonment of the site, the old dam begins to disintegrate and the water level soon falls. A new dam is constructed at another suitable basin. The result is a natural successional cycle favorable to waterfowl in forested regions.

THE WATERFOWL MANAGER applies his knowledge of plant succession and seasonal needs of waterfowl to guide land acquisition and to develop habitat on managed areas. Waterfowl are a product of early successional stages of aquatic vegetation and a proper interspersion of open water, aquatic plants, and emergents. These conditions may be brought about or maintained by accelerating or retarding plant succession.

This management by design yields the same types of habitat produced naturally through actions of water, drought, wind, ice, beaver, muskrat, and nutria. But the manager's ultimate goal is to maintain good habitat conditions for a longer time than normally occurs. This is the basis and objective of modern waterfowl management.

Major land acquisition programs aimed at maintaining duck production are concentrated in the grassland region. Here, depressions protected from draining and filling yield large dividends of ducklings. For the most part, managers merely preserve the natural basins and let Nature manage the aquatic vegetation. The natural water cycle perpetuates desirable types and patterns of plants without costly expenditures for development and maintenance. This has been the natural course of events since the shallow pothole depressions were spawned by glaciers.

In forested regions, Nature is a determined adversary, working to destroy what managers hope to gain. She changes deep waters very little, and they continue to lack ducklings. We would like to see it otherwise. The beaver teaches a lesson with his temporary shallow impoundments, and the beneficial effects of drawdowns are evident in other natural situations.

Managers of waterfowl attempt to improve on Nature's unscheduled drawdowns of varying duration. During a drought in the prairies, such a natural drawdown may last one, five, or more years. In forests, decades may be required for regrowth of popple to feed again a colony of beavers that would reconstruct the dam and reflood the waterfowl impoundment. But where water levels can be controlled and water supplies are adequate, a scheduled removal of surface waters in grassland or forest regions can produce a favorable environment for waterfowl plants in one or two growing seasons. By this means, managers maintain desirable conditions on wetland areas during most years.

This planned drawdown principle dictates that lands acquired for waterfowl have shallow basins and a dependable seasonal water supply. Only then can water levels be changed according to design. Completely landlocked depressions in woodlands, particularly the northern evergreen forest, are least attractive to waterfowl. Substantial investments in such areas offer disappointing dividends of seasonal use by ducks.

With increasing economic pressures and technological developments, people have converted waterfowl habitat to other uses. The loss by dragline has outstripped many thousandfold Nature's leisurely conversion of open water to marsh and high ground. The North-Central States are dotted with thousands of former waterfowl nurseries that now yield mint, corn, grain and truck crops. Presence of peat and muck soils betray their identity and location. By converting marshes to cropland, farmers capitalize on nutrients laid down by aquatic plants through a hundred centuries of history. Pheasant hunters now tramp crop fields in fall where waterfowl hunters formerly slogged or paddled.

Waterfowl managers and the interested public are attempting to insure the future of waterfowl by establishing special management areas. The possibilities are good on such units for accommodating more waterfowl on fewer acres through intensive developments.

How to manage vegetation for the best possible waterfowl use is one of the principal subjects of this book. For some situations we do not know the easiest or cheapest means to achieve what waterfowl require and we desire. But by understanding principles of plant succession, we know—for all situations—where we have been, where we are, and where we are headed. We also know what waterfowl need for a healthful and productive life. Bringing together this knowledge of what succession can offer and what waterfowl need helps to insure a continuing parade of waterfowl by working with the passing parade of plants.—LAURENCE R. JAHN and JOHN B. MOYLE

FULVOUS TREE DUCKS

Adventuresome Waterfowl

WHY, YOU ASK, do water-fowl fly thousands of miles each spring to the same northern breeding grounds and then, year after year, as millions of their kind have done, fly southward in fall to winter at the same marshes? Is it instinct, or habit, or the effect of an unknown mechanism in their brains, or (as we prefer to call it) merely tradition? Whatever it is, most birds during migrations follow ancestral flight lines with predictable regularity. They make the same stopovers, nest on the same breeding areas, and winter at the same marshes. Their flight patterns are distinct, and one would no more look for a black duck in California than he would a cinnamon teal on Long Island.

Yet tradition in birds, as in people, sometimes wavers. So, nonconformist pintails now breed in the Canadian Atlantic Provinces, where, as far as we know, they never nested before. Determined black ducks press westward into mallard range, and mallards are invading the domain of the eastern black duck. Canada geese have established nesting colonies in many places where they have

305

not bred for scores of years, if ever. Such originality in a few may well lead to new prosperity for many. The wayward tendency may offer managers of wildfowl a means to help build their numbers.

We use the term "migrational homing" for the tendency of birds to return to the same wintering grounds and nesting marshes. The annual return of the swallows to Capistrano is a well-known example. The tendency is strong in ducks. A female shoveler banded in. the Delta marshes in Manitoba returned to nest in the same meadow for 4 consecutive years. Wood ducks often return to their same old nesting boxes. A ring-necked duck in Maine used the same site for 4 years, each year building the new nest exactly on top of the previous one. Goldie, an albino gadwall hen whose name got in the newspapers, returned to nest in the same place at the Lower Souris Refuge in North Dakota each year between 1947 and 1953.

Homing by waterfowl operates primarily through the females. Even young hens that have never nested tend to return to the place where they were reared. Drakes, old or young, may be guided by the hens, wherever they go.

In this way biological traditions become established. Few are inherited. Some are acquired by young birds through experience. Many are passed from one generation to the next through the association of young birds with the veterans.

An example is the migration of the greater snow geese. They nest in many places in the eastern Arctic.

Their winter range is the Atlantic coast, largely Delaware to North Carolina. Yet, during fall passage, nearly all of them gradually gather and remain for several weeks at a single concentration point on the St. Lawrence River near the city of Quebec. They have done so for many years. It is not instinct that brings them to the tidal flats of Cap Tourmente and Isle aux Grus. It is habit, and group response and tradition that old birds pass on to the young.

But traditions are constantly being broken. New ones are established When prairie potholes dry up or are drained, few birds can nest. They may not nest for a year or so. Failure to breed is not part of Nature's plan, however, and sooner or later many of them will attempt to nest elsewhere.

NATURE WORKS FOR THE SURVIVAL of species in another way—through a wanderlust or adventuresome tendency we call pioneering. We see the trait in many kinds of wildlife. Even stay-at-home species sometimes travel far to seek new homesites Such ducks as the mallard, pintail blue-winged teal, and gadwall are strongly inclined to look for new and distant habitats.

Large-scale pioneering and accidental wandering are not the same Examples of wanderers are two pair of redheads that nested on the St John River of New Brunswick in 1944; an occasional pair of shoveler that also nest in New Brunswick; a pair of canvasbacks that bred in New York; a redhead found nesting in the Lake Erie marshes of Ohio and a shoveler discovered in Vermont. Ornithologists call such wanderings extra-limital breeding records. They may occur almost anywhere and usually are of slight significance in waterfowl management. Occasionally, however, these isolated wanderings may lead to new colonies.

Dabbling ducks, such as the mallard and blue-winged teal, among others, show a remarkable ability to adapt themselves to civilization. Even in the midst of large cities they nest and rear their young on remnant marshes, catch basins, water supply reservoirs, and lakes in city parks. They often choose unusual nesting sites—the foundation shrubbery of some lakeside dwelling, a clump of vegetation at the base of a powerline pole, the top of dock piling, or even a rose garden of a city park. But human disturbances, predation, and other hazards are severe for these fowl.

In the fall and winter large concentrations of ducks and geese often occur in water areas in or near towns and cities. It is surprising how soon they become tame and accept handouts from visitors. But when the breeding urge and desire to move northward again stir their wild instincts, natural wariness returns. Such adaptability, however, provides excellent opportunities for bird watching enthusiasts and hunters alike to observe many kinds of waterfowl at close range.

POPULATION CHANGES on a large scale have occurred oftener among mallards than any other ducks. Mallards have been extending their range eastward and each year we find more of these birds nesting within the Atlantic Flyway. Apparently it is a slow pioneering away from places of dense concentration, but it is also possible that the eastward extension of their range may be partly due to releases of mallards from game farms.

THE RING-NECKED DUCK is an example of pioneering on a major scale. Once ring-necks were birds of the West and Midwest. A sizable number of them invaded the Northeast in the thirties. It was not a gradual pioneering from existing centers; rather, breeding ring-necks leap-frogged from western Ontario and the Lake States into Maine and New Brunswick. From that nucleus, new colonies fanned out and then moved westward to fill in the gap. Ring-necks have become important to hunters and bird watchers in many parts of the Northeast.

The fulvous tree ducks wander widely, although they may not be true pioneers. They breed primarily in Mexico, southern California, Louisiana, and Texas. They were accidental visitors for many years on the lower Atlantic coast as far north as North Carolina. They began to appear as fall wanderers in the fifties in Maryland, New Jersey, and New York. A flock of 21 was identified on Grand Manan Island off the New Brunswick coast in 1961; 5 were shot near Fredericton, New Brunswick, that year. Eight tree ducks were taken in the Lake Erie marshes of Ohio and 3 near Monroe, Mich., in 1962. In Maine's Merrymeeting Bay 4 were shot in 1963.

The gadwall, a western bird, likes to form colonies far from its main range, as in New York, Virginia, Ontario, North Carolina, and Maryland. Most of the new groups are small and may be temporary. A colony at Pea Island in North Carolina, however, has grown steadily. The gadwall, like the mallard, is a strong pioneer within its normal range and is quick to occupy newly created habitat. Two other ducks, the blue-winged teal and the pintail, have similar traits. The shoveler and wood duck also have a slightly less strong spirit of adventure, but to a lesser degree.

HOW CAN A BIRD have a strong affinity for its ancestral range and at the same time have a wanderlust that leads it away from home and into the new and the strange? Maybe it is because of changes in habitat. We believe the homing instinct holds sway when conditions are favorable. When marshes are destroyed or deteriorate, birds are impelled to seek new homes and establish new populations. Adversity seems to foster restlessness and yearnings for a better life among all living creatures.

Unfortunately for their own welfare, some species do not show such wandering tendencies. Diving fowl (the ring-necked duck and ruddy duck are exceptions) are reluctant pioneers and have strict requirements as to habitat. Very likely that partly explains the marked reduction in populations of canvasback and redhead that follows droughts in prairie nesting habitat.

New impoundments and changes in the use of land often mean major displacements of waterfowl. An example is Horseshoe Lake Refuge in Illinois. A water impoundment for a rest area, protection from hunting, and plenty of food on nearby farmland made a cordial invitation to Canada geese to stop there. The fall concentration rose from about 1 thousand geese in 1937 to more than 200 thousand in 1962.

Large impoundments on the Missouri River have changed the fall migration and distribution of ducks in North Dakota and South Dakota. Before the Fort Randall Reservoir in South Dakota was filled in 1954, the number of wintering mallards seldom exceeded 50 thousand birds. More than a million were present in January 1958. Mallards also adapt themselves readily to small, newly created waterways. They have taken up residence almost immediately in manmade potholes and small impoundments, like those on the Lower Souris Refuge in North Dakota. Wildfowl moved in at once when a large dam created Luther Marsh of 4,500 acres, at the headwaters of the Grand River in southeastern Ontario. Within 10 years, 700 pairs of 11 species of ducks were nesting there.

THE REDISTRIBUTION OF MIGRANTS brings problems. As wetlands disappear, Federal and State refuges are called on more and more to preserve habitat and thus to influence the movement of birds. Many refuges in the United States have become hostels for Canada geese (especially during the hunting season) and for snow and blue geese. Land at the refuges must therefore be managed intensively to provide food, and nearby hunting must be regulated carefully.

That some species are changing their preferences for habitat and food has a direct bearing on management. We used to think, for example, that Canada geese sought only the open spaces and shunned small marshes and fields surrounded by timber, and we made an effort to clear timber from Federal and State goose-management facilities. Canadas may prefer the open for safety, but major concentrations in wooded districts in Pennsylvania, Maryland, Wisconsin, Michigan, Illinois, and Missouri seem to evidence the opposite. At the Horicon Refuge in Wisconsin, geese feed in oak groves. At Crab Orchard, Horse-shoe Lake, and Union County refuges in Illinois they use timber-fringed pools.

As to changes in diets: Canada geese did not feed on corn at the latitude of Sand Lake National Wildlife Refuge in South Dakota in 1947. Yet, when corn became more common there, geese began to eat it. The larger forms of Canada geese have learned to eat corn off the cob in unharvested stands. Whistling swans have begun to feed on field corn left in the spring at the Shiawassee National Wildlife Refuge in Michigan. Wood ducks, widgeons, black ducks, pintails, and green-winged teal in the Mississippi and Atlantic Flyways feed in grain stubble and picked cornfields much more than formerly.

Changes in feeding habits may be

Canada geese readily accept manmade structures as nesting sites.

thought of as learned responses—that is, birds follow the example of adventuresome individuals of their species. We can expect more changes as other acceptable foods become plentiful.

IT IS EVIDENT, then, that waterfowl are slaves to some habits and loyal to some traditions. But always there are exceptions—individuals that do otherwise and so establish a pattern. Evolution depends on variations of all kinds to insure the survival of species.

So, game managers ask: Can we encourage or force waterfowl to adapt to situations of our choice and thus produce more ducks and geese? We have tried to do so.

One starting point was to introduce game-farm birds into the wild in the hope they would establish themselves and multiply. In such efforts, failures have outnumbered successes. The use of ducks from game farms for stocking may result in poor-flying, semi-tame birds, of low sporting quality and low survival. It seems better to use wild or semi-wild birds for stocking.

Another way is to use half-grown birds, which are trapped where they abound and released (transplanted) in the locality where a new colony is desired. This technique and the others are based on the tendency of females to return to the site of their rearing and first fall flight—not to the place where they were hatched.

Game management officials in Wisconsin, Ohio, Pennsylvania, New York, and other States have conducted stocking programs. Most of them kept and later released mallards, but occasionally other species, notably the redhead, were also used. Many geese also have been reared and released in Pennsylvania. Workers in Wisconsin concluded that such a program was not economically sound. Those in New York concluded that stocking is biologically feasible if hunters are willing to give up local shooting near the release points for several years until the new colony becomes large enough to be harvested, and if the public will accept the high cost of the new birds.

THE ADAPTABLE MALLARD is a logical choice for introduction into new breeding areas, but wood ducks, blue-winged teal, gadwalls, pintails, and possibly others may be promising. As for diving ducks, establishment of new colonies by the transplant method may prove to be at least partly successful for the ring-necked duck and the redhead.

Although geese are not strong pioneers, they are flexible in their habits and build new traditions readily. Their firm attachments to family groups and to their breeding areas work in favor of purposeful establishment of new populations. Young geese, preferably those which have never completed a migration cycle, are live-trapped and taken to the site of release. There they are wing-clipped and kept in large outdoor enclosures until the spring or summer before they reach nesting age, which usually is the third year. They are then allowed to grow flight feathers and migrate. Because of a strong attachment to the foster marsh, some usually return to nest the following spring. A new breeding population thus may be formed if proper habitat and protection are provided.

MANY State and Federal refuges now have breeding populations of Canada geese where none existed for scores of years, if ever. Some of the flocks have reached sizable proportion, as in Montana, Utah, California, Michigan, Ohio, Wisconsin, Minnesota, North Dakota, and South Dakota. Even in the Atlantic Flyway, where opportunities for goose management are limited, small breeding colonies have been established in Maine, Vermont, Massachusetts, Pennsylvania, Maryland, Virginia, New Jersey and New York.

DURING MAN'S BRIEF OCCUPANCY of the land, major alterations have occurred. If waterfowl had not adjusted themselves to these changes, some would have passed from the scene. Species that are too specialized may not fare well in times ahead; others already have adapted themselves to new circumstances, mainly in migration and on the wintering grounds. So it is that we have witnessed changes from wildrice to corn, from smartweed to barley, from quiet marsh to hustling farmland, from peaceful slough to massive reservoirs.

We still have much to learn about ducks and geese. Their behavior during migration is one thing; the problems that drought, draining of land, and such have brought to the places they breed is another. Behind all this is a paradox: The strong urge a hen has to fly thousands of miles to nest repeatedly on the precise site of other years, and the pioneering urge that prompts individuals to seek new quarters far removed from others of their kind.

As we learn more about the requirements of waterfowl, we may find ways to duplicate these needs in areas away from the present range. We may find, too, that we have not yet fully utilized the inherent flexibility of some species.
—HOWARD L. MENDALL and HARVEY K. NELSON.

MUSKRAT
CINNAMON TEAL

Fur and Feathers

NO DUCK, goose, swan, or coot lives entirely apart from furred and other feathered inhabitants of ponds, lakes, and streams. It is the natural situation in waterfowl environments.

Muskrats, the commonest furred associates, flourish in every State and Province. There are also minks, raccoons, and river otters. Beavers and beaver ponds, from the Arctic to the Gulf of Mexico, are a part of the waterfowl scene. Nutrias, large rodents of South American origin, are infiltrating duck and goose wintering grounds along the Louisiana and Texas coasts, and have shown up in a dozen other States. Skunks, foxes, and weasels invade waterfowl breeding, feeding, and hunting grounds. Coyotes and bobcats work around the wetlands. Blackbirds and crows sieve through grain crops, or compete with ducks for water bugs, crawdads, and fairy shrimp. Simultaneous occupation of wetlands by furred and feathered faunas lends both aid and attrition to the birds. The current era of low raw fur prices, one reason for increased fur animal populations in recent years, can abet both situations.

MUSKRATS AND DUCKS are inseparable on most waterfowl range. The 'rats are scarce in pothole habitat, particularly during dry periods, and

313

*Muskrats are valuable fur products of the marsh. Their feeding and house-building
activities generally improve marshes for waterfowl.*

are rare or absent on the tundra.
They eat cattails, bulrushes, and
almost any other aquatic vegetation. Redheads, cans, and Canada
geese also feed on various aquatic
plants, and find cattails and bulrushes, at proper water depth, high-

quality nesting cover. Emergent
vegetation is also important nesting
cover for mallards, pintails, teals,
and other dabbling species. Peak
populations of muskrats simply eat
up the food plants of coastal wintering grounds—"eat outs" on the

Louisiana marshes. The same occurs in some degree in Oregon, Minnesota, and along the New Jersey coast. In short, muskrats and ducks live in the same "house" and share the same "dining room."

On the other hand, where emergent vegetation is too dense for good feeding grounds or nesting cover, or has attained an undesirable composition—too much cattail, for example—increasing 'rat numbers thin it out and so improve both the ratio of cover to water and the species combination. The muskrat trapper thus becomes a regulatory agent, but his catch each year must be guided by the marsh ecologist, who knows the habitat requirements of waterfowl, fur animals, and aquatic plants.

Muskrats in proper numbers benefit waterfowl. Geese nest atop old muskrat houses, grateful, it seems, for even the one-foot elevation above water level that permits a better visual patrol of the nesting area. Teals, mallards, and coots find these mounds of rotting vegetation good resting and brooding places all spring and summer. The cleaned-out areas around old 'rat houses produce much duck food both plant and animal.

Minks in the same waterfowl-muskrat marsh are a third dimension. They tend to keep the 'rats in check, thus serving, to a degree, the role of the trapper. Their valuable skins attract trappers and mink traps take ducks as well as minks and muskrats. In Maine, the loss was found to be heaviest in the spring, when about one duck for each 15 'rats was caught. About

half of the trapped ducks had drowned by the time they were found. Trappers released the others alive, most of them with an amputated foot or leg. Projected figures indicated that 2 thousand or so breeding ducks were lost or severely injured annually in Maine alone. Black ducks made up nearly half of the loss; wood ducks, green-winged teal, and pintails followed in order.

Muskrats, because of their burrowing habits, make for other waterfowl ills. Levees, weakened, sometimes break and spill the ducks' water; and ditchbanks, undermined, cave in, retarding water flow and raising maintenance costs.

THE NUTRIA, OR COYPU, is like an oversized muskrat in looks, habits, and habitat requirements. Strictly herbivorous, nutrias eat a wider variety of plants than do the smaller muskrats. Bulrushes, cattails, saw grass, and floating or submerged aquatics are staples in the nutria diet, but they also like to feed in croplands and forest plantations bordering inhabited marsh.

But feeding habits of nutria are different from those of muskrats. Nutria eat *off* emergent vegetation; 'rats eat *out* the roots and all. Nutria may improve quickly an over-grown marsh for ducks; 'rats, in uncontrolled numbers, slowly destroy marsh vegetation. Population control is the key to making either species work for the ducks.

Where the terrain permits, nutrias construct bank burrows, all bigger and more prone to cave-ins than muskrat tunnels. On bankless marsh they build floating houses, actually platforms, of aquatic vegetation. Bigger and flatter than typical haystack-shaped 'rat houses, nutria floats serve well as resting spots for ducks, geese, coots, and rails.

The first recorded release of imported nutrias in the United States was in 1899 at Elizabeth Lake in California. A nutria farm was established in the Green River area of Washington about 1932, but the breeding stock was released by flood waters in 1935. Other releases into the wild followed in this Washington locality, one, at least, as late as 1942. Nutria are now free-living in many places in western Washington and at several points in Oregon and California. A nutria farm was established at Avery Island in Louisiana, in 1937. Some of the animals escaped in 1939, and later that year 50 or more pairs were released—the beginning of the progressive establishment of the species on the coastal marshes of Louisiana, eastern Texas, and points east and west. Nutrias have since been reported in New Mexico, Michigan, Ohio, Iowa, Missouri, Mississippi, Alabama, Florida, North Carolina, Maryland, Virginia, and western Canada.

Where the nutria will finally place as a factor in waterfowl environments is yet to be determined. He is new, and he is being studied. Biologists of the Bureau of Sport Fisheries and Wildlife, now getting along with an extensive nutria investigation on duck and goose wintering grounds bordering the Gulf of Mexico, hope to assess the longtime ecological effects of the species.

NATURE'S ENGINEER, THE BEAVER, is a waterfowl manager, good and bad. To the extent that beaver works provide additional habitat, the entry is on the credit side; but in parts of the country, particularly in some of the mountainous western States, uncontrolled beaver populations may actually destroy duck nesting range. It's something to be examined East and West.

IN THE EAST, two ducks are special beneficiaries of beaver works. They are the black duck and the wood duck, for which beaver ponds in hardwood-conifer country, with their crisscross of drowned trees, acid water, aquatic plants, and seclusion, are good to excellent habitat. And ringnecks, greenwings, and the little hooded merganser draw some of these developmental dividends.

The significance of beavers in the eastern waterfowl picture is the very large area affected. The upper Appalachians to Hudson Bay, and westward to the Canadian prairies and northern Minnesota—the vast North Woods literally—is beaver territory, with beaver populations over much of the country equal to or greater than in the early Fur Trade era. Tens of thousands of beaver ponds and flowages over one-sixth of the Continent provide a lot of duck-nesting grounds.

This is not to say that beaver works are the last word in quality housing for either blacks or wood ducks. Often there is more emergent vegetation of better quality in open and less acid marshes. Duck weeds—tiny floating plants important to young wood ducks—are, however, usually abundant in beaver flowages, especially old ones; and aquatic insects—important food of all young ducks—are common to abundant. It is the vastness of the beaver "empire" in the Northeast that gives these animals their real significance in waterfowl environments in Maine, New Brunswick, Ontario, Quebec, and contiguous country. Actually, some natural wetlands along the streams of this great area, and some marshes along the upper Atlantic coast, are better producers of blacks and woodies.

IN THE WEST, beavers and ducks meet most frequently in the high country. In the Colorado Rockies, for example, and on similar terrain throughout the West, ducks are there primarily because of beaver ponds—and there is good reason for this situation: At 10 thousand feet spring comes a month or so later than a mile farther down. Here, snow goes off water areas in May instead of April—except on beaver ponds on south-facing slopes. And here, where the sun's rays strike mountain sides at nearly right angles, the heat and light, and clear air, hasten snowmelt and evaporation. Heat is then absorbed through the ice by the black muck

The nutria is an introduced animal in the marshes of the Southern States. It helps to maintain a balance between open water and marsh vegetation to the benefit of waterfowl.

Beaver ponds slow down runoff in the Colorado Rockies, and as a result are a help in water conservation. They are of significant value to waterfowl.

bottoms of the ponds. Under these influences, beaver ponds, often 30 or 40 to the mile of narrow mountain stream, open up 2 or 3 weeks earlier than ponds on north-facing slopes or on high-elevation lakes with deeper waters and lighter colored bottoms.

Though the beaver range in the western mountain country is large, a far smaller percentage of the land is actually affected by beaver presence than in the Northeast. In contrast to more or less continuous beaver occupancy in the less mountainous North Woods, beavers in the Rockies are limited to narrow, V-shaped, stream bottoms coursing down the mountain sides. And while there may be 50 or 100 beavers on a given mile of mountain stream, the population per square mile is relatively thin—certainly less than in parts of Maine, Ontario, and Quebec. And breeding ducks on western mountain range are correspondingly few, probably not in excess of one pair per square mile. Production, therefore, is limited mainly to a brood or two of mallards and green-winged teal per mile of mountain stream.

AND THERE ARE BEAVERS on the vast mileage of streams flowing eastward across the high plains. This is cottonwood-bottomland country, where water courses usually are wide, shallow, sand-choked, and meandering. Often, too, they have many channels, which create low, flat, willow-grown islands, often with exposed sandbar shorelines. As duck-nesting grounds, the bottoms have three main short-comings—flooding, overgrazing, and intensive use by man. Beavers, managed, make for some improvement.

ALONG THE thousands of miles of plains streams there are intermittent networks of shallow sloughs and still shallower depressions. The depressions are filled with water only during seasons of flood and heavy runoff. And nowadays, whether flooded, grazed, manhandled, or not, there are beavers on the streams. They cut down cottonwoods and willows, dam sloughs and some of the depressions, stabilize water levels, and set the stage for slough-side marsh development. Then, responding to food and cover, come the ducks. Not too many along most streams, but enough mallards, bluewings, and gadwalls to make a worthwhile addition to the whole.

BEAVERS HAVE TO BE MANAGED, regardless, if they are to serve best the needs of ducks. Management is mainly keeping numbers in balance with food supply. Even on the lower, more level, and more fertile bottomlands beavers may exhaust their food supplies; and food exhaustion is beset with environmental hazards in about direct proportion to gradient and elevation. Streams blocked by 100 dams to the mile on steep mountain sides hold the potential for vast environmental destruction when the beaver-made structures are breached during spring runoff and hundreds of tons of water are sluiced downstream. Such disasters are much more frequent under condition of excessive damming, always the manifestation of overpopulations of beavers and impending exhaustion of aspen and willow, their main foods and building materials. Breaching of dams in the North Woods, or even on the meandering stream of the Great Plains, exposes mudflats, readily invaded by weeds and willows. Beaver-dam breakage, regardless of locale, reduces for ducks the total area for feeding, nesting, and rearing of young. The best insurance of stability in this habitat type is a managed beaver population, systematically harvested in accordance with the beavers' food supply.

RACCOONS are swamp and forest dwellers by inclination. But when pushed by overpopulation or shortage of den trees, they take to rock dens, ground cavities, or to the marsh for daytime lairs or a place to raise their young. And the half-million or more ducks on areas such as Chautauqua National Wildlife Refuge in central Illinois in the fall

Beaver ponds afford good nesting areas for ducks but they may be either good or bad for fishing. Before this Colorado fisherman calls it a day he will have his own opinion on this matter.

or early winter has no deterring influence.

There, an appreciable population of Illinois River 'coons built up in the midforties and later to where tree and ground cavities and some dozens of wood duck nest boxes did not go around. What did the ringtails do? Up to a quarter-mile out on the marsh, at least in winter, the den-short 'coons went into muskrat houses. Whether the 'rats were evicted or whether the 'coons chose empty 'rat houses, we never learned. Maternal dens were found in hollow snags and stumps nearer the shoreline.

It is doubtful, however, if raccoons even in large numbers are of any great consequence to waterfowl in a competitive way. Of course, raccoons as predators are another matter, dealt with in the chapter that follows. Wood ducks surely feel the pinch on raccoon-filled range, and tree ducks along the Rio Grande and adjoining country dislike the proximity of duck-hungry neighbors. One can surmise one other minor direct effect: Very slight competition for food, involving crayfish, minnows, frogs, insects, and unharvested or residue grain.

PREDATION is treated in another chapter, as stated, but there is an environmental factor associated with predation that ought to be mentioned. This is the effect of cover on early nesting-season predation, in the pothole country of the northern prairies particularly, but observed elsewhere. Some studies show a nearly 100 percent loss of early nests to skunks, foxes, and badgers before vegetation reached a protective height. Thus, the first 2 or 3 weeks of the nesting season were lost or largely so; and because renesting birds lay smaller clutches the total loss is greater than the percentage of nests involved.

DUCK MARSHES are the part-time feeding grounds of certain birds, mostly blackbirds. Crows, gulls, herons, cranes, and soras compete lightly on the marshes, mostly for aquatic foods.

But there are myriads of blackbirds—rusties, Brewer's, redwings, yellowheads, and common and boat-tailed grackles. The last two work along the southern coast and up the major river systems, particularly the Mississippi, but actual competition with waterfowl eases upstream from the junctions of the Ohio and Missouri Rivers. Northerly from there, redwings, yellowheads, rusties, and Brewer's, millions strong, take over.

All blackbirds may feed over water and marsh, even though most of them spread out in nearby corn and small-grain fields at given times of the year. Nesting populations of blackbirds sometimes number into the hundreds to the square mile. That many mouths take a lot of filling, and when the filling is largely of aquatic life, plant and animal, it subtracts from the total that otherwise would be available to the ducks.

You can figure it simply: A boat-tailed grackle, adult or young, might eat a cupful of crayfish or aquatic insects every day; and two thousand cupfulls, say, out of a given section every day would make quite a difference to the ducks. At times, it is the difference between a plentiful and a marginal food supply.

Marsh grains and other seeds go about the same way. A big flock of redwings can scatter a good wild-rice stand in an afternoon. Of course a lot of the rice falls into the water, and dabbling ducks, excellent salvagers, go after it. But there is a big difference in 15 and 30 bushels an acre, a difference that may easily be due to blackbirds. The same sort of usage applies to the seeds of smartweed, wild millet, rice cutgrass, and other top duck foods.

Crows and gulls are also in the marsh—eating. But fish, frogs, and aquatic insects, rather than plant food, are their main interests. The crow-gull take is minor in the overall sense, but a wintering flock of 5 thousand crows, or a nesting aggregation of as many gulls, can make a real dent in the food supply of waterfowl on the affected marsh or coastal shoreline.

IN THE FUTURE, aquatic birds and mammals will continue to see a lot of each other. Waterfowl and muskrats, nearly inseparable, can and probably will be managed in such manner as to use the 'rats in improving wetlands for ducks and geese. We will learn a lot more about nutrias and, like muskrats, use them in manipulating aquatic environments. Beavers, with great potential for habitat improvement or destruction, will be kept in creative status so far as possible. Skunks, raccoons, foxes, weasels, and the native cats, neither vegetarians nor water engineers, hold no threat to the habitat of aquatic birds.

Management is inexorably the key to waterfowl's tomorrow. All associated animals, both as a resource and in behalf of the ducks, geese, swans, and coots, will be further studied, understood, and used in maintaining wetland harmony and equilibrium. All are integrals in the complex formula for waterfowl abundance in the future.

—LEE E. YEAGER.

To place all our bets on our industrial genius alone without covering the real source of wealth—natural resources—is to bet on the jockey and leave the horse entirely out of our calculations.

—DING DARLING.

RACCOON
YOUNG RUDDY DUCKS

Talon and Fang

W E WHO HAVE STUDIED the waterfowl of North American wetlands have seen enough plundered duck nests and remains of ducks to think that predation may seriously affect the populations of waterfowl. Yet immense numbers of them may live with remarkable security even in the midst of many predators.

We cannot easily explain the apparent contradictions in our well-studied case histories, the complexities in the ageless struggle of the eaters and the eaten, and the whole phenomenon of predation.

We must understand as much as we can about the predation suffered by waterfowl, however, if only to avoid mistakes in management, gain an idea of the chances that something similar will happen again, and detect whatever basic rules of order we can as a background for realistic thought. We should not expect that the findings from any particular investigation will necessarily apply throughout to another situation. Nature does not always work so neatly and reassuringly.

LET US FIRST take up predation during the reproductive season of waterfowl.

The special hazards of incubating

323

birds may increase vulnerability to predation. Agile foxes, coyotes, and minks may catch incubating hens on nests. Relatively clumsy predators, like raccoons, also may climb up and reach into holes in stubs or artificial nest boxes after wood ducks. Still, the larger waterfowl can be formidable defenders, and, of the lesser waterfowl, not all incubating birds will be tight sitters that allow predators to approach and kill them.

It is predation upon eggs and young that usually raises questions most difficult to answer, because its effect depends on the varying degrees to which the waterfowl may adjust to the losses. The destruction of a clutch of duck eggs or the death of a duckling does not always signify fewer ducks in the fall than otherwise would have been present. The losses may be compensated for by renesting efforts or by a sort of automatic balancing of mortality rates. Within limits, a destroyed clutch may mean only that another clutch will be laid; the death of a duckling may mean that another duckling has a better chance to live.

After all, our native North American waterfowl have been subject to Nature's experimenting for millions of years, and they have been living with many of the same hazards that they now have. That being the case, it may be that in the end much of the loss does not count.

Given the chance, crows and skunks can be egg eaters. Crows may take advantage of poorly concealed duck nests, especially those exposed by mowing; sometimes the nests best concealed from human eyes may suffer the more severely from depredations of crows. In some instances when the numbers of crows were reduced on breeding grounds, egg losses to other predators, notably skunks, increased. When the number of skunks was reduced, increased losses from still other egg predators seemed to substitute in something of a compensatory manner. We have data that show similar rates of total loss in different years despite great variations in the proportions of nests lost through different causes.

B. W. Cartwright, a Canadian biologist of long experience in the Prairie Provinces, has suggested that a light to a moderate degree of predation upon egg clutches may serve as a biological safeguard for grouse and partridges. Despite the usual dryness of late summer in central North America, I think that a similar safeguard may apply to some extent to waterfowl.

In a region like this that has occasional climatic emergencies for young birds, a species that hatched all of its young at such a time may lose its entire season's reproduction. Most species of ducks do not try to nest again during the same year if they succeed in hatching a clutch of eggs, no matter what happens to their ducklings. Light to moderate destruction of nests, followed by renesting, therefore would tend to stagger hatching dates and work against the likelihood of any one emergency claiming most or all of the season's young at a critical time of life. Besides, the young would appear later, when food and cover are more favorable for survival. It is hard to say how much depredation of eggs may be within desirable limits and how much may be excessive.

The losses of duck nests to bull snakes in the Nebraska Sandhills one season were 42 percent. The killing of some snakes cut in half the losses of nests.

An occasional fox, coyote, or dog may learn to go after nests. When I think of the hundreds of nests in northern Iowa that we found for research purposes by means of a trained dog during a few years in the thirties, I can readily imagine the destruction a free-hunting individual might commit if it got started of its own accord on such practice. I know of extreme cases of depredations by members of the dog family in which a fox or a coyote got out on an island covered with duck nests.

EXTREME CROWDING of waterfowl nests may occur on islands or other attractive nesting sites. Gadwall Island on Lower Souris National Wildlife Refuge in northwestern North Dakota has an area of less than an acre. In 1947 it had at least 160 nesting pairs of ducks which had a hatching success of about 90 percent of the clutches and a total production of about 1,350 young. Ding Island, slightly smaller, maintained a population of about 100 nesting pairs or more during 1949–1955. M. C. Hammond and G. E. Mann generalized that the absence of predation on Lower Souris islands led to concen-trations of 20 to 80 nests an acre for islands between three-tenths of an acre and an acre in size. High rates of reproductive success over periods of several years undoubtedly contribute to the building up of such populations locally.

Then, when something really goes wrong for such top-heavy nesting populations, the consequences may be devastating. It is to be expected that, aside from emergencies due to detrimental human activities or to flooding or extremes of weather, the great hazard to dense island-nesting populations would be concerted predation. Such populations may draw the eager attentions of weasels, dogs, foxes, raccoons, crows, ravens, gulls, or whatever predators can reach them.

Although the resulting havoc may be understandably conspicuous, it still may not be easy to appraise its biological significance. Waterfowl populations may adjust to predatory dangers by restricting their nesting to steep cliffs or to trees or other places beyond reach of mammals, whereas, when undisturbed, they customarily nest on open or flat ground. Following long periods of relief from molestation, the same species may expand their nesting areas to include once-dangerous sites. Or, waterfowl may learn that they gain protection, as from crows, by nesting in the midst of certain gull colonies. These adjustments reflect differences in experiences as well as innate behavior patterns and add up to the' broad generality that Nature's way is any way that works, so long as it works.

THE NORTHERN PIKE may be a voracious predator on young waterfowl, but the heaviest concentration of pike I ever saw was in a good waterfowl marsh in northwestern Iowa one summer. While paddling a canoe about the marsh, I could see the deadly-looking forms of pike through quiet water almost everywhere. Nevertheless, that summer was one of very high productivity of coots, ducks, and other waterfowl.

On the other hand, Victor E. F. Solman calculated that pike took 10 percent of the ducklings produced on the Saskatchewan Delta during the summers of 1940 and 1941. Most of the ducklings were less than a week old. The young of diving ducks seemed more vulnerable than the young of dabbling ducks. Of 2,658 pike of sizes large enough to prey on waterfowl, Solman reported that at least 23 contained one to four ducklings. Crows and other waterfowl predators characteristic of Canadian agricultural lands were absent.

An unwelcome guest. Providing safe nesting sites for wood ducks requires protection against raccoons.

Footprints tell the story. The metal guard was effective in preventing a raccoon from reaching this duck nest box on Maryland's Eastern Shore.

I HAVE SEEN LITTLE EVIDENCE in Iowa marshes of predation by snapping turtles on young birds. In one particular place, there must have been hundreds of snappers, but I saw nothing wrong with the waterfowl there. I seldom found anything except submerged plant material and bits of fish and crayfish remains in the stomachs and intestines of the snapping turtles.

Malcolm W. Coulter, however, collected snapping turtles in Maine at the peak of the brood season for ducks and in areas in which both turtles and waterfowl were abun-

dant. Of 171 turtles he examined, 157 contained food; 42 had remains of at least 52 birds, including 25 ducks, mostly black ducks and ring-necks up to 6 weeks old. A 31-pound turtle had eaten a ringneck, a goldeneye, and three pied-billed grebes. A 24-pounder had eaten two black ducks, an unidentified dabbling duck, and a grebe. Surface-feeding ducks were taken as turtle prey almost twice as frequently as divers. I should point out that northern pike and snapping turtles digest remains of ducks slowly and that snappers do much feeding on carrion.

EMERGENCIES may predispose waterfowl to predation losses. Flightless ducklings on drought-exposed mudflats have little chance to escape if a coyote or a large hawk discovers them. Drought conditions may increase greatly the amount of egg losses through predation and the significance of the losses to reproduction.

John P. Rogers studied the reproductive fortunes of lesser scaups on a square mile of pothole country in southwestern Manitoba. The tract contained 20 potholes one-half acre to 25 acres in size. In 1957, when water levels were favorable,

Red fox pups at Agassiz National Wildlife Refuge, Minnesota.

51 pairs produced 225 young in 25 broods. In droughty 1958, when mudflats surrounded what little water remained, 65 pairs produced only 20 young in three broods. Of 26 lesser scaup nests he found there in 1958, one hatched and 21 were destroyed by predators, mostly mammals. He found little evidence of renesting in 1958. That and the greater vulnerability of nests in dried-out shore vegetation may explain the severe decline in production.

PREDATION upon young waterfowl by the more active members of the weasel family deserves special mention. It is not strange that the stocky striped skunk, with its physiological need for the sulfur that is a constituent of its scent, should raid nests. It is not much of a predator upon agile prey, although it has wetland relatives that are avid killers of young and adult waterfowl—when they can. Biologists who visited a small Lower Souris island one summer day in 1936 found 59 ducks and coots that had been killed by one or more stranded weasels. Subsequent observations at Lower Souris indicated that minks, if present, usually preyed heavily on nesting ducks and ducklings.

My own observations on mink predation on ducks and ducklings in Northern States suggested equally severe predation drawn by crowded nesting populations. This took place regardless of whether nesting and rearing were done on the mainland or on islands accessible to the minks.

Of two extreme cases I have seen, one was a stretch of the shore of Lower Red Rock Lake in south-central Montana. More than 25 broods of ducklings per acre frequented the shallows and the margin. There they were with their mothers, broods of gadwalls, mallards, ruddies, and about all other duck species of the western marshes. On shore at one place was a den with four or five half-grown young minks scampering in and out.

The approximately 300 mink droppings that I looked over contained scarcely any recognized items except bird remains, and these could not have consisted of much other than bones and feathers of ducks. Dead ducks littered the holes and trails in the shore vegetation. The bodies of old birds and ducklings of two to six weeks were everywhere, partly eaten or left intact.

The second example involved young coots in northwestern Iowa. There the minks ate almost nothing but coots for about a month, and the heaped droppings and the strewed remains about dens and trails revealed the carnage that was going on. Concentrations of coot nests approached 15 to 20 to the acre in shore-zone tracts of marsh where the minks were accustomed to hunt. It was not surprising that these predators were taking advantage of their opportunities while they had them.

At other times and places, I have seen mink droppings made up almost entirely of yolk and shell fragments of coot and rail eggs when minks had access to large numbers of nests. Down feathers, red bills, and egg teeth in the droppings often had enough shell fragments mixed with them to indicate that the victims had been eaten while in the eggs.

SOME OF THE unanswered questions that I see in attempting to appraise mink predation on waterfowl—or any other kind of predation—relate to "normal" populations of birds living "normal" lives. Opportunism of predators and their opportunities can explain a great deal. We know that nothing is going to prey on something it cannot catch. We can assume also that neither a native predator nor its native waterfowl prey is completely lacking in adjustments to each other.

Outside of the breeding season, predation on waterfowl may have wide extremes. Birds helpless from botulism may be victims of hawks, crows, magpies, gulls, and four-footed flesh-eaters. There is nothing remarkable about that. Neither is it unusual to find feathers, blood, and bones and partly eaten carcasses where gunshot cripples or victims of lead poisoning are forced to remain about the last patches of open water at freezeup, or wander helplessly over the ice as long as they stay alive.

The genuine predation, itself, may vary greatly. Not always are the reasons apparent. We found one fall, for example, that 9 of 20 pellets of great horned owls contained duck remains. In another collection in spring of 158 pellets, from horned owls on an Iowa marsh, we found duck remains in 24, rail remains in 23, and coot remains in 17. On the other hand, it is often astonishing how little even horned owls living on marsh islands may prey on waterfowl, even at times when waterfowl are abundant.

Sometimes in spring and fall, up to 10 thousand ducks may cover the 135 acres of one of our study areas. They may feed or sleep or spend leisurely weeks drifting through; and pellets of horned owls collected under roost trees on islands in the middle of the marsh may still contain nothing but remains of blackbirds or land prey. Or the waterfowl that owls did prey on may be the grebes that the ducks vastly outnumbered. The only victim of predation I found about an enormous loafing congregation of ducks late one summer was a mallard, freshly killed by a mink. It was in good flesh but had several lead shot in its gizzard.

MY STUDIES of the bobwhite quail, a nonmigratory upland game bird well known in the Eastern States, brought out a point pertinent to our topic—that the dominant regulating factor of a quail population is its own psychology, its own intolerance of crowding within its environment. The biological structure of a quail population has in it tendencies to balance and counterbalance rates of gain and loss automatically. The compensations may reduce or nullify the net influence of predation.

We lack data on waterfowl that are technically comparable to data for bobwhites, but we know that waterfowl have psychological peculiarities that permit extremes of social tolerance and intolerance.

The preferences of migratory birds for congregating in one place one year but not necessarily the next may introduce variables into any efforts to appraise the real effects of predation on populations of waterfowl. Nevertheless, the data we have on waterfowl suggest that self-limiting tendencies and compensating adjustments may modify greatly the effects of predation — perhaps not to the extent suggested by the research on quail but enough to be worth considering.

FOR THE TRUMPETER SWAN, we have accurate data on numbers. For its range in the United States, chiefly northwestern Wyoming and south-central Montana, Winston E. Banko traced the growth of the trumpeter population from fewer than 100 in the early thirties to about 700 by the early sixties.

Predators known to prey on the swans were abundant in places and scarce in others. Predator control was practiced on some areas and not on others, and some movements of swans from one area to another were noted. But the trumpeter swans showed patterns of growth similar to those of the bobwhite quail. As the overall population increased, the rates of gain went down in ways that seem to indicate a considerable automatic adjustment in reproductive rates and survival of young, regardless of whether losses are due to predation or other causes.

WE HAVE SOME INFORMATION on the compensations and conformity to patterns of other waterfowl.

Frank C. Bellrose and Elizabeth Brown Chase compared losses suffered by mallards, black ducks, and blue-winged teal. The mallard, the most hunted by people, suffered the lowest "natural" losses; the blue-winged teal, the least hunted, suffered the highest "natural" losses; the black duck, subject to intermediate intensities of human hunting, suffered "natural" losses intermediate between those of the mallard and the teal. Mr. Bellrose and Mrs. Chase concluded that the shooting toll probably absorbed a large proportion of the mallard losses that otherwise would have occurred in an unshot population and that the blue-wings may be able to withstand more hunting by people without raising their total mortality rates very much.

Those contrasts may indicate that causes of death tend to substitute for each other in natural counterbalancings of waterfowl populations just as they do in bobwhite quail.

It follows that difficulties in appraising predation upon waterfowl and the knowledge we have of compensatory trends may arouse doubts as to the effectiveness of predator control in the management of North American waterfowl. We need more than conventional reasoning or simple observation as to whether predators do or do not prey upon waterfowl, for justification of any drastic control of predators.

On general grounds, I should advise against extreme attitudes on the subject of predator control on behalf of waterfowl managed as game birds. Overemphasis may lead to excessive expense and preoccupation with

measures of questionable effectiveness and may lead also to unnecessary sacrifice of outdoor values that
have their own importance. For the
predators themselves are a part of
Nature; they include species as
beautiful, as interesting, as splen-
didly adapted, and as rightly be-
longing in the natural out-of-doors
as even the waterfowl with which we
are here concerned. In my opinion,
it would be an inexcusable mistake
to sacrifice needlessly anything that
contributes to what may be called
the wholeness of Nature.

Waterfowl management should be
more than just another form of poultry husbandry. If it is to safeguard
the esthetic values associated with

our North American wetlands as
well as game birds to shoot, it calls
for balanced viewpoints on the part
of the people doing the managing.

As this chapter is written
(1962), I recommend for my home
region of the north-central United
States a reduction in numbers of raccoons. They have expanded their
geographic range and increased tremendously during the forties and
fifties. Red foxes likewise reached
and maintained a great population
peak at the same time and could
well stand reduction. But raccoons
and foxes are excellent animals for
sport hunting, and I would advocate
making increased use of them for

Two female pintails with broods at Lower Souris National Wildlife Refuge in North Dakota. They can take their young quickly to nearby protective cover if challenged by some predator.

such purposes, rather than unimaginatively campaigning to get rid of them.

As for other predators, I have no easy rule of thumb to propose as to which predators could be reduced in numbers for the benefit of waterfowl—or when and where to do so. Much depends on the local situations that pertain to northern pike, snapping turtles, bull snakes, coyotes, skunks, crows, and gulls. The status of our eagles is precarious, and I would not advise campaigning against them however much they were feeding on the commoner types of any sort of game. I have seen little to justify killing any of the hawks and small to medium owls because of their attentions to free-living waterfowl.

I can claim the mink and the great horned owl as longtime specialties as much as I can any of the predators upon waterfowl, but they are the species about which I have the most unanswered questions as to population effects of such predation. In terms of the severity of the predation sometimes observed, a pretty bad case could be made for either the mink or the great horned owl as an enemy of waterfowl. But, among other considerations, there is increasing evidence that the food habits of both species may reflect the relative vulnerability of many kinds of prey and thus serve for technical management purposes as valuable barometers of population well-being in a broad sense.

Besides—in my view—minks and horned owls properly belong around our north-central marshes, too; and I should be unwilling, indeed, to endorse any intensities of management that would eliminate either of these interesting and superlatively adapted forms of life from wide areas of their native range.—Paul L. Errington.

Botulism and Fowl Cholera

VISIT WITH US a marsh in the Great Salt Lake Basin of Utah. It is early August, the day is warm and sunny. We have a camera, so that we can photograph waterfowl in their natural state, and boots for protection against the brackish, alkaline water. Our boat, small and flat-bottomed so that it can move smoothly through the shallow water, is beached on the edge of the marsh where we left it yesterday.

We start off with light heart, but as we near the marsh, we stop abruptly in shock and horror. The shoreline, where only last evening we saw thousands of sleek, apparently healthy birds, is now littered with their bodies. Most of them are ducks, but here and there we see a Canada goose, a gull, an avocet, a black-necked stilt, a pelican.

At our approach, several pintails rise with difficulty to their feet, gain the water's edge, and swim slowly away. A green-winged teal, unable to walk, propels itself with desperately flapping wings across the damp soil toward the water. Others, still able to hold their heads erect, lack the strength to move away. This otherwise dismal picture is brightened by a raft of birds taking to the air, noisily protesting our presence. They give us hope that some, perhaps many, are still active and healthy.

Overcoming our apprehension that this may be a plague to which man is susceptible, we examine a few of the inert forms at our feet. Many are stiff and cold. Others, limp and apparently lifeless, are found to be still warm, still breathing feebly. Green-stained feathers around the vent and watery droppings, speckling the shoreline like daubs of bright green paint, give evidence of diarrhea. The eyes are sometimes bright and clear, sometimes filled with fluid or thick, yellow material that seals the lids together. In most of the birds, the membrane that normally snaps across the eye to keep it moist and clean functions sluggishly or not at all.

Searching further for the cause of the devastation around us, our probing fingers reveal that the dead birds are in good flesh. A cut through skin, muscle, and bone with a pocket knife removes the sternum from a plump mallard, exposing its internal organs. All are normal in appearance, except that the blood vessels of the intestine are congested. The stomach, its wall laid open by a slash of the knife, contains nothing but gravel and a few bits of vegetation.

What can have happened in less than a day to account for this desolation? From our knowledge of western marshes and the evidence before us, we are now almost certain that we are witnessing a conservationist's nightmare—an outbreak of avian botulism.

BOTULISM, or "Western Duck Sickness" as the disease was known before its true identity was determined, had probably been responsible for waterfowl losses for many years before 1910; but that year marked the beginning of real concern about its effect on waterfowl populations. That summer, outbreaks near Great Salt Lake and in California accounted for the death of millions of aquatic birds. In the years since, up to 1964, observed losses there and elsewhere have varied. An estimated 250 thousand ducks died at the northern end of Great Salt Lake in 1932. In other years, for reasons not at all clear, mortality has been relatively mild. Reports of the malady indicate that it occurs from Canada to Mexico, from California to New Jersey. It has been reported from Australia and Uraguay. For the most part, it claims its victims more frequently in the semi-arid areas of the Western States and Canada.

Alexander Wetmore, then of the Bureau of Biological Survey, began the first study to determine the cause of western duck sickness in 1914. He concluded that the malady was the direct result of the toxic action of certain soluble salts present in abundance in the vicinity of Great Salt Lake and its alkali flats and, therefore, gave the name "alkali poisoning" to it.

Outbreaks appeared occasionally thereafter in areas where salt concentrations were so low as to cast doubt on the idea that alkali poisoning was their cause. The Bureau of Biological Survey resumed its investigation of the disease near Klamath Falls, Oregon, in 1927. E. R. Kalmbach and C. C. Sperry conducted field observations and laboratory studies intermittently during the next 3 years. They had accumulated enough experimental data by 1930 to advance the hypothesis that duck sickness was a form of botulism. Supporting evidence came from pathologists in the Department of Agriculture who isolated the causative organism from decomposing bird tissues supplied by Dr. Kalmbach.

WHAT IS THIS DISEASE that strikes so quickly and severely? Botulism, a disease of both birds and mammals, is a bacterial poisoning, not an infection. The causative agent, *Clostridium botulinum*, does not invade the living tissues of its victims. Each of its cells can form a spore highly resistant to physical and chemical agents, and in this form it may lie dormant for many years. When conditions are favorable—suitable temperature, an organic medium to satisfy food requirements, and an absence of atmospheric oxygen (the organism is a strict anaerobe)— the spores germinate and multiply. In so doing, they produce a potent nerve toxin as one of the end products of their metabolism. A susceptible animal that swallows this toxin absorbs it through the lining of the digestive tract. By way of the blood stream, it reaches the peripheral nervous system. In some manner not yet clearly understood, it attacks the nerves and causes paralysis. If the dose of toxin is large enough, death of the animal results from paralysis of the respiratory system.

Clostridium botulinum is divided into six types, A through F, each of which produces a distinct toxin. An antiserum prepared by immunizing an animal against any one type of toxin can completely neutralize only that type. Types A, B, D, E, and F cause botulism in man and other mammals, but they probably rarely affect wild birds. The type involved in natural outbreaks in waterfowl is not always determined, but type C is the responsible agent in most cases.

Isolation of the bacterium from the tissues of a dead animal is not adequate proof of the cause of death. Probably most animals living in a botulism area harbor the organism in their intestinal tracts. The spores may be found in the livers of apparently healthy birds. After death of the host from any cause, the bacterium multiplies and produces toxin throughout the carcass. A definite diagnosis can be made only by demonstrating the presence of toxin in a sample of blood taken from a living bird. The test consists of injecting small quantities of the blood serum into two groups of mice (or other suitable laboratory animal), one of which is protected by doses of the proper antitoxin. If, within 6 days, the mice in the unprotected group exhibit the characteristic symptoms of botulism and die, while the protected group remains unaffected, we can assume that the bird had botulism.

Because an exact diagnosis requires laboratory tests, most outbreaks have been diagnosed on the basis of symptoms, the conditions surrounding the outbreak, and the absence of evidence of other diseases. An experienced observer can do this with reasonable accuracy, but the lack of proof makes it difficult to evaluate reports of botulism in many species of birds.

Almost every species of bird living on or near a botulism-producing marsh has been affected in one outbreak or another, and the degree to which it is affected can be explained largely by the nature of its feeding habits. Geese, for example, find less of their food than do ducks in the marsh mud where *Clostridium botulinum* thrives; they are less frequently victims of the disease. It is possible, too, that some species have acquired a degree of resistance to the poison through many generations of exposure.

There appears to be no such thing as a "typical" botulism area. Most marshes and lakes on which outbreaks occur are shallow, brackish, and on the alkaline side of neutrality; but depth, salt concentration, and alkalinity may vary widely from one marsh to another and within the same marsh from year to year. The kinds and abundance of vegetation and invertebrate life also vary within wide limits on such marshes.

BOTULISM is generally considered to be a warm-weather disease, but the influence of climate on the occurrence of outbreaks cannot be defined clearly. The most severe mortality in northern Utah commonly occurs between late July and mid-September. There, however, it is not unusual for milder losses to occur in the spring while some ice still is on the water. In the absence of proof, we can only speculate that these spring outbreaks result from toxin stored in some way from the previous summer.

Reflooding of a gently sloping, moist shoreline exposed by receding water levels is commonly followed by botulism losses. A possible explanation for this apparent cause-and-effect relationship is that the moist mud between water's edge and dry soil (the fringe area) serves as an incubator. Here, free of the diluting and heat-insulating effects of the water, *Clostridium botulinum* can grow and produce toxin in the entrapped organic materials. When subsequent reflooding covers such a fringe area with water and makes it attractive to waterfowl, toxin-containing materials are consumed when they feed.

What are these organic materials that *Clostridium botulinum* needs for growth and toxin production under natural conditions? Where both plants and invertebrate animals are present in abundance, the question is difficult to answer. Experience in the laboratory indicates that animal tissues support generally higher levels of toxin production than do plant tissues. Experimental evidence also suggests that a homogeneous sludge of decaying plant and animal matter is not the most favorable medium for toxin production. It appears that *Clostridium botulinum* prefers to grow within organized particles or units such as the carcasses of aquatic insects and other invertebrates that are abundant in marshes. These "microenvironments" provide the bacterium with both food and protection from the harmful salts and atmospheric oxygen that may be present in the water and mud that surround them.

If the latter concept has basis in fact, it follows that invertebrate carcasses must be available for toxin production prior to a natural botulism outbreak. Field studies in northern Utah will determine whether changes in the numbers of living aquatic invertebrates can be correlated with outbreaks of the disease.

Evidence is at hand that both living and dead invertebrates play a part in causing outbreaks of avian botulism. The presence of toxin has been demonstrated in extracts of several species of living aquatic organisms collected in the marsh. Also, after experimental exposure to the cells of *Clostridium botulinum*, these same species in turn become toxic. Presumably, even though the particular species of invertebrates do not normally feed on bacterial cells, they ingest them by chance. Under field conditions, then, they may concentrate or "package" toxin in a form palatable to waterfowl.

WHAT CAN BE DONE to prevent outbreaks or reduce waterfowl losses?

One control method grew out of the observation that stabilization of the shoreline of a nearly flat, shallow, alkaline impoundment created conditions favorable to toxin production in the fringe area. Experiments with water manipulation showed that the hazard to waterfowl resulting from reflooding of the fringe area could be reduced by steadily lowering water levels or by raising them rapidly to place the shoreline against steep banks.

There are disadvantages and limitations to water manipulation as a control measure. Waterfowl habitat is temporarily destroyed as

Waterfowl killed by botulism, a grim threat to western ducks.

J. Van Den Akker administering botulism anti-toxin to a sick duck at Bear River National Wildlife Refuge, Utah. This saves some but not enough.

water levels are lowered. In many botulism areas, enough water to effect rapid reflooding is not available when most needed. Moreover, water levels cannot be manipulated in lakes that get their water only from rain or in those that have no outlet.

MANY KINDS OF MEDICATIONS have been tested. None, except antitoxin, has been effective. A duck's chances of survival are increased appreciably by an injection of antitoxin. Because major outbreaks may affect thousands of fowl, however, any method of limiting losses by treating individual birds can be only a partial and expensive remedy.

If a cause-and-effect relationship between aquatic invertebrates is proved, it is likely that the chain of events that leads to an outbreak can be broken more easily at the invertebrate than at the bacteria link. With this idea in mind, biologists have undertaken studies to determine the feasibility of controlling the disease by controlling the invertebrates.

AND NOW, let us suppose that we had chosen for our photographic excursion a brackish lake near the Muleshoe National Wildlife Refuge in the Texas Panhandle or one in the San Francisco Bay area of California. Had the day been in late fall, winter, or early spring, our camera might have taken a picture almost as dramatic and as tragic as the one we saw in the Great Salt Lake Basin in August. At these places and within this time period, however, fowl cholera, more likely than botulism, would be the cause.

The environment may be remarkably like that of a botulism marsh, or it may be quite different. With the exception of the climates usually associated with outbreaks of the two diseases, there are no environmental characteristics that clearly define either. In fact, at least one western waterfowl area in the United States—Tule Lake National Wildlife Refuge in northern California—has suffered from both diseases.

Whatever may be the subtle differences that distinguish a Texas lake stricken by fowl cholera from a Utah marsh stricken by botulism, one grisly similarity may be expected—the bodies of dozens, hundreds, or thousands of dead birds will dot the shoreline or float grimly on the water.

OUTBREAKS of what undoubtedly was fowl cholera (pasteurellosis) in domestic fowl have been known to occur in European countries for more than 200 years. The first records of investigations of the disease in the United States and Canada appeared in the latter part of the 19th century. It has spread to most parts of the world, but its incidence in many countries appears to have gradually declined since about 1930. It was still a serious problem in North and South Dakota in 1963, primarily in flocks of chickens and turkeys. Heavy losses have occurred on the duck ranches of Long Island.

The first known outbreaks of fowl cholera in wild ducks occurred in California and Texas in early 1944. The vicinities of San Francisco Bay and the Muleshoe National Wildlife Refuge in the Texas Panhandle have continued to be epizootic areas since then. Losses from the disease have fluctuated greatly from year to year. Reports from the Muleshoe area have varied from only an occasional sick or dead bird in some years to more than 60 thousand in the winter of 1956–1957.

Besides ducks, other species of aquatic birds are susceptible. Losses, sometimes severe, have been reported in coots, whistling swans, geese, gulls, and shorebirds. Short-eared owls, marsh hawks, meadow mice, and a weasel were infected in an outbreak in California in 1958.

Fowl cholera, unlike avian botulism, is an infection. A tiny bacterium, *Pasteurella multocida,* must invade the tissues of its host to bring about its ill effects. Different strains of the organism vary with respect to the severity of the disease they induce. Some cause an acute, rapidly fatal infection; others, a more chronic form of the disease.

THE SYMPTOMS SHOWN by affected birds vary from one outbreak to another and within the course of a single outbreak. Particularly for the first few days after the disease strikes, it may be so acute that no sick birds at all are seen. Living birds are active and apparently normal at the same time the carcasses of others litter the area. Commonly the carcasses will be found in a sitting position, suggesting that death occurred suddenly.

As the outbreak progresses, and occasionally in its early stages, sick birds are seen in increasing numbers. Unlike those affected with botulism, they are apathetic and apparently unaware of an observer's approach. A few of the less seriously affected may make feeble efforts to escape. Weakness, as contrasted to paralysis, may become so extreme in some that they cannot hold their heads erect, and their condition may be confused with advanced stages of botulism.

In most outbreaks, other than the very acute ones, a few birds exhibit symptoms quite unlike those seen in botulism. Some shake their heads vigorously at frequent intervals. Others, or perhaps the same ones, swim or walk confusedly in small circles. When attempting to take off, birds so affected may tumble awkwardly back into the water. Diarrhea is a common symptom of fowl cholera, as it is of botulism and many other diseases.

Fowl cholera can be identified with certainty only by isolating the causative organism in the laboratory, but pathological changes may help in making a presumptive diagnosis in the field. In acute cases, the only internal lesions may be hemorrhages, pinpoint or larger in size, on the surfaces of the heart and gizzard or on any of the thin membranes that line the body cavities. Blood may be found in the intestine. Later in the course of the outbreak as the potency of the organism declines, or perhaps as the more resistant birds become infected, numerous small white or gray spots may be seen on the surface of the liver and throughout its tissue. If microscopic examination can be made, a stained smear of blood from an acutely infected bird may contain many small, oval-shaped bacteria colored more intensely at each end.

How THE INFECTION is introduced into a waterfowl population is not known. Losses in domestic fowl occasionally occur in the vicinity of some epizootic areas just before an outbreak among wild birds. Some observers therefore suspect that the disease is carried from farm to lake by way of drainage ditches or by mammals or free-flying birds.

Domestic fowl sometimes become carriers of the bacterium after recovery from the disease or even without having shown evidence of the infection. These "healthy" carriers are a source of infection when they come in contact with a susceptible population under conditions favorable to the spread of the disease. It may be hypothesized that a similar set of circumstances precipitates outbreaks in waterfowl. *Pasteurella multocida* can exist for at least 3 months, perhaps longer, in decaying carcasses of infected birds. Although no proof exists, the bacterium may survive from one year to the next somewhere in the problem area.

The mode of spread within a waterfowl population is also in doubt. The disease agent is present in both the nasal excretions and the feces of infected birds, and the environment, particularly on a densely populated lake, will quickly become contaminated. Domestic fowl appear to be more susceptible to experimental infection by the intranasal than the oral route. This supports the belief that the natural disease is primarily a respiratory infection.

OUTBREAKS OF FOWL CHOLERA in waterfowl are not well enough understood to permit a rational program of prevention and control. Elimination of infected birds and carriers from the flock, improvement of sanitary conditions, administration of medication, and other measures that can be used to control the disease in domestic birds are impossible or impractical to apply in the case of large, unconfined wild populations. A California lake was treated with copper sulfate in 1949 in an experimental attempt to control an outbreak, but the value of the treatment was not conclusively shown.

Overcrowding of a susceptible population favors the spread of contagious diseases. When such conditions exist in a waterfowl area, we may expect that management practices aimed at overcoming them will be helpful. Filling a lake to its full capacity, for example, would accomplish both an increase in its surface area and a dilution of the infective agent in the water. Dispersal of the birds by draining a lake, a measure that can be resorted to safely in the control of botulism, involves the risk of spreading fowl cholera to uncontaminated water.

Carcasses should be picked up daily and disposed of by burning, regardless of what other measures are taken. The influence that this practice may have on the course of an outbreak in an already contaminated habitat cannot be accurately determined, but it cannot fail to lessen the danger of scavenger birds introducing the disease into new areas.

WE HAVE REVIEWED BRIEFLY only two of many plagues of waterfowl. One, botulism, is a product of the environment. Its ability to kill is enormous. The other, fowl cholera, while not generated on the site, may become a chronic contaminant of concentration areas of waterfowl. It, too, is responsible for great losses on occasion.

While these two diseases cut like a scythe into numbers of waterfowl, others may whittle. Who can say which is accountable for the greater total over the years. As waterfowl management enters a new era, wherein today's numbers must be accommodated on less and less habitat, problems of disease and parasitism may take on a new significance. All factors that cut and whittle the populations—and disease is an important one—must be removed or throttled if our goals are to be realized.—WAYNE I. JENSEN and CECIL S. WILLIAMS.

CANADA GEESE

Blood Parasites

AMONG THE MANY causes of disease in waterfowl are the blood parasites, the most important genus of which is *Leucocytozoon*—so named in the mistaken belief that it invaded only white blood cells, the leucocytes.

The harmful effects of *Leucocytozoon* on waterfowl were recognized as early as 1915 when it was noted that the prevalence of the disease made it almost impossible to rear domestic ducklings in certain places in Canada. Its method of spread from duck to duck by means of black flies remained unknown until 1932.

TWO SPECIES OF THE PARASITE occur in waterfowl. *Leucocytozoon simondi* is very common in all ducks, although it can also infect geese. *L. anseris* is predominantly a parasite of geese. The former is widely distributed in many species of waterfowl in North America and has been extensively investigated in Canada and the United States. So far as is known, it infects only waterfowl. Little is known about *L. anseris*. Other species of *Leucocytozoon* occur in many woodland birds, but experimental evidence indicates that they cannot be transmitted to ducks or geese.

343

Leucocytozoon is a small, single-celled parasite related to the disease organism that causes malaria in man. As with malaria, an insect is essential to spread the parasite in nature. The black fly accomplishes this by feeding on an infected bird. Then, when taking a subsequent blood meal, it transmits the parasite to another susceptible duck or goose.

The leucocytozoan organisms invade some white cells but occur most frequently in young red cells. Extensive damage to red cells leads to severe anemia and death. The microscopic parasites in these cells are the sexual stages. These tiny organisms grow rapidly to reach maturity within 48 hours.

The parasite lies within the blood cell and close to its nucleus. It fills the cell as it grows, pushing the nucleus to one side. These spherical parasites are apparent early in the course of infection. Later they are replaced by oval forms, and most parasitized cells are enlarged and distorted. Seen in the most extreme shape, the parasitized cells have long, thread-like ends and no longer look like normal blood cells. The elongate forms are considered characteristic of the species, but there is reason to believe that many are no longer infective and that the spherical parasites are really the important types. These parasites undergo no further development until swallowed by suitable black flies that feed on the blood of ducks. Two kinds of black flies, and possibly others of the more than 50 species known in North America, are suitable hosts. Several species of black flies feed almost exclusively on birds. Furthermore some prefer certain species of birds.

THE BLACK FLIES that transmit *Leucocytozoon* to ducks show a strong preference for them and consequently are essential in spreading the parasite from duck to duck. Once within the fly, the one-celled parasites undergo a rapid transformation to sexual maturity. Fusion of male and female cells takes place within the stomach of the fly, and the resulting fertilized organisms enter the stomach wall. There the parasite changes its form, multiplies, and produces motile, comma-shaped structures, called sporozoites, within a cyst. The sporozoites escape through the membrane of the surrounding cyst and move from the stomach wall to the salivary gland of the fly. Sporozoites are the infective stage, and their development in the fly is completed in 4 to 18 days. The rate of development depends on temperature and other environmental factors. Sporozoites may remain for weeks within the salivary gland of an infected black fly.

When an infected fly feeds on a susceptible duck, some sporozoites move from the salivary gland into the puncture wound made by the fly. They are carried by the blood to the liver, spleen, heart, lung, and other organs, where they establish themselves. Developing stages of the parasite occur more often in the spleen than in any other organ. Here the growing parasite divides repeatedly. In 4 to 6 days, millions of minute sporelike structures are produced. These minute organisms escape into the bloodstream and invade young, red blood cells, in which they grow into male and female parasites, thus completing the life cycle. Ducks harbor these parasites from one season to the next and provide the source of infection for the black flies that transmit them.

BIRDS ARE THE SOLE HOSTS of *Leucocytozoon*. More than 150 species, including at least 20 species of ducks and geese in North America alone, are known to carry it. Associated most frequently with the disease are the mallard, black duck, wood duck, and teal.

The parasite is widely distributed throughout the world. It extends from Northwest Territories through the Midwest to New Brunswick and Maine. It is probably present in every State, Province, and county where waterfowl and black flies are present. Black flies responsible for its spread have been ascertained in only a few localities. Research since 1950 in Michigan, Ontario, and Wisconsin indicates widespread prevalence of the parasite in some places, but the exact distribution of the disease in other parts of the country is unknown.

LOCAL DISTRIBUTION of the disease depends on a number of factors, including the prevalence of black flies that feed on waterfowl. This necessitates a habitat in which the flies can feed, reproduce, and develop through their various stages, and survive. Conditions that favor one kind of black fly may be unsuitable for another. Running water of adequate depth, flow, temperature, and containing food for developing larvae is essential. The kinds and numbers of larvae in a stream will depend on differences in these factors and others, such as the nature of the streambed and the amount and kind of vegetation in it. If a stream is too cold, development of larvae of the black fly will be retarded, and the emergence of adult flies will not coincide with the hatching of ducks. Low air temperatures also interfere with feeding habits of the flies and retard development of the parasites in them. The local distribution of *Leucocytozoon* depends, also, on a population of infected and susceptible ducks and other waterfowl. These birds will be present only if the habitat is favorable.

HEAVY INFECTIONS MAY OCCUR in localities where the habitat favors the reproduction of both black flies and breeding ducks. Such conditions facilitate spread of the parasite from adult to young birds. The frequency of infection varies from place to place. In one instance, 100 percent of the mallards were infected at one locality, but the incidence 50 miles away was less than 10 percent. The intensity of infection also varies considerably among individuals. It is difficult in some parasitized birds to find a single parasite in the blood; in others, hundreds can be observed in a single microscopic field.

The organism is present in blood and tissues throughout the winter, but often few parasites are detectable. Toward spring and the onset of breeding, a mild relapse occurs in some birds, and the number of parasites in the blood increases. This favors transmission of the disease by black flies, which begin to emerge from streams in late April and early May. Infected flies then spread the disease rapidly.

During late May and June, another species of black fly, *Simulium rugglesi*, emerges and becomes the dominant vector. During this period, ducklings are hatching, and chances for transfer of the parasite to them are excellent. This is especially true when the parents have a large number of parasites in the blood as a result of infection by flies that emerged earlier. Absence of early black flies prevents spread of the parasites among adult birds prior to hatching time. With fewer parasites, the chance of large-scale transmission from adult to young is reduced. Transmission ceases toward the end of summer, when black flies disappear. The number of parasites in ducks then declines to the chronic level characteristic of those examined during the winter.

EARLY EMERGING BLACK FLIES involved in transmission feed largely on ducks, but if ducks are absent they will feed on other birds. This preference insures that a large percentage of the flies will become infected in habitats that support diseased waterfowl. In one locality in Ontario, 50 percent of the black flies *(S. rugglesi)* carried the organism. Such a high rate of infection has great potential for initiating an outbreak of the disease in ducks.

(Epidemics of malaria can occur when 1 percent of a mosquito population is carrying the infective stage of the parasite.)

Many black flies are known to live for weeks and appear to feed every 5 to 7 days if environmental conditions are favorable. Consequently, if the first feeding is on an infected duck, the parasite can be transmitted at each subsequent meal. Also, by means of radioactive isotopes, it has been found that flies move along a watershed for at least 2 to 6 miles. With a high percentage of infected flies that move freely up and down a stream and feed by preference on ducks, circumstances are favorable for widespread transmission. This may occur even when the population of flies and ducks is relatively small. All ducks become infected in one season in some localities.

KNOWLEDGE of the pathological changes is derived mostly from observations in domestic ducks and geese in which the disease is severe. Mortality rates as high as 90 percent were found among ducks in Michigan and in Canada. Mallards and occasionally black ducks succumb to infection. As a result of the susceptibility of the mallard to this disease, some investigators have suggested that *Leucocytozoon* is a factor limiting the successful extension of the mallard breeding range into black fly areas. Conversely, the presence of such species as black duck, wood duck, and the Canada goose within black fly areas, plus the high incidence of infection among these birds, suggest that they are comparatively resistant to the disease. The mortality rate in all cases is much higher among young than adults. The debilitating effects of the disease render ducks more susceptible to other maladies and predators.

Parasites in the blood are not noticed usually until 6 days or more after infection. If the infection is light, the organisms may not be seen in the blood for 10 to 14 days after exposure. The parasites become more numerous for 5 to 7 days after they first appear, and this increase is accompanied by an increase in the production of red blood cells and leucocytes. Despite the formation of new red blood cells, the total number drops because of the destruction of those parasitized. This destruction may involve more than half the normal number of cells. A marked anemia results. The blood becomes thin and watery in appearance. Birds suffering from such severe anemia seldom survive. The liver and spleen often are enlarged enormously. The spleen may be five to ten times the normal size. Most of the deaths occur 8 to 15 days after infection by flies.

Birds acutely ill with the disease refuse to eat, are listless, and have rapid and labored breathing and an unsteady gait. Some show signs of nervous excitement and disturbance immediately before death, which may occur suddenly. The rapid onset of the disease often is an outstanding feature of an outbreak. Death usually occurs in 2 to 4 days after the first signs of illness. Young birds that recover may not develop normally. Retarded growth is especially noticeable in ducks with heavy infections.

Adult birds frequently are chronically affected. The disease develops slowly, and they become thin and listless but rarely die. Regardless of age, all birds that recover remain carriers. Infection does not confer complete immunity, but a tolerance develops in birds subjected to continued reinfection. This resistance is lost in the absence of such repeated stimulus.

CONTROL OF THE DISEASE is possible but is hardly feasible on a large scale. The larval stage of black flies is easily killed, and local eradication has been accomplished where the insects were a nuisance to humans. Considering the vast range of these flies, however, a general program of control to destroy the chain of disease transmission to ducks is out of the question. We can, however, use our knowledge of the relationship in other ways.

If we know the types of habitats favored by ducks and flies that spread the parasite, we can investigate areas proposed as sanctuaries or as management units for waterfowl. Changing watercourses or creating artificial waterways, without considering the possibilities of creating or improving black fly habitat, could be detrimental rather than favorable to the production of more ducks. Few diseases of waterfowl are more intimately related to habitat than *Leucocytozoon*, and waterfowl management in black fly areas should consider this relationship.

FOUR OTHER KINDS of blood parasites *(Haemoproteus, Plasmodium, Trypanosoma,* and *Microfilaria)* are known in waterfowl in North America. Their incidence and distribution are only vaguely understood. Even less is known of their effects on populations. In some sites in Wisconsin, 24 percent of the waterfowl was found to be infected with *Haemoproteus,* and mortality of ducks was attributed to this parasite. Obviously more detailed investigations are needed to appraise the possible importance.

Undoubtedly many of the relationships between the habitat of waterfowl and associated chronic and fatal diseases await discovery.

Their presence, sometimes as severe outbreaks, in widely separated localities is well known and probably more significant than realized. Losses from disease may have been overlooked in the past when habitat and ducks were plentiful. In the future, however, management of waterfowl will be more intensive, necessitating a reappraisal of factors causing losses. Diseases described herein arise only if the environment is favorable; assessment of their impact on waterfowl and consideration of methods of coping with them should be included in our programs of research and management.

—A. MURRAY FALLIS and
DANIEL O. TRAINER, JR

BUFFLEHEAD—HEN AND BROOD

Blue-Greens

WE OFTEN SEE changes in the color and transparency of the water in lakes and potholes we know well. The cause is a complex interaction between the physical environment and a multitude of microscopic or near-microscopic, free-floating plants, the algae. These organisms usually are designated as plant plankton. Sometimes they grow so thickly as to produce a noticeable change in the color or turbidity of the water; then we say that a lake or pond is blooming. The phenomenon occurs the world over, and several languages have terms for it, all of them meaning water bloom.

Many kinds of algae grow in waters that ducks use. Most of them are harmless. A few are poisonous to wildfowl if they occur in tremendous numbers. When a toxic strain becomes predominant in a water bloom, hundreds of birds may die in a few hours. Then any living creature that drinks the water is a potential victim, and shorelines may be strewn with bodies of mammals, land birds, and waterfowl.

Algae blooms occur commonly. Their poisonous nature may not always be recognized, and the prevalence of algae poisoning may have been underestimated. Poison-

349

ous water blooms have been reported in nearly all regions where scientists have investigated them.

MANY KINDS OF ALGAE may be found in a bloom, but ordinarily one or two species outnumber all others. In a study of typical Minnesota blooms selected at random, technicians found seven genera and a total of 10 species of algae. All of them were blue-greens. Besides chlorophyll, the blue-greens have a blue pigment (phycocyanin) and sometimes a red one (phycoerythrin). The color of the Red Sea is attributed to the red tint given it by one of the blue-green algae.

The name "blue-green algae" is generally applicable but is somewhat misleading. Some are not blue-green but may be blue, black, red, purple, green, yellow, or various shades depending on the proportions of the pigment present. The group has been referred to as the rainbow algae. To the scientist they are known collectively as the cyanophytes.

BLOOMS OF BLUE-GREENS are commonest from midsummer to early fall, but they may occur at any time. Even in winter, when the ice may be several feet thick, algae blooms are not rare.

Under the ice of a lake, I have seen growths of *Oscillatoria rubescens* so luxuriant that the water, wherever I took a sample of it, resembled red wine. Millions of algae filaments, bluish green by transmitted light but red by reflected light, made the water cloudy. Because

this species floats easily, large numbers of filaments floated close against the ice, and many had been frozen in as the ice increased in thickness. The result was beautiful pink ice with scattered blotches of scarlet.

The usual winter bloom is not very distinctive—more like a green or bluish-green cloudiness. Summer blooms tend to be more concentrated. Often the organisms are so numerous that the water has the consistency and color of pea soup. They may even jell and form an opaque mass, like green gelatin.

The concentration of algae may not be uniform within a given lake, and day-to-day variations may occur as a result of changes in the weather. Heavy rains and cloudy days, for example, may temporarily reduce the concentration, as filaments or colonies are dispersed to greater depths and into greater volumes of water. A strong wind can shift a bloom from one part of the lake to another and usually will concentrate the algae along the lee shore. Any study that attempts to relate algae blooms to the welfare of wildfowl therefore must also take into account the physical features of the body of water.

IN THE LABORATORY, scientists have found that some algae can produce substances which will slow or stop the growth of others. One substance of this kind is an antibiotic (chlorellin). It is less efficient than penicillin but has marked effects against several types of bacteria.

The point is that if microscopic

aquatic plants can produce substances that may retard and poison other algae, it is not difficult to imagine that they can produce compounds harmful to animals and man. We have only limited information on algae toxin, but such a substance was recognized more than 85 years ago, and a number of losses of animals that can be laid to algae poisoning have occurred since then.

THE FIRST RECORD of algae poisoning was reported by George Francis, of Adelaide, Australia, in 1878. In a letter to a scientific journal, he described the phenomenon that we commonly refer to as toxic algae poisoning or water bloom poisoning. He mentioned the low water level and the high temperatures that year in Lake Alexandrina, one of the Murray estuary lakes, and the heavy bloom of algae that preceded and existed at the time domestic animals died along the shores of the lake.

Other references have been made since to losses of livestock and domestic animals in the United States, Australia, Canada, South America, South Africa, and other places.

My own interest in algae poisoning began in the winter of 1928, when I was snowbound for 2 days in a hotel in Waterville, Minn. I met an old resident who had witnessed cattle poisoning along the north shore of Lake Sakatah and Lake Tetonka in 1882 and 1883. Investigations at the time established that blue-green algae were responsible. His story prompted me to check the facts and led to an inter-est that has continued over the years.

On Aug. 10, 1941, I collected a toxic bloom of *Microcystic aeruginosa* less than 100 yards from the spot on Lake Sakatah where the cattle kill of 1882 occurred. The bloom, and material I collected later that fall, I still have. A frozen sample tested in 1957, 16 years later, was still potent. Dried material and alcohol extracts also have remained toxic. In 1947, poisonous algae were again found at Waterville, this time about 200 yards from the original site. This demonstrates that in certain lakes in the United States poisonous algae may be found repeatedly in a given area, a phenomenon that has been reported for the Murray estuary lakes where algae poisoning was first observed.

Because the reports of algae poisoning emphasized the death of livestock, many persons are skeptical of statements that algae are poisonous to wildfowl. They prefer to believe that such losses are actually brought about by the potent bacterial toxin that causes botulism. Circumstances at a waterfowl die-off often permit either interpretation. Field work at the time of the outbreak therefore must be planned so that one can later be certain that botulinus poisoning was not involved.

TWO STUDIES illustrate typical and undisputed algae poisoning episodes involving waterfowl. Each is presented in the form of a case history, and each represents a waterfowl kill in which botulinus toxin played no part. The first involved domestic animals and chickens as well as wild birds. The second for all practical purposes was restricted to wildfowl.

FOX LAKE, a shallow body of water a little more than 3 miles long, is in Martin County 12 miles east of Fairmont, Minn. At no point is it wider than a mile. Its surface area is about a thousand acres. Because its long axis has an east-west orientation, the lake is exposed to the full sweep and power of east and west winds. In summer, the shape of the lake and the wind direction usually have a marked effect on the distribution and concentration of algae. In winter, a heavy snow cover is usually laid down over the ice, and light is often shut out early in the season. Frequently this leads to a pronounced and progressive depletion of oxygen, which reaches its peak in February or March. Blooms of blue-green algae, common in all the shallow lakes of the region, tend to keep the dissolved oxygen high in summer.

During the first week of September 1948, an unusually heavy bloom of algae occurred in Fox Lake. Many sheltered places had extensive accumulations of heavy, green scum. After a few warm, sunny, and calm days, during which the microscopic plants continued to increase, a light northerly wind swept great masses of the floating algae toward the south shore. There they accumulated until a thick porridgelike suspension of tightly crowded cells and colonies occupied all of the shoreline and extended 5 to 20 yards into the

lake. Hogs, ducks, chickens, dogs, and other animals that had access to the south shore died in large numbers after they had consumed algae-laden water.

When the wind changed, a few days later, the algae were swept across the lake to the north side, where the sequence of events was repeated. Deaths ceased promptly when the algae were swept away from the south shore, and began just as promptly on the north side when the heavy algae scum accumulated there. Within about a week, the toxic bloom was responsible for the deaths of 79 hogs, 2 horses, and an uncounted number of chickens, ducks, geese, cats, and dogs. Many wildfowl and wild animals also were destroyed.

All losses of domestic animals occurred in approximately the same manner. A farmer on the north side of the lake kept a diary of events related to his farm operations. At sunrise on Sept. 3, according to his notes, he watched his valuable breeding hogs as they went down to the lakeshore to drink. All were in good health and normal in every way. At 7:00 a.m. he was surprised to find four of the animals dead. All of the others were seriously ill. By 10:00 a.m., 10 animals had died, and within the next 2 hours 24 hogs were dead or dying.

Many other losses occurred at other points on the lake. Only one dog, of many associated with farms around Fox Lake, remained alive on Sept. 19. He had been tied up during the critical days. Every farm lost poultry and cats.

An investigation was made on

Sept. 19 of the area and the circumstances of the outbreak. Many wild animals and birds that had drunk the water had died. Along the shoreline, remains were found of gray squirrels, muskrats, ducks, various species of shore birds, sparrows, and many carp. Pigeons had died in the barns and haylofts where they had taken refuge after drinking lake water. A partly paralyzed phalarope and an English sparrow, easily captured as they fluttered along the shoreline, were examined. Their legs were extended and useless. The wings, partly paralyzed, were being used to propel the birds along the ground. The nictitating membrane was found to be functional and not paralyzed. Such paralysis is usually considered as one of the characteristic symptoms of botulinus poisoning.

An offshore wind had broken up the blanket of scum on the lake, but the lake as a whole had a deep, blue-green color. The water was highly turbid with suspended algal filaments. Samples taken in the shallow areas about 15 feet from the shoreline contained a moderate suspension of extremely toxic algae cells. A small amount of the water killed mice in 20 minutes. An amount 10 times larger killed mice within 5 minutes. A small dose of algae produced extreme salivation and severe prostration in a rabbit. A heavy dose caused death in 17 minutes. A chicken, fed some of the algae by mouth, died in 84 minutes; paralysis was an important symptom.

Hamsters and guinea pigs inoculated with similar suspensions of the toxic material died within a few minutes. The guinea pigs and some of the mice produced foamy tears that contained a fat-staining substance, which was attributed to the discharge of the harderian gland. Boiled samples and samples treated with polyvalent botulinus antitoxin were as lethal to mice as untreated samples, demonstrating that a botulinus toxin was not involved. The species predominant in the samples was *Anabaena lemmermanni*.

EARLY IN THE FORENOON of Sept. 22, 1955, two game biologists were making a routine check of wildfowl in one of the leading duck hunting areas of northern Minnesota. They found large numbers of dead and dying ducks and other water birds along the east and southeast shores of Lake Reno near Glenwood. Taking note of the vivid, blue-green color of the water and the strange symptoms of the birds, they concluded that this was an outbreak of an algae poisoning and promptly referred the matter to their superiors. The same day, at the request of conservation authorities, I visited the area to see the outbreak firsthand and to determine, if possible, the cause.

Lake Reno is roughly pearshaped. Its longest axis runs southwest to northeast, with the narrowest dimension at the north end. It is 4 miles long and just over 2 miles wide. It has a total surface area of 3,940 acres and is less than 15 feet deep in most places. The lake is open to the full sweep of strong westerly winds, which frequently whip its surface into high waves. Since it is shallow and well fertilized by local runoff, the lake is highly productive, and algae blooms may be expected as a normal event. When the lake was visited on September 22 and 23, the wind was blowing strongly from the west, and a blue-green algae bloom was concentrated along the eastern and southeastern shores. So efficient was this wind transport that only a scattering of filaments could be seen on the west shore. On that side, the water was almost clear, and although I made a thorough search, I could not find a single dead or dying bird.

Directly opposite, on the east side, the situation was different. There filaments of the alga, *Anabaena lemmermanni*, were so numerous as to form a paintlike green scum. Dead birds lay everywhere. Moribund birds lay shivering in the cold wind, and apparently were suffering from exposure as well as from effects of the toxin. Along a strip of beach, less than 500 yards long, I picked up 26 red-winged blackbirds, a herring gull, 2 horned grebes, a blue-winged teal, and a great blue heron.

Farther south, dead and ailing birds lay entangled in rushes or partly awash on the sand bars. I undoubtedly missed many dead birds that may have been hidden in the vegetation. I counted 20 pied-bill grebes, 8 American coots, 2 black-crowned night herons, and one each of American bittern, mallard, and blue-winged teal. There was 1 muskrat. I saw many sick and dead frogs but no evidence that fish had been affected. Dogs permitted to visit the lake died shortly thereafter.

Other searchers who checked the shore the same day reported similar findings. Two men reported 108 birds. A flyway biologist made an aerial check of the lake about 2 weeks later and reported seeing 500 dead waterfowl.

That the Lake Reno outbreak of duck sickness was due to algae poisoning was established in later laboratory tests. One may also make certain inferences from the field experience itself. The weather was cold enough to prevent the algae from disintegrating rapidly. Since there was no opportunity for anaerobic conditions to develop, a botulinus toxin could not be produced in the algae mass. Boiling the algae suspension or treating it with an antitoxin did not protect test animals or birds. Finally, the symptoms produced were identical to those seen in other poisoning episodes where the same algae had been involved.

Microscopic examination of the bloom in the field showed that the filaments were normal. There was no sign of breakdown of cells or filaments. This may be attributed to the cold weather and to the fact that the filaments had only recently been concentrated by wind. The species was *Anabaena lemmermanni* and (for practical purposes) the bloom was composed of this one species. When four teaspoonfuls of the unconcentrated suspension were later fed to a great blue heron, it died within 14 minutes. Similarly, an American bittern fed a small dose died within 3 hours. A mallard duck died in 13 minutes. Thus, an oral dose of as little as one-fifth teaspoonful of fresh algae was enough to cause death.

Later, to ascertain more exactly

the potency of the poison, a larger number of animals and varying dosages of the algae suspension were used.

Without going into all the details of our tests. I found, for instance, that mallards were more resistant than mice. There was evidence of individual differences in resistance among ducks. In general, time of death was related directly to the size of the dose.

The symptoms produced by the algae toxin from Lake Reno were typical of those usually associated with blooms of *Anabaena lemmermanni.* In this type of poisoning, mice stretch and arch their backs soon after injection. The tail assumes a characteristic tense, flexed curve, the eyes bulge, and the fur becomes rough. At the end of 2 minutes the eyes project alarmingly and foamy tears may appear. Within seconds the mouse develops violent convulsions and dies.

Ducks react more slowly and during the first stages they lose their sense of equilibrium and fall forward on the breast. Later, they lose their voice, and their eyes water. In 20 minutes paralysis is evident, and soon the head and neck are strongly drawn back over the shoulder in an S-shaped curve. After this point has been reached, the bird usually dies within a few minutes.

ALGAE TOXIN can exist in water outside the cells. It passes through cellophane and animal membranes by dialysis, is nonvolatile, and relatively heat stable. It is soluble in water, alcohol, and acetone, but not in benzene, ether, or chloroform. It is resistant to changes in acidity, and does not respond to specific tests for nitrite, pilocarpine, saponins, or glycosides.

P. R. Gorham, of the National Research Council, Ottawa, has demonstrated that there are both toxic and nontoxic strains of *Microcystis aeruginosa* and *Anabaena flosaquae.* This means that with no apparent change in the species or of the algae concentration which characterizes a bloom, there may be a waxing or waning of its toxicity. The potency will depend on the genetic strain which prevails. This phenomenon was demonstrated in the Fox Lake episode in 1948.

If we examine the facts further, we find evidence of slow-kill and fast-kill algae toxins. The slow-kill type, the first to come to my attention, has been associated with blooms in which *Microcystis* was the chief component. Mice inoculated with this type usually died within 20 minutes to 2 hours. The fast-kill has been associated with *Anabaena* blooms, especially those in which *Anabaena lemmermanni* was predominant. In this case, experimental animals given a moderate dose could be expected to die in 2 to 20 minutes.

AN ADDITIONAL POINT should be kept in mind. Not all blooms are poisonous, and not all species that produce a bloom are toxic. This was demonstrated by a field study in Minnesota in 1948–1950, when 92 algae blooms collected at random were examined. It was found that only nine species of algae were consistent and important constituents of heavy blooms and that all were blue-greens. *Microcystis aeruginosa,* the most important species, occurred in 87 percent of all blooms and also made up the bulk of the growth. In half the blooms, it comprised two-thirds of the volume; in one-third, it was practically the only species.

Aphanizomenon flos-aquae was half as frequent and second in importance. *Anabaena lemmermanni,* the most toxic to wildfowl, occurred in only 16 percent of the blooms and reached a volume ratio of 80 percent in only two instances. It was important but not dominant in eight blooms. Field tests with mice showed that 49 (about half) of all the blooms examined were toxic. The potency varied greatly.

EXTENSIVE ALGAE BLOOMS are potentially dangerous to waterfowl, especially where the principal component is *Anabaena flos-aquae* or *Anabaena lemmermanni,* which may be the same algae. More than one-half of the blooms encountered in random collections have been toxic to some degree. One can appreciate the potentialities when weather conditions favor the production of a heavy blue-green bloom or when the wind may concentrate a moderate bloom.

To forestall wildfowl losses, it would be desirable to keep surface waters free of heavy algae growths. Unfortunately, this is an unrealistic goal for the 1960's, and perhaps beyond, because of the many unknowns. But as a part of our conservation responsibility, we hope that some solution to the problem may come from an energetic program of research on the quality of water and control of algae.

—THEODORE A. OLSON.

Habitat is then the starting point for any and all successful game increase. If we are to increase a game species, we must first know the habitat requirement of the species, then find or create and preserve that environmental type.

—WALLACE GRANGE.

Men at Work

SHOVELERS

Dredges and Ditches

THE FACE OF AMERICA is being changed. Water that once remained in low spots and provided habitat for wildlife now collects in ditches and tile lines and is rushed to the nearest stream. Millions of acres that once grew cattails, wildrice, and pondweeds now support wheat, corn, houses, factories, airports, and roads. Of 127 million acres of wetlands present in the United States in colonial times, more than 45 million acres have been drained for dry land use.

And reclamation goes on. The Census of Agriculture for 1959, showing 92,269,864 acres in farm-land drainage projects, reported that 5,336,593 acres were added between 1950 and 1959. This does not mean that all wetlands suitable for waterfowl are now part of drainage projects. Most of the project acres are lands too wet to farm but not wet enough to provide waterfowl habitat. However, many millions of acres of good waterfowl habitat have been destroyed and the loss continues.

Dredges and ditches have had a profound effect on our agriculture, our industries, our economy, and our waterfowl. They were not used deliberately to destroy duck domain, but were used to convert waterways and wetlands to more profitable channels and lands. Our economy is one of dollars, not ducks, but that does not mean the two are totally incompatible. In many places throughout the continent waterfowl are important economic assets and nearly everywhere they are desirable esthetic assets. Ducks have been hurt by unwise drainage of good waterfowl wetlands but they are far from being knocked out.

The public, if it wants waterfowl, must be militant in seeing that vital habitat is not destroyed and that wetlands not now productive and not economically feasible of being drained are flooded and managed for ducks.

Hopefully, understanding and resolvement may be in sight. The beginning of multipurpose water programs in both Canada and the United States signals recognition of the continent's wetland values. The next main step is coordinated planning by all groups having interests in wetland use. Initial instances of this are mentioned later in this chapter.

IN CANADA, the principal breeding ground for most North American waterfowl, many millions of acres of wetlands remain. But most of the acreage is in the infertile forest and tundra region, or rocky shield, where waterfowl production is generally low.

The more fertile prairie-parkland regions of Manitoba, Saskatchewan, and Alberta, upon which hunters depend so heavily for their sport, are in the early stages of a potentially great drainage program. This vast 220,000-square-mile nesting ground for ducks also is an important agricultural region of the world and unless a solution is forthcoming soon the "handwriting is on the wall" because nesting waterfowl and farmers share the fertile Canadian prairie. During the wet mid-fifties, these prairies had about 6.5 million areas of surface water and attracted a breeding population of about 25 million ducks. In dry 1961, water was reduced to 1.7 million areas and duck production was only a fraction of that in a wet-cycle year.

Large but unrecorded acreages of wetlands have been lost because of road construction. Roadside ditches act as drainage channels, draining one slough into another, or into a creek or river system, where much of the water is eventually lost to waterfowl. Roadside ditches further the drainage efforts of farmers since they serve as channels into which nearby ponds can be emptied. In some parts of the prairies this type of drainage has destroyed more waterfowl areas than any other.

More recently, most land drainage in Saskatchewan has been done through the Conservation and Development Branch of the Department of Agriculture, working with locally organized Conservation and Development Area Authorities. The Conservation and Development Act of 1949 enabled the Department of Agriculture to provide all technical assistance and 50 percent of the construction costs, including drainage, on private lands and land-reclamation projects. Projects are listed as flood control (most are drainage) and irrigation (some are drainage with temporary early

The dragline is not always used to drain wetlands. This one is operated by the Michigan Department of Conservation to improve waterfowl habitat on Shiawassee Flats, Michigan.

spring backflooding), and only the costs of construction, operation, and maintenance are given.

However, Ducks Unlimited has recorded at least 22 major marshes totaling 57 thousand acres which have been destroyed. The records also show that 26 out of 743 large marshes in the prairie region have been ditched, a loss of 39,330 acres

of wetlands out of 1,882,000 rated
as valuable to waterfowl. Losses
among the more valuable smaller
marshes are expected to run higher,
especially as emphasis in drainage
has shifted from flood relief in the
cultivated areas to the development
of hay-producing lands in the parkland and forest-fringe regions.

Drainage through Conservation
Authorities by the Department of
Agriculture in Manitoba has followed about the same pattern as in
Saskatchewan. Alberta has been
more aware of water conservation,
especially in the drier south, but
the parkland can be expected to
suffer from drainage losses.

Another form of wetlands loss is
the diking of coastal marshlands in
the Maritime Provinces against
ocean tides. Nova Scotia, New
Brunswick, and Prince Edward Island have 123 diking projects to
protect more than 80 thousand
acres from such floodwaters. E. L.
Paynter, Wildlife Director of Saskatchewan, reported in 1962 that
reclamation of agricultural marsh in
Nova Scotia had taken 63 thousand
acres of waterfowl habitat; and in
the St. John River basin, plans were
afoot to reclaim more than 50
thousand acres of inland marsh.

Wetlands have also disappeared
on the west coast of Canada.
Drained are 6 thousand acres of the
Fraser River Delta; 135 acres of
the Boundary Bay marsh; and 600
acres of marsh have been diked and
pumped for agriculture at Beach
Grove. Applications are filed for the
development of an additional 8
thousand acres in Boundary Bay for
industrial, residential, and park
usage. Marshlands of Iona and Sea

Islands are now used for sewage-
disposal; and 4 thousand acres of
Burns Bog were drained and turned
into sanitary fill. All of the fields in
the Benson Road area near Ladner
have been tiled, and choice waters,
formerly heavily used by waterfowl,
have been eliminated.

STATESIDE in the Atlantic Flyway,
as in Canada, agricultural drainage
and flood control have taken their
toll of duck habitat. Eliminated by
canal construction, drained for mosquito control, destroyed by highway building, industrial or commercial expansion, and filled for
new residential and city parks, are
millions of acres of marsh and
swamp. More than 9 million acres
of coastal marshes have been ditched
for mosquito control, channeled for
navigation, and drained for agricultural production.

Dismal Swamp in North Carolina and Virginia once covered
1,500 square miles. Since colonial
days this unique area has been
ditched, channeled, and dredged,
and now only 600 square miles are
left. Back Bay and Currituck Sound,
famous for waterfowl and comprising 300 square miles, were nearly
lost from excessive salt-water intrusion and pollution in the twenties,
when the guard lock in the Albe-
marle and Chesapeake Canal was
removed and the canal enlarged.
Installation of a suitable lock
stopped the inflow from Norfolk
Harbor 10 years later. Subsequent
ditching and continued dredging
dumped silt and heavily stained
waters directly into Back Bay, destroying much of the aquatic vegetation, the ducks' food supply. The

eventual status of this important segment of the Atlantic Flyway is cause for concern.

Marshes in the Northeastern States have been ditched, dredged, drained, diked, and filled to the point where few good waterfowl areas remain. Mosquito-control ditches traverse every sizable salt-water marsh along the coast. Their grid pattern is interesting as viewed from a plane, but their effect on the marshes is all bad for black ducks. Waters now rise and fall with the tides and choice food plants pass with each ditch and dike.

Studies by the Bureau of Sport Fisheries and Wildlife have shown that most of the large marsh areas along the Delaware River have been destroyed during the past two centuries. In 1957, only 2,450 acres of good waterfowl habitat remained along the Delaware between Phila-delphia and Trenton, and only 300 acres of good marshland were scattered along tributary streams close to the main river.

The largest and most important of these wetlands is the Crosswicks Creek-Trenton Marsh of 990 acres just south of Trenton. Philadelphia Conservationists Incorporated, and the Broad Street Park Civic Association, have purchased large sections of the marsh to insure its preservation. If the Army Engineers follow the study-team report of the Fish and Wildlife Service and acquire, through the Coordination Act, the five key areas recommended, the remaining marshes can be saved.

The wetlands of Long Island, with their marshes, mud flats, and tidal shallows, are an important waterfowl asset. These, and the South Shore complex of bays, furnish more than 5 million waterfowl

A drainage ditch in prairie country. The dragline adds to wheat surplus and aggravates waterfowl deficit.

use-days each year between October 1 and April 30. Such waterfowl
use, practically in the shadows of
Manhattan's skyscrapers, seems incredible. Postwar development of
Long Island has nearly doubled
the human population, and resultant demands for space are eating
away the wetlands here at an
alarming rate.

The towns of Hempstead and
Oyster Bay own a large share of
the tidal wetlands. And, encourag-
ingly, after State and Federal
biologists informed town officials of
the need for wetland protection,
they requested recommendations for
fish and wildlife preservation and
development of the marshes for
recreational uses.

The results of this survey, made
in 1959 by the New York State
Conservation Department and the
Bureau of Sport Fisheries and Wildlife, revealed that 12.5 percent of
the wetlands had been destroyed
since 1954, 30 percent of the remaining wetlands were in danger
of being destroyed in the next 5
years, and 39 percent may go after
a longer interval.

The report, published in 1961,
recommended that the South Shore
marshes and lands under water
owned by the towns within the
area—15 miles long and 3.5 miles
wide—be dedicated to fish and
wildlife conservation for the public
benefit. After dedication, it was suggested that management be guided
by recommendations prepared for
each of the 17 units comprising the
Hempstead-Oyster Bay area.

The Long Island Wetlands Bill
of 1959 provided a legal means for
the State to give financial assistance
to Long Island towns or counties
for wetlands preservation and development. To date, none has taken
advantage of this legislation, but
public opinion regarding wetlands
is changing as more and more people become aware of the recreational values of this land type.

IN THE MISSISSIPPI FLYWAY, extensive marshes, sloughs, oxbows, and
river bottoms have been ditched
and dredged from northwestern
Minnesota to coastal Louisiana.
The 1963 Census of Agricultural
Drainage showed nearly 73 million
acres of land in Mississippi Flyway
States involved in drainage programs. Although millions of wetland
acres have been eliminated or depleted, there is still in the flyway
about 11 million acres of high or
moderate value to waterfowl, more
than in any other flyway.

Drainage has hit especially hard
some of the choicest wetlands in
the flyway. The near total elimination of the Kankakee River marshes
along 240 miles of that river in Indiana is a major example. The
fabulous bottom-land areas along
the Illinois and Mississippi Rivers in
Illinois are another example of extensive drainage. Many of these
bottom lands were formerly lakes
and marshes that have been leveed
and drained for agriculture. About
half of the flood plain of the Illinois
River valley has been blocked off
by raising and improving levees.

In Iowa, once an important
duck-producing State, ditches by
the thousands have reduced wetlands until today Iowa turns out

but a small fraction of its former
wildfowl crop. Ditching for agriculture in Minnesota has squeezed
water from more millions of acres
of marsh. Fortunately for waterfowl,
many of the larger projects in the
northwestern section of Minnesota,
and in Beltrami, Marshall, and
Roseau Counties, were agricultural
failures, and the State and Federal
Governments have taken title to
much of the land in the affected
localities and are developing them
for waterfowl use. Thief Lake and
Mud Lake in Marshall County
were entirely drained in 1923, but
have now been partly restored and,
under management, probably are
more productive than ever before.
The Great Horicon Marsh in Wisconsin is another excellent example
of successful restoration after unwise
drainage.

At the southern end of the Mississippi Flyway, Louisiana still has
nearly 2.5 million acres of wetland
of high or moderate waterfowl
value. This most important wintering ground can still supply the
winter needs of ducks and geese
despite the vast number of wetlands
adversely affected by water-control
structures, the Intracoastal Canal,
highway and railroad grades, and
canals for transportation, irrigation,
and drainage.

The Gulf Outlet Channel Project
in Louisiana, begun in 1957, was
about half finished in 1964. Approximately 2,100 square miles of coastal
marsh will be affected by the channel, which is 36 feet deep and 500
feet wide at the bottom and which
will cut through the marsh from
Lake Ponchartrain to the Gulf. In

its construction, safeguards have
been taken to maintain as nearly
as possible the original drainage
patterns and marsh elevations. Lock
systems have been designed to retain existing bayou flowage systems.
The dredged silt is being settled in
a series of lagooned basins 4 thousand feet wide, stretching, when the
project is completed, for 70 miles
across the coastal marshes. It is too
early to tell how this huge under-
taking will affect the vast marsh so
highly valuable for waterfowl and
many other kinds of wildlife.

IN CENTRAL FLYWAY STATES wetlands used by ducks and geese have
much the same history of dredging
and ditching as those of the other
flyways. The important waterfowl
breeding grounds in North Dakota,
South Dakota, and Nebraska have
been severely affected by agricultural drainage; and the great river
systems of this flyway have been
modified by dams, ditches, dikes, and
channels. Some of the largest reservoirs in the country have been built
in these three States.

A wetlands inventory of the Central Flyway States, made in the
mid-fifties, classified as of high or
moderate waterfowl value a total
of 5,008,700 acres. The 1959 drainage census listed approximately
9,408,000 acres of agricultural lands
as having been "benefited" by
drainage. It is interesting to note
that Texas, the main wintering area
for waterfowl in the flyway, contained more than half the drainage
acreage, while the most important
duck-breeding States, North Dakota,
South Dakota, and Nebraska, con-

tained approximately one-third, or 3,039,000 acres, of the total treated.

Another threat to the 1,368,000 acres of coastal wetlands remaining in Texas is entirely different. The Texas Water Plan calls for a level coastal canal that will cut across the Neches, Trinity, Brazos, Colorado, Guadalupe, Nueces and several smaller rivers. This construction will almost certainly change water salinity in lagoons important to wintering waterfowl. There is danger that this change will upset the delicately balanced biotic community and make the areas much less productive of waterfowl food.

THE PACIFIC FLYWAY, although some of its greatest inland wetlands have been plundered, still is in relatively good shape for ducks, geese, and coots. Its six States had about 1.8 million acres of wetlands of high and moderate value in the mid-fifties. But about 2.6 million acres of farmland had been drained by this time, including approximately 1.9 million acres in California. The Pacific Flyway has only about 3 or 4 percent of the nation's wetlands but they are of exceptional quality for wintering waterfowl.

The Great Central Valley of California originally had a belt of marshland along its entire length. By 1929, drainage and irrigation had reduced the marshes by at least 90 percent. Throughout California, agricultural drainage and irrigation have taken a tremendous toll, and the best waterfowl marshes remaining in 1964 were owned and managed by duck clubs, or had been purchased and developed by the State or Federal Government. In spite of this history of drainage and irrigation, the remaining California wetlands and the nearby croplands winter excellent numbers of waterfowl. This indicates that high quality wetlands and adjacent good croplands can support waterfowl, at least some species.

Water for irrigation has been the largest factor in changing the Oregon wetlands east of the Cascade Range. Here, the critical water supply has been largely soaked up by agricultural lands, but important wetlands like Klamath and Malheur have been restored by the government.

But there are some bright spots. The development of irrigated lands in the Columbia River Basin of Washington has greatly improved conditions for wintering ducks. This experience suggests that necessary canal and reservoir systems may be devised in such manner as to serve the needs of both agriculture and waterfowl.

Wetlands, countrywide, have been, and are being, drained and diked, or filled through industrial, urban, and recreational expansion; and roads and airports, dumps and city parks, are taking over former waterfowl lands and waters as shown in the foregoing.

Obviously, as the human population expands, wetlands for wildlife will wither. The jobs of saving present marshes and building new ones will grow. So will the costs. Never before has it been so necessary to find ways and means of preserving and managing habitat to meet the needs of waterfowl, and to provide space for people to enjoy outdoor recreation involving either watching or hunting wildfowl.

In our present economy, dollars and ducks are about as compatible as mustard and mumps. The basic problem is not man versus ducks, as many believe. Nearly everyone likes ducks. Instead, it is that nearly everyone likes dollars more; and society, therefore, condones drainage for greenbacks—at the expense of greenheads.

This is not surprising, since society has seldom shown sustained concern for its environment. Man drains water from land to convert newborn acres to (excess) grain production in the hope of faster dollar gain. He has not stopped to balance long-term gains and losses, for only recently have men come to know the value of marsh environments. Now, there is evidence of people awakening . . . the beginning of a change in public opinion. The public must come to know the true value of the continent's wetlands; and the people must be shown that rampant destruction of these lands is fast-buck folly.

In coastal drainage, the delicate balance between wet and dry areas and between fresh and salt waters, which creates the enormously productive environment so favored by many species of waterfowl, has been disrupted. Here, other than waterfowl has paid the price: Fin fish and shellfish, dependent on these wetland types as nursery waters, have been especially hard hit.

Other factors favoring loss of wetlands have to do with growing populations and increasing demands on water and land. Frank Shefrin and M. W. Menzies foresee an increase of 70 percent in the total physical volume of food consumed in Canada, and an 80 percent increase in world demand, before 1980. A. Leahey has said that of 40 million acres of arable land in Canada not under production, 24 million acres lie in the Prairie Provinces, with 6 million in their prairie regions.

Getting down to the individual, the private landowner will ditch and drain simply to be rid of nuisance water. Economics will determine other private drainage, and presently operating subsidized drainage programs will be a major factor in those that would otherwise be uneconomical. Also, pressure will continue to be strong for drainage of public lands for the benefit of local interests, where the government pays the entire cost.

As noted, probably the most promising sign is the recognition given in some places to the multipurpose approach in water management, which recognizes drainage in wetland management. The Prairie Farm Rehabilitation Association and Ducks Unlimited have created or improved wetlands in the Prairie Provinces, and this is an encouraging effort at recouping losses. The former, however, has been instrumental in destroying wetlands; and, at the present rate of loss, wetlands being developed for wildlife will fall far short of balance.

ANY PLAN leading to success in maintaining significant wetland acreage must first be provided with basic data on what the needs are, and what is presently available to meet those needs. Actually, we are not certain of the extent of damage to the resource by drainage in Canada, other than locally. It is virtually certain that this habitat loss will continue before final adjustment of the wetland type, for bulldozers and draglines are already at work. Now, it is time to plug some ditches, build some levees, and actually set aside some still undrained wetlands for ducks and geese.

In reality, the wetlands are being "managed" for us, and if we do not come up with more than a hands-off attitude they will be "managed" to extinction. Agricultural agencies don't need wildlife biologists; and private landowners know biologists as people who count birds, set the conditions of duck hunting, and oppose draining of water-logged land! But landowner-supported agencies are open to the expressed interests of their constituents, and these sturdy men of the land are as fair-minded as they are understanding. Our cue is to provide understanding: That wetlands are a part of the landscape, that wetland products are of recreational interest and material value to all; and that these products can be provided for all in an equitable program of wetland zoning, purchase, and lease, according to detailed prelaid plans formulated on a watershed basis.

And then, once acquired, the larger and more important wetlands must be managed; and management will require the services of engineers and land-use specialists, as well as guidance by wildlife biologists. The basis of management must be a broad consideration of interests, not the will of a particular clientele. And where there are conflicts of interest, as there will be, resolvement must be from the broad, over-all standpoint, predicated on watershed needs not only now but in the future.

But acquisition and management of wetlands by conservation agencies are not the whole answer by a long shot. Think of the task of acquiring and managing 5 million potholes! No agency or combination of agencies would have the money and manpower to go it alone. It was previously pointed out that the basic problem is one of economics. Perhaps the only real assurance of an understanding or a workable basis is to use the "money in the pocket" approach. Farmers, like everyone else, will exchange greenheads for greenbacks. This is the medium of exchange universally acceptable on the North American Continent. Wetlands will be saved if it is worthwhile financially for the landowner to save them. Reimbursing the farmer for reclaimable acreage committed to waterfowl use or for services rendered must be part of any plan to guarantee waterfowl for tomorrow.—ALLAN T. STUDHOLME and THOMAS STERLING

Potholes—Going, Going . . .

WE DROVE QUIETLY through the half-light before dawn toward Mallard Marsh. There, as the sun rose we would see, as we often had, dozens of ducks, shorebirds, muskrats, pheasants, and maybe a white-tail buck and some Canada geese.

Light was in the eastern sky when we stopped at our usual spot and got out in the morning chill to get our gear from the trunk. We sensed that something was different, but it took us a minute or two to realize what it was. Always before there had been sounds of contented quacking, of cackling as pheasants awoke and flew from the marsh, and of singing as small birds greeted the morning.

Now, only silence.

We walked up a ridge where we would be able to see the sunrise reflected in the waters of Mallard Marsh. But there was no reflection. There was no water. Now, only a broad mudflat with dying clumps of cattail and bulrush.

We had seen Mallard Marsh in really dry years. Drought comes to this country every few years. But how could Mallard Marsh be empty of water and wildlife in this wet year? We knew many smaller marshes were full of water.

We began to edge around the 40-

acre expanse. Then we saw it—a 20-foot gouge in the prairie lay across our path. It was an open drainage ditch, new.

Now, in full sunlight, we could see the scar leading across the empty marsh. We followed it to where it branched from three smaller potholes, also dry and devoid of wildlife. Retracing our steps, we walked down the ditch until we came to a deep delta of eroded silt, where the drain ended in Prairie Creek. Here the waters of Mallard Marsh had gone on a journey of no return.

Here was permanent drought. What had happened to Mallard Marsh had happened to countless numbers of the myriad potholes that dotted the northern prairies when the white men settled there. Uncounted flocks of ducks reared their young in these prairie waters. They continued to thrive as the immigrants plowed the soil and planted their crops as they had done on the lands they left.

A change came in the late 1800's. New kinds of machinery increased the amount of work a farmer could do and the land he could till. He drained the potholes to increase his acreage. Reclamation of potholes began in the rich soils of the Midwest—first in Iowa, then Nebraska, Minnesota, the Dakotas, and Canada. As drainage became more complicated, judicial drainage districts were established. Everyone seemed to want to get water off the land faster and faster.

The Government gave free engineering services as far back as the 1930's and during the Second World War began to share the cost of

drainage with the farmer so as to raise more food. This assistance continued after the war. Thus private, judicial, and Federally assisted drainage were alined to remove water from the potholes.

POTHOLES CAN BE DRAINED and destroyed in several ways. Drainage by open ditches—the way it was done at Mallard Marsh—has been most widespread. You can see the scars of the operation for many years. It is simply ditching from a wetland to an outlet at a lower level—to another wetland basin, a roadside ditch, a river, or a flat within the field. Open drains are used to dry out temporary as well as permanent wetlands.

When you dig a ditch to drain a pothole, you have to put the fill material someplace. Often this spoil is dumped into another pothole. Thus when one pothole is destroyed by ditching, another may be destroyed by filling. Other potholes may be lost through incidental drainage in the ditching process, when the ditch must pass through other potholes to reach an outlet. The drainage of small, temporary wetlands often causes incidental drainage of better marshes.

Tile drainage, another method, is used in deep, flat soils, large marshes, and waterlogged fields. A network of tile, properly installed under the ground, completely drains an area. Surface water percolates through the soil into the small tiles, then to larger tiles, a ditch, a river, and finally out of the country. Tile leaves no evidence of drainage because farming operations continue over the buried system. Tile drainage is popular in southern Minnesota, southern South Dakota, Iowa, and Nebraska.

Terraces often dry out wetlands. They are built across sloping fields so as to slow down the movement of rain and snow-melt to control runoff and erosion. Terraces do protect soil. Constructed without thought for wildlife, however, terraces can destroy wetlands by holding back water needed to replenish them.

A diversion, one kind of terrace, intercepts runoff, but it diverts the water to an outlet that takes it away. A South Dakota farmer in 1961 started a 10-year plan to dry up a hundred-acre marsh by making 100 miles of terraces. The success of such a project no doubt would encourage others to do the same.

Land leveling also eliminates breeding areas of waterfowl. Common in the Rain Water Basin of central Nebraska, it has spread to other States. This practice fills the pothole with soil, leaving a level field. Sometimes a field is shaped or graded to improve drainage or leveled for irrigation or to prevent erosion. All make for efficient farming, but they are permanent land treatments that destroy habitat of wildlife.

MANY WETLANDS near centers of population become city or town dumps and are filled eventually. Builders of highways and roads sometimes drain wetlands. Wetlands are filled for housing developments.

County and judicial drainage ditches go through the middle of some of the finest wetlands in the prairie pothole area. These large ditches drain the potholes; they also provide outlets for the ditching and tiling of all wetlands in the vicinity of the main or lateral ditches.

The soil material that flowing water picks up is dropped when the water reaches a depression. Deposition of sediment is a continuing process. It can fill wetland basins completely. The rate at which wetlands are filled with silt depends on nearby farming practices, such as stripcropping and contour plowing, the kind of crops that are grown, and the intensity of rainfall. Depending on how he handles his land, a farmer can slow and almost halt siltation or he can increase the rate greatly. Some potholes have been filled up with silt after one heavy rainstorm.

A farmer who plows around a wetland in one direction can actually plow his low hills into a basin and fill it over in a few years. Generally that is done only on small, temporary potholes.

ONCE STARTED IN AN AREA, drainage tends to spread. Heavy, expensive equipment has to be used if it is to give a reasonable return on a large investment. Most of the drainage is done by small contractors, but large contractors, consulting engineers, suppliers of material and equipment, and some farmers also have a part in the drainage industry. They of course are looking for work. County commissioners and members of county agricultural committees are prone to approve drainage projects which provide work for local labor and increase the acreage of high-tax lands. So it goes. So do the potholes.

WHAT EFFECT does the drainage of potholes have on waterfowl? We have strong evidence that the effect is bad.

F. R. Kenney and W. L. McAtee in the 1938 *Yearbook of Agriculture* said that drainage of the most productive waterfowl breeding places in the northern Great Plains was one of the prime factors in reducing the waterfowl populations of North America

Clay Schoenfeld in an article, "Good-by Pot-Holes", in *Field and Stream* in 1949 pointed out that 6,285 acres in some 1,400 pothole areas had been drained in Day County, S. Dak. The potholes ranged from one-eighth acre to 90 acres and averaged 4 acres. Some 350 farmers had participated. The Government paid them 17,285 dollars for digging 43 miles of ditches in 1948.

Nearly three potholes to the square mile were drained in an areas of 15,803 square miles in west-central Minnesota during 1945–1950. The area had 14.2 potholes to the square mile in 1950; thus over 16 percent of the water areas were drained in the 5 years. Some 64 thousand potholes, whose total surface area was 188 thousand acres, were destroyed in Minnesota and North and South Dakota in 1949 and 1950. That was done with subsidy payments; many others were drained without payments and did not appear in the records.

FEDERAL ASSISTANCE was given for the drainage of about 72 thousand individual potholes in 89 counties in Minnesota and the Da-

Erosion can destroy potholes as effectively as drainage or drought. This extreme case was in Minnesota, near Fergus Falls.

kotas in the 8 years following 1953. This drainage destroyed more than 79 thousand acres of waterfowl habitat. The average annual amount of subsidized drainage in the 89 counties was 9,885 acres. The average size of the wetlands was 1.1 acres. Fifty-eight percent were small wetlands that usually dried up in late spring, but were used by ducks for courtship and nesting; 39 percent were wetlands of the type that usually are bigger and hold water longer; the rest were deep marshes where ducks nest and rear broods.

In Cerro Gordo Township, Lac Qui Parle County, in Minnesota, the 1,668 acres of potholes at the end of 1954 were reduced to 627 acres by 1962. Drainage had eliminated 62 percent in 7 years.

Farmington Township in Lake County, a good duck-production section of South Dakota, had 385 potholes before any artificial drainage. By 1961 only two-fifths or 147 of the original potholes remained. Drainage had destroyed 83 percent of the acreage and 62 percent of the number of potholes. Federal technical and financial assistance was used during the 8 years beginning in 1954 to drain 2.3 percent per year of the number of potholes remaining at the end of 1953.

The annual report of the Agricultural Stabilization and Conservation Service for Minnesota for 1960 showed that 141,908 acres were drained by permanent open drainage systems to dispose of excess water. This assistance cost the Government 575,850 dollars on 2,886 farms in 74 counties. Assistance of 638,906 dollars was provided for tile drainage for 26,747 acres on 2,464 farms in 50 counties. The report did not specify the extent of waterfowl habitat lost, but undoubtedly a great deal was included in the drainage of 168,655 acres.

Drainage of potholes was at the same rate in 1962 as in 1961 in Minnesota and North Dakota but was less in South Dakota. Wetter conditions in 1962 probably emphasized the need for additional drainage in some places. Apparently much of it was done privately, because Government assistance was more restricted.

If subsidized drainage in the primary 89 counties of greatest importance to waterfowl in the three States should continue at the average rate for 1954–1961 of 9,885 acres a year, about 375,630 more acres of waterfowl habitat will be eliminated before the year 2000. The figure is for subsidized drainage, not drainage or losses of habitat by other means.

So far we have considered only the direct effect of drainage on waterfowl. Indirect effects also are serious. For example, networks of drainage ditches empty into many tributaries of the Minnesota River. They increase the rate of runoff so that more silt moves into streamside marshes. Many places that once were marshes are so filled with sediment that they are now covered with noxious weeds and dense stands of willows. You can see examples of streamside marsh siltation in southern Minnesota between Fort Ridgely and New Ulm, between St. Peter and LeSueur, and east of Shakopee along the Minnesota River.

DESTRUCTION OF WETLANDS on the Canadian prairies is occuring in the 1960's although not as rapidly as in prairie States. Drainage is the commonest method and usually is effected by open ditches. Tile drainage, hitherto little used, probably will expand because of its greater efficiency, particularly in unstable soils.

Most drainage in Canada is undertaken to reclaim wetlands for agricultural crops, hay, or pastureland. Temporary water on grain fields in the spring is a nuisance to farmers; that is often sufficient reason for its removal. Losses of wetlands also result from urban and industrial development and construction of airports, and particularly from highway development.

Flood control, irrigation, and land reclamation projects also take their toll. Water in a marsh may flood surrounding farmland in wet years; the removal of the floodwater may lead to the drainage of the whole marsh. Because lack of control structures at the outlet is usually the cause, what sometimes is called flood control actually is complete drainage.

Road building has led to the draining of many potholes in the Canadian prairies by providing farmers with a readymade trunk ditch. It is more serious than agricultural drainage in some districts. On many parts of the prairies, a grid of roads surrounding each section of land has been or is being constructed. Many potholes bisected by this network of roads are drained into roadside ditches. While more permanent marshes sometimes result from road drainage, the net result is an overall loss of waterfowl breeding habitat.

A minor loss attends draining or pumping water from shallow sloughs into stock watering dugouts. The dugouts are more permanent than the original slough, but they generally are less productive of waterfowl.

Pothole destruction in Canada by filling and brush clearing has been increasing through the use of modern machinery. It is more serious than drainage in some districts, particularly in the parklands. Aspens and brush around the margins of potholes are bulldozed into these depressions where they are burned or left as a brush pile.

DURING A SERIES OF DRY YEARS, potholes cleared of trees frequently become arable and are cultivated. With the return of wet years, larger depressions may again fill with water and provide good habitat.

Many Canadian potholes are drained in wet years following a drought. Wetlands that dry up during a drought usually are cultivated, planted to hay crops, or pastured. Sometimes roads are constructed through dry marshes. When the depressions again hold water, farmers are reluctant to lose the use of additional land they have gained, and they think of drainage.

Some drainage occurs in nearly every part of the prairie pothole region, but the greater part occurs in regions with higher precipitation and less evaporation. These regions lie mainly in parklands and include central Alberta, central and southeastern Saskatchewan, and southwestern Manitoba.

Water is at a premium, and stable waterfowl habitat is scarce on the plains of southwestern Saskatchewan and southern Alberta. Agriculture there probably has created more permanent water areas in the form of dugouts, stock dams, irrigation reservoirs, and ditches than it has destroyed by draining and filling.

SEVERAL FACTORS have a bearing on drainage. Topography and soils must be suitable. Gently rolling terrain lends itself to drainage. Steeply rolling land where potholes exist in deep depressions is difficult and costly to drain. Effective drainage on flat plains may be impractical. Drainage where the soil is light and erodable is not desirable.

Drainage of Canadian potholes began in the late 1800's and reached its first peak in the 1920's, following a dry period between 1917 and 1921. Wetlands were considered a liability in the early years of settlement. The only good wetlands were those that could be bought cheaply and reclaimed at low cost. Settlers were encouraged to purchase such wetlands with a view to reclaiming them for agriculture. Thus the twenties saw coniderable drainage, most of which was government-sponsored.

Drainage declined during the drought of the thirties. Many wetlands dried up naturally, and little money was available for drainage. The return of higher farm prices and the wet cycle of the forties again encouraged drainage. It has continued since then—probably at a growing rate.

Improved techniques and heavier equipment have reduced the cost of land reclamation at a time when higher costs of farm operations and declining farm income have stimulated development of more arable lands. Wetlands are all that remain to be reclaimed in many districts.

CONSIDERABLE LEGISLATION pertaining to water use in the three Prairie Provinces has been enacted. Until 1960, none of the acts recognized nonconsumptive uses, such as those associated with recreation and wildlife.

The Saskatchewan Water Rights Act was amended in 1960 to include recognition of those uses. It indicates a trend toward broader thinking in terms of water conservation and use among people responsible for administration of the resource.

Drainage resulting from activities of the Prairie Farm Rehabilitation Act usually is a byproduct of flood control and irrigation projects. Some reclamation is undertaken, however. The Pasquia Reclamation Project along the lower Saskatchewan River in Manitoba is an example. There 110 thousand acres of flat, marshy delta were reclaimed from a total of 135 thousand acres. Investigations for similar reclamation projects have been started.

Participation by Provincial Governments varies among the Prairie

Provinces. In Manitoba, little drainage is financed by the Province. Some contributions are made to projects under the Prairie Farm Rehabilitation Act. One is the Pasquia Project, in which the Province provided the secondary drainage systems. In the pothole country most drainage is done by private landowners.

The Saskatchewan Provincial Government participates in considerable drainage for flood control and land reclamation on private and public lands. The work is done under authority of the Conservation and Development Act of 1949. The Government pays up to 50 percent of the cost for land reclamation on private lands and up to the full amount on land owned by the Government. The existence of a main Conservation and Development ditch often makes it possible for individual farmers to drain their wetlands by means of short lateral ditches.

The Water Resources Branch of the Alberta Department of Agriculture shares costs of projects for drainage and flood control with towns, villages, counties, municipal districts, drainage districts, and local improvements districts. The Government will pay one-half of the cost up to a stated maximum. The nine drainage districts in Alberta in 1961 represented 189,200 acres, of which 75,647 received direct benefits. All the districts are in the parklands.

Herb Moulding, of Ducks Un-

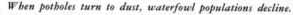

When potholes turn to dust, waterfowl populations decline.

limited (Canada), assembled data on drainage in Saskatchewan up to 1960. Wetland loss is of greater magnitude in that Province than in Manitoba and Alberta. There were 563 registered ditches and drainage projects that affected 115 thousand wetland acres. Ninety-five percent of the wetlands affected were under 40 acres. Of 843 licensed flood irrigation projects, 257 drained 27 thousand wetland acres. The drainage of 21 large marshes and lakes involved 55,580 acres. Thirty-nine additional lakes and marshes, totaling 115,149 acres, have been proposed for drainage.

Some idea of the extent of unregistered drainage is evident from two investigations by Ducks Unlimited. In an area of 605 square miles, 80 water areas each more than 10 acres in size were inspected. Twenty-three had been ditched— 13 by farmers, 8 for roads, 1 for a railway, and 1 by authority of the Prairie Farm Rehabilitation Act. In a 245-square mile block, 5 of 18 lakes were lowered or drained by farm or municipal ditches. Twenty-nine percent of the wetlands investigated in these surveys had been affected by drainage.

The Canadian Wildlife Service and Ducks Unlimited surveyed a sample township in the Saskatchewan parklands and found that 40 percent of the farmers had drained some of the surface water from their land either by themselves or with government assistance.

A survey by the United States Fish and Wildlife Service in the Minnedosa pothole area of Manitoba in 1961 revealed that in 13 years, 14 percent of 120 potholes had been altered. Of these, 4 percent were lost to roads and fields and the remaining 10 percent were partly drained but would hold some water in wet years. Road building was a major cause of the destruction of potholes.

The pattern in Alberta is similar to that in Saskatchewan, though probably not so extensive.

So we see how in Canada and the United States prime prairie breeding habitat has been decreasing gradually and may be reduced to a fraction of its former value unless it is protected by effective, large-scale measures.

Development of manmade wetlands can offset some of the drainage losses, but it is impossible physically and economically to replace all wetlands lost to reclamation activities.

The best alternative is to protect remaining wetland habitat from destruction. No one plan offers a complete solution.

The united states congress has recognized the need to protect wetlands and has attempted to further that objective through a number of legislative accomplishments.

Public Law 85–585 in 1958 provided for the purchase and lease of waterfowl production areas. Public Law 87–383 in 1961 provided for an interest-free loan to the Bureau of Sport Fisheries and Wildlife to buy and lease wetlands in all parts of the country. More than half of the important waterfowl producing areas in the prairie pothole region of the United States are included.

The Congress passed Public Law 87–732 in 1962 in an attempt to save waterfowl production habitat in North Dakota, South Dakota, and Minnesota. The law obligated the Department of Agriculture to refer all requests for drainage to the Department of the Interior for a determination of wildlife value. The law provided an opportunity for the Bureau of Sport Fisheries and Wildlife or a State Government to offer to purchase or lease areas of high waterfowl value in which drainage assistance was requested. The landowner could not receive Federal drainage assistance for 5 years if he refused the offer.

The Agriculture Appropriation Act for 1963, Public Law 87–879, contained a provision that prohibited the use of Federal funds for the drainage of certain wetlands for that program year. The same provisions were included in the Agriculture Appropriation Act for 1964, Public Law 88–250.

The Department of Agriculture under its Agricultural Conservation Program, effective in 1962, was authorized to pay farmers up to 50 percent of the cost of installing certain wildlife practices on farms. Farm ponds for fish and wildlife are included in these practices.

A plan was authorized in 1962, on a pilot basis, to return soil-bank lands to a grassland economy; the Federal Government subsidized the transition period with cost sharing and long-term, low-interest loans. A grassland economy has been generally recognized as compatible with the conservation of wetlands in the prairie pothole region.

Land acquisition efforts by State Governments in the Dakotas and Minnesota have preserved many wetlands for wildlife. Federal funds have assisted the States in many of these purchases. Minnesota increased its small game license fee by a dollar; the proceeds are used to purchase wetlands. Nine dollars from every nonresident hunting license were set aside by South Dakota for purchases of wetland. Wisconsin added a State tax on cigarettes to help with its acquisition efforts.

An independent organization, Wetlands for Wildlife, was incorporated in Milwaukee in 1961 to purchase wetlands in the United States and give them to the Federal or a State Government. Anyone can join the organization on payment of 3 dollars or more.

LITTLE HAS BEEN DONE in Canada to curtail drainage or compensate for wetland destruction from settlement and agriculture, even though the need has been recognized.

As early as 1925, an Order-in-Council establishing several new Federal prairie waterfowl sanctuaries included this statement:

"That the Great Plains region of Canada contains probably the most valuable breeding grounds in North America for the wildfowl of the continent and that it is important that measures be taken to set apart permanently certain areas for the propagation of bird life, a resource of economic value in providing sport and food . . . That the advance of settlement, following cultivation of the land, the drainage of lakes and marsh areas for development purposes has seriously restricted the areas suitable for the propagation of wild waterfowl and under present conditions it is necessary that proper means should be taken to check the decrease in the number of these birds and to guard against the danger of extermination . . ."

Only in recent years has widespread interest in wetland conservation been evident. This interest has been stimulated partly by the rapid loss of waterfowl habitat in the United States and partly by the alarming effects of drought on prairie waterfowl production.

The Parliament of Canada passed the Agricultural Rehabilitation and Development Act in 1961. ARDA, as it is called, is concerned with resource conservation and rural development. A section of the act deals with alternative land uses and is aimed at making more efficient use of submarginal farmlands. Production of wildlife would be an alternative use on many lands — particularly wetlands. The cost of the program is to be shared by Federal and Provincial Governments.

THE CANADIAN WILDLIFE SERVICE began pilot studies in 1962 to determine how ARDA may be used to preserve habitat. It is expected that long-term easements on wetlands can be obtained from farmers similar to those under the program in the Prairie States. Such easements in effect would pay farmers not to destroy waterfowl marshes. The payments may also help to compensate some farmers for losses from crop depredation, which by itself can be a major obstacle in the way of wetland preservation.

Another possibility under ARDA that would protect some wetlands is that of taking submarginal farmlands out of intensive agriculture and using them for forest production, community pastures, wildlife production, and recreation.

It remains to be seen how effective ARDA will be in preserving waterfowl habitat in Canada. We know that preliminary activities under ARDA have focused considerable attention on the need for wetland preservation. That is good. The task will be much easier when people are informed about it.

IN SUM, THEN: Each year our prairie waterfowl habitats are shrinking. Already we have lost many of them. The loss of more than a million acres has been recorded; the loss of millions more has not been. Our choice is clear. If we do not preserve our wetlands we shall have insufficient ducks for hunting, on the scale to which we are accustomed.

We feel some cautious optimism. Federal and State programs to preserve wetlands in the prairie States are gradually accelerating. On the Canadian prairies similar programs are likely.

More and more landowners are becoming aware that natural wetlands have value for recreation, grazing, and water conservation.

Saving wetlands is more than the absence of drainage. Except on carefully managed tracts, conversion of cropland to grassland will be needed to halt erosion which destroys wetlands on many parts of the prairies.

Much has been done to preserve wetlands, but much has yet to be done. ROBERT W. BURWELL and LAWSON G. SUGDEN.

Like winds and sunsets, wild things were taken for granted until progress began to do away with them. Now we face the question whether a still higher 'standard of living' is worth its cost in things natural, wild, and free. For us of the minority, the opportunity to see geese is more important than television, and the chance to find a pasque-flower is a right as inalienable as free speech.
—ALDO LEOPOLD.

Reservoirs

LAKE TEXOMA covers 143 thousand acres in Texas and Oklahoma. The Army Corps of Engineers created it in 1943 by building Dennison Dam on the Red River for flood control, navigation, and hydroelectric power. It is one of the largest of reservoirs constructed in the last 20 years, but it is typical of many of them and it exemplifies the point of this chapter—the effect of manmade lakes on waterfowl.

The Tishomingo National Wildlife Refuge was established in 1946 on the upper Washita arm of Lake Texoma to take advantage of the opportunities it offered for waterfowl development.

The refuge includes about 13,450 acres of water. Its upland comprises high, densely wooded hills on the south and east, gently rolling hills on the north, and flat valleys. It provides resting and feeding places for ducks and geese that use that portion of the Central Flyway. During fall migration at least 30 thousand geese and 50 thousand ducks concentrate there to feed in the 600 acres of farmland. They include Canada, snow, blue, and white-fronted geese and mallard and pintail ducks. Egrets, herons, wood ibises, and many other birds use it in summer. More than 200 species of birds have been seen in the refuge.

Lake Texoma by itself would have benefited waterfowl, but specific management, of the kind carried on at Tishomingo, was necessary to get the full benefit.

Developments on the refuge include several 10- to 25-acre lakes, small ponds, and waterholes, which provide resting and feeding areas. Corn, sorghum, wheat, and vetch are planted on the farmlands to supply winter feed for the fowl.

Water-impoundment projects like Texoma used to be developed to provide water for a single purpose, such as household use or irrigation or the generation of electricity. The lakes they created generally were small. Now the projects are designed to serve several functions, such as irrigation, flood control, navigation, power, municipal and industrial water, pollution abatement, fish and wildlife conservation, and water-related recreation. A manifest of their popularity as places of recreation is that visitors spend an aggregate of more than 6 million days a year at Lake Texoma.

Among the other large manmade inland lakes are Lake Mead in Nevada-Arizona, which has 146 thousand surface acres; Franklin D. Roosevelt Lake in Washington, 83 thousand acres; Garrison Reservoir in North Dakota, 390 thousand acres; John H. Kerr Reservoir in North Carolina and Virginia, 96 thousand acres; and the Falcon Reservoir on the Rio Grande between the United States and Mexico, 113 thousand acres.

The 1,300 reservoirs in the United States in 1954, each having a capacity of 5 thousand acre-feet or more of water storage, had a total surface area of about 11 million acres. Reservoirs completed since 1954 raise the total area to 13 million acres.

The Select Committee on National Water Resources of the United States Senate predicted in 1961 that 442,200,000 acre-feet of additional storage would be needed by the year 2000. This would amount to 17 million additional surface acres, if the relationship between acre feet and surface acres existing in 1954 is used as a yardstick.

ARTIFICIAL LAKES have various effects on waterfowl. There is ample evidence that large reservoirs in association with grain farming areas in certain western river basins have delayed southward migrations. If open water prevails on them longer than elsewhere in the region, waterfowl may be held north of a climatically safe winter range. Impoundments in the Western States also have created hundreds of thousands of acres of shallow water habitat and countless miles of shoreline, canals, and drains, which have attracted sizable numbers of waterfowl to places where natural bodies of water previously had been lacking.

In the Pacific Northwest, most reservoirs have little value for nesting waterfowl, unless specific management is provided, because water levels fluctuate and food and cover are lacking. Reservoirs in the vicinity of agricultural lands do provide resting use for field-feeding species consisting of mallards, pintails, and various races of Canada geese.

Impoundments made by a number of dams along the Columbia and Snake Rivers in Oregon, Washington, and Idaho for power, flood control, and irrigation have increased the extent of high-value duck habitat, especially when they are not far from irrigated fields of small grain and corn. The fall and winter populations of mallards rose sharply in the Pacific Flyway between 1951 and 1959 and then decreased somewhat through 1962. During the period, however, the States of Washington, Oregon, and Idaho accounted for an increasingly higher portion of the total in the flyway. For example, in 1962 these three States contributed 77 percent of the total as compared to 48 percent in 1951.

Depending on location, size, method of operation, and the use of nearby land, reservoir projects may have beneficial, adverse, or insignificant effects on the numbers, distribution, and movement of waterfowl.

Nearly all reservoirs with permanent water storage provide some resting opportunities for waterfowl, but this may be the extent of their value if the local food supply is not adequate.

Impoundments in irrigation projects often provide splendid opportunities for waterfowl, since they generally are near canals, ditches, and sumps, which have desirable small areas of water, and to cultivated croplands, which provide supplemental feed.

Reservoirs that eliminate bottom land, nesting islands, marsh areas, and natural oxbows may result in serious damage to waterfowl populations. Such damage may result from actual inundation or by the regulation of stream flows below dams so that beneficial flooding of bottomlands at periodic intervals is eliminated.

Some reservoirs in sparsely vegetated canyons at high elevation or in hilly, wooded terrain have negligible effects on waterfowl.

With proper plannings, most projects can be developed and operated with little or no harm to waterfowl. With specific management, many reservoirs can benefit the waterfowl resource. Management for waterfowl may include such techniques as the creation of shallow subimpoundments, establishment of desirable natural food plants, controlled agricultural production on nearby lands, and the manipulation of water levels.

Generally speaking, the use of reservoirs by waterfowl is increasing. This is a reflection of the adaptability to changing conditions of several important species, notably the mallard, pintail, and Canada goose, and to a lesser extent the American widgeon and the black duck. Most reservoirs have little in the way of food for ducks and geese. Over the years, however, there has been a change in feeding habits of the abundant species toward greater use of waste grain and other field crops as a sustaining source of food. Since reservoirs usually provide open water areas where birds can rest undisturbed, the combination of reservoirs plus grainfields in the vicinity often provides all the elements of high grade migration and wintering habitat required by our most popular sporting ducks. When the few adaptable species that accept this manmade habitat are considered, it is significant to note that more than half of all the waterfowl in North America are no longer completely dependent on traditional marsh-type habitat for survival during the fall, winter, and spring.

LEGISLATION HAS BEEN ENACTED in the United States to facilitate the conservation and development of waterfowl resources at reservoir projects. The President in 1934 signed the so-called "Coordination Act," which required that the Bureau of Biological Survey (a predecessor of the Bureau of Sport Fisheries and Wildlife) be given the opportunity to use reservoir projects for migratory bird resting and nesting areas. The act was amended in 1946 to require that consideration be given to the protection of fish and wildlife resources whenever water-development projects were proposed for construction or license by the Federal Government. A further amendment in 1958, termed the Fish and Wildlife Coordination Act, specified that consideration be given to the development and improvement, as well as the protection of fish and wildlife, in the planning, construction, and operation of reservoirs. It authorized Federal construction agencies to acquire lands for wildlife as well as for other project purposes.

The provision for the establishment of waterfowl areas at water-development projects was carried forward into both the 1946 and 1958 acts. Under this provision, such waterfowl areas may be administered by the Bureau of Sport Fisheries and Wildlife or by State fish and game agencies under an appropriate general plan and cooperative agreement.

About 4 thousand water-development projects have been studied by the Fish and Wildlife Service and State fish and game agencies. Many have included measures for waterfowl management based upon recommendations by the agencies.

Consequently a number of national wildlife refuges and State-administered wildlife management or public shooting areas have been established at water-impoundment projects. Thirty-three national waterfowl refuges, containing nearly a million acres of land and water, have been established at such projects. These refuges constitute about 27 percent of the total area in the national system of wildlife refuges for waterfowl. The Bureau of Sport Fisheries and Wildlife expects to establish additional waterfowl refuges, totaling about 780 thousand acres, near reservoirs in the coming 35 years.

On the areas administered by the Federal or State Governments, varying types and degrees of management practices are applied to increase the usefulness of the reservoirs to waterfowl. They include creating and controlling smaller water bodies, growing aquatic food plants, producing land plants for food or shelter, growing grain as a source of supplemental feed, and restricting in certain ways the use of the waterfowl area by people.

Fifty-four State-administered waterfowl management areas covering nearly 564 thousand acres have been established at such projects and developed under the program of Federal Aid in Wildlife Restoration. Their number and acreage also are expected to increase substantially.

LAKE TEXOMA is one example of the waterfowl lands available for management. We cite a few others.

Lake Mead, which was formed by Hoover Dam in 1936 for flood control, irrigation, municipal water, and hydroelectric power, is important for waterfowl and recreation. The Lake Mead National Recreation Area, operated by the National Park Service, had more than 2 million man-days of recreational use in 1961.

The Overton Wildlife Management Area, also on Lake Mead, is administered by the Nevada Department of Fish and Game. The area obtains its water from waste and return flows of the Boulder Canyon Irrigation Project. It is about 9,700 acres in size and supports waterfowl use of about 600 thousand duck-days and 40 thousand goose-days annually. The Overton area provides the major waterfowl hunting opportunities within 100 miles of Las Vegas and receives about 1,500 man-days of hunting each year. Nevada has constructed two ponds of 40 and 70 acres for waterfowl use. Grain is grown on about 500 acres for supplemental feed.

Sardis Reservoir in Mississippi exemplifies the management of a large reservoir to provide greater use by waterfowl. This flood-control reservoir of about 60 thousand acres was completed in 1940 by the Army Corps of Engineers on the Little Tallahatchee River in northwestern Mississippi. It has become important for recreation and receives about 1,500,000 man-days of use a year. In an average year the reservoir fills rapidly in late winter or early spring, reaching a maximum storage in April. The rate of discharge into the river is planned so that the reservoir recedes to a conservation pool level of 9,800 acres by November 1. The conservation pool, representing 10 percent of the total land and water area of the reservoir project of 98 thousand acres, provides an excellent attraction to visiting waterfowl, which begin arriving early in November. The Mississippi Game and Fish Commission assumed the responsibility of developing and managing fish and the wildlife habitat on the reservoir.

A tract of about 14 thousand acres of the reservoir land surrounding the conservation pool is exposed gradually between August 15 and November 1 as the water level is drawn down. The land supports a growth of native annuals, which furnish grazing and feeding to ducks and geese at the beginning of their stay. Reflooding begins by the first of December.

Above this tract is another area of 14 thousand acres, which usually is exposed by reservoir drawdown before August 15, the latest practical date for planting. About 25 percent of this land is in bottom land hardwoods. The State curtails the growth of willow, buttonbush, cocklebur, and trumpet vine, the most serious pest plants; constructs subimpoundments for advance flooding; and manages the wooded areas under a sustained-yield program. Once the pest plants are eliminated, the area is disked and planted to grain. The State does some planting; local farmers do some on a sharecrop basis. A portion of the grain crop is left standing in the fields for wildlife. Every third year or so, high water and a late drawdown make farming impractical, but heavy stands of wild millet and smartweed are produced in those years.

BECAUSE Sardis Reservoir is operated primarily for flood control, no waterfowl developments can be made that might adversely affect its storage capacity. A number of small impoundments have been built within the reservoir area. However, terraces were found later to be more successful than dams in providing these ponds. Farming operations are carried out at the base of the terraces. The ponds are kept under water as far into spring as possible in order to provide a moist seedbed for germinating duck food and water areas for duck broods. About 3 thousand wood ducks breed there each year.

Above the 28 thousand acres are 60 thousand acres, or about 60 percent of the total project lands. This tract is too steep for ponds, but has value to waterfowl during the high-water stages when crop residues,

vetch, and annuals become available.

Intensive management has demonstrated that a flood-control reservoir of this type can provide outstanding habitat. The number of geese increased from none to more than 10 thousand, and the number of ducks from about 500 to 50 thousand after 4 years of management. Two refuges 10 miles apart on the reservoir provide ample protection during the hunting season. The reservoir area provides more than 10 thousand man-days of waterfowl hunting each year.

Since flood-control reservoirs like Sardis must be drawn down in summer, they have high potential value for waterfowl management. The summer growth of millets and smartweeds can be made available by winter flooding or by the construction of subimpoundments.

The Jackson Lock and Dam Project of the Army Corps of Engineers on the Warrior, Black Warrior, and Tombigbee Rivers in Alabama is an example of a project that has been modified to provide benefits to waterfowl. The original plans in 1954 for the replacement of existing navigation locks and dams would have flooded about 30 thousand acres of valuable bottom land and reduced the wildlife-carrying capacity of adjacent uplands. The natural lakes, sloughs, and backwaters of this area were important to migrating and wintering waterfowl.

In accordance with the Fish and Wildlife Coordination Act, the Bureau of Sport Fisheries and

Wildlife and the Alabama Department of Conservation investigated the project site and recommended major modifications in the plans to protect, develop, and improve waterfowl resources. The modifications, authorized by the Congress in 1960, included the establishment of a national wildlife refuge to be administered by the Bureau of Sport Fisheries and Wildlife and a public shooting area to be administered by the Alabama Department of Conservation. Funds were appropriated to the Corps of Engineers by the Congress in 1962 for the acquisition of lands needed to establish the two areas.

When fully developed, the Choctaw National Wildlife Refuge at the Jackson Lock and Dam Project will include 4,250 acres of land and water. The State public shooting area will include some 2 thousand acres of leased private lands east of the project pool, and some project land.

The waterfowl area has both national and local significance. Birds from eastern Canada originally followed the Atlantic Flyway along the coast or entered the Mississippi Flyway by way of the Great Lakes and the Ohio River. The construction of T.V.A. reservoirs created a new flyway route below the Ohio along the Cumberland and Tennessee Valleys and attracts large flights into Kentucky, Tennessee, and the northern parts of Alabama and Georgia. Construction of the Jackson pool, with a stabilized water level and the associated waterfowl development, is an important link between those areas

in this new reservoir flyway and the wintering grounds on the Gulf coast.

When completed, the waterfowl development will comprise shallow backwaters, islands, and the margin of the navigation pool on the west, with extensive timbered bottom lands subject to controlled seasonal flooding on the east. Aquatic and terrestrial waterfowl feeds will be planted within the refuge. Corn, milo maize, and millet will be planted as necessary on certain of the agricultural lands acquired.

The Fontanelle and Flaming Gorge Reservoirs on the Upper Green River in Wyoming and Utah will destroy nesting areas presently used by the Great Basin Canada goose. These losses will occur along a 158-mile stretch of the Green River from LaBarge, Wyo., through the Flaming Gorge Reservoir area in Utah. Nesting habitat, consisting of islands, marshlands, oxbows, and meadows, will be destroyed when reservoirs are flooded, and stream regulation will eliminate the periodic natural floods. The Seedskadee National Wildlife Refuge and State waterfowl management areas in Wyoming and Utah arc being developed to provide compensatory nesting habitat.

ACCORDING TO THE Water Resources Branch of the Canadian Department of Northern Affairs and National Resources, the generation of hydroelectric power has had an important effect on the economic development of Canada.

Canada has shifted from an essentially agricultural economy to one that is increasingly industrial. The shift has coincided with the development of its water resources. An indication of the extent of reservoir development in Canada for hydroelectric power is reflected in the total installed turbine capacity of more than 26 million horsepower by the end of 1960. Canadians expect an even greater development in the northern regions.

The Grand Rapids Hydroelectric Project on the Saskatchewan River in Manitoba is an example of a reservoir that benefits waterfowl. The project was studied by the Bureau of Sport Fisheries and Wildlife in cooperation with the Game and Fisheries Branches of the Manitoba Department of Mines and Natural Resources in 1960.

As originally planned, the reservoir, of 1,600,000 acres, would have flooded out several hundred thousand acres of prime, waterfowl-producing habitat in the Saskatchewan River Delta between Lake Winnipeg and The Pas. An average of about 168 thousand ducks have been produced there each year. Construction of the reservoir as originally planned would have reduced this production to an estimated 40 thousand ducks, a loss of about 75 percent.

The joint report of the two wildlife agencies to the Minister of the Manitoba Department of Mines and Natural Resources recommended that a large subimpoundment be constructed to protect an extensive area from flooding by the reservoir. Such a subimpoundment would reduce waterfowl losses substantially. Management of water levels in the subimpoundment and further developments there would increase the value of the protected area to waterfowl and offset losses in other parts of the project.

The Manitoba Government made detailed studies to develop engineering and management plans for the subimpoundment. Other potential developments in the delta above The Pas also were investigated to determine additional possibilities for mitigating the waterfowl losses. As a result of these efforts, it is expected that substantial measures for waterfowl protection will be included in this project.

Mexico also has developed a number of reservoir projects for irrigation, water supply, and hydroelectric power. The impoundments in 1960 had a storage capacity of more than 27 billion cubic meters, roughly equivalent to 22 million acre-feet or 880 thousand surface acres.

It is apparent that reservoir projects on the North American Continent have had a significant effect upon the size, distribution, and habits of the continental waterfowl population. With the increasing emphasis on reservoir construction and the high estimates of water requirements by the year 2000, we may expect even greater effects on our waterfowl resources. It is extremely important that every effort be made in connection with future reservoir planning to insure that adequate consideration is given to the continental waterfowl needs. Reservoir projects should be designed and operated in such a manner as to prevent waterfowl losses insofar as possible and to insure optimum use of the areas by waterfowl. Waterfowl refuge or management areas should be established by the Federal or State wildlife agencies when appropriate and operated in such a manner as to meet the habitat needs of the waterfowl population.—WILLIAM M. WHITE and G. W. MALAHER.

The future of the Canada goose is bright as long as its breeding grounds in the Far North remain secure.

Stock Ponds and Dugouts

NOT ALWAYS is water where we want it. In the central and eastern portions of the States of North and South Dakota, and particularly during wet years, natural water areas hinder farming operations. The western Dakotas are not blessed with abundant natural ponds and the problem, there, and elsewhere in arid parts of the West, is to provide a scattering of ponds to distribute cattle over the extensive grazing areas. These manmade waters are called stock ponds and dugouts depending on how they are constructed.

STOCK PONDS are formed by building dams across natural waterways. Dugouts are large holes excavated to catch runoff water or to intercept ground water. Both are constructed primarily to furnish water for livestock, but some are sources of domestic water or are used for irrigation. Most of the stock ponds are located in the semiarid plains. Dugouts are more closely associated with the prairie pothole region to the east and north. Both types occur in some areas.

Because of their special values to waterfowl, we consider mainly the stock ponds and dugouts in North Dakota, South Dakota, Minnesota, Montana, and the prairies of Manitoba, Saskatchewan, and Alberta. In the United States, the impoundments may be constructed with technical assistance of the Soil Conservation Service and financial assistance from the Agricultural

391

Conservation Program. In Canada, they are built with financial and technical assistance furnished by the Prairie Farm Rehabilitation Branch of the Canadian Agricultural Department.

THE NUMBER OF STOCK PONDS and dugouts is hard to determine. The Department of Agriculture has an annual accounting of the number of structures in which its agencies participate, but those made by individual operators without assistance are not recorded. According to the records and our estimates, approximately 220 thousand stock ponds and 40 thousand dugouts have been constructed in North Dakota, South Dakota, western Minnesota, and Montana. The Prairie Provinces of Manitoba, Saskatchewan, and Alberta have 10 thousand stock ponds and 185 thousand dugouts. The estimated total therefore is 230 thousand stock ponds and 225 thousand dugouts for this region. This program is popular among landowners and is becoming increasingly so. Information from the States and Provinces indicates that 10 thousand additional stock ponds and dugouts will be constructed each year for years to come.

Stock ponds differ from dugouts in size, construction, and geographic location. The importance of each type to waterfowl varies. The surface areas of stock ponds vary from a fraction of an acre to 30 or 40 acres. Maximum depths of the impounded water may be a few feet up to 20 feet or more.

Most stock ponds in the Northern Plains are in the rolling rangelands west of the Missouri River in North and South Dakota, and Montana, and in the Prairie Provinces, where livestock production is a major industry. There are few natural sources of water for livestock. Before stock ponds came into being, the parts of the range that were close to water often were overgrazed and distant parts were underused. The strategic location of stock ponds makes it possible to more evenly distribute cattle over the range. When natural construction sites are available, the ponds are spaced so they average one to two for every 640 acres.

Most stock ponds have gently sloping shorelines except at the dam or fill end of the pond. Even dams built in fairly steep-sided gullies usually have a gentle slope at the upstream end of the pond. Water levels fluctuate in response to dry and wet cycles, as do natural areas, and the alternate drying and flooding undoubtedly enhance the fertility of the impounded water. Marginal and submerged vegetation begins to appear during the second year and is well established in 3 to 5 years. The long, irregular shorelines serve well the requirements of breeding waterfowl, and most ponds furnish the food and cover necessary for survival of broods.

WATERFOWL WERE NOT IN MIND when the program of building stock ponds began a generation ago. No one thought then that they would furnish breeding grounds for waterfowl on the rangelands of the Plains, which previously had few natural wetlands for nesting waterfowl.

A Minnesota dugout provides water for stock and a place for ducks to nest and feed. Fences prevent overgrazing of vegetation needed by ducks.

That, however, has been an extra and growing dividend.

Year-to-year production of waterfowl on the stock ponds reflects many of the same conditions that affect natural wetlands of the prairies to the north and east. Moisture, land use, and the numbers of waterfowl determine the number of birds that use and nest on stock dams. On 50 ponds west of the Missouri River in South Dakota, an average of 5.5 breeding pairs per pond were found in 1950 and 6 pairs in 1951. Eighty percent of the ponds were occupied. Tallies made from aerial surveys in 1950 of 16 thousand square miles in western South Dakota showed an average of 1.27 stock ponds to the square mile and an average of 2.75 breeding pairs per pond.

We computed from this information that there were 20,320 stock ponds and 56 thousand breeding pairs on the area. Brood studies disclosed an estimated annual pro-duction of 200 thousand waterfowl in 1950 and 1951. Later surveys by the Bureau of Sport Fisheries and Wildlife in 1958 showed that breeding pairs and production had increased 67 percent. This tract covers less than one-half the stock pond region in South Dakota.

The Bureau's survey of South Dakota in 1958 showed about 89 thousand stock ponds in the State. Blue-winged teal, mallards, and pintails are the major breeding species there. The shoveler, gadwall, American widgeon, and ruddy duck occur in lesser numbers. The coot is a common nesting bird. Green-winged teal, canvasback, redhead, lesser scaup, bufflehead, common merganser, and Canada goose use the stock ponds during migration.

In Montana an estimated 120 thousand stock ponds, including a few irrigation ponds, are used by the same species. Canada geese are also reported as nesters on some. Aerial counts made in the early fifties of 442 stock ponds showed 3.8 ducks per pond.

North Dakota had about 11 thousand stock ponds in 1962; an average of 2.5 waterfowl used each of them during the 1961 nesting season.

The Prairie Farm Rehabilitation Administration reported that about 10 thousand stock ponds have been constructed in Manitoba, Saskatchewan, and Alberta. The number constructed without cost-sharing benefits is not known.

We can figure reasonably that stock ponds in the Northern Great Plains of the United States and Canada produce upwards of a million waterfowl a year. Production on the ponds is more stable than that on natural wetlands of the prairie pothole region, and acre for acre, over the years, the artificial impoundments will outproduce many natural wetland areas. During droughts, natural wetlands go dry until above-average moisture conditions return. That is not true of stock ponds. Heavy rains that leave little water in a natural wetland locality may fill a stock pond of equal size.

Stock ponds have larger, steeper, and more efficient drainage areas than do the average natural wetland areas. But that does not mean that stock dams are better than all natural areas in years when both types function to capacity. Prime natural marshes are utilized by divers as well as dabbling ducks; stock ponds, which are primarily

This 10-acre stock pond has more than 6000 feet of irregular shoreline. It supported 30 breeding pairs of ducks in 1950 and 1951.

for watering cattle, do not equal natural marshes in overall quality.

GOOD PRODUCTION in the stock pond country is due to good success in nesting. In Montana in 1950 and 1951, 77 percent of the waterfowl nests hatched. In South Dakota, 65 percent of the breeding pairs brought off broods. In natural wetland areas near Waubay, South Dakota, a nesting success of 30 percent and 39 percent, respectively, was noted for the same years. Nesting success was 56 percent in the aspen-parklands near Minnedosa, Manitoba. The higher than normal nesting success in the stock pond country may be due to the abundance of nesting cover and less disturbance from farming operations, and possibly fewer predators.

Ducklings occasionally fall prey to bass and snapping turtles in stock ponds. Losses to skunks, badgers, and other animals are greater. In Montana an overall mortality of about one duckling per brood occurred between the time young reached the water until they were near the flight stage. Newly hatched broods averaging 6.2 ducklings were reduced to 5.1 flight-stage ducklings.

The type of land use surrounding the ponds determines, more than anything else, their use by waterfowl. Overgrazing destroys shoreline vegetation and nesting cover. Such bare shorelines are not attractive to waterfowl. Grassy shorelines support nearly three times as many breeding pairs as the bare, mud type—greater turbidity of water in ponds with muddy shores lowers the amount of aquatic plant and animal foods.

Stock ponds that have no agricultural use at all do not necessarily support many breeding pairs. Shallow, completely protected shorelines grow up to tall emergent plants, such as cattail and bulrush, and are not suitable for dabbling ducks, although occasionally diving ducks use this emergent vegetation. The greatest use is had when the range is grazed within its carrying capacity. Good range management is also good waterfowl management. Fencing the upper, or shallow, end of the pond area and part of the waterway is desirable when overgrazing is an annual occurrence, because siltation in the pond is reduced and there is some grass on the shoreline.

MOST DUGOUTS in the Northern Great Plains and prairie region are in the eastern parts of North Dakota and South Dakota, western Minnesota, and the Prairie Provinces of Canada where small grains and livestock are produced.

A dugout, or a stock watering pit, is a hole dug to a depth of 8 feet or more in a place where it can catch runoff or intercept ground water. They may be big or small, depending on the number of livestock to be watered, the method of construction, and the source of water recharge. They usually are about 165 feet long and 65 feet wide. Most of them have a surface area of one-eighth to one-fourth acre. One or both ends slope gently to permit easy access for livestock, but the sides are generally steep.

About 185 thousand dugouts have been made in Manitoba, Saskatchewan, and Alberta, and about 40 thousand have been constructed up to 1963 in the Dakotas, Montana, and western Minnesota. In 1958, there were only 6 thousand west of the Missouri River and 17 thousand east of the Missouri. This increase from 23 thousand to 40 thousand in a 5-year period gives some indication of the rate of new construction.

Their location in relation to natural wetlands that waterfowl use, type of construction, and depth of water along the shorelines determine their use by waterfowl.

Dugouts are of three types, two of which are subject to flooding.

One type is constructed in temporary and semipermanent natural wetland areas. Many waterfowl use them under average conditions; during dry periods, they provide habitat not otherwise available because wetland areas then are dry. Spoil banks of dugouts, when they are near natural wetlands and are covered by vegetation, provide an attractive nesting place. The second of the flooded types is a dam-dugout combination on waterways where excavated material is used to dam the water below the dugout. A shallow, flooded place is thus made around the dugout.

The third type, or regular dugout, is constructed in intermittent waterways or on level ground. It is usually in a level place and away from natural wetlands. Waterfowl use this type when water comes up to the ground level of the steep sides. Once the water drops to more than 3 feet below the level of the banks, the use by waterfowl drops or stops.

Dugouts are used less than stock ponds by waterfowl. The ponds often are the only water areas available to ducks. Dugouts when associated with natural water areas are used more frequently, but their relative contribution is difficult to determine. As a rule, they do not furnish the good habitat afforded by stock ponds. Shorelines are short and regular, and often the high piles of spoil are not attractive to breeding pairs.

F. Graham Cooch of the Canadian Wildlife Service inspected 347 dugouts during the summers of 1948 and 1949 in Manitoba. He found 43.5 percent of the flooded dugouts occupied in 1948 and 63.2 percent in 1949. Regular dugouts, which were not flooded, showed only 16 percent usage in 1948 and 12.5 in 1949. Ninety-eight of the 347 dugouts he examined were of the flooded type. He recommended that dugouts be built in natural wetland depressions, the spoil banks be flattened out, and cattle kept from destroying nearby cover. He also noted that usage of dugouts is related to the density of ducks and their use of nearby natural areas.

BLUE-WINGED TEAL, mallards, pintails, and shovelers are the species found most commonly at the dugouts in Canada. Territorial drakes and breeding pairs of buffleheads and American goldeneyes use the dugouts in the Peace River Country of Alberta during the spring. Scaup sometimes use dugouts as nesting sites. In North and South Dakota and Minnesota, dabbling ducks are the commonest waterfowl at dugouts, although other species, including divers, use them during migration periods.

Biologists of the Soil Conservation Service have made observations of the use of dugouts in the Dakotas and Minnesota. In South Dakota, 33 dugouts in 1958 had an average of about one duck each during the spring migration. In North Dakota, the average was more than two breeding pairs on each of 30 dugouts. The highest use in North Dakota was on 7 dam-dugout combinations, where water was stored outside the excavation. Of 36 dugouts in southwestern Minnesota in 1958, 28 percent were utilized during the spring migration, but 31 percent of 145 natural wetlands of less than 1 acre were used during the spring migration.

Acre for acre, dugouts in temporary or semipermanent wetlands and dam-dugout combinations have heavier use than those made on intermittent waterways and level terrain. An air survey of stock ponds and dugouts in South Dakota in 1958 showed four ducks per dugout in natural wetland areas and only two ducks per unit on types not associated with natural wetlands. Dugouts within the natural water areas received the highest waterfowl use.

BIOLOGISTS HAVE MADE several observations of waterfowl production in dugouts. Five broods were reported in 1962 on 14 dugouts in Wright County, Minnesota. Sixteen broods were observed in North Dakota in 1958 on 30 dugouts, all of which were on dugouts where water was impounded outside the excavation by a dam-dugout combination.

During drought years in the early sixties, dugouts in Canada frequently held the only water for miles around and therefore contained the only broods in the entire area. Even so, the number of ducklings per dugout usually was small, an indication that these water areas alone cannot sustain duck production at a reasonable level. Without the dugouts, however, there would have been no production.

During extremely dry conditions, in 1960 and 1961, South Dakota reported 50 broods per 100 dugouts constructed in temporary wetland areas, 175 broods per 100 dugouts in more permanent natural wetland areas, and 10 broods per 100 regular dugouts on intermittent drainages.

In Minnesota and North Dakota, between 1958 and 1962, 37 of 118 dugouts were utilized by 53 broods of ducks.

We can suggest several ways to enhance the use of such structures by waterfowl. They should be built in or near natural wetland areas, where water levels are good in years of good rainfall and in dry years, when they store water that would ordinarily disappear from natural wetlands. The dam-dugout combination on good watersheds also assures new and productive habitat. To have a shallow shoreline, where emergent vegetation will grow, one or both ends of the dugouts should be constructed with a

7-to-1 slope. Grasses should be planted on the banks.

Dugouts in heavily grazed places should be fenced, except for access points for cattle. Placing the fence about 40 feet from the margin will lengthen the life of the dugout and furnish good nesting cover for waterfowl and upland game. Breeding pairs use dugouts more when 4-foot rafts of logs or boards are placed in the water to furnish loafing sites. The rafts should be anchored in the center of the pond.

To CONCLUDE: The natural wetlands of the prairie pothole region are the backbone of waterfowl production. We should keep them wherever we can. But we realize that many will be drained. Stock ponds and dugouts will compensate for some of that loss. Agricultural and wildlife agencies should set guidelines for building and managing them, for they offer us good opportunities to improve breeding habitat in the Northern Plains. Tens of thousands of good undeveloped sites exist throughout the Plains.

Some ranchers and farmers have all the stock dams they need, but in many places more water areas would mean better management of the livestock enterprise. Very likely, if water facilities for livestock were included, many landowners would welcome the development of more wetland areas by public agencies or private organizations interested in preserving waterfowl. Long-term easements for building stock ponds may help in the United States as they have in hundreds of projects in Canada.

Stock dams and dugouts are good conservation practices in themselves. That they help waterfowl, too, is an added inducement to encourage farmers and ranchers to construct more of them.—

INGALF G. BUE,
HANS G. UHLIG and
J. DONALD SMITH.

We will be judged by our offspring and in that judgment if all they can contemplate is muddy and polluted rivers, eroded hillsides, burned forest lands and wildlife behind glass, stuffed, then they will have a right to ponder just what type of improvident barbarians sired them.

—ERNEST SWIFT.

Farm Ponds and Waterfowl

OF ALL THE WINDS that tried men's souls in the depressed, droughty, dust-bowl 1930's, one blew farmers, the land, and waterfowl much good. It was a dry wind: It carried tons of topsoil off the prairies. It dried up the places where people and cattle got their water. It abetted the forces that cause soil to erode. But it also woke us up to the need and value of farm ponds. In the generation since, more than 2 million ponds have been built all over the United States. All of them serve one or several purposes; about two-thirds of them provide some use to waterfowl.

The onslaught of the great drought brought Federal programs of drought relief into being. Many small impoundments for livestock use were built on ranches and farms, mainly in the Great Plains States, on public grazing lands and private land. Some were built by the husky, willing young men of the Civilian Conservation Corps. Workmen on relief projects made others. Several public agencies provided technical help, assistance, and encouragement, among them the Soil Conservation Service (established in 1933 as the Soil Erosion Service), State and Federal extension services, and public land agencies.

Many of the early structures built by SCS were stream dams much like old mill ponds. A rubble masonry dam in North Dakota backed water nearly 3 miles upstream. Another CCC dam in Kansas created a 250-acre lake. The bigger ones were mostly CCC jobs—1,109 of them built in 1936 had an average capacity of 25 acre-feet. About 2,900 drought relief projects in the Western States comprised thousands of impoundments and excavations for water conservation, of which SCS built about 5 thousand.

In its first year—1936—the Agricultural Conservation Program of cost-sharing assistance helped 4,167 farmers and ranchers in 12 Great Plains and Western States finance livestock watering ponds. The total reached about 50 thousand in 17 States within 2 years.

The pressing need and primary hope of soil conservation in the early years were to control erosion; fewer than 10 percent of the ponds built today have control of erosion as a major purpose. I mention it as a matter of historical interest and to point out how a great good may develop into a greater good.

When the 74th Congress was considering legislation in 1935 to establish National policy in soil conservation, Congressman William Lemke of North Dakota asked this question at a meeting of a committee of the House of Representatives, "In this matter of soil erosion control, your plan, or your suggestion, would be to build a lot of reservoirs to collect the water in basins, and hold the water in the country where the rain falls, and where it naturally belongs, rather than sending it to the ocean, flooding out other people below?"

The late Hugh H. Bennett, head of the Soil Erosion Service, replied "Our plan includes, in part, the building of thousands of small dams and reservoirs. Of course, part of that water will infiltrate laterally from the little pools back of the dams and contour embankments and probably seep down the slopes. We do not, however, believe that the building of reservoirs alone will control either floods or soil erosion."

A reorganization of the Department of Agriculture in 1938 assigned

Moderate grazing around ponds is not harmful to duck nesting; overgrazing is another story

several new responsibilities to SCS, including irrigation, water facilities projects in the West, drainage, farm forestry, land utilization projects, and flood control surveys. This broadened soil conservation program increased the opportunities for ponds. The enactment of State laws to set up soil conservation districts began in 1937. Districts were organized in State after State, and as a result landowners almost everywhere had access to technical help for pond building.

Biologists of the Soil Conservation Service and others quickly saw the potentials in the broadening concept of farm ponds for wildlife. SCS engineers developed design standards of ponds to make them easier and cheaper to build. Technicians were trained to locate pond sites in any natural drainageway where the watershed was not too large and the soil could hold water. Several persons had a hand in creating the standard type of farm pond design used today—a simple earth fill with a small pipe through the base to take the regular flow and a sod emergency spillway around the end. The Department of Agriculture in 1949 isued a comprehensive bulletin, "How to Build a Farm Pond," by Walter Atkinson.

INTEREST IN FISHING furthered the interest in ponds. Research at Alabama Polytechnic Institute by H. S. Swingle and his associates spurred a new enthusiasm for them. SCS, with Dr. Swingle's help, began testing the results of his studies throughout the country. The Fish and Wildlife Service enlarged its hatcheries to accommodate the new demand. Tens of thousands of fish ponds came into being on farms. In 1945, 4,319 ponds were stocked with 6 million hatchery fish, almost double the previous total.

I am not sure how many ponds have been built for fishing. At first, most ponds had another main purpose, usually to hold water for livestock, but lately more and more are designed as a place to fish. Unfortunately, the ideal fish pond and the ideal duck pond are not much alike. In size, depth, water flow, vegetation, and location, their needs tend to be opposite. Particularly is this true of ponds for duck breeding; it is less true of ponds for the ducks' transient use.

ANOTHER BOOST was given pond building by the wartime development of improved types of bulldozers, cranes, carryalls, and other types of earth-moving equipment, which made the projects easier, less expensive, and faster and within the reach of landholders almost everywhere.

As the interest in ponds grew, technical standards and specifications were refined to fit the several uses. Cost-sharing for irrigation reservoirs was begun, and SCS separated those reservoirs from farm ponds in its records. Floodwater detention reservoirs were similarly recognized. Requirements for the use of ponds for fire control were established. Recommendations for plantings to improve wildlife habitat near ponds were made. SCS issued technical materials for "wildlife" or waterfowl ponds in the Northeastern States and for waterfowl farming in the West.

The New York Conservation Department, in collaboration with SCS, was among the first to work with the wildlife (or shallow) pond—which they called a "small marsh." This variant of the farm pond differed from the fish pond type in several ways. It emphasized shallow water. It used flatter sites to get greatest size. It used a flashboard drop-inlet box, instead of a trickle tube in order to vary the water level seasonally. It encouraged some types of aquatic vegetation, rather than discouraging almost all but plankton. It tolerated continuous flow of water. In practice, all variations from the "perfect" fish pond to the "perfect" wildlife pond were built, depending upon circumstances. The State assisted landowners in building more than a thousand of them and some 1,500 small, dugout "potholes" near the small marshes.

Wildlife ponds now are popular in many parts of the country. In the Southeastern States they are called duck fields, fresh-water duck ponds, woodland duck ponds, widgeongrass or brackish-water ponds, saltmarsh bulrush ponds, and snipe fields. Most are built near the coasts, but many are in rice-growing areas, Piedmont river bottoms, and elsewhere.

ANOTHER VARIANT of the farm pond is the impounded brackish tidal gut in the Eastern Shore counties of Virginia and many coastal areas. Built on deep muck by special techniques, it converts

a salt marsh or shallow water area to deep, fresh water. These impoundments are designed for irrigation, but they are in good waterfowl districts and are used a great deal by the birds.

Between 1936 and 1962, the Department of Agriculture helped people in soil conservation districts build more than 2 million ponds.

Their distribution over the country is not even. Many are in livestock regions that may be subject to drought, such as Texas, Nebraska, South Dakota, and Oklahoma; in sections where interest in fish ponds is great, as in several Southeastern States; and in States where public agencies have given special encouragement, as in Missouri.

Many sections have few ponds because of certain limitations—arid lands (such as in parts of Arizona and Nevada) because of lack of water and strict water rights laws; areas of excessively permeable soils; and mountainous regions. Except in the very dry sections, lack of urgent need and strong interest has been the major limitation, but as more and more people want to have ponds for recreation, ducks, irrigation, fire control, and so on, the number will grow.

About half of all ponds in the United States are in the Great Plains. One-fourth are in the Southeast. The Far West has the fewest. The number of ponds in the Corn Belt and the Northeast very likely will increase because of the growth in population and a greater desire for outdoor recreation.

In some States, one farm or ranch may have 2, 10, or even

more ponds. The development of recreation facilities for fees on farmlands will mean more and more ponds.

How WILL the nearly 2 million acres of new water in ponds over the countryside affect waterfowl?

To answer the question, I can cite some scientific studies and a number of field observations, all of them generally favorable and encouraging.

Stock ponds in the high plains of Colorado, New Mexico, and Texas have been used for nesting and rearing of young by blue-winged teal, mallards, pintails, and ruddy ducks. Fifty young were raised in 1938 on five such ponds in Colorado, none of which had more than an acre of water surface; 11 ponds supported 107 resident ducks. Ponds were visited during migration periods by surprisingly large numbers of waterfowl and shore birds.

In the northern Great Plains, specifically in North Dakota, South Dakota, and Montana, a prime duck breeding area, surveys showed that breeding populations can be established by building large numbers of ponds. Ducks make good use of dugouts for courting and breeding if the nearby cover is favorable and the water level is within a foot of the ground level.

Research workers in Missouri checked on the use of 91 ponds by all birds and mammals. Blue-winged teal were noted 19 times on 16 ponds, mostly in April. Mallard, green-winged teal, shoveler, lesser scaup, and Canada geese were seen on one or several ponds. Three nests of Canada geese were found. The use by ducks was rather low, probably because the ponds were too small and did not produce desirable feed for ducks.

Three studies were made in Ohio during 1952–54. In one survey, owners of 1,406 farm ponds were interviewed. About 65 percent of the ponds were used at some time during the year by waterfowl. About 40 percent were used during fall migration. On about 26 percent, at least one brood of ducks was raised. Many raised a brood every year. The mallard, wood duck, blue-winged teal, and black duck were most prevalent. Only 13 percent of the ponds were hunted; on 85 percent of them, ducks or geese were harvested, the number ranging up to 35 on a pond. The average was 4.5. Mallard, wood duck, blue-winged teal, black duck, and lesser scaup made up 90 percent of the bag.

Another study in Ohio was conducted on 43 ponds, averaging three-fourths acre each on a public hunting area of 4 thousand acres. All were within a mile of a 1,200-acre reservoir. They were used by 28 duck broods having 176 young, an average of 4 ducklings to a pond. The 30-odd large reservoirs in Ohio would seem to offer a good opportunity to increase the number of nesting waterfowl if ponds are built near them.

About 2 thousand wood duck nesting boxes on ponds were checked in Ohio. The utilization on farm ponds was 17 percent. On one area of 3 ponds, 7 of 8 boxes were used the first year and yielded 50 young woodies. Four years later, 14 of 19 boxes were filled and produced 102 young.

In a study in Oklahoma of farm ponds as resting and feeding areas during migrations, 5,402 ducks were counted on 44 ponds.

A report from Vermont in 1961 showed that of 153 ponds checked on 79 farms in 6 counties, 129 (84 percent) had some use by waterfowl. Broods of ducks were raised on 32. Black ducks were the commonest. A few wood ducks, mallards, and Canada geese were observed.

'Of 117 ponds in Wisconsin, 3 percent were constructed for wildlife, but 78 percent had some use by ducks and 24 percent were used for nesting. At least 17 percent raised broods. Geese used 31 percent of the ponds. Fair to good hunting was supplied on 49 percent of all ponds. On ponds used for breeding, 65 broods, totaling 444 ducklings, were reported—an average of 6.8 per brood and 3.2 broods per breeding pond.

In New York, 80 percent of small, impounded wildlife marshes attracted breeding pairs in the spring, 70 percent reared broods, and fewer than 5 percent failed to attract ducks at any season. Similar small marsh impoundments in Maine were observed to be equal to natural ones in duck productivity. Manmade marshes of 5 to 10 acres were more productive than larger or smaller ones, and they produced birds at costs comparable to costs of artificial propagation.

Two hundred ponds in New York were studied for their value to waterfowl. They constituted a random selection of 15 percent of all the ponds in three counties, two of which were hilly and naturally poor in duck waters. Most ponds were one-fourth to one-half acre in size. Few of them had fenced land, but three-fourths had good vegetation nearby. Three-fourths of the ponds were used by waterfowl in the spring, 39 percent in the summer, and 68 percent in the fall. Ponds in the lake plains were used more than those in the hilly counties. About a third of the ponds had raised broods of mallards, black ducks, wood ducks, and blue-winged teal. At least 81 ducks were killed on 17 of the ponds, and 18 geese on 9 of them.

Hans G. Uhlig made observations of ponds each spring from 1957 to 1960 in several southwestern and northwestern counties of Minnesota. Ponds averaged an acre in size and dugouts (pits) less than one-fourth acre. He reported widespread use of ponds and pits by blue-winged teal and lesser scaup and some use by pintail, mallard, shoveler, ruddy duck, and coot.

From limited summer observations in southwestern Minnesota, where few broods were found, he concluded that utilization of these water areas by ducks is primarily confined to migrating birds, but are of some benefit to birds during the courting and breeding period. Utilization of ponds by ducks increases as the ponds become older. Good shoreline vegetation appears to be an important factor in the use of an area by ducks. Stable water levels appear to be an important secondary influence. Ducks use ponds more than pits because of the larger size and the irregular and shallow shorelines of the ponds. Fencing is of value to waterfowl around dugouts and may also be needed around ponds. Loafing sites in stockwater dugouts are attractive to waterfowl and should be highly recommended as an improvement measure. Anchored rafts, 4 by 4 feet or larger were placed in dugouts as loafing sites.

FROM THESE OBSERVATIONS, a number of general conclusions seem warranted.

Even though most farm ponds were not built with waterfowl use in mind and are not ideally located or constituted for waterfowl use, a surprising number of them received some use by wild waterfowl.

Spring use is most frequent; fall use is next.

Almost all ponds that are not close to buildings, under one-half acre in size, or devoid of shore vegetation receive some use by waterfowl.

Ponds with good shoreline and adjacent cover, several hundred yards from buildings, not badly grazed, and situated in the breeding range of ducks will have a sub-

A farm pond in Marathon County, Wisconsin. Ponds like this can be useful in waterfowl management, providing overgrazing and excessive human disturbance are avoided.

stantial breeding use. Even if close to buildings, some ponds are used heavily if other conditions are favorable.

New breeding populations of waterfowl can be established in areas previously lacking water by the building of large numbers of ponds or dugouts if they are properly constructed.

Dugouts or pit-type ponds are less useful to waterfowl than dam ponds but do have substantial use if adjacent cover is good and water-level is not over a foot below ground level.

Clusters, or groups, of ponds, especially if they are near a large body of water, have a cumulative beneficial use by waterfowl.

Ponds can furnish a moderate amount of duck shooting, especially if they are in clusters or near other duck waters and are several acres in size.

IF PONDS are built with proper standards and specifications in suitable locations it is guaranteed that they will have good use by waterfowl. People having such ponds are assured of many pleasant hours watching the interesting antics of these birds.

Productivity of ponds for growing ducks varies with soils, locality, and topography, as well as with other factors. Productivity of the best pond areas may equal that of prairie potholes, but most will not exceed half that rate.

The distribution of waterfowl is markedly influenced by farm ponds, especially in sections more than a feeding flight away from major

natural waterfowl areas such as coasts and rivers.

Farm ponds are a valuable addition to waterfowl habitat and less subject to disturbances such as drought, flood, and pollution than much natural water.

Farm ponds already, and more so in the future, will furnish new and good habitat for waterfowl that will have beneficial effects on waterfowl production and hunting.

SINCE THERE IS GREAT variation in use of farm ponds by waterfowl, it may be well to set down the important factors that influence this use.

Flyway pattern and geography. A pond location in the natural flyway of waterfowl is most likely to be used. Substantial water developments anywhere will eventually be found by ducks, however. Locations that are isolated in rough terrain are less likely to be used than others. Birds will not ordinarily breed on ponds outside of the natural breeding range of the species.

Soils. Prairie soils and lake or coastal plain soils are the best pond sites for duck breeding areas. Most soils suitable for ponds are also adequate for some use by ducks.

Size and depth. Breeding use by waterfowl is higher per acre on ponds of one-half acre to about 10 acres than on very small ponds or on larger ones. Ponds with substantial shallow water and some aquatic vegetation plus deep water are better than those with all deep water or marshy types of all shallow water.

Location. Ponds should be separated as far as possible from human disturbance. Isolated ponds seldom receive as much use as those in close proximity to other water areas. Wood ducks make more use of ponds close to woodland cover than those where such cover is far away.

Water characteristics. Ponds with stable water levels or ones where the level can be controlled seasonally are favored. Turbid water discourages waterfowl use. Fresh-water ponds provide drinking water in salt water areas.

Vegetation in and around the pond. Aquatic plants that provide foods for ducks are desirable. Bare and overgrazed shores discourage nesting ducks. A good cover of grass and weeds near the pond and not overgrazed is favorable for duck nestings. Heavy growth of emergent aquatic plants, such as cattail and bulrush around the entire shore, reduces the use by ducks, however. Small clumps of shrubs and evergreens, scattered near the pond, are beneficial. Small grain grown in nearby fields provides a source of food. Winter wheat, winter barley, ryegrass, and annual bromegrass may be useful to geese. The pattern of vegetative cover needed by ducks varies with the season and species of duck.

Management. Proper use of wood duck nesting boxes on poles over the pond, islands in the pond, and artificial loafing sites anchored in the pond often are useful in encouraging ducks. Fluctuation of the water levels seasonally to induce growth of duck foods, sometimes with seedings, will improve fall use by ducks and facilitate hunting. Periodic draining may be necessary to maintain maximum fertility and productivity.

FARM PONDS already have improved the status of waterfowl in the United States. I estimate that of the 2.2 million ponds in America in 1962, at least 1,400,000 ponds were of some use to waterfowl.

I believe prospects are good that 1.3 million additional farm ponds will be built by 1980. They will be even more useful to waterfowl than the first 2 million because they will be larger, more will be built with waterfowl benefits and recreation in mind, and there will be a cumulative value based on the cluster principle.

The result then should be over 2.5 million ponds covering nearly 3 million acres of usable water. The number of waterfowl benefited will depend partly on the number of birds; if that is reasonably stable, some 7 million to 12 million birds should make some use of farm ponds.—FRANK C. EDMINSTER.

MALLARDS AND PINTAILS

Waterfowl in the Canadian Breadbasket

NEARLY THREE-FOURTHS of all occupied farmland in Canada is in the three Prairie Provinces of Manitoba, Saskatchewan, and Alberta, a vast hinterland whose fabulous crops of spring wheat make it a renowned breadbasket and whose sloughs are the home of so many ducks as to be a problem to farmers.

The Prairie Provinces grow more than 90 percent of the wheat that is the major Canadian agricultural export and 66 percent of her oats and barley. They make a triangle that extends from the southeastern corner of Manitoba to the Rockies and from Peace River in northwestern Alberta to the United States border.

The area is the northernmost part of the continental Great Plains. It extends into the transition zone between grasslands and boreal coniferous forest.

Prairie farms account for almost half of Canada's farm cash income and employ about 40 percent of Canada's farm workers. The fur trade stimulated exploration of the Canadian West, but its development followed the plow and the cultivation of small grains, particularly spring wheat.

The average annual production of small grains has been about 900 million bushels. All (except about a million bushels of winter rye) were spring sown. About half has been wheat; the remainder, oats and barley.

The triangle has 10 to 20 inches of rainfall. Two-thirds falls during the growing season, which averages 80 to 100 frost-free days. The commonest rotations are grain-summer fallow and grain-grain-summer fallow. The first rotation is usually used in drier areas. Summer-fallowing, a moisture-conserving technique in which fields are cultivated but not seeded, promotes penetration of rain into the soil and prevents moisture loss from growth of weeds. A typical farm has about 600 acres.

The farmer's first job in spring is to prepare a seedbed. That chore begins in April as soon as the soil is dry enough to cultivate. When seeding is completed in late May, there is time to start summer fallowing before spraying for weeds and insects in June. After the second summer fallowing operation is completed in July, the crop is about ready to harvest. Harvest usually begins in early August. Then, given 4 to 14 days of warm, dry weather, threshing begins. With harvest completed, summer-fallow receives one final cultivation. If a 3-year rotation is being followed, stubble to be seeded in the following spring is mulched to promote tilth.

The land mostly is gently rolling. Some areas are rough and broken. In them are many shallow depressions, which are called sloughs when they contain runoff water.

The sloughs, interspersed among the grainfields, are home for part of the year for 18 species of ducks, 4 species of geese, and the American coot. Ducks that breed on the prairies may be classified by habit as aquatic feeders or upland feeders. The upland feeders are the mallard, pintail, American widgeon, and green-winged teal. Mallards and pintails comprise about half of the total duck population of the prairies. Other species of upland feeders are fewer; only a small number leave the marshes to feed regularly in fields.

UPLAND FEEDING, or field feeding, by mallards and pintails occurs from the time they arrive on the Canadian prairies in April until they leave in November. They feed commonly on ripe kernels of small grains, which, following harvest, are present as waste grain, sometimes even after stubble has been tilled or burned.

Two field-feeding flights usually are made each day. The first begins about sunrise or before; the ducks return to the water about midmorning. The second begins about midafternoon, and birds return to water about sunset. During stormy, overcast days, which often precede fall migration, mallards and pintails also make field-feeding flights in the middle of the day. Hunting pressure may also alter the feeding time. There is little evidence that they feed in fields during the night on Canadian prairies, but their departures to fields may be in the semidarkness of predawn and the returns to water may be an hour or more after sunset.

During harvest, feeding on the ripened kernels causes damage to fields of small grain, particularly when the crop is lying in swaths.

A swath is a windrow of cut crop that lies on stubble to dry for several days before threshing. Swathing is used widely on the Canadian prairies. It reduces hazard of crop losses from shattering and lodging, avoids reduction of grade from damage to unripened kernels by early frost, and makes possible a uniform dryness in the harvested crop for storage. The swath lodges on the stubble cut about 6 to 10 inches above the ground. Feeding ducks can reach it easily.

Ducks also cause damage when they stand on the swaths. They trample the grain to the ground and contaminate it with their droppings. It gets dirty and loses grade. It may be impossible to pick up if the crop germinates, grows, or freezes to the ground. The trampling by ducks causes kernels to drop to the ground, where it is unavailable to both ducks and farmers. Such damage also carries over to the following year, because the shattered grain and damaged swath sprout and make extra cultivation.

DAMAGE BY DUCKS to small grain is related to the distance between the grainfields and water areas on which the flocks congregate. The amount of damage is in proportion to the degree with which swathing and harvest schedules synchronize with flocking and migration of mallards and pintails. And, of course,

the longer small grains are in swath, the greater is the damage likely to be.

A survey by mail in 1961 indicated that about 27 thousand grain farmers lost 4.3 million dollars worth of small grains because of damage by ducks. Losses were incurred in 1960 by an estimated 24 thousand farmers in the amount of 7 million dollars. An estimate of damage was derived from a smaller sample sent in 1959 to agricultural officials and farmers. An estimated 45 thousand farmers had losses totaling 12.6 million dollars. In 1955, a questionnaire as to pest damage was sent out by Federal and Provincial departments of agriculture in Saskatchewan. About half of the respondents reported damage calculated to be about 10.6 million dollars in that one Province. All these estimates may be subject to bias in reporting.

It may be assumed that losses reported represent what the farmer believes ducks have cost him. The significance, therefore, only partly concerns a comparison of duck damage to total production or a comparison with other forms of crop loss caused by insects, weeds, hail, and gophers. The attitude of farmers who have experienced crop losses and whose lands produce ducks is important, too. As one small-grain farmer put it: "Prairie agriculture has only progressed at the expense of the buffalo and the coyote. Why should we let ducks stand in our way?"

Five out of eight ducks taken by Canadian and American hunters are produced on these privately owned lands. The growing resentment of aggrieved landowners toward waterfowl cannot be taken lightly. Prairie agriculture will progress.

THE PROBLEM as the farmer sees it is that he bears the burden of economic loss caused by an animal given protection primarily for recreational purposes. Early accounts indicate that geese and ducks have used small grains from the beginning of their cultivation on the Canadian prairies. Tolerance shown by pioneer farmers to that form of competition has been tempered in their successors by a change in farm economics. Probably the most important single influence has been the shift from stack threshing to stook threshing and, finally, to combine harvesting with swathing techniques, which greatly increases the vulnerability of the ripened crop to damage.

Combine harvesting came into general use on the Canadian prairies by the midforties. Soon it was the predominant method of harvesting small grain. That change, through increased use of machinery, reflects the changes in farm economy that have taken place. One aspect of it is referred to as the cost-price squeeze. Another reflection of this change in the economic status of farmers is the increase in farm size and in the number of tenant farmers. The overall effect is that the margin of profit for farmers now is less than it used to be. To the average farmer whose fields are susceptible to duck damage, the 300 bushels or so that he loses annually represent relatively more than he used to lose under older methods of harvesting and mean a lower margin of profit; it adds to his costs.

While the farmer has more troubles from ducks, the public is better able to enjoy wildfowling. Higher standards of living, more leisure time, and more money to spend on recreation add up to more demand for ducks. That demand has skyrocketed since 1945. More protection has been given to waterfowl. More money has been spent on conservation of waterfowl. More publicity has been given to the protection and conservation effort. One acute effect is a worsening of relationships between sportsmen and landowners. The net result has been bitterness among farmers, who take the position that they raise ducks in their sloughs, the ducks come back to plague them in their grainfields, and the birds are protected for some city-hunter who is a pain in the neck because of his carelessness and indifference.

Farmers in Alberta and Saskatchewan, furthermore, are prevented by law from leasing or renting hunting rights to their land. A realization of income from hunting as a means of offsetting losses from duck damage therefore is impossible.

To administrators of the waterfowl resource, the damage to crops by ducks adds up to a king-sized problem. Ducks have a recognizable value in outdoor recreation. At the same time, they are a liability to the grain farmer, who often owns habitat on which they are raised. The resource manager has the responsibility of finding a solution that will be fair to farmers, hunters, and others who have an interest in waterfowl.

FOUR COURSES OF ACTION may offer possible solutions. The duck population could be limited at some level that would result in less damage to the grain farmer. Control methods might be developed to keep ducks out of grainfields. Ducks might be made an asset to grain farmers, through a hunting-supported subsidy, for example. Shifts in land use or agricultural practice might be developed that would reduce a farmer's susceptibility to damage by ducks.

Research and operational efforts have been made and are continuing along these lines.

Farmers often have the same attitude toward ducks that feed in fields as they do toward such other pests as grasshoppers and gophers. A conventional method of dealing with the latter has been to destroy them. Many grain farmers believe that the duck problem should be solved in the same way.

Legal means of destroying ducks have been extended through changes in the crop-damage permit sections of the Migratory Bird Regulations. Hunting seasons have been made as liberal as possible. Yet many farmers press for further reduction of the duck population. The drought of the late fifties and early sixties provided a natural limit on the duck population, but duck damage in fields continues to be a widespread problem. It seems clear that reducing duck numbers to a level tolerable for all farmers would re-quire duck populations too low for hunting.

MANY METHODS have been tried to keep ducks out of grainfields.

Some techniques have been tested by farmers themselves on a trial-and-error basis. Others have been tested as part of research programs sponsored by Government and other agencies interested in the welfare of waterfowl.

Variations of traditional scarecrows are frequently used. A 4- to 6-foot post with a crossarm attached near the top is put in a field. Clothing, bits of cloth, or pieces of metal are attached to the crossarm so that the wind will move them.

Farmers have noticed that ducks normally will not feed close to harvesting machinery or oil barrels. Consequently many farmers leave such objects in fields.

The deterrent effect of these practices, however, usually is limited to a maximum of 10 acres and their effectiveness decreases in time, even when they are moved from place to place in the field.

SHOOTING AT DUCKS with a shotgun has been used to prevent ducks from landing in grainfields. It is done during the regular hunting season and at other times under authorization of crop damage protection permits. Manitoba has had special hunting seasons in which shooting was allowed only on cultivated fields and not within 100 yards of water. The earliest allowable season under terms of the Migratory Bird Treaty is September 1. Because much of the damage to grainfields occurs in August, it is necessary to issue permits to allow shooting at that time. Under conditions of the permit, decoys, calls, or blinds may not be used.

If shooting is done at frequent intervals, while ducks are flying over the field, they may be prevented from landing. That form of protection is expensive. It is normal for ducks to feed twice a day, morning and afternoon, for a total of about 8 hours. To achieve relief over this period, one person firing shells at the rate of one a minute would involve an expense of about 55 dollars a day. A cure by that method is as bad as the illness.

Acetylene exploders have been used to protect grainfields from feeding ducks. They ignite a measured amount of acetylene and air mixture to cause an explosion that sounds like the discharge of a shot-gun. At the rate of one explosion a minute, these machines cost about 15 cents a day to operate if the acetylene is generated from carbide and water. The cost is about 50 cents a day if acetylene is supplied from a portable tank. The tank holds at least five times more fuel; its lower maintenance more than offsets the higher cost.

A TEST carried out in Saskatchewan in 1960 showed that 70 percent of the grainfields in the test area could be protected from duck damage with one exploder per field. These seem to offer most effective and economical means for keeping ducks out of grainfields. Of course, ducks excluded from one grainfield simply go to another to feed. Exploders have never been widely used on the prairies, and problems we do not know about may arise

A normal sheaf of barley from a Saskatchewan grain field.

in diverting ducks from one field to another. Some fields are harvested sooner than others. The problem would be solved if, as an end result, ducks could be diverted from unharvested fields to waste grain of stubble fields or other sources of food.

ANOTHER METHOD of keeping. ducks out of grainfields is to provide feeding areas where they can do no damage. Since birds feed in stubble after harvest is completed, farmers can contribute to such a program by not plowing stubble until after the depredation period is over. It can also be done by providing special areas managed as duck pastures. This may involve seeding specific areas to grain that will then be eaten instead of farmers' crops. Also, grain can be spread in strategic locations to divert the birds from unharvested fields. Both techniques have been used in Canada.

Crops of grain have been planted to provide feeding areas for ducks near Last Mountain Lake in. Saskatchewan. Grain has been spread to the edge of Delta Marsh in Manitoba to reduce duck depredation on nearby grainfields. Although effective, feeding techniques are expensive, and their usefulness seems limited to areas of special importance to both waterfowl and grain farming.

SHIFTS IN LAND use can be made that will reduce the landowner's susceptibility to duck damage. A few farmers have changed from a small grain to grass-legume rotation in fields where persistent damage has occurred. Similar changes might be made to oilseed crops, such as

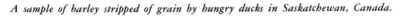
A sample of barley stripped of grain by hungry ducks in Saskatchewan, Canada.

rape and flax, which are not damaged by ducks on the Canadian prairies.

WILDLIFE INSURANCE has been made available to farmers by the Governments of Saskatchewan since 1953 and Alberta since 1961. The insurance payments do not cover completely the cost of the damage to the farmer. He must pay a premium for the insurance—2 percent of the insured value in Saskatchewan and 3 percent in Alberta. Maximum coverage is 25 dollars an acre in Saskatchewan and 15 dollars in Alberta. Often crop loss exceeds that amount. Only a small percentage of farmers who suffer damage from waterfowl have taken advantage of this program in Saskatchewan. Since its inception, however, some 1400 claims have been paid, amounting to more than 536 thousand dollars.

In 1961, two events took place that could aid in solving the problem.

One was formation of the International Waterfowl Committee, whose membership comprises senior wildlife and agricultural administrators from the Governments of Canada and the United States. It is expected that this international committee will review continental waterfowl management in relation to the plight of the grain farmer. A foremost need is for funds to develop a sound management program, including acquisition and development of wetlands.

The other event was passage by the Government of Canada of the Agriculture Rehabilitation and Development Act to provide for rehabilitation of agricultural lands and development of rural areas in Canada. This legislation could be of great importance in maintaining wildlife habitat, including wetlands, and conversion of duck populations into an asset. For the first time, much of the land in western Canada will be considered with multiple use in mind. One outcome is certainly to be a trend toward more livestock production and with it, a reduced competition between farmers and waterfowl for grain.

Ducks feeding on cereal crops in Canada represent competition to the small grain farmer which he finds particularly objectionable because of limitations put on methods of reducing his liabilities. A solution to the problem is clearly a responsibility of waterfowl resource administration agencies on both sides of the border. Greater efforts to meet that responsibility should be made through research and operational programs.

The operational programs should attempt to: disseminate information on how to keep ducks out of unharvested fields, promote changes in land use or agricultural practices that will reduce susceptibility of a particular site to duck damage, seek means of making ducks of value to farmers, and, during years of bumper crops of ducks, reducing their numbers through liberalized hunting regulations.

Research is needed, too. We need to know more about ducks and about agriculture if the two are to coexist in harmony on the Canadian prairies.—

ERNEST L. PAYNTER and
W. J. D. STEPHEN.

MALLARDS, PINTAILS, AND WIDGEON

Ducks, Grain,
and American Farmers

SPRING IS A raging battle of the air masses on the northern prairies. A warm day is apt to be followed by a gale that hurls clouds of dust aloft. A blinding blizzard may sweep in from the north, bringing polar air at temperatures below zero. He who greets the vanguard of ducks on the prairies should not consider them an omen of spring; he will shiver and shake and frost his ears for weeks to come.

Pintails and mallards venturing from southern quarters into the nesting ranges on the northern prairies often encounter such weather—and even greater hardships. They are seldom out of sight of farmland on their flights northward. Water usually appears in grainfields before the

ice melts from the deeper sloughs, potholes, lakes, and marshes. In wet years, millions of ducks and hundreds of thousands of geese move leisurely northward. They feed on the abundant waste grain in newly flooded depressions and potholes or in upland stubble nearby. Fall-plowed fields, flooded by spring freshets, provide food and are regularly used. Abundant water in the cropfields means a heavy runoff and deep flooding of the lakes and marshes. Dabbling ducks and divers use them for resting and make daily flights to surrounding field potholes to feed. Water and feed reasonably close together is the combination that brings in birds.

Sometimes on prairie farms in

spring a light snow melts quickly and puts shallow water into many potholes. Flocks of pintails and mallards are likely to use them. Some birds may even begin to nest near them. But the plug is pulled in these temporary potholes when frost goes out of the ground. The water rapidly disappears, and the ducks must then give up and seek other places to fulfill their destiny.

ONLY A PART of the United States small-grain farming region has the abundance of water areas needed for a high potential in waterfowl breeding. The better U.S. pothole habitat during 1948–1962 held populations of 50 to more than 100 pairs of breeding ducks the square mile—but this is considerably less than in some Canadian pothole localities: At Lousana, Alberta, Allen G. Smith of the Bureau of Sport Fisheries and Wildlife found 300 pairs to the square mile in 1958. Nevertheless, stateside production can be substantial, except in drought years. During the peak of the drought in 1961 many square miles were down to a few pairs or none. Similar reductions were recorded in Canada.

Not all of the land in the small-grain belt is in crops. You may see blocks of several square miles without an acre of grass, trees, or weedy cover, but it is more usual for individual farms to have pasture, hayland, alfalfa, and corn in the rotation along with windbreaks, shelterbelts, and odd acres of idle grassland or weeds. Since the beginning of the Soil Bank program in 1957, many acres of cultivated grasses were established, and some will be left idle or used only in emergency conditions, such as drought, through 1970.

Cover conditions during April and May vary greatly from one locality to another. Where there are only bare, plowed, or disked fields, prairie ducks find few places to nest. On farms in hilly areas and on sandy soils, substantial acreages are in grasslands. Nesting cover there generally is much better than it is on farms planted to grain alone.

During May, June, and July, the main nesting period, both cropland and grassland offer many good nesting sites. In the North, small grains start growth too late to be of much value as cover, but greater use is made of grain fields in southwestern Minnesota, South Dakota, and Nebraska. Mallards readily accept wheat and barley fields in irrigated districts of the Sacramento Valley in California.

Conditions and factors that lend diversity to grain fields generally help to improve the quality of nesting cover. Acceptable nesting sites, for example, may be found on idle ground adjacent to low, wet areas and around patches of brush and trees.

Weather influences the timing of farming practices and affects the growth of domestic and native plants. Major changes in land use also have widespread bearing on nesting conditions. In 1947, a year of peak flax prices, thousands of acres of native prairie grasslands in the Dakotas were plowed and planted to flax, thereby reducing nesting habitat. In contrast, the Soil Bank and grassland restoration practices, encouraged by farm programs, have reestablished much good nesting cover.

Farmers who regularly burn stubble fields, pastures, and idle land in spring destroy early duck nests along with the unwanted vegetation. Many farmers do not have equipment to handle heavy vegetation, and spring seeding is simplified if fields are burned to rid them of excess straw or heavy stands of weeds. This kind of land use hurts ducks.

DUCKS HAVE VARIOUS PREFERENCES for nesting sites on prairie farms. Mallards are not inclined to specialize. They will nest in plowed fields, in weeds and grasses, in nest boxes or abandoned crows' nests, and in the marsh over water.

Other species are more particular. Most dabbling ducks will not nest where the ground is wet or soggy unless a layer of ground litter provides a dry nest base. They prefer to have dead, standing vegetation in the nesting cover. Then they can avoid flooding by using the dead material to raise their nests above ground level. Poorly drained cut hay fields and cultivated sites are of little value to nesting dabblers.

Redheads, canvasbacks, ruddy ducks, and coots usually nest over water; they use cattails, bulrushes, grasses, or sedges as nesting cover.

Scaup normally nest on land, usually within 15 to 50 feet of water. When the margins of water areas are hayed, heavily grazed, or farmed they no longer lure scaup as nesting tenants.

Blue-winged teal and shovelers usually nest in grass. Bluewings also like alfalfa. Both will use weeds.

Gadwalls and widgeon prefer herbaceous cover, although widgeon at times may nest in cover where brush and trees are present.

The pintail seems best adapted to intensive land use in small-grain country. Most individuals of this species actually seek out more open nesting sites, such as stubble fields, heavily grazed pastures, and hay meadows in preference to tall or dense types of cover. Those choosing stubble-field nesting sites are usually destined to have their nests destroyed by spring plowing.

NESTING pintails and mallards averaged 34 and 11 to the square mile, respectively, in agricultural land within 10 miles of the Lower Souris National Wildlife Refuge in North Dakota in 1949. Most of the nests were in small-grain stubble. Waterfowl biologists elsewhere have found pintails and mallards, to a lesser degree, selecting stubble as a choice nesting site.

It is easy enough to observe and describe the diversity in nesting habits of waterfowl.

But what does it mean in terms of their overall prosperity?

Does cover limit the number and kind of ducks that will use a body of water?

Does cover limit productivity?

We cannot say exactly how much cover is needed, what kind is desirable, how it should be dispersed, or just when it must be present. But if cover of the kind and quality an *individual* duck requires is absent when she has the urge to nest, she will leave the locality and move elsewhere in search of the proper cover,

delay egg laying until conditions improve, or fail to nest.

With most ducks, selection of a water area is determined by many factors besides cover. Availability of food and loafing sites, protection from wind and waves, water quality, and freedom from disturbances caused by man or animal all have bearing on the use of an area.

The amount and quality of nesting cover often seem secondary in importance to other factors. Considering prairie ducks collectively, good cover within the water area is desired by redheads, canvasbacks, ruddy ducks, and coots. Cover on and around the water margin may be used by canvasbacks and is preferred by scaup. An area within 200 yards of the water's edge is used by mal-. lards, gadwalls, widgeon, pintails,. bluewings, greenwings, and shovelers.

NESTING IS ONE THING. Bringing off a brood is another. Nesting ducks on farmland face hazards aplenty.

What it amounts to is this: *If* seeding and summer fallow are greatly delayed, *if* the farmer does not burn or destroy the nests he accidentally finds, *if* crows or skunks do not find the eggs, and *if* the weather cooperates—a good hatch may come from cropland nests.

Needless to say, it is only rarely that all factors are favorable, and usually success is poor. But in southern latitudes, where some species nest in green crops, success may be very good. J. P. Earl measured 61-percent success for mallard nests in growing wheat and barley in Sacramento Valley. He felt that his trails to the nests increased predation rates and that success of nests not visited was even greater. Hayfields, though, are essentially death traps to ducks. Alfalfa and other legumes or grasses attract nesting ducks in numbers, but losses from mowing are high, and few ducklings hatch.

Nesting in stubble fields by mallards and pintails often leads to widespread destruction of nests. Biologists of the North Dakota State Game and Fish Department reported losses from late plowing as high as 20 nests per square mile. In Saskatchewan 23 nests of pintails and mallards were found to be plowed under in 320 acres. Competition with plows, cows, and cutterbars does not help bring off broods.

As things stand, nesting cover is unlimited for mallards and pintails— but so are the hazards.

High losses of nests and young are normal. A stable mallard population has an average of 1.25 young per adult in the prehunting season. To provide this ratio, 40 to 50 percent of the pairs must raise a brood. Production is best in areas with at least 40 percent uncultivated lands. But whether production is good, fair, or poor, the ducks that come through in the prairies have a banquet set for them.

TO PUDDLE DUCKS AND GEESE, particularly to mallards and pintails, few things are more attractive, more alluring, than a harvested grainfield.

Snow geese feeding in a barley field at Tule Lake National Wildlife Refuge, California. The grain was planted for their exclusive use.

The methods of harvesting in the prairies create nearly ideal feeding conditions. In the southern and western prairies, wheat is usually combined straight. The uneven terrain, climate, and farming practices in the North usually make straight combining impractical. Here, the swather is used almost universally to cut and windrow the grain before it is dead ripe. After it has dried enough for safe storage, it is harvested with combine and pick-up attachment.

Regardless of method, waste grain is left in the fields. The amount varies with the variety of grain, weather conditions, and the density of the stand. Waste grain is available to ducks and geese in some fields until spring farming operations begin. In others, it is gone in a few days or weeks if fall seeding, plowing, or disking are done. Measurements taken near Whitewater Lake in Manitoba indicated that the amount of waste wheat available was 1.5 to 3.6 bushels an acre. In two barley fields, the amounts were 4.7 and 7.1 bushels an acre. At this higher rate, 160 acres would have 1,136 bushels of waste grain, enough to feed about 7 thousand mallards for 20 days.

Ducks and geese coming through in the fall soon find fields with large amounts of waste grain of preferred varieties, usually wheat and barley. Both Canada and white-fronted geese feed on grain and greens in lightly disked fields and in summer fallow, where only green plants are present. Green shoots of winter wheat, rye, and legumes are also important foods for Canadas and snow geese in some localities. Waste corn, whenever available, is preferred by mallards and is often used by geese.

Feeding flights in fall of mallards, pintails, and geese are made morning and evening between resting areas and grain fields. These forays, sometimes by thousands of birds, are awesome spectacles to hunters and nonhunters.

Waste grain undoubtedly makes it possible for ducks and geese to use many water areas that were sparingly visited before the appearance of grain farming.

It is certain that the fall migration of some field feeders now is less hurried and, in fact, often delayed. This works to the advantage of hunters in the grain States, because it prolongs their hunting.

The amount of waste grain available to ducks and geese in the small-grain belt has declined since 1950. The drop was not due to greater efficiency of harvest methods but rather to the smaller acreages of wheat and barley and an increase in fall tillage. Such crops as grass, legumes, and safflower are replacing small grains in farm programs.

OTHER THINGS ARE HAPPENING, too, to reduce the ability of the small-grain belt to sustain waterfowl in the spring. Several developments have cut into the potentials of duck production of the Prairie States. Much of the original waterfowl habitat has been drained. Small potholes are being filled by pushing trees, brush, and earth into them. More potholes are being filled by windborne soil.

One who has seen the dust clouds of the northern prairies can guess at the tons of soil that are carried through the air.

An even more important filling agent, although less spectacular, may be the steady downward movement of soil driven by rain from cultivated margins of potholes. A violent rainstorm may splash more than 100 tons of soil per acre into the atmosphere. On a 10-percent slope, three times more soil creeps downward than moves upgrade. Gully erosion into cultivated potholes is less common in the low-rainfall belt, but some occurs with every cloudburst.

Land that has been farmed for 50 to 75 years appears to have many shallow depressions, where once there must have been deeper potholes. The rate of filling has never been measured, but it seems likely that most water areas in cultivated fields eventually will be filled by Nature and man. Just how long remaining potholes will last under the action of wind and rain is more than an academic question. The future of prairie ducks is involved.

CROP DAMAGE BY DUCKS AND GEESE is a vexing problem. Many farmers have sustained heavy losses by flocks of grain-eating birds. Heavy damage to crops occurs in California, southern Oregon, northwestern Minnesota, northeastern and central North Dakota, and occasionally at scattered localities elsewhere. For the most part, losses are heaviest when harvesting of small grain is delayed for one reason or another. The waterfowl damage zone in the prairies is essentially the region where spring wheat is grown. There a flock of a thousand mallards using a large prairie slough may cause a heavy loss to one farmer. Flocks of this size may be widely scattered in wet years, and many farmers may be directly affected. At larger lakes and marshes, total numbers of field feeders may range from 10 thousand to 150 thousand birds.

At Tule Lake and Lower Klamath National Wildlife Refuges on the California-Oregon border, peak migration totals several million ducks, and the depredation problem often is substantial. In that area, one farming operation whose gross was 3 million dollars, is said to have spent 65 thousand dollars in a year for herding ducks from crops with airplanes, searchlights, shotguns, and other devices. Losses of small grains (including rice) in California formerly ran to thousands of dollars to individual farmers and a total of a million dollars or more in the State.

The potential for damage may be estimated from the number of feeding ducks and the cash value of grain in the field. The average flock consumes grain at the approximate rate of a bushel a day for each 125 ducks. The amount of damaged or wasted grain in the swath may be 1.5 to 5.5 times the amount actually eaten. On individual farms, damage by unmolested flocks has run as high as 44 dollars a day per thousand ducks. The average loss is considerably below this figure.

Losses of 100 to 200 dollars a day because of the feeding of flocks of 5 thousand to 10 thousand ducks in fields have been fairly common.

At some of the larger concentration areas, such as the Lower Souris Refuge, populations have often exceeded 125 thousand ducks during peak seasons. If damage control measures were not used, the potential loss could amount to 2,500 dollars a day or 112,500 dollars during a 45-day harvest season. Annual losses at Lower Souris declined from an estimated 100 thousand dollars to about 1,200 dollars after damage control techniques were employed. In the worst of the depredation seasons between 1940 and 1955, possibly a hundred farmers had individual losses ranging from a few dollars to a thousand dollars or more. During 1956–1962, a program of depredations control reduced the annual losses to about 1,200 dollars a year, distributed among a dozen or so farmers.

AT MANY larger national wildlife refuges and at some State management areas, reasonable solutions to the problem of crop depredations have been found. Leaving small grain crops unharvested for ducks is one approach. On Tule Lake and Lower Klamath Refuges, about 7 thousand acres are managed in this manner.

Spreading harvested grain on specially prepared feeding stations at the water's edge is another method. That is done on the Lower Souris Refuge and the Agassiz National Wildlife Refuge in Minnesota. It is also practiced at Delta Marsh in Manitoba. About 10 thousand to 25 thousand bushels are fed annually at Lower Souris. In some localities, farmers alone or with assistance from refuge personnel haze the occasional field-feeding birds and drive them back to the refuges.

Widely scattered flocks present a more serious problem. Game management agents of the United States Fish and Wildlife Service investigate complaints and instruct farmers in the use of frightening devices. Herding birds out of damage areas by frightening measures, as authorized by Federal permits, is partly successful, but we need better methods for coping with the problem.

THE SMALL-GRAIN FARMER holds the future of waterfowl in the palm of his calloused hand. At times he is in the mood to throw it away. Hordes of ducks gorge on his fall crops. Sometimes they trample and spoil more than they eat. Hunters in pursuit of these grain-fed ducks may scatter his swaths, leave his gates open, throw away beer cans to pass through his combine, and thumb their noses at him if he protests their carelessness. No wonder the western grain farmer has reservations about the values of waterfowl.

Hunters and the rest of us—all who are concerned with soil, water, wildfowl, conservation, and the well-being of living things—have to understand his problems; know how his operations affect waterfowl and how the birds affect him; and convince him that ducks and geese are natural treasures worth their keep.

Let me offer an interim solution. This country has a surplus of one crop (grain) and a shortage of another crop (ducks). Payments to farmers, for concessions and operations in behalf of migratory waterfowl, may well prove rewarding to this grain-rich, recreation-hungry Nation.—MERRILL C. HAMMOND.

WHITE-FRONTED GEESE

The Cornfielders

BETWEEN THE WIDE wheatlands of Manitoba and Saskatchewan and the ricelands of Louisiana lies a fine larder for people and waterfowl. It is a heartland of rich soil and heavy grain—winter wheat, rye, late alfalfa, and pastures for the grazing geese, and soybeans, barley, wheat, and rice for ducks. But most of all, in the upper and middle reaches, there is corn.

Corn is a prime food for waterfowl. It is abundant. Birds easily find its golden kernels on the ground between the rows of stalks. It is nutritious and fattens wintering and traveling ducks even when savage Midwestern winters exert se-

vere demands on their energy and reserves.

WHEREVER CORN IS GROWN, ducks and geese seek it out. They come together in all four flyways, but when we speak of the golden grain we usually think of the Mississippi Flyway in general and the upper Midwest in particular. This is corn country. In 1963 the States in the Mississippi Flyway produced nearly 3 billion bushels; the North-Central States alone grew more than 85 percent of the Nation's corn crop.

A vast residue of this immense crop is available to waterfowl. Since mechanical cornpickers came into

425

use in the thirties, the amount of corn left in fields has at least trebled. A good handhusker might leave less than 3 bushels of corn on an acre, but machine picking is not nearly so thorough. (It is faster, perhaps cheaper, and more easily available than farmhands.) Corn shanks may be brittle and easily broken by machines. Corn borers and dry weather may weaken the stalks further. The dry ears of late harvests shatter easily. So, an average of 10 percent of the standing corn crop in the United States may be left scattered in the fields. That loss is the birds' gain.

The States in the Mississippi Flyway (excluding the cornlands of South Dakota, Nebraska, and Kansas) had a total corn production in 1962 of about 2,807,159,000 bushels. That was grain; it does not include the corn harvested as silage or used as livestock forage. If we assume—and perhaps we should not— a "loss" of 10 percent of the crop of grain corn through machine picking, we can figure that about 280 million bushels of corn were left in the fields of the Mississippi Flyway. In all the North-Central States, it is possible that 313 million bushels of corn failed to reach the crib or bin.

It was not all waste. Farmers salvage much of it. They hog down picked cornfields or open them to cattle. Cattle, though, tend to seek out waste ears first and may not bother with scattered kernels. If the total cornpicker "loss" was half shelled corn and half ear corn, and if livestock salvage all the lost ear corn, more than 150 million bushels of corn still were available to wildlife in the North-Central States in 1962.

And this isn't all. The Bureau of Sport Fisheries and Wildlife and the State conservation departments have been increasing the acreage of corn grown on areas managed specifically for waterfowl. A survey by the Mississippi Flyway Council in 1960 revealed that about 20,000 acres on managed areas in the Mississippi Flyway produced a corn crop for ducks and geese. Waterfowl are allowed to harvest additional acres of corn grown on private areas. It is estimated that enough corn is being grown on waterfowl areas in the

Flooding has placed this corn within easy reach of hungry mallards.

Mississippi Flyway to feed 5 million mallards for 50 days if the grain were all available to them.

So THE TABLE IS SET. All down the great funnel of the Mississippi Flyway, millions of bushels of corn await the winged gleaners each autumn. Many puddle ducks find and use the grain. Mallards, pintails, black ducks, and wood ducks all gorge on the kernels. In one study in Missouri, corn was found in the gizzards of every species that biologists examined except the blue-winged teal.

Even diving ducks visit cornlands, especially if tile drains remain frozen in spring and heavy runoffs flood the fields. Larry Jahn, of the Wildlife Management Institute, once told of watching an old bull canvasback float serenely in a flooded cornfield with half an ear of corn in his bill. But the diving ducks are not a very adaptable group, and buffleheads, scaup, cans, redheads, ruddies, and ring-necked ducks prefer open water to open lands.

Geese are foragers that subsist mainly on greens, but they can pack away huge amounts of corn. The big Canadas can feed on unpicked corn as high as 43 inches above the ground. Some standing cornfields in goose country exhibit clear-cut browse lines.

Biologists at Horicon Marsh in Wisconsin found that 38 inches is about as high as the average Canada goose will feed. An effort was made therefore to plant refuge corn that ears out below 38 inches; nearby farmers may plant taller varieties that ear out higher than that.

As field corn ripens, the ears hang. A hungry goose, stretching to his utmost, can push his head inside the husk and thoroughly strip the ear. The field may appear intact from a distance, but closer examination will show that almost every ear has been shelled on the stalk.

Pete Carter, a Federal refuge manager, and I once were discussing a 10-acre cornfield on the big Crab Orchard National Wildlife Refuge in southern Illinois. Some of the stalks had been ridden down and broken by geese, but the field seemed to be in good shape. I asked Pete how much corn he thought still remained on that 10 acres.

"I'd bet a day's pay that there isn't a quart of corn in the whole field," he said.

We walked through the field and examined three rows of standing corn carefully. The cobs still had their husks wrapped neatly about them, but not one bore a kernel. Nor did we find any kernels on the ground.

ALTHOUGH THE 30 THOUSAND geese wintering at Crab Orchard in 1962 ate nearly 25 thousand bushels of corn, this food item probably was a second choice in that locality. At Crab Orchard the birds generally turn to corn only after they have cleaned out pastures and soybean fields on the big refuge.

In this regard, waterfowl managers in Missouri, Wisconsin, and Illinois balance on a tricky tightwire. If they fill all the needs of the geese, hunting success in the area will fall off. Yet they must plant enough food to hold geese on the refuge until nearby crops are harvested, or drastic depredations may result. By the time the geese have cleaned out the refuge fields, most nearby landowners have completed their harvests. Pity the farmer, though, who was rained out of his bottomland fields before he could harvest his corn. By December or January, he may have several thousand honking volunteers doing the job for him.

Corn and the mechanical picker surely are factors in the shift of the old migration routes of Midwestern blue geese. Traditionally they migrated along the Missouri River only in spring. In autumn they usually made an almost nonstop passage from Baffin Island and James Bay to the gulf coasts of Texas and Louisiana. That has changed.

Since the early forties, flights of blue geese have made their fall push down the Missouri and have established a new tradition for geese and gunners alike. The late Bruce Stiles, who was director of the Iowa Conservation Commission, lived and worked for years in western Iowa. In 1942 he wrote: "I have never seen a blue goose in more than 20 years of hunting on the Missouri River." But even as he remarked, the "cobheads" were beginning to revisit in September and October their spring stopover points.

A FEW LESSER SNOW GEESE always have made autumn flights down the Missouri. It has been only a few years, however, since both the blue and white color phases of the

lesser snows began making this fall flight in large numbers. Many hunters and wildfowl experts attribute the shift to a change of cultural practices—and especially to an abundance of waste corn. This change of migration habits coincides pretty well with the general use of the cornpicker along the Missouri. At the same time, however, there has been a westward shift of blue phase birds on the breeding grounds

Today's goose hunting along the middle Missouri hinges almost directly on the availability of corn If the harvest is late and fields are unopened and unpicked, most of the blue and white snows may scarcely pause in their southward flight. But when one speaks of waterfowl and corn, he refers to the puddle ducks and geese in general and to the common mallard in particular.

THE CANNY GREENHEAD invariably is the first duck to discard tradition and tailor his habits to changing times. Today he is the duck most generally associated with corn, although authorities in 1918 and 1930 did not mention corn as an important food of mallards While mallards have been known to feed in shocked cornfields, one veteran Midwestern hunter recently told me that he had never seen mallards feeding in corn before mechanical pickers were used.

A big drake mallard can eat up to 400 kernels of corn in one meal Corn comprised more than 26 per cent by volume of the total fall foods of more than a thousand mallards in Missouri one year. In Illi nois, corn has made up more than 47 percent of the total food of the mallard. Jim Sieh, a biologist in Iowa, estimated in 1958 that "several million mallards" used Iowa fields during migration each year.

Like many of the geese, mallards have altered their migration and wintering patterns to coincide with the immense new food supply. Great concentrations of mallards now carry on northern waters until late winter. They cruise out from these resting areas to feed in cornfields at every point of the compass. Some mallards fly more than 40 miles to the feeder fields and descend in cloud-like flocks on picked cornlands.

Frank Bellrose, of the Illinois Natural History Survey, has seen 40 thousand mallards at one time in a 20-acre cornfield. In one of his field notes he wrote: "At this time the mallards are arriving in the cornfield at the rate of 1 thousand birds per minute." Such great flocks remind you of a cyclone as hundreds of echelons spiral down from altitudes of a thousand feet or more to feed in fields.

Ducks often ignore cornfields in the dissected, broken lands immediately behind the flood plain bluffs of large rivers. They may bypass them and keep going until they reach the flatter fields of the upland prairies. Ideally, such fields are within a few miles of the resting areas and offer good visibility.

The mallard's favorite cornlands are clean, open fields that have

A flooded cornfield near Ringgold, Louisiana. Up to 1,000 mallards fed here over a winter season.

plenty of waste grain, a minimum of debris or cover, and mostly broken or flattened stalks. Machine pickers open the fields and make it easier for waterfowl to alight in them. Handpicking may break down only a third of the stalks; the tall fodder makes problems for fliers and sentinels.

Mallards can eat ear corn when it is partly frozen in the ground. They often snuffle through light snow to find buried corn, "snow-plowing" in it with heads and necks completely buried. An inch or two of snow does not discourage many mallards, although some birds will leave the region. A few may persist in an area and feed on corn in 12 inches of snow, but snow more than 4 inches deep discourages most cornfielding mallards.

CORN IS NOT A PERFECT FOOD— natural aquatics such as coontail surpass it in calcium and protein content—but it is readily available and mallards may subsist on it to the exclusion of all other domestic grains. Mallards may feed on corn near a soybean field and ignore the beans. When greenheads do feed heavily on soybeans, as in Arkansas, the fields are often flooded and the beans soaked. In a parallel situation, corn may not be so attractive, for it appears to deteriorate rapidly in water.

Corn is such an attractive duck food that birds will continue to feed where corn is available even in the face of considerable gun pressure. There are many examples, however, of ducks shying off or being "burned out" from favored feeding areas by

hunting. Thus the degree of use of any duck food is inversely proportional to the hunting pressure on areas where it is available. In cornfields, hunting effort is often thinly spread, and space alone may give enough protection to feeding ducks.

Thinly spread duck hunting is a relative term now. Some cornfields sustain a surprising degree of hunting effort, (although nothing to compare with the average marshland). The shifty mallard therefore has been quick to mold his habit to the new sport of hunting in cornfields. Mallards once may have left resting waters and flown to corn fields at altitudes of 300 feet. Today they may fly to the feeder field at levels of a thousand feet or more, and often it is hard to tell such feeding birds from travelers. In most of the Midwest, mallards now seem to leave for the corn lands later in the morning and afternoon and at greater altitude than they did a few years ago. They lose some of this native caution only on overcast, snow-spitting days in early winter. Then mallards may work the fields all day with great urgency and singleness of purpose—and the experienced hunter follows their example.

Corn depredation by mallards generally is not serious. If a corn field is flooded, or crusted with deep snow, the birds may feed on corn in the husk and even break down stalks to get it. But little stalk breaking occurs in standing dry corn; the ducks prefer picked fields.

Mallards, however, may be found in unharvested cornfields in places where other food is scanty. On

North Dakota game area one winter, mallards easily stripped more than 20 acres of standing corn. In Colorado, where more than a million mallards congregated one January on the Arkansas and Platte River drainages, the huge flocks took 4,500 dollars' worth of corn a day.

HOWEVER ATTRACTIVE a corn diet may be, it sometimes has sinister overtones. As mallards dabble in shallow, heavily hunted marshes, they often ingest lead shot pellets. Many pellets are expelled from the ducks naturally. If this occurs before there is drastic erosion in a mallard's gizzard, the bird will not be poisoned. And if the mallard eats lead pellets and follows that with a diet of small seeds or leafy materials, it may still have a fighting chance. But if a mallard feeding on corn eats only one number-6 shot pellet, chances are that it will die. The flinty kernels evidently promote mechanical abrasion of the lead pellets in the gizzard and accelerate absorption of deadly lead compounds into the bloodstream.

Such factors, however, are surely offset by the advantages of corn-yielding. Barren waters that lack aquatic foods may hold sizable flocks of mallards as long as heavy snows do not blanket adjacent cornfields. Large numbers of mallards may pack into municipal reservoirs, park lakes, flooded sandpits, farm ponds, and even little prairie creeks in parts of the upper Midwest, where they rarely wintered a generation ago. Today, thousands of hunters go cornfield-

ing for mallards—a type of gunning that requires neither club memberships nor special leases. Only adequate resting waters, where the mallards will be safe and undisturbed, are needed. The broad, picked cornlands provide the rest.

BUT A NAGGING WORRY PERSISTS in the minds of some biologists. Most traditional feeding grounds along the major midwestern flyway routes no longer exist. Siltation has wrecked clear backwaters that once grew emergent aquatics that mallards love. Low alluvial benches of nut trees have been destroyed along many old river routes.

Certain places along the Illinois River illustrate the history of duck habitat and food supplies and their manipulation by man. The bottom lands of the Illinois originally were forests of bur-oaks, pin oaks, pecans, and other mastbearing trees. Ducks made the most of this food supply and fed heavily on the nuts and acorns and aquatic plants that flourished in the clear backwater lakes.

During the early 1900's, the Chicago River was reversed from Lake Michigan, and the level of the Illinois River was lifted about 3 feet. Many lowland nut forests were flooded and killed. As the watershed was put to soybeans and corn, turbidity and siltation clouded the clear backwaters, and most of the best aquatic duck foods were smothered.

When the alluvial forests perished in the rising river, duck hunting nearly ended along many parts of the Illinois. The Sangamon River delta, comprising about 15 thousand acres of prime duck habitat, was the first and hardest hit of the major hunting areas. It was here that the first deliberate duck baiting began in the early 1900's—a manmade substitute for the vanished attraction of natural food supplies. Acorns and pecans were gone. They were supplanted almost overnight by hunting areas intensely "salted" with corn.

IN THE TWENTIES, when cheap corn was available during the depression, baiting began with a vengeance. In the Illinois bottoms near Beardstown, duck clubs were spreading as much as 7 thousand bushels of corn each season on 20-acre tracts. It was estimated that 6 million bushels of corn were fed by Illinois hunting clubs during the open season in 1933.

In a sense, this was the beginning of corn in the waterfowl tradition of the Mississippi Flyway. And no sooner was baiting outlawed in the midthirties than the first of the new mechanical cornpickers came clanking onto the National scene. By sheer, undeserved luck, the hunters had won again. One of the very factors that silted the oxbow lakes and overflows—the upland fields of cash corn—had helped compensate for the lost wild foodstocks of waterfowl.

But if corn ever vanishes as a major food supply of ducks along the upper Mississippi Flyway, midwestern ducks and duckhunting will suffer a grievous loss. At best, the mallards may fly almost non-

stop to southern wintering grounds and pass a half mile high over Cornbelt guns. At worst, they may find the situation little better in the South, as more efficient rice harvests and accelerated southern drainage and marsh destruction penalize waterfowl. And if grain crop residues vanish, can manmade refuges and wildfowl food plantings take up the slack? It is doubtful and some waterfowl experts are viewing new farming methods with grave concern.

ON MOST FLAT CORNLANDS—particularly on bottom lands—farmers dread wet springs that prevent early plowing. Some corn farmers may not even attempt spring planting on lands that were not plowed in the fall. Many of them therefore dress their fields in autumn. Tractors, coupled in tandem, pull combines that precede plows—picking, shelling, and plowing the cornfield in a single operation. Such plowing is done half a year in advance of planting, and great quantities of waste corn are plowed under by the time the main waterfowl flights arrive. Fall plowing of cornfields is increasing—especially on land of less than 3-percent slope. That includes nearly all bottoms and a great many of the best uplands.

In many cornfields, in an attempt to reduce corn waste and weather risk, farmers harvest early and place the high-moisture corn in drying bins. New drying techniques permit corn to be picked early; the lowest corn losses take place when kernel moisture ranges between 24 and 28 percent, a time when the stalks also contain some moisture and stand more strongly to the picker.

Agronomists in Iowa have developed a new schedule for planting and harvesting corn. The goal is to achieve the most economical harvest with the least loss of corn, and the harvest of corn with fairly high moisture levels. By carefully using calendarized hybrid corns that mature in varying stages, total field losses may not range above 5 percent, and up to 30 percent of the total harvest may be in by September 20.

Planting such calendarized varieties provides a buffer against bad weather that might completely halt the harvest of a single variety that matures on a single date. Later maturing corns that are picked early show high moisture levels similar to those of the earlier maturing varieties. If necessary, the entire harvest can be cured in driers to a highly controlled degree.

Strong stalks of new corn hybrids further reduce losses. Mechanical cornpickers are being improved constantly. The best may cause corn losses little higher than some oldtime handpicking losses.

Some new corn combines, however, may work to the advantage of waterfowl. Of the total corn lost with such machines, as little as one-third may be ear corn. The remainder is widely strewn shelled corn. This presents a problem in efficiently hogging down a field, and it is nearly impossible to sal-

Cornfields are often chosen as places to hunt.

vage anything but ear corn when cattle glean a field. So, even though the picker-sheller combines may harvest corn more efficiently than older cornpickers, an increased percentage of lost shelled corn may actually benefit wildlife.

IN THE LONG RUN, however, corn harvests are certain to become increasingly efficient. As this occurs, manmade wildfowl food will diminish, and some waterfowl authorities may have good reason to predict gloomily that the current cornfielding tradition of ducks and geese is a transient pattern that will be encompassed within a few fleeting decades and that there may be nothing to replace it on a large scale.

An agricultural engineer recently said to me: "I'm no duck expert, but I know something about corn production and harvesting methods. We'll always be feeding ducks in the fields. Even with greatly increased harvest efficiency, there'll always be more than enough waste corn in Iowa alone to give every mallard in the flyway a bellyache. Besides, our high experimental corn production is one thing; the commercial production of the average farmer is quite another."

The last point is borne out by the Iowa farmer who was being urged by his county agent to attend an agricultural short course at the State college. Nels reflected: "Aw what good would it do? Heck, I ain't farming as well now as I know how to!"

For the sake of the cornfielders let us hope he never does.—

JOHN MADSON

MALLARDS

Rice and Waterfowl

WINTERING waterfowl were here long before domestic rice was grown, but some ducks, especially mallards and pintails, now depend heavily on ricefields for food. Rice and the birds get along pretty well together.

A few acres of rice were grown on upland sites in Virginia in 1650. By the end of the Revolutionary War, and until the Civil War, production was centered near the mouths of the major rivers from North Carolina to southern Georgia.

Over the years, rice growing has shifted, and today the primary producing regions in North America are the coastal prairie of southwestern Louisiana and southeastern Texas; the delta areas of Louisiana, Mississippi, Arkansas, and Missouri; the Grand Prairie of Arkansas; and the Sacramento and San Joaquin Valleys of California. About 1,803,-000 acres were in rice in 1962—320,300 acres in California and 1,482,700 acres in southern and southeastern United States.

ORIGINALLY the rice producing areas along the southern Atlantic coast were fresh-water marshes, which a variety of ducks utilized, and swamps, which wood ducks and mallards liked. Waterfowl shooting in the ricefields was a major sport of plantation people. Ever since, after commercial rice production

435

ceased, many of the old fields have been maintained for waterfowl shooting.

The coastal prairie of Louisiana and Texas, just above extensive coastal marshes, was covered by tall grass interspersed with trees which grew along streambanks and in swamps. Meandering bayous formed natural levees cutting off sumplike areas which were wet during winter and spring but dry during summer and early fall. Fires set by lightning or Indians burned many acres every year. Then it was excellent habitat for Canada and white-fronted geese and fair habitat for ducks.

The ricelands of Mississippi, northeast Louisiana, eastern Arkansas, and southeastern Missouri are on old river deltas.

Oaks in the virgin hardwood forests gave ducks a bountiful supply of acorns. Many stranded stream channels, low ridges, and flats made a washboard pattern. Acres of shallow, permanently flooded swamps were wintering grounds for wood ducks and the largest mallard concentrations ever known in North America. Open lakes wintered other species. Drainage and land clearing reduced the number of waterfowl and caused changes in their distribution.

Perennial grasses covered much of the Grand Prairie of southeastern Arkansas. Waterfowl concentrated in the nearby bottoms of the major

Estimate the snow geese on this burned-over rice stubble near the Sacramento National Wildlife Refuge in California. If your figure is 20,000, you are close.

streams; some utilized flooded prairie ponds. When rice came to be grown on these prairies, myriad ducks began feeding heavily on the shocked rice and later on shattered rice which remained after harvest.

RICE IS GROWN in California in the rather flat Sacramento and San Joaquin Valleys, known as the Central Valley. It is the ancestral wintering grounds of many of the waterfowl in the Pacific Flyway and is vital to their existence. Early Spanish padres, soldiers, and travelers wrote about the vast tulares (tule marshes) in the valleys and of the ducks and geese associated with them.

The flat floor of Central Valley has a fall in elevation of about a foot per mile. Mountains rim it. A break at about midpoint to the west is a drainage outlet to the Pacific Ocean. Rain comes in fall, winter, and early spring, but not in summer.

Once there were many seasonally flooded fresh-water marshes, some alkaline marshlands in the San Joaquin Valley, native grasses, sedges, spikerushes, bulrushes, cat-tails, pondweeds, smartweeds, and, along the streams, willows, cotton-woods, and sycamores. Oaks flourished on the somewhat higher valley lands. All in all, it was an excellent waterfowl habitat.

Rice, first planted in 1910, has had ups and downs—504 thousand acres in 1954, for example, and 319 thousand acres in 1962.

Of the original 6 million or so acres of overflow or wetlands in the State, about 560 thousand acres of natural marsh remained when the last survey was made in 1954. A considerable but unknown acreage has since been devoted to agriculture—220 thousand acres (less now) were in the rice section of California.

THE GENERAL REQUIREMENTS for efficient production of rice are fairly level land, a subsoil that prevents seepage, a growing season of 120 to 180 days, a mild temperature, and a large supply of water. Ricelands generally are leveled to 0.2 foot fall between contours. In the southern areas, levees 8 to 12 inches high are common. Some are 3.5 feet high and 5.5 feet wide at the base. In California, a height of 2 to 3.5 feet and basal width of 4 to 6 feet are common. Plants on the larger levees provide food and cover for waterfowl and for pheasants in California.

Most rice is sown in April and May. Rice may be planted with a drill or endgate seeder on dry or flooded land, but aerial sowing on flooded fields is replacing other methods. Rice is raised in standing or circulating water. Practices vary regionally. In some places, the water is lowered after the seed germinates, and flooding is resumed when the rice is 6 to 7 inches high.

In California the water level is maintained so that rice plants are emergent and progressively raised to prevent growth of wild millet, locally called watergrass. The water is retained on the field until 2 weeks before harvest. Rice is generally harvested with combines from August 15 to November 15.

Along the Gulf coast, rice is grown on the land every third year. During the intervening years, the land may lie fallow or it may be put into improved pastures or some other agricultural crop. Arkansas farmers often rotate rice with oats, lespedeza, and soybeans. California rice growers rotate every other year with such crops as barley and safflower, or the land may be plowed in fall or spring and left fallow over summer.

NORMALLY, little waterfowl damage occurs to newly planted rice, except along the Gulf coast where fulvous tree ducks feed on rice planted in flooded fields. Before they breed, these ducks remain in flocks and fly from the marsh to feed during the night in water-planted ricefields. They are gregarious feeders. Flocks of a few hundred may cause serious damage to some parts of a field. If they are not disturbed, they return every night to the field and feed on the newly sown grain until the sprout reaches a length of 2 or 3 inches or until the field is dewatered.

If the ducks take the seed rice, the stand is thin and the yield is less, but the total loss may be small. Planting germinated rice shortens the length of time the rice is exposed to depredation by fulvous tree ducks. Damage rarely occurs in fields in which rice is drilled on dry land and then flooded. Farmers employ exploding devices, scarecrows, and shotgun patrols to discourage the depredations.

Fulvous tree ducks nearly always nest in ricefields in Louisiana and California. Early nests are generally on levees and checks. Nesting activity causes little or no damage, but because of spring feeding, farmers

often destroy both nests and broods in Louisiana. These ducks nest as far north as the middle San Joaquin Valley in California. They do little damage to planted rice. The main damage consists of creating small, open-water areas along the rice checks. It is not easy to scare them away from a California field. They are decoys for pintails and mallards in August and September, before the harvest.

Geneticists have developed high-yielding varieties of rice that have a growing season of 105–110 days. Since most tree ducks in the South do not nest until rice reaches a height of 8 to 10 inches, the rice matures and is harvested before the ducks reach flight age. When early maturing rice is dewatered for harvesting, the brood must walk to water—usually a field in which a later maturing variety is growing. Predation then is rather high.

Little or no damage is done to rice in the South and Southeast in the fall. This is the reverse of the situation in California, where spring damage is negligible and fall damage has been severe. Occasionally seeded rice is damaged by late migrating flocks of blue-winged teal along the Gulf coast. Mottled ducks, wood ducks, and snow geese rarely feed on newly sown rice. Coots may damage sprouting rice in California.

Since most waterfowl are absent in all rice sections during the summer in the South, there is little conflict then. A resident mallard population in California does not do great damage to growing rice. Different farming practices, however, intensify or lessen waterfowl damage to rice crops in California in August and September, and lessen the amount of food available to waterfowl in the fall.

LAND LEVELING, a common practice on ricelands, permits a uniform depth of water, and eliminates poorly drained and open water spots in which sedges and other weeds thrive. Leveling leads to rapid drainage of fallow fields and a reduction in weeds, such as smartweeds and millets, which prefer a moist site. Leveling also reduces the number of interfield levees, which often produce waterfowl food and cover. Since leveling permits the use of a minimum amount of water to flood a field, it reduces the cost of rice production and likewise the cost of flooding for waterfowl use after harvest.

Many tree ducks in Texas have been killed by the insecticides, such as aldrin, that are used to treat planted seed. Only moderate losses have been reported in Louisiana and few in California, however, perhaps because a different formulation of the insecticide is used. Mortality of waterfowl has occurred after fields have been sprayed with endrin. Experimental work is being done to develop a repellent that can be applied to seed rice so as to end the depredations and also the fatalities.

Rice growing takes large amounts of water—about 30 to 36 inches in the South. Some farmers in the South and Southeast collect water in large impoundments during the winter. These reservoirs frequently are used by large numbers of wintering ducks. As the water is drawn down during the summer, smart-

weeds, wild millet, and other waterfowl food plants grow on the exposed land.

A marshy section of Mermenteau River Basin in Louisiana is a shallow sump, from which water is pumped for irrigation. Holding water over it in winter and spring tends to prevent establishment of climax-type plants. Dewatering it for rice production exposes many sections at a time favorable to moist-site annuals, such as wild millet, Leptochloa, fall panicum, and smartweeds. The use of this wide section for water storage reduces the possibility that it will be drained for grazing. The rice industry in the South and Southeast therefore is responsible for the preservation and maintenance of a large block of marshland for waterfowl. In California, though, water is impounded in large reservoirs, such as Shasta Lake, and then released through a system of large irrigation canals. These reservoirs, whose water levels fluctuate, have little value for waterfowl.

HERBICIDES ARE USED by most southern rice farmers. Nearly all broad-leaved weeds can be eliminated thereby. New, selective chemicals are said to reduce grasses by 95 percent. The weedkillers, the regulation of water levels, and water-planting of rice all have reduced drastically the fall waterfowl food supply in ricefields.

Research and field tests at the Rice Experiment Station in California indicate that the use of herbicides may permit control of all weeds in ricefields and revolutionize cultural practices. Instead of producing rice in circulating water, the fields would be kept moist by periodic irrigation. The elimination of watergrass (wild millet), sedges, and other duck foods will deprive waterfowl of a large supply of their fall and winter food. Lack of these foods and water in early fall, before harvest, would probably reduce depredation on rice.

BEFORE THE DAYS of the combine and drier, rice was cut with a binder, bound in sheaths that were shocked, and left in the field to dry before threshing. Waterfowl fed heavily on the shattered grain and shocks, notably on the Grand Prairie of Arkansas. In California, some rice was swathed and allowed to remain on the ground to dry before combining. Waterfowl caused serious losses by feeding on the swathed grain.

Practically all rice today is combined as it stands in the field and is dried at mills. Since the introduction of driers, rice is harvested when it has a high moisture content. The shattering loss is cut thereby to about 3 to 5 percent of the crop. In a field yielding 3 thousand pounds an acre, this means a loss of 90 to 150 pounds an acre.

A 2-year study in Louisiana on nine farms, after the rice harvest, disclosed that during the first year the loss was 61.8 to 296 pounds an acre. The average was 142.2 pounds. A severe hurricane had shattered and blown down considerable rice. In the second year, the loss was 2.5 to 215 pounds an acre. The average was 73 pounds. The average amount of waterfowl food (seeds) produced per acre on the nine

farms was 176.8 pounds in 1958 and 163 pounds in 1960.

Competition for food is high in ricefields. Small birds, insects, and rodents (plus factors like poor germination and decay) caused a loss of 80 to 90 percent of rice residues between the time of harvest and February. The loss of wild seeds ranged from nothing to 55 percent. In California, the waste rice after harvest amounts to 200 to 300 pounds an acre.

Along the Gulf coast, much riceland remains fallow for 2 years, when some farmers convert the fields to improved pastures. They produce little duck food, but geese frequently graze them.

Grazed fallow land produces some food for waterfowl, but ungrazed fallow land produces a great deal the first year and even more the second year. Fallow fields on the nine farms in Louisiana averaged 489 pounds of waterfowl food per acre. Clearly, ungrazed fallow fields have a high potential use for wintering waterfowl, if the key ingredient, water, is added to them.

Crops planted in Arkansas and California in rotation with rice (soybeans, lespedeza, safflower, barley, or others) furnish good forage for some species of ducks.

A rice-fish rotation is developing in Arkansas in which fields are flooded to a depth of 18 to 24 inches between rice crops. Buffalo fish or catfish are grown during the period of flooding. Since the field generally is in fish production 1 year and many of the fish do not reach marketable size that soon, they are transferred to another field the second year. Farmers say this

Airplane seeding rice.   Harvested rice fields are important feeding sites for waterfowl.

kind of rotation increases their yield of rice. Waterfowl use these flooded fields mainly as loafing areas, from which they fly at night to feed in ricefields.

A new development in Louisiana is a rice-crayfish rotation. The ricefield is flooded soon after harvest. Water is kept on it until July, when it is dewatered. It is reflooded in September, and the water stays on it until the following planting season. Two crops of crayfish are produced from the wild-stocked crustaceans. Farmers report higher yields of rice follow the crayfish.

Grand Prairie has produced rice for more than half a century. At first, water was obtained from shallow wells, but ground water supplies were overtaxed and the first water storage reservoir was constructed in 1928. Another was built in 1932. It was soon discovered that these reservoirs attracted ducks, and the farmers found that hunters were willing to pay enough for their sport to offset initial and maintenance costs of the reservoirs plus pumping costs to fill them. Twenty or more were constructed during the late thirties and early forties, mostly during the height of the duck depression, and Grand Prairie enjoyed some of the best duck hunting to be had at that time.

The rice reservoirs have changed the wintering habits of a large segment of the Mississippi Flyway mallard populations. Formerly, very large numbers of mallards fed and rested in the flooded bottomlands. Now most of the birds rest on rice reservoirs and feed in nearby fields, returning to the bottoms only during periods when high water covers new and particularly attractive feeding grounds.

In general, it appears that grain-feeding waterfowl will flourish in any locality that has a large enough acreage of rice and where plenty of daytime loafing areas free of disturbance are available.

Because rice production is limited by Federal control programs, the rate of development of new land for rice production is quite low. The end of Federal controls could mean a rapid increase in some sections, especially on the delta lands of Arkansas, Louisiana, and Mississippi.

IMMEDIATELY after the First World War, rice production in California went up. Lands were unlevel. Ducks used the open water areas and fed upon maturing rice. Herding of ducks by airplane came into practice. Rice was harvested at that time by combines but oftener by binders or swathers. Ducks alighted on the shocked bundles or swaths and ate or shattered much of the grain.

A situation that arose during the late thirties developed into a serious problem. Waterfowl were recovering from the low totals of the twenties. By 1940, pintails, mallards, and some other ducks ran into the millions in interior valleys. Waterfowl marsh had been reduced by drainage and farming. Shasta Dam on the Sacramento River and Friant Dam on the San Joaquin River regulated much of the runoff from the two drainages. Overflow upon lowland areas approached nil.

The Fish and Wildlife Service acquired 10,770 acres near Willows for the Sacramento National Wildlife Refuge. It afforded protection for birds during the hunting season. California had the 2,542-acre Grey Lodge Refuge near Gridley, the 3,000-acre Los Banos Refuge near Los Banos in the San Joaquin Valley, and the 1,887-acre Suisun Refuge in the Sacramento-San Joaquin delta. None of these was well developed. Not enough water was available, and irrigators objected to use of any water for ducks until agricultural needs had been met. So the refuges were short of water and food. Hungry ducks had to go out for food every evening to nearby ricefields.

Unlevel fields with open water, other wet places, and some dry, high ground provided good habitat. Weeds in ricefields ripened in August and September. As the rice matured, it was not uncommon to see 30-acre fields stripped of rice in a few days.

The California Farm Bureau made surveys of the losses of rice— 607 thousand dollars in 1941; 600 thousand in 1942; and a million dollars in 1943. Rice and other losses brought the 1943 total to 1,750,000 dollars.

Demands for relief were insistent. A committee was formed of representatives of the California Chamber of Commerce and all groups concerned with the depredations. This committee recommended that additional lands be leased by the Fish and Wildlife Service and that they be flooded and supplied with grain out of the sack. Land was bought later, developed, planted to rice, barley, and watergrass, and left for the birds. Marauding birds were herded by rice growers, from rice-fields back to those feeding lands.

The Congress passed the Lea Act and under its provisions appropriated funds for acquiring and developing more land for waterfowl by the Fish and Wildlife Service. California, through its Wildlife Conservation Board, spent nearly 6 million dollars for similar management areas. Depredations dropped sharply, and have remained at a satisfactory level.

WHAT HAVE WE LEARNED? What preparation has been made for future management? Quite a lot.

The following suggestions pertain to the management of ricelands in central and southern United States to provide greater benefits to waterfowl: Flood the field after harvest to prevent loss of waterfowl foods to seed-eating birds, mammals, and insects and to prevent germination and decay. Drive early flights of teal and pintail from fields. Restrict hunting to half-days and not more than two times a week. Provide undisturbed resting areas. Permit rank growth of vegetation along field edges, canals, and levees. Plant supplemental waterfowl food, such as brown-top millet. Delay plowing until spring. Restrict grazing in fallow fields.

In California a different situation exists. Supplying fish and wildlife needs is now considered a beneficial use of water.

It is carrying capacity and not the number of acres of marsh or management area that counts in maintaining a compatible relationship between our waterfowl and agriculture.

About 560 thousand acres of natural marsh remain out of the original 5 million to 6 million acres. Some of this remnant has low waterfowl carrying capacity. Some is being developed for other uses each year. About 500 thousand acres of land is devoted to wetland agriculture. Much of it now provides wintering grounds for ducks and geese.

The problem of perpetuation of waterfowl in California is now one of competition between waterfowl and people for suitable habitat.

Because of the growth of population and industry in California, perpetuation of waterfowl wintering in California will depend more and more upon management areas. Waste rice and other cereal grains will continue to be an important part of waterfowl maintenance.

Substitution of an acre of rice for an acre of marsh is looked on with favor by several important species of waterfowl. In some locations, such as Grand Prairie in Arkansas, rice culture with its attendant reservoirs, has provided wintering areas for millions of birds. The growing of rice is one of the few activities which can be added to the credit side of the ledger in man's relation to waterfowl.—E. E. HORN and LESLIE L. GLASGOW.

AMERICAN WIDGEON

Forage and Truck Crops

FLOOD PLAINS, river deltas, and tidal flats were the water-fowl pastures of yesterday. White-cheeked geese fed on their grasses and roots. American widgeons grazed on their new growth. Coots cropped the sprouts down to bare soil. Snow geese grubbed for roots.

Periodic surges of floodwaters scoured these flood plains and often lay down new silt beds. Wildfire sometimes swept the accumulations of vegetative growth that withstood the freshets. Annual grasses and forbs quickly occupied the new ground as it became exposed. The surviving roots of perennials sent forth new shoots. Thus Nature once cultivated the waterfowl pastures.

Man cultivates or uses them now. He has changed the normal regimen of rivers, large and small. Floods and silt deposits that served to maintain waterfowl pastures have been reduced or eliminated. Industries and subdivisions occupy thousands of acres of deltas.

Thousands of acres of tidal flats, including those of Puget Sound and the Middle Atlantic and Gulf coasts, ditched for drainage and diked to exclude high water, have become pastures for livestock. Up-stream storage of water for flood control, electric power, and irrigation has fostered agricultural development on alluvial flood plains. Big marshes once important to ducks and geese now are truck gardens. That has happened to the Skagit River Flats of Washington, the Sacramento and Suisun Rivers in

445

446

California, the Connecticut River marshes, and many more.

Winter runoff and spring freshets that once spread over the valleys and sinks of the Western States have been harnessed for irrigation. Thus destroyed were marshes of the Tulare Basin in California and the famed Carson Sink marshes in Nevada, at one time an important nesting ground for Canada geese, canvasbacks, redheads, and several other species of waterfowl. In the San Joaquin Valley of California, grasslands agriculture has replaced much of the wetland pasture that formerly furnished food and cover for waterfowl. The waterfowl pastures of the Mississippi River system were the most extensive in the United States. The modification of this habitat, underway for more than a century, is marked by changing patterns of waterfowl abundance and distribution and the increased use of croplands by ducks and geese.

THROUGHOUT THE GREAT PLAINS— and other regions of the United States and southern Canada that were important as waterfowl breeding grounds—an unbounded acreage of native prairie has been converted to improved pasture or developed for growing forage crops. Introduced grasses and legumes have been planted extensively. Forage consisting of a single species replaced thousands of acres of mixed grasses. The new forage plants may require mowing during the vulnerable nesting period or pasturing practices that eliminate all nesting cover.

Originally the United States had

about 750 million acres of grassland. At least 250 million acres have been converted to growing crops or forage. Grasslands mean food and cover for nesting and rearing young, protection from the weather, and concealment from enemies. These essentials have declined in quality as pristine grasslands have given way to agriculture.

Of all the many types of habitat that waterfowl need, and that will determine what happens to them in the future, the need for suitable breeding grounds is most critical. As the late Ding Darling once remarked, "Ducks can't nest on fenceposts." Breeding grounds are more than just water and cover; they must be of particular types and in particular combinations to suit the varying needs of many species.

Boxes, baskets, and platforms for nesting have been used in some locations to make up for a shortage of natural nesting sites. For a few species, notably wood ducks and Canada geese, the results have been gratifying. But acceptance by waterfowl is influenced by the overall character and quality of the immediate breeding ground environment and, for most species, standing vegetation continues to be indispensable for successful nesting.

MANY GEESE start nesting in early March as the melting snow exposes vegetation of the previous year. Other species begin in late March and this activity continues through April, May, and early June. Most nesting gets underway before the growing season, however, and early nesters select sites largely on the basis of remains of the previous year's vegetative cover. Late nesters have the benefit of cover afforded by growth of the current season.

Mallards and pintails accept short grass cover. Blue-winged teal seek a clump of tall grass. Gadwalls choose a patch of low brush or perhaps thistles. Redheads, canvasbacks, and ruddy ducks require good emergent or shoreline cover. Pintails and mallards are the only ducks that habitually nest in grain stubble. The Canada goose seeks not cover, but a "platform" with good visibility in all directions, such as is afforded by a muskrat house, a small island, or a dike top.

Farming practices bring about many departures from normal habits of nesting. Even diving ducks occasionally nest in stubble or a cultivated field, if preferred habitat is lacking.

Blue-winged teal usually nest less than 100 feet from the water. Pintails and mallards are more tolerant of intensive grazing than other species of dabbling ducks. Thus, methods and means of harvesting forage crops—haying or grazing—do not affect all species in the same way.

Close grazing along the shore and little grazing on uplands, as in the rolling terrain of pothole country, encourage nesting. Moderate grazing tends to maintain a good ground cover of palatable forage interspersed with clumps of uncropped grasses and forbs. Such a combination near a semiopen marsh attracts breeding waterfowl. Surveys of breeding grounds in the Valen-tine National Wildlife Refuge in Nebraska showed that waters with a semiopen shoreline had twice as many ducks as did waters with a barren shoreline.

Losses from haying may be high. Hay is cut at a time when its nutrient content and palatability are at their peak. It often happens that the quality of forage is best when duck nesting is at a peak. Losses of nests and eggs may be considerable therefore, and some hens are killed even when a flushing bar is used on the mower.

Heavy losses occur when ducks nest in irrigated alfalfa fields, because two or more hay crops are harvested in a season. The first crop is usually cut well before the peak of the nesting season. Pintails and mallards prefer stubble fields, and late nesters and hens making a second nesting attempt are vulnerable at the time of the second cut.

Opinions differ on the relationship between grazing and predation on nesting grounds. On the Valentine and Crescent Lake National Wildlife Refuges in Nebraska, bullsnakes may take many eggs. Because bullsnakes, like many other reptiles, cannot endure long exposure to the sun, ungrazed or unmowed meadows adjoining nesting territory are much to their liking and make their search for eggs easier. Skunk predation is noticeably greater on nesting grounds where vegetative litter and rank growth border the shoreline of ponds, sloughs, and potholes. The raccoon also seems uninhibited by the coarse vegetation surrounding prairie marshes as it searches for food.

How well nests are hidden seems to have little bearing on how many eggs mammals and predators find and destroy, but an abundance of dead vegetation, such as accumulates in two or more seasons without grazing or mowing, attracts predators as well as ducks.

PLANTS OF WET MEADOWS and seasonally flooded lowlands that are important as waterfowl food and also used by livestock include wild millet, Bermudagrass, bentgrasses, mannagrasses, paspalums, sloughgrass, bulrushes, sedges, cyperuses, and smartweeds.

Marsh grasses, bulrushes, and sedges may be used when upland vegetation is unattractive. Cattle frequently wade far from shore to graze on water plants. On several occasions I have seen cows swim from shore to feed on wildcelery and naiad in the St. Marks River near Newport, Fla. At times they may literally devour all waterfowl food plants if the range is depleted or if upland vegetation generally is mature, coarse, and low in food value. On the other hand, grazing helps maintain openings, which afford access by waterfowl to swales and sloughs where food is available. This type of benefit is readily apparent in the extensive fresh-water marshes of Cameron Parish in Louisiana.

AMERICAN WIDGEONS on Pacific Flyway wintering grounds readily forsake natural feeding grounds during fall and winter for an alfalfa field, improved pasture, or truck garden. There they feed extensively on young, fall-planted barley, alfalfa, clover, and pasture grasses. If other food is not readily available, they are not above raiding a cabbage patch or a field of lettuce. They devour all leaves, leaving only the tough stump. Not even the rutabaga is immune, but the choice in this instance is the seedhead of mature plants, not the foliage.

Widgeons regularly visit new seedings of cereal grains, grasses, and legumes near resting grounds. A widgeon can consume about 4 ounces of green feed a day. Thus, in a week, a flock of a thousand ducks can make great inroads on the forage of a field, especially if they go after young plants. Near Brawley, Calif., one February, a 300-acre field of head lettuce, nearly ready for market, was destroyed in 10 nights by a flock of about 10 thousand widgeons. Generally, however, the wildfowl feed on marsh vegetation and are no problem.

Coots also may be a problem, particularly in the Pacific Flyway. There they winter in sloughs, ponds, drainage ditches, and creeks near pasture and croplands, but they range less widely in feeding than widgeons and geese. Coots are less discriminating in their feeding habits; they like vegetables, sugarbeets, legumes, and grasses. They feed on the roots and foliage. They are more gregarious than usual in spring, and flocks of several hundred may invade golf courses and park lawns. Their droppings on the turf usually are more objectionable than the loss of ground cover.

Trampling by livestock or waterfowl on ground made wet by rain or irrigation causes puddling. The ground then becomes hard when the surface water is removed, cultivation becomes more difficult, and some plants are lost. Waterfowl graze more closely than cattle, and their continued, excessive clipping of the tips of leaves and stems retards plant growth. Droppings of the birds do not harm the forage but may cause cattle and sheep to avoid the contaminated area for a time.

Tender, succulent foliage attracts geese, ducks, and coots. The variety of plant is another factor. For example, even the new growth of newly mown tall fescue is less acceptable to Canada geese than is bluegrass. In Maryland, alsike and ladino clovers, in all stages of growth, often are favored over red clover. One April I saw small flocks of Canada geese search out and feed on patches of quackgrass in potato fields bordering Merrymeeting Bay in Maine. Apparently they preferred it to the newly sprouted grain in nearby fields.

The volunteer growth of grassland forbs that flourish when an irrigation reservoir is drawn down affords excellent "pasture" for Canada geese, widgeons, and coots. The tender new growth of goosefoot is equally attractive, whether in Montana on sagebrush flats in early spring, on exposed reservoir slopes in Oregon in September, or following winter rains on grasslands of San Joaquin Valley. Nutrients and

minerals alike are in the tips of the young foliage. The protein content is high. As growth progresses, the forage becomes coarse and less digestible, and the vitamin and protein contents decline.

GRASS OR GRASSLIKE PLANTS are practically a staple diet of Canada geese most of the year. One hunting season, I saw flock after flock of Canada geese leave cornfields on the Blackwater National Wildlife Refuge in Maryland to feed on eelgrass beds of Chesapeake Bay. When saltmeadow cordgrass was shallowly flooded by high tides or winter rains, the geese often abandoned cornfields to feed on its foliage and rootstocks.

A confirmed grazing habit like this makes domestic geese good eradicators of weeds. Each year 100 thousand goslings are let loose in cottonfields of the San Joaquin Valley to help control grass and weeds. They are put to similar use in other areas and in different crops including the mintfields of Oregon and Idaho. Yearlings are most useful for this purpose. Older geese are less active and feed more selectively on weeds.

Ladino and Dutch white clovers in mixtures with palatable grasses are taken readily by Canada geese. Alfalfa has little attraction for Canada geese and widgeon, except as seedling growth or when tender shoots are available after mowing. Irrigated pasture crops and young grain are especially attractive to white-fronts as well as Canadas from late winter through the spring migration. But if these are not available, the geese will feed heavily on legumes as long as the foliage is tender. Wheatgrasses grow quickly and are planted widely for pasture because they tolerate a variety of soil and climatic conditions. Such pastures are used a great deal by Canada geese during spring migration.

Seedling barley and wheat are the first choice as grazing plants among the cereal grains and are taken in preference to oats. Geese use Burmudagrass extensively in the Southeast. In the Pacific Coast States, bentgrasses are favorites. Kentucky bluegrass is comparatively abundant over much of the waterfowl wintering area and is readily taken by geese, widgeon, and coot.

CANADA GEESE are the gourmets of the grasslands. They move slowly and deliberately over the greensward, selecting choice, tender leaves of the best forage. Where cattle have cropped close, geese follow through and crop a little more. Then they return again as new growth appears. Geese and cattle may graze together for a few days to several weeks, depending on the weather, plant growth, disturbance, or other factors that could influence the movement of the birds. Then, as plant growth progresses and palatability declines, the birds move on. Each bird consumes 10 ounces, or more, of forage a day.

Grazing waterfowl often uproot seedlings not yet anchored to the soil and even young plants where heavy rains have loosened the soil.

Thus a flock of geese on newly sprouted grain often is accepted as evidence of damage. But seedling root growth is rapid, and once plants are anchored to the soil, "leaf pruning" by geese can be a help. For example, in the spring of 1961, several wheat ranchers near Moses Lake in Washington told Game Management Agent Ed Carter that geese were grazing their winter wheat "into the ground."

To help the ranchers recognize what was actually taking place, Ed established several plots of grazed and ungrazed wheat in two different fields. He marked each plot by a 30-inch wire ring. He rechecked them on July 26, when the grain was ready for combining. By counting kernels of grain, Ed found the yield from the grazed plots was 35 percent greater in the first field and 30 percent greater in the second field. According to Ed, stand density was visibly heavier where pruning of leaf tips had caused the young grain to stool out.

Game Management Agent Ray Lawhorn obtained similar data from field studies he conducted on several wheat ranches near Pendleton, Oreg. Field studies repeated across the country have shown that yields from wheat and barley plants grazed by geese equal and frequently exceed yields from ungrazed plants.

WHITE GEESE (except Ross') grub and graze. The lesser snows, along with white-fronted geese and a few cacklers, even invade potato fields in the Klamath Basin of California and Oregon. There they dig potatoes in the loose peat soil, if culls are not readily available. It appears to be a localized feeding habit that began about 1925 and developed gradually.

As blue and white phase lesser snow geese move northward from their Gulf coast wintering ground, they graze briefly in grainfields, especially in the lower Missouri River Valley. If the soil has been loosened by alternate freezing and thawing, some grain is uprooted by geese. They may cause further damage by trampling new sprouts into the mud.

Greater snow geese may choose marshland plants, especially common threesquare, Olney threesquare, saltmarsh bulrush, and saltmarsh cordgrass. Generally they denude a feeding ground before seeking new range. Young cattails are relished by white geese while on Pacific Flyway wintering grounds. Each year several hundred acres of the Salton Sea National Wildlife Refuge in California are managed specifically to grow such feed. By the time the geese leave, the ground has the appearance of being freshly plowed—and no wonder, for the utilization is complete: They grub out and eat the roots before departing. This rather specialized feeding activity of the snow goose in southern California and the lower Colorado River often sets the stage for a plant succession that may afford temporary habitat for other waterfowl and even cattle at times.

The coastal prairies of Texas and Louisiana are pasture for both livestock and geese. Cattle graze on

the foliage of saltmeadow cordgrass, saltgrass, paspalums, bulrushes, and many other marsh plants. Ranchers burn the marshes in late summer or early fall to remove dead vegetation and stimulate new growth. Blue and white snow geese flock to the new burns in search of rootstocks. If surface water favors digging, they may lay waste hundreds of acres of pasture in a short time. In alluvial soil, such eat-outs usually become revegetated in one growing season.

In peat soils, loss of the root matrix often results in the formation of ponds, which in turn may become new feeding grounds for dabbling ducks. I have seen several such ponds near Fortescue in New Jersey and Assateague and Parramore Islands in Virginia that resulted from feeding by snow geese.

Competition between white geese and cattle or muskrats is a matter of water relationship. Geese dig roots in hard ground only as a last resort. Prolonged drought limits the choice of food; cold weather causes flocking and abnormal concentrations of white geese on feeding grounds. Then there may be extensive, though not necessarily permanent, damage to wetland meadows and marshes.

Waterfowl tend to specialize in their food habits, but they are adaptable, and when they cannot get their preferred food they can subsist by turning to other plant materials. A temporary shortage of eelgrass in Humboldt Bay in California, for example, caused brant to graze barley, clover, and even garden peas. One winter, during an extended period of severe weather throughout the West, hundreds of mallards survived by eating stacked, chopped hay. Ensilage likewise is eaten by ducks and geese when other feed is lacking.

FORAGE AND TRUCK crops have supplanted a considerable acreage of waterfowl wintering grounds. Some of the crops are highly palatable to geese, widgeon, and coots and are a welcome substitute for native plants no longer available. A continuing dependency on these crops by wintering waterfowl is inevitable.

Grassland agriculture has changed the character of thousands of acres of breeding-ground habitat and reduced waterfowl production in many localities. Partly making up for it are the development of land for irrigated pasture and the growing of forage crops, which have created new nesting grounds and enhanced the production of fowl in some localities.

Regulated grazing generally tends to improve shorelines of breeding grounds. Well-managed pasturelands afford browse for geese and are important in their protection and management. In water, however, cattle sometimes prevent vegetation from becoming established. Depending on the density of emergent vegetation and the intensity of grazing, livestock can either improve or destroy the value of a marsh for waterfowl.

Some waterfowl gains or losses from forage and truck crops are transitory. For example, hundreds of acres of barley in the Upper Klamath Basin, where cackling Canada geese, white-fronted geese, mallards, and pintails fed on grain residues, were converted to pasture because of difficulty in controlling quackgrass. Production and market problems caused some farmers in the Basin to shift from seed potatoes (geese fed on the culls) to onions, broccoli, horseradish, and sugarbeets—crops of no benefit to waterfowl. Winter flooding, an established practice for managing certain alkaline soils, contributes feeding and resting habitat for waterfowl in some areas of the Pacific Flyway. This type of land management eventually had to be abandoned in parts of the Upper Klamath Basin because increased soil alkalinity reduced crop yields.

Marsh and upland areas of prime use to waterfowl yesterday serve more intensive needs of people today. This competition no doubt will grow. In some places, at some times, the conflict has become so acute as to raise the question: Can waterfowl tomorrow survive alongside of an intensive agriculture that is increasingly exploitive of land that once belonged to ducks?

I think they can. Waterfowl are adaptable, and most species (except divers) adjust with surprising speed and success to new conditions in their environment. People are adaptable, too, and ingenious. Some ways already have been found to ease the impact of displaced waterfowl in cropland.

—RICHARD E. GRIFFITH.

REDHEADS

Fish and Fowl

WILLOW SLOUGH in Indiana proves the simple proposition that we can manage lakes, streams, and waterfowl marshes to the benefit of fish, waterfowl, and people at the same time and place.

Indiana created Willow Slough from 8,368 acres on the eastern edge of the famous Kankakee Marsh astride the Illinois-Indiana boundary. The area was purchased and developed with one hundred thousand dollars of Pittman-Robertson funds obtained from taxes paid by sportsmen and administered by the Bureau of Sport Fisheries and Wildlife.

A lake and marsh covering 1,500 acres were created within this area. Fish already present in the old marsh drainage ditches were augmented with fish from Federal and State hatcheries. The waters soon teemed with largemouth bass, bluegills, and crappies. In 1962, the area was used by 21 thousand fishermen and 15 thousand hunters from the crowded cities of northern Indiana and Illinois.

There are many other examples of multiple-use marshes. Louisiana made tidal marshes by driving sheet piling across estuaries in such a way that the pools fill at high tide, and

453

boats can cross over the piling caps. When the tides recede, the pools remain full. The marshes produce large numbers of largemouth bass.

Tuckahoe Marsh in New Jersey, Cheyenne Bottoms in Kansas, and many artificially created marshes in Iowa offer as much to the fisherman as they do to the hunter.

Or the approach may be from the other direction. States have used Dingell-Johnson funds obtained from fishermen, and administered by the Bureau of Sport Fisheries and Wildlife, to make fishing lakes. That purpose has been well served, and a secondary value to waterfowl has become apparent.

Sport fisheries managers use many tools to provide enough desirable fish for anglers. Sometimes these tools may harm waterfowl unless they are used carefully.

Unwanted fish must be controlled. Carp, occasionally bullhead, and several other species are removed from lakes by nets. Sometimes chemicals are used. Toxic materials frequently sprayed from airplanes to reduce overabundant fishes have killed waterfowl resting on the surface of the lake. Caution is mandatory. Use of rotenone will remove fish without harm to the birds, but toxaphene persists unduly long in soft waters and builds up into risky concentrations in organisms that fish and fowl feed on. Toxaphene is not used in projects sponsored by the Bureau of Sport Fisheries and Wildlife, and is not recommended by the Bureau.

Waterfowl food plants respond quickly after plant-destroying fish are controlled. When fisheries man-agers do not want overabundant plants, lakes and ponds are fertilized with nitrogen and phosphorus to encourage algae blooms and thereby shade out unwanted aquatic weeds. Fertilization also creates new forms of fish food, particularly in southern waters.

Fertilization carries problems for waterfowl. It deprives ducks of certain food plants that the fisheries managers believe are unnecessary for fish.

Chemicals sometimes are used to control plants in fishing waters just as they are used to control weed fish species. Here, again, they are not an unmixed blessing, for they can disperse too widely and kill more plants than intended.

Clean water is essential for both fish and waterfowl.

The Izaak Walton League, a national organization of individuals working together for the conservation and enjoyment of outdoor America, awakened our concern to keep unpolluted our lakes and streams. Its first interest was on behalf of sport fish; now the effort includes the welfare of ducks and geese and their wetland environments.

Clean water comes with intelligent use of crop, forest, and pasture land to reduce silt loads in waterways. Efficient industrial processes can remove or reclaim chemical wastes from factories. Thorough treatment of sewage, with its load of modern household chemicals, can reduce the oxygen-consuming debris that enters streams from sewer outfalls. Every possible approach must be used to prevent pollution.

NEW FISHING WATERS, constructed in the form of large reservoirs or small farm ponds in all sections of the country, are habitat for fish, and feeding and resting areas for several kinds of ducks.

On the open water of Fort Randall Reservoir on the Missouri River of southeastern South Dakota, about 141 thousand ducks and 15 thousand geese were counted in January 1962. The reservoir is 140 miles long and covers 118 thousand surface acres at full pool. Major functions of flood control and power are augmented by the recreational advantages for people and the habitat provided for fish and waterfowl. The birds usually feed in adjacent cornfields, but sometimes fly as much as 40 miles from the reservoir.

The tailwaters of reservoirs must be managed so that enough water will be released through the dams to maintain good fish habitats downstream. In the Fort Randall Reservoir, for example, mallards particularly use the open tailwaters in the winter. They feed on small fish that run into the tailwaters until stopped by the dam. Up to 100 bald eagles also feed on birds and fish in the open waters of the reservoir tailrace.

CONTROL OF WATER LEVELS is one procedure perfected by workers in wildlife conservation to meet the requirements of fishermen and waterfowl. Drawdown (intentional raising and lowering of water levels) benefits both fish and fowl.

This technique is used to control the spawning of unwanted fish, such as carp, and to improve the avail-

ability of soil nutrients to plant and animal organisms living in the water. Some species of rooted vegetation that fishery managers do not want also can be killed thereby. The practice can be detrimental at times to the development of a good waterfowl lake.

Waterfowl enthusiasts usually favor a late spring and summer drawdown of water so that millet and quick-maturing grains can be planted on the muddy edges of the pool. The greater food supply that results helps attract and hold fall migrants.

THE DRAWDOWN also encourages germination of seeds of millets, smartweeds, sedges, and other plants. The plants help control silt levels as the reservoirs refill by protecting the shoreline and by inducing an organic chemical reaction on colloidal soil particles.

The extent and frequency of drawdowns vary to meet different needs of fish and wildlife. The topography of the impoundment basins, the character of existing vegetation, water fertility, and local opinion are taken into account before drawdowns are made for waterfowl or fishery management.

Fishermen do not like a summer drawdown because they cannot fish from the bank in a shallow lake and cannot launch their boats over the muddy flats. Often a compromise between anglers and duck hunters is possible, so that fishing will be available in spring or summer and hunting will be good in fall. Sometimes there is no choice, as when waterfowl must be thought of first or when sites for spawning fish must be protected by keeping water levels stable.

DREDGING of shallow, marshy lakes is often requested by fishermen and boat operators to give better access to a lake. Dredging is of little benefit, though, and may be a disservice to waterfowl that prefer shallow lakes. The spoil from the dredging often is pumped into nearby marshlands and so removes them from use. Dredging to improve sport fishing is expensive and results do not warrant it. Many managers of fisheries believe that a lake that has become senescent to the point of being a marsh should be left to the ducks, muskrats, mink, and shorebirds.

SOME DUCKS EAT FISH. Successful management of fisheries sometimes depends on the control of fish-eating birds. When American mergansers winter on a small Michigan trout stream, for example, or on an Atlantic salmon stream in eastern Canada, they can cause damage. Sometimes expensive, hatchery-reared, newly-planted, legal-sized trout have disappeared at an alarming rate. Young salmon on their way from their river spawning sites to the Atlantic may be taken in large numbers by hungry birds. In New Brunswick, the control of American mergansers and belted kingfishers to the point where only one bird was permitted to survive on 50 acres of water or 15 miles of stream increased at least fivefold the average output of fish.

Studies at a lake in the Nebraska sandhills showed that a temporary concentration of mergansers that fed on stunted black bullheads could reduce noticeably the poundage of the fish. The result was beneficial, because the surviving bullheads grew rapidly to a size local anglers like.

ARTIFICIAL PROPAGATION results in the rearing of about 25 species of freshwater fish in State and Federal hatcheries for introduction into lakes, streams, and reservoirs. Rearing techniques, especially for largemouth bass and sunfish, include the use of artificial ponds of varying sizes. The ponds and the grassy dikes between them provide a varied habitat for resting and nesting waterfowl.

The national fish hatcheries at Tishomingo, Okla., and Hebron, Ohio, annually provide wintering areas for ducks. Several pairs of breeding Canada geese have visited the State hatchery at Lake St. Marys, Ohio. Grassy margins of natural ponds in Minnesota, in which the State rears walleyed pike, often contain many nests of mallards and blue-winged teal which rear their broods on the hatchery ponds regardless of the presence of hatchery employees.

The activities of fish-eating waterfowl must be controlled on fish hatcheries. Mergansers rarely invade the shallow ponds, but terns skim the surface to pick up the tiny fry of northern pike and walleye in the spring. Sometimes the birds pick up small fry from one pond and accidentally drop them in a nearby pond that contains a different species. Such mixing of species plays havoc with pond production schedules. No effective device has been developed to eliminate the birds without harming them, although occasionally scaring devices are useful.

Many parasites of fish have a life cycle in which the adult stage is found in the digestive tract of fish-eating birds. Eggs pass from the birds into hatchery rearing ponds, and the first larval stage invades aquatic organisms, such as snails or microscopic water fleas. The parasites develop into intermediate stages in the bodies of the fish that ingest them. Often the fish are harmed; always they are objectionable to anglers.

Producers of minnows and other small fish for commercial use often treat their ponds with a light oil to kill air-breathing insect larvae that live in the water and prey on the fish. This treatment has no effect on the fish, because they swim under the oil film, but it is not good for ducks that land on the surface and are coated with the oil.

Fishery managers believe that a heavy harvest of fish is possible and necessary if fish stocks are to maintain a rapid rate of growth and remain vigorous. Increasing numbers of fishermen visit our lakes and streams each year, but only rarely does this increase in angling reduce the numbers of fish.

If, however, waterfowl use heavily fished waters for breeding, resting, or feeding, they will be disturbed often by anglers who use boats or fish from the banks. This conflict can be resolved by zoning certain water areas for use by waterfowl or by anglers or by restricting fishing during the season when waterfowl are nesting and raising their broods.

COMMERCIAL FISHING nets placed in deep waters of the Great Lakes account for the capture and killing of waterfowl of several species. At times, gill nets set for herring in Lake Michigan enmeshed hundreds of oldsquaw ducks that wintered near sheltered shorelines. Nets set for tullibee in Lake of the Woods, Rainy Lake, and Namekan on the Canadian boundary once took their toll of ducks that had dived deeply to catch their food. American goldeneye also were trapped under water in trammel nets placed in the Mississippi River to capture buffalo fish and sheepshead.

A SUBSTANTIAL mortality of redhead ducks occurs in the Laguna Madre of the Texas coastal area when the birds gather there each fall and winter. Commercial fishermen lay out thousands of trotlines in the shallow waters. The lines, from which dangle millions of closely spaced hooks on short leaders, are designed to take channel bass, redfish, and weakfish. The hooks also snag redheads, scaup, and cormorants. Most drown. Others are injured by tearing out the hook or by being shaken off the lines by fishermen. A fisherman may remove from 10 to 100 birds each morning he runs his lines.

When long seines are dragged through beds of vegetation to catch carp, food plants of waterfowl may be uprooted and destroyed. The loss is not overly serious, because few plants may be left in a lake overrun by carp and because the disturbing of the plant beds may help to disperse cuttings of vegetation, which can take root elsewhere.

458

WATERFOWL TOMORROW

FISH PROCESSING INDUSTRIES may contribute indirectly to the decline of numbers of waterfowl. When wastes from fish processing plants in some New England communities are dumped into nearby tidal waters, gulls and other fish-eating birds are attracted. Garbage disposal piles near the shorelines of some coastal communities may also bring in scavenging gulls. When the birds seek nesting areas each spring, they often select small offshore islands within easy flying range of the points where they receive their handouts. Shore birds and possibly waterfowl originally using these islands for breeding undoubtedly are crowded out, or their eggs and chicks are destroyed by the rapacious gulls.

BOTH FISH AND DUCKS are worthy of protection and management. Both need the benefit of good land and water conservation practices. With a little seasonal adjustment in management techniques and human behavior patterns there should be room for both resources. The future then will hold fewer conflicts of ducks versus fish, and more promises of ducks plus fish.

—RAYMOND E. JOHNSON.

Insecticides

IT WAS a spring day in 1960. A low-flying plane crossed back and forth over a flooded Texas rice-field sowing partly sprouted seed. It was standard practice: The field had been flooded in the usual way to control weeds; water planting of seed is common. But fulvous tree ducks that had come to get an easy meal soon started to die, quickly and violently. Some flew a short way, then flopped around. Others fell from the air. Fifty ducks died, the victims of a single change in the usual procedure.

That year the seed was coated with aldrin, a powerful insecticide—only 4 ounces to 100 pounds of rice seed planted per acre—to prevent damage to the young plants by the maggot of the rice water weevil.

The fatalities could have been predicted.

Studies at the Patuxent Wildlife Research Center near Laurel, Md., and field investigations by the North Dakota Game and Fish Department had shown that aldrin is highly toxic to birds. Less than 4

459

one-millionths of an ounce a day over a 100-day period is enough to kill adult bobwhites. Ducklings die following single applications of 2 ounces an acre. It is evident why the practice of water planting aldrin-coated seed is hazardous to waterfowl.

The incident in Texas is just one of a number in which waterfowl and other birds have been harmed by applications of chemical insecticides. Sometimes damage has resulted from failure to follow the directions on the labels of containers. At other times, damage has followed applications carried out exactly as planned; then, losses of wildlife have resulted because people had no consideration for wildlife values or because not enough testing had been done to permit suitable cautionary labeling.

In this modern day, insects must be controlled in order to grow the food and fiber we need to protect our health and to keep us comfortable—not even the most ardent fisherman or hunter enjoys the harassment of biting insects.

The issue is: How can we control insects without damaging other resources? We could do so in several ways with different degrees of success. If the ways are not perfect, we must discover better ones.

Several physical methods are available. Those that are directed toward mosquitoes touch on waterfowl most directly.

Generally, they are based on the manipulation of water levels, as when wetland is converted to dryland. That method, however, is unacceptable for waterfowl. An

extreme course is to use earthen fil to remove all traces of a wetland But filling is expensive, and few acres have been filled in for the sole purpose of controlling mosquitoes

Another method, less drastic in effect but widely applied, is open ditching. Ditching drains surface water, however, and may lower the water table to the point that marsh ponds shrink and disappear and weedy dryland plants replace the marsh vegetation. During the thirties workers in the Civilian Conservation Corps drained about 90 percent of the 625 thousand acres of Atlantic coastal marshes from Maine to Virginia, many of which produced few mosquitoes in the first place Much of the ditching has not been maintained, and mosquito breeding conditions are as bad or worse now than they were before the program began, although some ditches have clogged enough to permit some marshes to regain part or all of their former values for wildlife.

WATER MANAGEMENT need not be to the disadvantage of wildlife Wildlife and mosquito-control agencies have devised methods of water management that control mosquitoes but do not harm waterfowl One is based on the knowledge that the eggs of floodwater species (*Aedes* and *Psorophora*), which include the well-known saltmarsh mosquitoes are laid only in temporarily dewatered sites generally next to higher ground. When the tracts are flooded by rains or high tides, the eggs hatch and may produce adults in a week or less. Diking the sites and keeping them flooded throughout the mosquito breeding season is as effective as drainage in preventing the production of the mosquitoes. At the same time, impoundment greatly enhances the value of tidal marshes to water birds. A study in Delaware by scientists of the Agricultural Experiment Station and the Patuxent Wildlife Research Center disclosed that 16 times more waterfowl used impoundments than unditched marshes.

Other research has suggested physical ways to control mosquitoes without harming waterfowl environment. One way is to dewater early enough in summer so that moist-soil plants, on which waterfowl feed, can make ample growth before the area is flooded again. Sump drainage is another way. Controlled and level ditching to assure stable water levels is a third method.

Other physical methods are used against upland insect pests. Because they are practiced in locations little used by waterfowl, they generally do not affect these birds. The burning or cutting of vegetation to eliminate insect wintering quarters is an exception; it destroys early nesting cover used by waterfowl.

BIOLOGICAL METHODS of insect control generally do not harm waterfowl and may benefit them.

Many disease micro-organisms that attack mosquitoes are quite re-

The gas chromatograph used by Bureau of Sport Fisheries and Wildlife chemist Calvin Menzie can measure concentrations of some pesticides in waterfowl tissues as low as 1 part in 1 trillion.

stricted in their activity and neither harm nor help waterfowl. However, some blue-green algae that limit mosquito breeding may also be toxic to warm-blooded animals. Fish and aquatic insects that prey on mosquito larvae and pupae provide forage for certain ducks.

Many new techniques loosely referred to as biological control are useful in insect control. Disease-causing organisms, including bacteria, fungi, and viruses, and parasites of insects are capable of being mass cultured and distributed at a reasonable cost. For example, a bacterium *Bacillus thuringiensis* has been used with some success for control of the gypsy moth and other insects with caterpillar-like stages.

Insects that prey on pest insects, and antibiotics produced by various micro-organisms, are also helpful biological control agents.

The restriction of insect reproduction through various sterilization techniques is a proven success. The virtual elimination of the screw-worm fly in the Southern States through release of male flies sterilized by irradiation with cobalt-60 is evidence of this. Sterilization also can be achieved by chemicals. The production and release of large numbers of insects of inferior genetic make-up offer possibilities as a space-age approach to insect control.

Baits and sex attractants on the one hand and repellents on the other make use of biological reactions that may be employed effectively in control programs. The development of strains of corn and other crops that are resistant to insect attack is yet another approach.

While many of these biological methods are still in the experimental stage they offer exciting new possibilities for control of insects in waterfowl environs minus the harmful side effects inherent in chemical methods.

CHEMICALS ARE A THIRD MEANS of combatting insects, and man's ingenuity in controlling his environment and the insects that threaten it has resulted in many new chemicals being introduced into the habitats on which waterfowl depend. We need to examine just how much of a problem, real or potential, these chemicals pose.

Several chemical control agents have subtle but important effects on growth and reproduction. We should not overlook the indirect effect of insecticides in reducing food for waterfowl. Beyond that, a serious problem arises from the ability of many organisms, which are consumed by other creatures, to store or accumulate pesticide chemicals in their bodies at levels above those in the environment.

There are several groups of chemical insecticides. Inorganic materials such as Paris green and other arsenicals, largely have been supplanted by organic compounds. The latter include chlorinated hydrocarbons such as DDT, TDE (DDD), lindane, toxaphene, chlordane, heptachlor, aldrin, and dieldrin; organophosphates, such as malathion and parathion; and carbamates, such as carbaryl. Pyrethrum, rotenone, and ryania are among the insecticides from plants.

The production of organic pesticides in the United States has increased more than fivefold since

1950. A total of 250 million pounds (active ingredients, not including carriers) of all types of insecticides was used in 48 States by 1961. Canada uses about one-tenth and Mexico about one-twentieth as much as the United States. New materials are added constantly to the chemical arsenal, but DDT has maintained top position. Nearly 67 million pounds of it were used in the United States in 1961.

Part of the steady growth in the use of insecticides is attributed to the practice of preventive insect control by more and more growers. Cropland and pasture lead the land types in acreage treated annually (68.6 million) in 48 States. Other large-use areas are marshes and swamps (2.5 million acres), forest lands (1.8 million acres), and rangelands (1.6 million acres). Fifteen million acres in towns, industrial sites, military installations, airports, and railroad and highway rights-of-way are treated each year.

WHAT HAPPENS to these chemicals after they are applied? At the time of treatment, not all the insecticide reaches the ground, at least on the area of application. Some drifts with the wind. Some may be picked up

William Reichel, Bureau of Sport Fisheries and Wildlife chemist, prepares a thin-layer chromatography plate, a valuable tool used in the analysis of waterfowl tissues for pesticide content.

later in dust from the ground. Pitifully little is known, however, of the general distribution of pesticides in the air. In California chlorinated hydrocarbons found as residues on forage and feed crops were determined to have drifted through the air. A change was made from these persistent chemicals to parathion, a somewhat less stable material.

After they reach the ground, insecticides last for various periods. Research in Ohio showed that some chlorinated hydrocarbons remain in detectable amounts in the soil more than 10 years after application. Studies by the United States Public Health Service disclosed that parathion residue persisted in soil for at least 9 months; it had been thought that it and some other organophosphates broke down fairly fast and did not leave residues. Other organophosphates, such as TEPP, detoxify more rapidly.

Not all insecticides remain where they are deposited. Water as it runs off the land carries with it, either by attachment to silt particles or in solution, a part of the insecticides applied to control crop, forest, and range pests. Nearly all major rivers sampled by the Public Health Service since 1957 have been found to contain insecticides, although the chemicals occur in tiny amounts.

Insecticidal residues have been found in impoundments on the Tule-Klamath Refuge in California. Its water supply is the runoff from surrounding irrigated land treated with chemicals. Several hundred water birds have died from insecticidal poisoning on the refuge each year for several years. Thus aquatic

environments may be subject to the greatest contamination because they are the ultimate repositories into which all persistent chemicals drain. In this manner, they may well act as chemical traps for their animal inhabitants.

A study made near Yellowknife, Northwest Territories, by scientists from the Denver Wildlife Research Center, showed that pesticides somehow do contaminate remote regions. Nearly half of the samples of aquatic vegetation they collected in 1962 contained DDT or related compounds. Many of the ducks, eggs, and ducklings taken the previous year also had residues. Yellowknife is more than 500 miles north of any known insecticidal application.

With the continuing, widespread contamination of the environment, it is no wonder that many waterfowl carry an insecticidal burden, for, unlike people and domestic animals, wildlife cannot be kept from areas to be treated with insecticides. A sample of wintering waterfowl on the Gulf coast of Texas, taken by the Denver Wildlife Research Center in 1961, showed that more than half the birds had DDT or related compounds in their systems. Some of these chemical probably were picked up during migration. Waterfowl obviously are exposed to a greater variety of hazards than are nonmigratory birds, because of the opportunities for multiple exposure as they move south and north between breeding and wintering grounds.

Some of the chemicals are sufficiently toxic and are applied in large enough amounts that they have killed birds directly, soon after treatment. Oftener, though, they have indirect or subtle effects that can be either beneficial or harmful.

Of the few studies made of the direct effect of insecticides on waterfowl, most have measured only obvious effects. We know that statistics on total losses are low, because dense marshy vegetation hampers discovery of all victims. Repopulation from nearby untreated areas also obscures the true mortality and can result in continued losses as long as the area retains toxic substances.

Because many waterfowl nest north of the regions of principal insecticidal use and migrate south late enough to avoid direct exposure to most treatments, the likelihood of heavy mortality is less. Because croplands and rangelands get the most toxic chemicals and often the greatest amount, they offer the greatest direct hazard to waterfowl. Lower amounts or less toxic insecticides are generally applied to wetlands and forestlands.

The use of aldrin-treated seed in ricefields in Texas, Louisiana, and Arkansas has been growing.

DDT has been the chemical of choice for the same purpose in California. Studies by the California Department of Fish and Game show that its use at recommended rates constitutes a dosage of 1 to 3 pounds an acre, an amount that is lethal to mallards. The recommendation for use of DDT on rice seed was withdrawn in 1963. Besides aldrin and DDT, various mercuric fungicides, some known to be toxic to waterfowl, are added to rice seed.

Aldrin applied for grasshopper control at 2 ounces an acre also has caused a known mortality of 16 to 37 percent among young waterfowl. The losses occurred in marshes interspersed among cropland and rangeland in North Dakota. Mortality continued up to 25 days after treatment. Applications of chlordane at 1 pound an acre and toxaphene at 1.5 to 2 pounds an acre caused similar or heavier losses. Adult waterfowl were affected less than ducklings.

OTHER INSECTICIDAL PROGRAMS on agricultural lands have killed waterfowl and their relatives. These treatments include parathion at an estimated 4 ounces an acre for green bugs (aphids) in wheat and alfalfa in Oklahoma and toxaphene at 2 pounds an acre for cutworms in barley in California. Toxaphene in water is a hazard to waterfowl, as shown by an experimental program for control of trash fish. The California Department of Fish and Game found at Big Bear Lake in 1960 that only two-tenths part of toxaphene per million parts of water killed or sickened about 200 coots and ducks. An estimated 1,500 birds were on the lake at the time of treatment.

When oils were applied to marsh ponds to control mosquito larvae, waterfowl suffered some losses from poisoning, and small aquatic animal life and aquatic vegetation were damaged. A pyrethrum larvicide developed as a substitute and applied at a rate of four-hundredths of a pound of pyrethrin per acre did not harm waterfowl in tests by the New Jersey Agricultural Experiment Station.

Since the end of the Second

World War, emphasis has been placed on the use of chlorinated hydrocarbon and organophosphorus insecticides for mosquito control. Ordinarily, immediate losses of waterfowl do not follow applications of these materials, but treatments of DDT, dieldrin, and toxaphene killed some waterfowl in California, according to the State Fish and Game Department.

Even though millions of acres of forest land in the northern United States and Canada are treated with insecticides each year, little attention has been directed to the effects on waterfowl. Observations by the Wisconsin Conservation Department did show that some young mallards died as a result of spraying for the jackpine budworm with 1 pound of DDT per acre.

THE POSSIBILITY of impaired reproduction may be of even greater importance than immediate poisoning.

Pen tests at the Patuxent Wildlife Research Center show that sublethal concentrations of certain chemicals in the diet of mallards will affect their reproduction. For example, an average daily intake of less than one one-thousandth ounce of aldrin a day during the winter and breeding season reduced hatching by 63 percent.

Another chlorinated hydrocarbon, Kepone, caused similar effects at higher levels. It also upset the hormonal balance so that males grew feathers like those of females.

Research reported by the California Department of Fish and Game in 1962 revealed that reduced fertility is not just a laboratory phenomenon. On riceland treated with DDT and dieldrin, in accordance with usual agricultural practice, the reproduction of pheasant was lower than on untreated land.

CHEMICAL INSECT CONTROL might offer nominal benefits to waterfowl indirectly. Destruction of black flies in woodland streams prevents them from transmitting leucocytozoon, disease organism known to be factor limiting the population of black ducks.

Bird malaria and encephalitis also are transmitted by insect vectors but native birds apparently do no suffer greatly from such attacks. No-see-ums (gnats) are vectors of another type of malaria and of other parasites in ducks.

Investigators at the Bear River National Wildlife Refuge in Utah learned that some aquatic insect are suitable media for the development of the bacillus that cause botulism, or western duck sickness. Waterfowl can contract this deadly disease by ingesting blow flies that have fed on botulism-killed animal. Other aquatic animals also are intermediate links in the botulism cycle, so the control of insects alone would be of limited value in reducing the incidence of the disease. We have no evidence that insect-control programs influence vectors of waterfowl diseases to such an extent as to alter significantly the incidence of wildlife diseases.

More frequently, the indirect effect of insecticides on waterfowl harmful. Most of these chemicals are indiscriminate in action; more than the target organisms—suscep tible forms such as other insects, crabs and other crustaceans, and certain fish—may be victims. Many of the susceptible forms also provide food for wildlife.

As an illustration: Up to 90 percent of the summer diet of the clapper rail, which is an important bird in Atlantic coastal marshes, consists of fiddler crabs. A large reduction of these crabs, from operations to control mosquitoes, could affect the welfare of the rails. Fortunately, waterfowl are not tied so closely to a single dietary item, but the young do partake heavily of insects during their first month of life.

Pesticides need not kill organisms in order to affect the animals that feed on them. In any food chain, resistant animals may accumulate enough chemical residues to poison animals higher in the chain.

The process of biological concentration usually begins far down the line, as shown by an incident at Clear Lake in northwestern California.

Midges, an abundant and abiding pest in Clear Lake, do not bite but create a nuisance by the sheer numbers that are attracted to artificial lights. TDE was applied to provide a concentration of 1 part of the chemical to 50–70 million parts of water. Three treatments were made between 1949 and 1957. Subsequent sampling by the California Department of Fish and Game showed that micro-organisms in the water contained residues of 5 parts of TDE per million parts of their body weight. Fish contained residues of hundreds to thousands of parts per million in their fat. This concentration was enough to kill grebes feeding on the TDE-charged fish.

So far we have discussed mainly the influence of single insecticides. We know, though, that animals are exposed to many different compounds. The impact of some of these is additive. Some, however, actually enhance the effect of other compounds, so that the overall effect is greater than the sum. For example, the combined effects of the organophosphates malathion and EPN are ten times the sum of the individual effects. We are only beginning to explore these synergistic reactions.

BECAUSE OF THE impossibility of studying the toxicity of insecticides under all of the conditions encountered in the field, it has been necessary to seek other ways of obtaining this information.

One method has been to measure the survival of penned mallards fed diets containing insecticides. Results of tests at the Patuxent Wildlife Research Center show that endrin, Baytex, phosphamidon, aldrin, Zectran, endosulfan, dimethoate, heptachlor, dieldrin, Kepone, Co-ral, and lindane are more toxic than DDT; that BHC and toxaphene are of about the same order of toxicity; and that TDE, mirex, and naled are less toxic.

Although we have made significant advances, our knowledge of the effect of insecticides on waterfowl is still sketchy.

We recognize that while these chemicals can harm waterfowl,

there are numerous instances in which detrimental effects are minor. We know, too, that much of the damage caused by insecticides is unnecessary and can be avoided.

Comprehensive surveys are needed on the incidence of damage and more research is necessary to determine how the toxic effects of chemical applications can be reduced.

Studies conducted so far tell us that adherence to the following rules will greatly reduce losses of wildlife:

Be sure the chemical has to be used and that other control methods will not suffice.

Select the chemical and carrier that will be least dangerous and still do the job. Ordinarily these are the most specific and least toxic and persistent materials. For example, indications are that carbaryl is safer than aldrin against grasshoppers, although it does pose problems with pollinating and aquatic insects.

Apply chemicals strictly according to label instructions.

Use minimum dosages and a minimum number of applications.

Treat the least area possible. Guard against drift. When large areas are treated, leave blocks,

Fresh-water amphipods, or "scuds," abundant in many waterfowl breeding grounds, are important in the nutrition of ducks and ducklings. They are extremely susceptible to poisoning by pesticides.

strips, or headwaters untreated at the first application whenever possible to facilitate repopulation of wildlife if damage occurs.

Avoid direct and indirect contamination of water. Prohibition of treatments within 165 feet of water bodies, as required in South Dakota, will reduce waterfowl losses from grasshopper control programs.

Avoid treatment during periods of principal wildlife use and the nesting season when possible. If the area must be treated and waterfowl flocks are present, scaring devices sometimes are effective.

Follow practices that will lessen the chance that wildlife will be in contact with insecticides. For example, most of the immediate loss of waterfowl from treated rice seed could be avoided if it were worked into the ground, as it is in many places, instead of being water planted.

Seek the advice of wildlife biologists for other ways of reducing losses to wildlife from insecticides.

BECAUSE they are based on primary ecological factors that limit the numbers of insects, the physical and biological methods generally are preferable to chemical methods as the basis for control programs.

All too often we tend to minimize or ignore the role of natural physical and biological factors in depressing insect populations, not appreciating that outbreaks would be many times more severe without their aid.

Physical and biological factors also have a definite advantage over chemical methods in that they have a longer lasting effect in depressing populations of noxious insects with-out the disadvantage of toxicity to beneficial life, including insect predators and parasites.

With our present knowledge, it is not always possible to achieve the desired level of insect control through physical and biological means, and recourse must be made to chemical methods. The chemical methods employed, however, should always be safe and not create problems greater than those they are intended to resolve. For that reason, there has been an increasing tendency to consider chemicals as only one group of weapons among a whole arsenal and to give greater attention to insect control that combines the best of each of the various weapons in an integrated plan of attack rather than relying on the use of chemicals as the sole, matter-of-course approach.

For example, A. D. Pickett, of the Canadian Department of Agriculture, has selected insecticides and fungicides that are of specific action and of low toxicity to insect parasites and predators that aid in biological control. Through carefully timed applications, he has been able to accomplish control of insects in apple orchards in Nova Scotia that is less hazardous and as effective as large, repeated dosages of more toxic chemicals that were employed previously at four times the cost.

WE CONCLUDE with a note of hope. More and more of us have become aware of the problems of insect control. We have a growing fund of knowledge that makes it possible to devise more specific control methods. The same ingenuity that has provided us with a bountiful supply of food and reduced the inroads of disease surely can provide us with a better choice than between bugs and birds on the one hand or elimination of both on the other. It is up to those of us who want waterfowl tomorrow to provide the necessary stimulus for development of insect control measures that permit us to control the bugs without destroying the birds.

—JOHN L. BUCKLEY and
PAUL F. SPRINGER.

OIL-SOAKED SCOTERS

Clean Water, and Enough of It

OIL POLLUTION on the Detroit River killed 12 thousand ducks, mostly canvasbacks, in March 1960. Sportsmen were outraged; their bag limits already had been reduced because the ducks had become scarcer and scarcer. Heavy losses of wild waterfowl have occurred on the Detroit River and Lake Erie in many of the past 20 years. In instances more than one type of pollution was identified as the cause of death, but in general oil flows were involved. Between 1948 and 1960 losses of 28 thousand on this one river were caused mainly by oil.

Earl Rose, Chief of Fish and Game for the Iowa Conservation Commission, reported: "The Santa Fe Railroad yards at Fort Madison on January 16, 1962, dumped waste diesel oil into drains which emptied into the Mississippi River. A large lake of oil was formed on the ice, attracting waterfowl. All oil-soaked ducks died. Most of them sank through holes in the ice adjoining the oil pool. Estimated loss 200."

Alfred L. Hawkes, in the Transactions of the 26th North American Wildlife and Natural Resources Conference, in 1961, stated: "With the advent of oil burning ships, the automobile, the airplane, asphalt roads, and a thousand other devices and processes, which demand that oil be produced, transported, and

471

disposed of, oil pollution of the sea has become an international problem which is reaching the proportions of a disaster in some of the aspects."

L. M. Tuck, of the Canadian Wildlife Service in Newfoundland, estimated that one nesting colony of auks in his area has been decimated by nearly a quarter of a million birds in 2 years due to oil pollution. The colony cannot survive comparable losses for more than 2 or 3 years.

Lester Giles, Director of the American Humane Society, counted approximately 4 thousand oil-soaked birds on Nantucket Island in December and January of 1960–1961, a time of year when currents actually are carrying oil away from the area. In Narragansett Bay, some 4 thousand ducks, nearly one-fifth of the entire wintering flocks, were killed by an oil spill in February 1961.

During December 1962 at Mankato, Minnesota, a storage tank containing 3 million gallons of soybean oil burst and spilled into the Minnesota River. Shortly before this material entered the Mississippi River near St. Paul, some 3 months later, it was joined by 1 million gallons of distillate which had escaped from a tank at Savage, Minnesota. Together these wastes destroyed an estimated 10 thousand ducks and an assortment of other wildlife and of fish.

Oliver Beckley, Supervisor of Game Management for the Connecticut Board of Fisheries and Game, estimated 4 thousand ducks dead as a result of an oil spill in Long Island Sound in mid-December 1960.

Clean water is a valuable natural resource. It sustains both man and wildlife and provides opportunity for an abundance of healthful, outdoor recreation.

A report from Germany indicated a kill of over one quarter of a million birds in the North Sea, mostly as a result of one oil spill.

Mr. Hawkes concluded from such evidence that: "These figures represent typical reports from many sources . . . but only begin to indicate the real extent of the problem since, without doubt, the major portion of bird kills go unnoticed at sea."

The birds' insulating feathers and down become matted, so that cold water and air reach the skin. Body heat is then lost faster than it can be generated. In cold weather, an oil glob the size of a quarter can be fatal. Larger amounts of oil prevent flight. Starvation may then be the direct cause of death. Ingestion of the oil while drinking or preening kills birds. Internal examinations have revealed the alimentary canal sometimes is coated with poisonous oil. Oil coated birds lose buoyancy, climb onto the ice and freeze to death, or, if they remain in the water, drown.

Mr. Hawkes mentioned shipping as the chief source of oil pollution on the seas. Oil is spread from ships when taking on fuel, pumping bilges, and washing tanks. Much oil also may be lost through leaking hulls. Damaging spills occur when ships go aground. Offshore oil drilling and natural seepage add more.

Efforts to halt oil pollution on the high seas are being made. The International Convention for the Prevention of Pollution of the Sea by Oil was opened for signature at London on May 12, 1954. The Convention was approved with certain reservations by the Congress August 30, 1961, and implementing provisions were enacted in Public Law 87-167. Thirty-two countries, including the United States, had signed the convention by 1964.

POLLUTION of water by oil is just one of the ways in which we befoul water and make it unfit and lethal for ducks and geese. Less obvious, less spectacular, and probably more serious and widespread is the slow, insidious, steady deterioration of water that destroys by degrees the aquatic vegetation and animal life so necessary for waterfowl.

Harder to understand and appraise than direct poisoning or loss of environment is the kind of pollution that may trigger a major disaster. An example is the development of poison in decomposition of certain blue-green algae—"green scum" plants that exist in most waters. Sometimes these plants develop incredibly fast and in great abundance in water into which sewage or other organic wastes are dumped. We have many records of fatal poisoning of waterfowl, gulls, livestock, and even domestic pets from this cause.

Serious and widespread also is the loss of waterfowl habitat. Wastes from industrial operations or mining may destroy the ability of a body of water to support vegetation and the animal life on which waterfowl feed. High temperatures resulting from industrial use of water for cooling is often harmful. Countless contaminants from industrial, agricultural, and domestic wastes may

Pulp from a paper mill has made this stream worthless for recreation or wildlife.

change slowly the character of a waterway until it is no longer of use to waterfowl because it has gradually ceased to produce waterfowl food and shelter.

ACID MINE WATER has destroyed or seriously damaged the waterfowl value of more than 4 thousand miles of streams in the United States. Working and abandoned coal mines discharge an estimated 3.5 million tons or more of acid each year into streams, most of them east of the Mississippi River.

Acid mine water is associated usually with coal mining, both anthracite and bituminous. Acid water also may come from other types of mining, including zinc, lead, gold, bornite, and manganese. The free acid in drainage from coal mines is sulfuric acid. As the coal seams were formed, marcasites and pyrites were laid down in rocks above and below the coal and in ribbons in the seams themselves. This sulfuric material oxidizes and produces acid when exposed to air and water. The process will continue as long as sufficient atmospheric oxygen reaches the sulfuric material.

The most serious and widespread damage to ducks by acid mine water is due to the destruction of food organisms. Toxic mining wastes have killed outright the fish populations in many places. In other less acid stretches of streams, the pollution may kill organisms that are food for fish and ducks.

A CLASSIC EXAMPLE of continuing waterfowl loss from mining operations is the 75-year-old history of "lead poisoning" on Coeur d'Alene River and Lake in Idaho. For many years, mine tailings and other wastes were discharged directly into the stream. Siltation basins were developed there, and pollution is now reduced, but some mine tailings still are discharged into the river. During periods of high water, they are flushed downstream for long distances, and large amounts of silt of a high mineral content settle out in slack-water sections of the river.

The construction of the Post Falls Dam at the outlet of Coeur d'Alene Lake shortly after 1900 greatly enlarged the lake and backed up water into the Coeur d'Alene River. Marsh and aquatic vegetation became established in the shallow bays and "drowned" stream channels. This habitat is particularly attractive to waterfowl during spring migration.

When the contaminated alluvial deposits are flooded in the spring, feeding by waterfowl is comparatively heavy, and then losses occur. Whistling swans, among the first spring migrants, are followed by Canada geese, mallards, pintails, a few diving ducks, and coots. During their feeding on flooded marshlands, the soils of which contain mine waste deposits, the birds ingest lethal quantities of lead, zinc, and copper.

Waterfowl losses on the lower Coeur d'Alene River first received widespread notice in 1934 and have been a matter of concern over a long period of years. Losses have been worst among whistling swans. In mid-March of 1948, an estimated 300 to 400 swans were using the area. Losses became evident about 2 weeks after they arrived. The total mortality that season was put at 100 to 125 birds. In the spring of 1955, about 2 thousand waterfowl used the area. Between March and June, 26 swans, 10 Canada geese, and 80 ducks and coots died there.

HUMAN WASTES in moderate amounts are not detrimental to plant life. In fact, they are a fertilizer that stimulates growth of aquatic and marsh plants. Newer chemicals (including weedkillers) that reach sewers from almost every home and yard create hazards to plant growth unless they are fully treated in a modern, well operated disposal plant before they are discharged into streams. Even under the best treatment, though, some wastes do not break down but flow almost unchanged into the receiving waters. Increased domestic sewage adds to light-blocking turbidity, and is a factor in the destruction of plant organisms which ducks like.

The Public Health Service does not know of any scientific investigations on the health effects in ducks of exposure to radiation. Some biological effects are assumed to occur with radiation exposure of any kind or any amount received by any living organism. Such effects have been occurring since the appearance of life on earth and are considered to have had a major role in evolutionary processes.

SILT is one of the sneakiest destroyers of waterfowl habitat. Excessive turbidity, which excludes sunlight, often is responsible for a scarcity or total absence of duck food plants and animals. The com-

monest cause of turbidity is prolonged suspension of fine clay silt in
running waters, a condition always
aggravated by heavy rains, especially in areas of disturbed soil.

Turbidity created by industrial
and domestic pollution is believed
by some ecologists to be a greater
menace to the growth of submerged
plants than even the toxic materials
commonly found in industrial wastes.

Industrial activities that commonly
cause turbidity (or staining, with
corresponding results) include paper
and pulp production, mine operations, and oil production and processing. Wastes from tanning, dye,
and chemical manufacture all add
to stream turbidity, as do those from
canneries, creameries, and packing
houses.

The solution is the construction
and proper operation of treatment
or disposal plants at the source of
contamination.

Investigations were conducted at
Back Bay and Currituck Sound in
1958–1962 by the Fish and Wildlife
Service, the Virginia Commission
of Game and Inland Fisheries, and
the North Carolina Wildlife Resources
Commission.

Some of the findings: "Portions
of the famous Back Bay, Virginia,
and Currituck Sound, North Carolina, are buried . . . under tons of
silt. Approximately 40 square miles
of some 225 square miles of bay
and sound bottom are literally
smothered under tons of silt unsuitable for anchorage of waterfowl
food plants. At the caprice of the
wind this silt can become suspended
and result in turbid water."

The study found that in only 2
months of 1960 did 5 percent of the
total sunlight reach a depth of 6
feet. In recent years, submerged
aquatic plant production has been
estimated as high as 50 million
pounds dry weight for the 225-
square-mile area, but the 40 square
miles of Back Bay proper and the
North Landing River produced less
than 1 percent of the total.

Between 1947 and 1956, the report continued, more than "100
miles of main canals and 700 miles
of lateral ditches were dug in the
watershed to drain agricultural fields
that for the most part have no winter
cover crop. One subwatershed of
the area now delivers 13 tons of
silt after every one and one-half
inches of rain that falls over a 24-
hour period. Work was begun in
1960 to 'improve' this watershed
and a similar rain after completion
of the canal will bring in 175 tons
of silt. . . ."

WATER TREATMENT and waste
treatment to control pollution stem
from State and local concern a
century before the Federal Government took action. Our Federal
legislation to control water pollution
today is based on the premise that
such control is primarily a State
responsibility.

The Department of Health, Education, and Welfare is charged with
implementing the Federal Water
Pollution Control Act. Its primary
responsibility is to maintain water
quality for all uses. The Departments
of Defense, Interior, and Agriculture
have responsibilities as to the quantity of water.

The Public Health Service Act

of 1912 authorized surveys and studies of water pollution, particularly as it affected human health. In consequence, the first stream pollution control laboratory was established in Cincinnati. But not until 1948, after a half century of evaluating the growing pollution problem, did the Congress enact the first Water Pollution Control Act. Its administration was lodged in the Public Health Service, which became a part of the Department of Health, Education, and Welfare when this Department was created in 1954.

The act of 1948 was temporary legislation, to be reviewed after 5 years and revised on the basis of experience. It was extended for an additional 3 years to June 30, 1956. In 1956 the Congress enacted the first permanent, comprehensive Federal Water Pollution Control Act, Public Law 660. The Congress amended and strengthened the act, and it became Public Law 87–88 on July 20, 1961.

The new legislation does five important things. It increases Federal financial support for the construction of municipal waste treatment facilities. It broadens and strengthens the enforcement authority of the Federal Government. It calls for an intensified program of research looking toward more effective methods of pollution control. It authorizes increased Federal financial support of State and interstate pollution control programs. It establishes in law the principle of including storage in Federal reservoirs for regulation of streamflow to control quality of water.

In addition, both the old and new Water Pollution Control Acts require development of comprehensive river basin programs; provide for technical assistance to other agencies, Federal, State, and local; and provide that basic data on water quality shall be collected and disseminated for the intelligent planning and management of water pollution control.

Unchanged since the first act of 1948 is the declared policy of Congress "to recognize, preserve, and protect the primary responsibilities and rights of the States in controlling water pollution." The act further requires that "due regard shall be given to the improvements which are necessary to conserve waters for public water supplies, propagation of fish and aquatic life and wildlife, recreational purposes, and agricultural, industrial, and other legitimate uses."

In this retracing of the Federal Government's entry into water resource development, we see that the Congress has extended its activities and authority slowly and only after it became clear that problems were not being met or could not be met solely by local, State, or private effort.

THREE MAJOR PROBLEMS in water resource management are of greatest concern to Federal agencies at the present time.

The first is quantity of water. Particularly in the drier sections of the West, we are spending billions of dollars in conservation, land management, and impoundment programs to save water.

Our reservoir management recognizes the value of multi-purpose impoundments. Flood control, navigation, irrigation, power, public water supplies, and fish and wildlife are all involved in the programs of the Corps of Engineers, of the Department of the Interior, and the Department of Agriculture. To these we are adding another criterion, that of dilution of pollution—and pollution can be of agricultural, industrial, municipal, or even natural origin. The principle streamflow regulation is now part of our law and is being considered whenever a Federal reservoir is being planned.

The second problem before Federal agencies is quality of water. Our industrial society and our growing population are now dumping six times as much waste into our waters as 60 years ago. Our demand for water is increasing. The result is that more and more of our communities are using water that has already been used by other communities upstream.

In order to protect the public health and provide good water for industry, recreation, and other uses, we must see to it that our rivers, lakes, and estuaries are clean. This means building more and larger waste-treatment plants. It also means research so that we can make these plants more efficient. The Federal Government is helping in both.

Our third need is a reflection of our culture and our economy. Particularly in the past generation, the leisure time of Americans has increased immeasurably. The recreation Americans now seek means an annual outlay of 40 billion dollars, or more than 8 percent of the gross national product. An estimated 30 million Americans participated in sport fishing and hunting in 1960.

ACCORDING to Resources for the Future, outdoor recreation in the next 35 years may increase tenfold. Because so much of our outdoor recreation is water-oriented, that will mean in years to come that recreation will become coexistent with the industrial, municipal, and agricultural uses of water. This imposes upon us the responsibility of maintaining water as a safe, enjoyable, and healthy environment for our people.

The late President Kennedy in a message to the Congress March 1, 1962, said:

"Our Nation's progress is reflected in the history of our great river systems. The water that courses through our rivers and streams holds the key to full national development. Uncontrolled, it wipes out homes, lives, and dreams, bringing disaster in the form of floods; controlled, it is an effective artery of transportation, a boon to industrial development, a source of beauty and recreation, and the means for turning arid areas into rich and versatile cropland. In no resource field are conservation principles more applicable . . .

"Our goal, therefore, is to have sufficient water sufficiently clean in the right place at the right time to serve the range of human and industrial needs."

—GORDON E. McCALLUM.

GREEN-WINGED TEAL
MALLARDS

Spent Shot and Lead Poisoning

EACH YEAR tens of thousands of ducks and geese fall victim to spent shot, a loss that borders on wanton waste. It is a consequence of hunting, and we can do something about it.

Waterfowl get lead poisoning by swallowing lead shot that they pick up on the bottoms of lakes and marshes. The average hunter fires 5 shots for every duck he bags. A 12-gauge shell contains about 280 pellets of number-6 shot. Accordingly, as many as 1,400 pellets may be deposited on waterfowl hunting grounds for every duck killed.

Because most blinds on any body of water are on the best waterfowl feeding grounds, shot pellets fall in greatest numbers in the very places the birds are most attracted to feed. Shooting tends to keep waterfowl away from them when hunters are in the blinds, but when hunting is over, these feeding grounds can be death traps.

On most marshes there is fortunately little carryover of shot pellets from year to year. Lead shot sinks into the soft bottom and within a few months is beyond the reach of many feeding birds. In the sand, gravel, and thin layer of plant debris on the bottom of Lake Puckaway in Wisconsin not long ago, 118,048 pellets an acre were found.

479

A portion of the Horicon marsh, which has a deep peat and muck bottom, had only 3,485 shot pellets an acre in the surface layer, even though it is one of the most heavily hunted places in Wisconsin.

In California, the number of shot pellets an acre ranged from 9 thousand in the Delta marshes to 60 thousand in the marshes of the San Joaquin River. Counts from several Minnesota lakes varied from none at Rush Lake to 64 thousand an acre at Heron Lake. Two localities on Delta Marsh in Manitoba had 17 thousand and 51 thousand pellets an acre. At Willow Slough in Indiana, 41 thousand pellets an acre were found in the spring and 47 thousand in the fall.

WATERFOWL are most apt to pick up shot pellets from late autumn through winter. Spring floods create new feeding grounds and often inundate fall feeding areas to the point where they are little used. Also, with a few exceptions, marshes on the breeding grounds are not hunted intensively; therefore, from late spring through summer, relatively few waterfowl succumb from lead poisoning.

Shot pellets resemble the seeds of numerous plants, especially the pondweeds. This seems to explain why birds ingest them and why the birds that feed most actively on the bottom pick up the most shot. During the fall and early winter, young ducks eat more than adults do and they swallow more lead. Drakes consume more food than hens, and they, likewise, ingest more lead.

Geese feed less in lakes and marshes and more on farm fields than do ducks and so swallow less lead shot than ducks. Birds which feed extensively on the foliage of aquatic plants, like the American widgeon and gadwall, ingest fewer shot than the mallard and pintail, which feed a great deal on seeds in the bottoms of lakes and marshes. Also, a bird feeding on greens requires less grit than a grain-feeding bird and might pick up fewer pellets even if they were available in abundance.

Lead shot is retained in the gizzard for varying periods. The grinding action of the gizzard on the shot and dissolution by digestive juices reduce its size. As lead is eroded from the surface of the pellet, soluble lead salts pass into the digestive tract. The first toxic symptom is a lessening of food intake, as the gizzard is partly paralyzed.

In most waterfowl, the malfunction of the gizzard leads to starvation. Birds lose their appetite and eat little, or the ingested food is not digested. The glandular stomachs of birds that continue to take in food become greatly distended and impacted. Fowl that have starved to death because of lead poisoning weigh about half of normal. In 3 or 4 weeks the birds either die or begin to recover. Occasionally, waterfowl ingest such large numbers of shot pellets that a highly acute form of lead poisoning occurs; blood, kidney, and liver tissues are severely damaged, and birds die in 1 to 2 weeks.

Losses from lead poisoning occur almost every year in some localities; in others, they occur only now and then. The numbers of deaths also vary from year to year; one place may lose a few dozen or none one year but 10 thousand ducks another year.

Mortality has been greatest and most frequent in the Mississippi Flyway, especially in Louisiana, Illinois, Missouri, Indiana, and Arkansas. Mallards, pintails, and Canada geese have suffered the heaviest losses. Whistling swans, sometimes in large numbers, have been reported dying from lead poisoning at Back Bay and Currituck Sound in Virginia; Lake Mattamuskeet in North Carolina; marshes of the Great Lakes in Ohio, Michigan, and Wisconsin; and Bear River in Utah.

Almost all species of waterfowl have been reported at one time or another to be victims of lead poisoning.

SYMPTOMS of lead poisoning usually are distinguishable from those of other ailments. Gizzards of most dead birds contain eroded shot pellets, although some void the shot before dying. Among mallards found dead from lead poisoning in the Mississippi Flyway, 10 percent of the drakes and 13 percent of the hens had voided the shot.

In most cases of lead poisoning, the birds show extreme emaciation. The flight muscles are a remnant of their normal size. The keel bone protrudes prominently. Fat deposits are absent from the body cavity. The gall bladder is several times normal size. Liver, kidney, and heart are much reduced in size. The horny lining of the gizzard, which

is smaller than in healthy birds, is usually stained green or dark brown. Dark, ulcerated spots may penetrate the horny pads, which are abnormally stiff and easily separated from the rest of the gizzard. The vent is usually stained green.

In outbreaks, dying birds are often seen. They swim in a hunched position with the head back, the wings forming a roof over the back. They have difficulty flying and walk unsteadily. In late stages of the disease, the chest and wings droop. Most sick birds seek isolation and concealment in dense vegetation on the bank or shore.

Degenerated flight muscles in lead-poisoned birds make them easier to shoot than healthy birds. Tests with banded mallards showed that ducks experimentally dosed with lead shot were brought to bag up to two times more readily than normal birds. Dosed birds began to show increased vulnerability to hunters near the end of the first week and even more in the second and third weeks.

Unless waterfowl are badly emaciated, hunters are unaware that they have bagged a lead-poisoned bird. Very thin birds, often termed "straw hats" by hunters, usually are discarded. Many hunters attribute the condition of such birds to old gunshot wounds.

Waterfowl hunters need not be concerned about becoming poisoned by eating the flesh of birds suffering from lead poisoning. Laboratory animals that received doses of lead salts showed little or no deposition of lead in skin or flesh. The kidney and liver are the organs most likely to contain lead, yet the livers of lead-poisoned ducks were found to contain such low-level amounts of lead as to be harmless to man.

Large losses of waterfowl and emaciated birds discarded by hunters are the most obvious indicators of mortality from lead poisoning. However, day-to-day losses are prevalent on waterfowl marshes through autumn, winter, and spring, and the cumulative total of these could be substantial and yet go unnoticed. Predators make quick work of many sick waterfowl, and the remains of dead ducks are consumed by many scavengers in and around marshes. Only when waterfowl die in such large numbers that predators and scavengers are unable to keep pace with the death toll are losses likely to be apparent.

Because individual carcasses are seldom seen, the day-to-day losses are difficult to appraise in total. An effort was made to estimate this mortality by determining the incidence of ingested lead shot, noting the amount of lead in infected birds, and establishing in experiments the levels of lead necessary to cause death.

Examinations have been made of 36 thousand gizzards from 20 species of waterfowl. Samples were obtained from the main waterfowl zones in much of the United States in autumn and early winter.

Lead shot was recovered from 6.7 percent of all ducks and 1 percent of the geese. By species, the incidence of lead in gizzards was less than 2 percent in bufflehead, green-winged teal, merganser, wood duck, shoveler, and gadwall; more than 2 and less than 5 percent in blue-winged teal, American widgeon, and common goldeneye; more than 5 and less than 10 percent in ruddy duck, mallard, black duck, and pintail; and more than 10 percent in canvasback, lesser scaup, redhead, and ring-necked duck.

Among waterfowl that swallowed lead, 65 percent contained only one pellet, 15 percent contained two, and only 7 percent more than six. The largest number of shot pellets ingested was 179 by a pintail.

Among mallards that survived the ingestion of lead, the average period of retention was 18 days. Mallards that died carried lead in the gizzard for an average of 23 days, and the average interval of shot retention was about 20 days. Beyond 20 days, the bird usually either voids the shot and lives, or retains it and dies. Hence, during the most critical time that waterfowl are exposed to lead poisoning—November through February—there are about six 20-day periods of exposure. On the average, a sample taken during this period represents only one-sixth of the actual occurrence of lead shot in waterfowl populations during the year.

THE NUMBER OF SHOT that can kill fowl varies among individuals. One shot may cause death in some birds. Others that ingest several shot are unaffected. The variation in the expression of lead toxemia is attributed to the volume and kind of food eaten. As long as birds continue to eat at near normal rates, those which have ingested lead have an excellent chance to survive. The passage of food through the digestive tract apparently results in the elimination of many of the soluble lead compounds, and the longer the gizzard continues to function adequately, the more likely is the passage of ingested lead.

Three tests, in which the volume of food consumed appeared to influence survival, demonstrate the importance of this factor. Captive drake mallards consumed 15 percent more food than did hens during fall and winter, and mortality in drakes was only half that of the hens. Conversely, during spring, hen mallards consumed about 17 percent more food than did drakes, and survival was more than twice as high in hens as in drakes. Juvenal mallards ate considerably more food than did adults most of the fall, and their survival rate was several times greater than that of adults.

The type of food consumed also bears on survival. On experimental rations, birds fed whole corn experienced the highest mortality, and losses were progressively lower with grain and weed seeds, foliage of aquatic plants, and commercial duck pellets. Mallards fed cornmeal survived longer and eliminated shot pellets more quickly than those fed whole corn. Lesser scaup dosed with lead shot and fed clam meat showed less toxemia than mallards fed small grains and weed seeds.

The prevalence of corn and other large seeds in the diet of mallards suggests the reason for high suscep-

tibility of this species to lead poisoning. The high percentage of mallards found in die-offs supports this premise.

BECAUSE of its abundance and its susceptibility to lead poisoning, the mallard was selected for extensive studies under natural conditions.

Mallards trapped in central Illinois were dosed individually with one, two, or four pellets of number-6 shot. In eastern Colorado, other mallards were dosed with six pellets of number-6 shot. The treated birds were banded and released, along with an equal number of control birds which contained no ingested lead shot. Subsequent recovery of bands provided a basis for judging comparative mortality. Returns indicated that one number-6 shot caused 12-percent mortality among adult drake mallards; two shot, 44 percent; four shot, 41 percent; and six shot, 66 percent. The loss among juvenal drakes was less; one shot caused an apparent loss of 4 percent; four shot, a loss of 32 percent. A marked seasonal difference in mortality was noted among mallard hens. A group dosed with one shot in the autumn had a mortality of 22 percent; a group treated in late winter with six shot suffered a loss of 8 percent.

IN ARRIVING at an estimate of waterfowl losses—due to lead poisoning, we considered these factors: The incidence of shot among various species; the effect of various shot levels on amount of mortality; bias in the sampling procedure, because lead-infected birds are bagged more readily during the hunting season; the mortality interval represented by a given sample during the critical period from late October to March; the effects of diet and the volume of food consumed on survival; and amount of mortality at times of large die-offs.

These factors are the basis of an estimate, which seems reasonable to me, that lead poisoning causes an annual loss of 2 to 3 percent of waterfowl.

MORTALITY is most severe among mallards in the Mississippi Flyway and may amount to as much as 4 percent yearly. Pintails also have large losses, but deaths are relatively low among blue-winged teal, green-winged teal, shovelers, and wood ducks, because few individuals of those species swallow lead shot. Lead poisoning is even less important among American widgeons and gadwalls, since they ingest few shot pellets and their preference for soft food minimizes the hazard.

Redheads, ring-necked ducks, canvasbacks, and lesser scaups have the highest rate of shot ingestion among all species. Although Canada and snow geese usually ingest few shot, large numbers are known to die from this disease. Wisconsin biologists estimate that more than 1500 Canadas met death from lead poisoning in their State between 1940 and 1963. One goose had 110 lead pellets, but this is only a drop in the bucket compared to 451 pellets recovered from a trumpeter swan in British Columbia.

A WAY to reduce losses caused by lead poisoning may be to use shot made of something other than lead. Mallards given massive doses of iron shot pellets show no harmful effects. Obviously, such a material would eliminate lead poisoning as a hazard to waterfowl.

After considerable experimentation, the Winchester-Western Cartridge Division developed a true, spherical pellet from an iron alloy. Repeated annealing in furnaces with controlled atmosphere resulted in a substantial reduction in hardness of the metal. The firing of thousands of rounds has demonstrated that pellets of annealed iron have little or no adverse effect on modern gun barrels and adjustable chokes.

Iron shot does not measure up to lead shot in range. Comparisons of iron and lead were made with number 4 and 6 shot-loads fired from a 12-gauge, full-choke gun. No difference in power was evident between the two, at 35 yards. Beyond that range and up to 60 yards, the superior power of lead became increasingly evident, especially with number-6 shot.

However, two factors tend to balance off the lesser effectiveness of iron shot at long ranges: The average hunter bags most ducks at less than 35 yards; and for any given shot size, there are more pellets of iron than of lead in the load, because of the lower density of iron.

A standard 12-gauge load contains about 169 number-4 lead shot. A shell loaded with iron shot of the same size has about 250 pellets.

Conversely, iron shot of larger size may be used to achieve a load of the equivalent weight and pellet count of lead. As the size of shot increases, so does its impact potential at long range. The larger iron shot would reduce the difference in power between it and lead at ranges over 35 yards and still provide similar patterns.

Since lead persists for long periods in water or on the ground, it will continue to accumulate in certain types of situations for as long as shells with lead shot are fired there. This accumulation has already reached the point where annual loss is averaging close to the total number of ducks produced in the States of North and South Dakota. If lead shot continues to be scattered in waterfowl marshes across the country, it is inevitable that losses from lead poisoning will increase. A substitute for lead shot is needed.

—Frank C. Bellrose, Jr.

BLACK DUCKS

No Place to Hide

MIGRATORY DUCKS and geese may have to dodge shotgun pellets for as much as half their existence.

No sooner are the summer molts over for the old ones and the flight stage reached by the fledglings than they all become fair game for an army of hunters.

Hunting begins in Alaska and Canada as early as September and along the northern row of States by October 1. Shooting does not stop in the Southern States until after New Year's. Birds may be taken in Mexico until March 1 which is close to the time when the urge to migrate and breed sends them northward again. Let not the hunter, then, bemoan the limits on his bag and time for hunting. About the only place the birds can hide during the 6 months they are under constant pursuit is a refuge or sanctuary.

But that is not all. During the period of nesting, brooding, and rearing young, interference by man continues. Sharing our public waters now with the ducks and geese are a growing number of fishermen, speedboaters, water skiers, and skin divers. Over parts of the northern waterfowl breeding range, speedboaters and water skiers are taking command. So, also, on the wintering grounds.

Consider the lower Columbia River. There we have watched great flocks of ducks and geese drift wearily in to a landing after long flights from the autumn staging grounds at Izembek Bay at the base of the Aleutians. From Izembek they have fought their way through storm and fog to the coastal bays of Puget Sound and the lower Columbia. There the tired, hungry migrants find welcome beds of aquatic plants and waste grain and stubble in harvested grainfields nearby. They also find their haven bustling with boaters and thousands of fishermen trolling among restless swells for salmon and steelhead. Night falls on the Columbia and the salmon fishing boat. The skipper cuts across the broad river, paying out a half-mile of gill net, a lighted float at each end.

Murres and gulls pay little attention to the ceaseless activity, but ducks and geese must seek quiet and safety at Summer Lake in Oregon, Klamath and Tule marshes along the California border, and other inland places where the waters are too shallow for sport and commercial fishermen.

Farther south, the interior valleys of California may harbor 10 million ducks, approximately one-half of them pintails, in December. In earlier days they used the broad rivers for resting, and moved to adjacent marshlands and grainfields to feed. Now the open waterways are the recreation grounds of sport

fishermen, speedboaters, and water skiers, as more and more roads and facilities are built for the convenience and pleasure of people.

And along the Atlantic coast: Many of the canvasbacks reared on Canadian and Dakota prairies move eastward across the Great Lakes and settle for the winter in Chesapeake Bay, the lower Potomac estuary, Pamlico and Currituck Sounds, and other coastal waters. There scaup, redheads, widgeons, blacks, ruddies, and other ducks join them. Great flocks of geese come from nesting grounds bordering Hudson Bay.

In the coastal estuaries they feed on a rich variety of plant life growing in extensive submerged beds. The divers go down to feast on the tender stalks. Surface feeders relish the surface plants. This, waterfowl have done since prehistoric times.

Now the growing traffic of pleasure craft harasses the autumn flocks. Later in winter come the crabbing, oystering, and fishing boats and keep the feeding flocks on the move.

Along the Gulf coast, fleets of shrimp boats and sport fishermen disturb the wintering redheads and other divers that use the shallow coastal waters.

ALL THIS GROWING *use* of public water is not in itself a serious threat to the welfare of waterfowl. The point is that to the older types of water uses have been added new disturbances to waterfowl. They merit attention.

Two factors enter in: Pleasure boating is a major recreational pursuit; it is also big business. An example, perhaps atypical: People in the vicinity of Detroit own 180 thousand or so boats, the value of which approaches 260 million dollars. The investment in some 200 clubs and marinas exceeds 150 million dollars. More than 60 million dollars were spent in 1961 for boats, accessories, supplies, and services. We estimate that 8 million Americans own boats and that 400 thousand new pleasure craft are launched each year.

BOATING IS ADMINISTERED in 30 States as a function of official conservation agencies. This is where it belongs so that consideration for all groups may be assured in the sharing of our lakes, streams, and seashores. State administrative agencies are attempting to resolve the differences of uses and requirements of water users. Some are adopting restrictive regulations for specific bodies of water. Others attempt to divide the public waters by means of buoy markers or by designating hours of the day or days of the week for different groups.

Measures have been taken in Pennsylvania to provide a degree of control. Motor boats are excluded on all lakes created for fishing and on most impoundments provided for general recreational purposes. On some lakes, motors of 6 horsepower or less are permitted. Speeds generally are confined to 6 miles an hour or less in narrow channels and near streambanks.

Groups representing owners of large craft, speedboats, high-powered motors, and water skis sometimes have defeated State efforts to improve the administration of public waters for the benefit of all. They usually have the support of National and State organizations financed by equipment manufacturers.

Few State agencies have adequate regulatory authority. Their function usually is to license and inspect. Regulation of speed and zoning of waters for various uses are left to local authorities. Only man's uses are considered, not those of wildlife.

Two exceptions are Minnesota and Wisconsin. The Minnesota Department of Conservation has authority to post a maximum of six lakes as resting places for migratory waterfowl and to ban motorboats and aircraft. The Wisconsin Conservation Department also posts large lakes used by waterfowl, but on tenuous authority, which has not been challenged because fall boating is largely by sportsmen.

Game managers seem to agree that the turmoil created by speedboats and water skiers is not a major problem. Most ducks like shallow, weedy areas, which motorboat operators usually avoid. In many areas, most pleasure boating ends before migrant ducks arrive. Lake Geneva, in Wisconsin, is almost urbanized, but thousands of waterfowl rest there on spring and fall migrations.

Ducks can become quite tolerant of man and his machines—except guns. The mallard that waddles from a city park pool to accept a handout little resembles its wary cousin in a marsh. We have seen flocks of ducks feeding in fields beside heavily traveled roads at the

490

WATERFOWL TOMORROW

edge of Milwaukee and thousands ignoring passing trains and switch engines to feed on spilled grain in railroad yards in the Twin Cities. Large flocks remain all winter on a pond called Roaches Run near National Airport in Washington, D.C., where airplanes land and take off all day and night.

Yet, if we consider the overall picture of influences that detract from waterfowl welfare, water sports that turn placid streams and lakes into churning waves upset the normal pattern for ducks. Gerald Eddy, former Director, Department of Conservation of Michigan, has said: "Tolerance limits and net effects are difficult to appraise or measure, but they exist and must be recognized. The absence of some species, the decline in abundance of others, and the length of stay is more than likely in a given environment."

Intensive boating has almost eliminated waterfowl use of the Ochlawaha River and parts of the St. Johns River in Florida. Airboats have done the same in parts of the Everglades and Lake Okeechobee. Boating and heavy fishing use of large lakes in southern Missouri are believed to be driving waterfowl away, and cause serious disturbances in resting areas that the State Conservation Commission has established on such lakes as Bull Shoals.

On the Ninepipe National Wildlife Refuge in Montana, refuge waters were closed to fishermen in 1962. Their use by waterfowl increased twofold over that of the year before.

THINGS ASSOCIATED WITH pleasure boating also have an effect. Dwellings, boathouses, docks, and marinas have burgeoned, often accompanied by dredging and filling. Aquatic plants are cut or are killed by chemicals. Fertilization by wastes from dwellings and boats produces such dense growth in some lakes that there is little water surface for ducks.

Other examples of waterfront and wetland developments: Where the Raisin River flows into Lake Erie, a big harbor development is surrounded by industries and a superhighway with cloverleaf turnoffs. A bronze plaque beside the road reminds motorists that the famous Monroe Marshes once occupied the area. Steel mill activities are destroying the Cottonport managed shooting area on Chickamauga Reservoir, near Dayton, Tennessee. An oil refinery is proposed on Delaware Bay, where a major company has asked that protected shore be rezoned for industrial use. An industrial area attracts more industry. Even if adjacent marshes, which for centuries have wintered thousands of waterfowl, were not filled, there would be harassment and danger of pollution. A proposal to build a harbor threatens the famous Indiana dunes at the southern tip of Lake Michigan, an area remarkable for its variety of birds and plants.

Oil wells once were regarded as a major threat to refuges, but the showdown brought on by a liberal Federal leasing policy in the fifties had a salutary effect. Large companies particularly proved that they could operate with very little damage to habitat.

Highways follow valleys and cross watersheds. Wetlands are filled. Drainage is sometimes obstructed, sometimes accelerated. In most States there is little control. Highway fills could serve as dikes to create pools and sometimes do, mainly in small watershed projects under Public Law 566.

A bay shore highway in Delaware crossed marshes on dikes. Water control structures were built to relieve pressure. When the possibility of damage to duck hunting and fur trapping was pointed out, the Highway Department turned water control over to the Game and Fish Department, which has since managed water levels to enhance the productivity of the marshes.

Wisconsin since 1953 has required that notices of proposed highway changes be sent to the Conservation Department and the State Soil Conservation Committee. The Highway Department has gone further. It sends preliminary plans so that the other agencies may suggest changes in plenty of time. Similar legislation has been considered for all Federal-aid highways.

AFTER EXAMINING these other activities of man, we come back to his recreational urge as a basis of conflict with waterfowl needs. A burgeoning population with more leisure and more income is rushing for the great outdoors, preferably where there is water. What has happened and will continue in the Mississippi Flyway gives an idea of the dimensions and urgency.

States in the flyway contain more than a third of the National population. Recreation seekers spread out from nine metropolitan centers of more than a million each, ranging up to nearly 7 million in the Chicago area. The Twin Cities, Milwaukee, Detroit, Cleveland, Cincinnati, St. Louis, Kansas City, and New Orleans all contribute to the throng that wants summer homes, all-year residences, camp sites, resorts, and boat launching facilities on lakes and streams.

The urban-suburban impact on waterfowl is exemplified at Detroit. The Detroit River, Lake St. Clair, and the west end of Lake Erie have production and wintering habitat for migratory waterfowl that use the Mississippi Flyway and a tributary of the Atlantic Flyway.

Much of the habitat has been gobbled up by lake-front dwellings, parks, bathing beaches, and marinas. More than 3 thousand boats are berthed along a half-mile of Lake St. Clair shore once used by waterfowl. A metropolitan beach on the lake was made by filling a productive waterfowl marsh. A water-ski school here trained a thousand persons in 1961. Flocks of diving ducks still use an offshore area at the end of the beach.

The Detroit area still is one of the few places on the Great Lakes with significant waterfowl habitat. The Michigan Department of Conservation and the Bureau of Sport Fisheries and Wildlife are trying to save what is left of the habitat, but it seems to be a losing fight.

Famous old Mississippi River sloughs above St. Louis, Missouri, have been invaded by shacks, trailers, and rickety boat docks. Waterfowl no longer use places they once frequented by thousands. A Tennessee State refuge on the U.S. Corps of Engineers' Old Hickory Reservoir has been made useless by home building and boating. Homes are being built adjacent to the Tennessee Valley Authority's pools, and commercial boat docks are increasing, along with pleasure boating. TVA developments attract both industrial and recreational activities.

Dwellings are scattered along the Mississippi from Illinois to the Twin Cities on land held by the U.S. Corps of Engineers in connection with its navigation development. In 1960, the Bureau of Sports Fisheries and Wildlife and conservation departments of five States induced the Corps to revise its land-use regula-

tions to protect wildlife values. Nonconforming uses must have approval from the States and the Bureau.

Control is not so simple along waterways where land is privately owned. Cottages have sprouted on the north shore of Green Bay, an arm of Lake Michigan, near marshes heavily used by ducks. Summer and all-year dwellings are increasing along streams. One of these is the Wolf River in Wisconsin, which has wilderness stretches, white water, and marshes used by waterfowl. To make more cottage sites on this natural area a dam was being planned to create a shallow lake. It took action by the 1964 State Legislature to stop this.

Recreational developments have affected waterfowl little in the southern part of the Mississippi

Flyway but a glance eastward to Florida finds cause for apprehension about the effects of population pressure. Many persons in Florida want boats moored alongside their lots. The developers put bulkheads offshore and use sandsuckers to make land behind them with fill taken from the adjacent bottoms. A channel is dredged from the sea and lateral canals create "waterfront" for all of the lots. The U.S. Corps of Engineers District Office at Jacksonville has been issuing about 180 permits a year for dredging and filling in navigable waters. This same type of canal subdivision has also appeared in the Midwest and caused the destruction of marshes.

THE FULL IMPACT of recreational development is seldom assessed. Wisconsin has started a survey of lakes and streams to provide a basis for classification and regulation. Fifteen counties, containing perhaps 5,500 lakes and streams, have been covered.

"Improved shoreline for human habitation," said C. W. Threinen, the project leader, "means short grass and sand, no food or cover for waterfowl, no nesting. The cottage owner wants no underwater or shore weeds of emergent or wetland types. Shallows are the principal habitat of such desirable types as sago, wild celery, wild rice and others. Without cover, invertebrates, amphibians, and fish are scarce or absent.

"Waterfowl can continue to use open water for feeding and resting, provided there is not excessive interference by fast boating. This does disturb waterfowl. On big waters, they simply move to another location; on small waters there is no other location; waterfowl numbers decline.

"Intensive boating will influence the quantity and types of vegetation. Emergent vegetation vanishes. Aquatic plants of many species poke their heads above water for fertilization. Heavy boating traffic effectively prunes the upper portions of plants to propeller depth. Formerly, shallow waters were immune to boat traffic. Now the water jet boats can traverse all depths, and at faster speeds."

Threinen added that shallow lakes of some size (often excellent for ducks) had a precarious status and if converted to open water would produce algae rather than rooted plants, with carp the most abundant fish.

Despite laws that forbid lakeshore filling and require a State contract for bottom dredging, modern machines work faster than officials can act. There have been about 30 cases a year of unauthorized lakefront filling. Resort and cottage owners also try to make beaches by having truckloads of sand dumped on winter ice over muck bottom. Since 1959, Wisconsin has required permits for these so-called sand blankets. Applications average 200 a year. About 25 percent are denied, so as to protect fish and wildlife values.

AND SO IT IS that city dwellers in their pursuit of peace and quiet are trading the stresses of the workday week for the weekend harassment of motor boats and water skis. This mass exodus from towns to the countryside—and water—bears implications for waterfowl. Duck habitat—no matter how good—does not serve well the concurrent use of nesting mallards and people at play.

This is not a new problem to a world whose human population is, as they say, exploding. All uses of the land and its resources bring conflicts of sorts. It requires giving and taking to achieve multiple use of limited land and water areas. In the months and years ahead, waterfowl will yield their place to people at play in some areas. Elsewhere, they will gain the protection from harassment necessary for their continuing use of nesting and feeding grounds.

Legal zoning of water will preserve habitat in many situations. New areas will be created to help offset habitat sacrificed to intensive users of water. And waterfowl adaptable as they are, will likely adjust in considerable measure to the growing invasion of their domain.—ALBERT M. DAY and RUSSELL G. LYNCH

These days people think more and more in terms of dollars. By those standards all of our wilderness will be chewed up by machines. Yet dollars do not express all the values which we Americans cherish.

—WILLIAM O. DOUGLAS

AMERICAN WIDGEON

Places to Hide—
and Seek

CANVASBACKS
WHISTLING SWANS

Federal Refuges

ON THE GROUND behind the refuge signs, geese chattered and an occasional duck called. Overhead, out of gunshot, a formation of geese broke ranks and descended to join the others. Here they had safety from the hunters' guns, as well as food and a secure place to rest.

Hunters listened and watched from the other side of the refuge fence. Some felt cheated, because shots had been scarce that day. Others, who knew the area before the refuge was established, were pleased. They remembered the days when by this time of year all the geese and most of the ducks would have been chased out of the country by the opening day's gunfire or taken away in some hunter's car. Now the birds lingered until cold drove them farther south; when conditions were right, they provided good shooting for sportsmen and birding for naturalists.

This is the waterfowl refuge, the kind of refuge most people know best. There are other kinds. Some were established long ago. Ancient kings of Asia Minor and Egypt set up wildlife preserves, and the practice moved north and westward. Medieval European princes and noblemen made great parks or woodland preserves for their enjoyment and the preservation of native wildlife. The early refuges preserved the famous white cattle of western Europe and England and the wisent, or European bison.

Present-day refuges differ in many respects from those of the past, although they have points in common. Their object may be to preserve from extinction a notable piece of habitat, a distinct ecological unit of plants and animals, or a single species. Some refuges are as small as an acre in size. Others like certain western game ranges and refuges for waterfowl, may exceed a million acres.

Usually it is necessary to employ some kind of management measure to improve or maintain the conditions that led to the establishment of a refuge. The refuge thus has become a basic instrument in modern management of game.

Our waterfowl fared well until 1900–1916. They were distributed widely and were shot primarily for food. Then came the modern repeating and automatic shotguns, more effective ammunition, contin-

Bird watchers enjoying the waterfowl sights at the Malheur National Wildlife Refuge, Burns, Oregon.

ued year-around shooting, and more market hunting. Many persons became alarmed at the waning of waterfowl in North America. The alarm led to the signing in 1916 of an International Treaty involving Great Britain (Canada) and the United States to protect and regulate the taking of migratory birds. It was ratified by the Congress in 1918.

THE HISTORY of the national wildlife refuge program in the United States began with the establishment of the Pelican Island Refuge in Florida in 1903 by an Executive order of President Theodore Roosevelt to protect a magnificent colony of brown pelicans and other colonial nesting birds. Their existence was threatened by ruthless slaughter for their plumage, which was sold to the millinery trade. It was the first of a series of such Executive orders. Three more refuges of the same type were set aside by 1906. In 1908, 36 more small refuges were set aside, again primarily for the protection of colonial nesting species.

From this small beginning, interest grew until in June 1924 the Congress authorized the appropriation of 1.5 million dollars for the purchase of bottom lands along the upper Mississippi River. This permitted creation of the Upper Mississippi River Wildlife and Fish Refuge, a complex of waterfowl habitat extending from Wabasha, Minn., to Rock Island, Ill. It preserved a valuable core of the Mississippi Flyway habitat that was

becoming engulfed by the intensive development of our growing Nation. Today it furnishes excellent habitat for Mississippi Flyway waterfowl and provides excellent hunting, fishing, and other recreational opportunities to some 30 million people who live within a half day's drive of its boundaries. This was the first time a refuge area was established on which public hunting was specifically authorized.

An appropriation of 350 thousand dollars was made by the Congress in 1928 to establish the Bear River Migratory Bird Refuge, on the delta where the Bear River flows into Great Salt Lake. Under its former natural conditions, the delta produced thousands of waterfowl. At times, though, it was a death trap for other thousands. In many seasons, the extensive marshes of the delta dried up to make expanses of exposed mudflats and sheets of shallow water, an ideal situation for the development of the causative agent of botulism. After it was bought, dikes and other structures were built to permit regulation of the water levels. Today Bear River still produces thousands of waterfowl, and losses by botulism have been reduced. The authorization for the Bear River Refuge also provided that parts of the area could be opened to public hunting.

Senator Peter Norbeck of South Dakota and Congressman August H. Andresen of Minnesota in 1929 introduced a bill, which was enacted as the Migratory Bird Conservation Act. The Act, which was based on the Migratory Bird Treaty with

The rare whooping crane winters at the Aransas National Wildlife Refuge, Texas, along with Canada geese and other waterfowl. With wings widespread these adult cranes are fighting over territory. Picture taken January 1964.

Great Britain, clarified and enlarged Federal conservation operations. The Act strengthened the enforcement of Federal regulations, which govern the extent of waterfowl seasons and bag limits, and authorized a system of waterfowl refuges. Shortly thereafter, money was appropriated for the purchase of inviolate waterfowl sanctuaries.

THE YEAR 1929 also marked the beginning of a great drought, which nearly brought disaster to the duck population. Gradually it grew worse, peaked in severity in 1934, and continued another 4 years before relief came. The prairie nesting grounds of the United States and Canada shrank to a small part of their former size. The need for drastic action became so acute that President Franklin D. Roosevelt took a hand.

First he named a waterfowl committee composed of three great conservationists: Jay N. "Ding" Darling famous cartoonist; Thomas Beck well-known publisher; and Aldo Leopold, a pioneer conservation leader and teacher at the University of Wisconsin. The committee singled out preservation of the breeding grounds as the key to the problem and recommended a 50-million-dollar restoration program to purchase and rehabilitate nesting marshes.

To implement the program, "Ding" Darling was named chief of the Bureau of Biological Survey (predecessor of the present Bureau of Sport Fisheries and Wildlife), whose responsibility it was to administer the Migratory Bird Treaty Act and the Migratory Bird Conservation Act of 1929.

A better choice could not have been made. "Ding" informed the public and the Congress about the emergency and aroused so much enthusiasm for the restoration idea that the first part of the restoration fund was soon forthcoming. Actually, he obtained a total of 8.5 million dollars in 1934 from Emergency Acts relating to retirement of submarginal lands, drought relief, and Works Progress Administration, and a special fund of 1 million dollars. The refuges started with Migratory Bird Conservation funds were completed with emergency funds. Because most of this money had to be used in an officially designated drought belt of 18 States, the early refuge purchases and restorations were largely in the upper Mississippi Valley and the Great Plains States. Hundreds of W.P.A. workers and Civilian Conservation Corps enrollees were soon hard at work on the new refuges, restoring the habitat for wildlife use.

The early emergency funds for land purchases had been obligated by June 15, 1935. So pleased was the Congress and the conservation world with the results of this expendi-

Cormorants share a six-floor "apartment building" at Agassiz National Wildlife Refuge, Minnesota.

It is hatching time for more than waterfowl. Two young clapper rails have hatched, and a third seems to be in the process under watchful eyes.

ture that the Congress voted another 6 million dollars to extend the program. The kindly and devoted conservationist, Senator Peter Norbeck, succeeded in getting the Congress to appropriate this money by unanimous consent, a legislative feat reserved for dire national emergencies. This time the authorization for acquiring refuges also included the Atlantic Coast States and the lower half of the Mississippi Flyway. This period of great activity lasted through 1940.

The emergency funds were augmented when the Migratory Bird Hunting Stamp Act was passed in 1934. The thinking behind the Act was that the hunter should help restore the marshlands on which he depended largely to produce waterfowl for his sport. Every duck hunter 16 years of age and over was required to obtain a one-dollar duck stamp at any post office, and have it in his possession while hunting. The income was to be used to purchase and develop refuges.

On hand at this time were almost 2 million acres of refuge lands already acquired, plus lands of the public domain and holdings of other Federal agencies that were available for refuge purposes. The C.C.C. and W.P.A. provided a large labor pool, but no money was available for lumber, hardware, cement, reinforcing steel, fenceposts and wire, draglines, bulldozers, trucks, and other materials with which to start the actual construction on the refuges. The Duck Stamp income, therefore, was used largely for the habitat restoration program. This action was widely criticized, because many believed the funds should be used exclusively to acquire land, but the course followed made it possible for the refuges to be made effective much earlier than would otherwise have been possible.

ALONG WITH the restoration program in 1935 and 1936 was an auxiliary program, which today is significant in habitat preservation. This was the program of perpetual easements, which enabled the saving and restoration, without the need to purchase the land, of many small breeding areas that had dried up in the long drought. Dams and control structures were built on many of these areas, and by 1937 many were holding water and were used by nesting waterfowl.

Another act that helped enlarge the refuge system was the Fish and Wildlife Coordination Act of March 1934. It expanded the scope and authority of the Biological Survey and its successors by recognizing wildlife and recreation values on Federal water development projects. Under this Act, a number of new Federal refuges have been established.

AS PART OF THE relief endeavor in the early thirties, the Government had embarked on a program of purchasing submarginal lands. This program was under the Resettlement and Farm Security Administration. The program was abandoned in 1939 and areas purchased were turned over to other Government agencies. At least seven major refuges were established on lands secured in this manner.

These great achievements came about because of the tenacious devotion of Congressmen and private citizens who were awake to the country's conservation needs. Among them were Senators Norbeck, Key Pittman, Charles McNary, and Congressmen George Shiras III of Pennsylvania, Daniel Read Anthony of Kansas, August H. Andresen of Minnesota, and A. Willis Robertson of Virginia.

DURING THE YEARS of the Second World War, the refuge system received a serious setback. Understandably, the Congress made no further appropriations for land acquisition, and only token amounts were made available for operation and maintenance activities. Serious deterioration occurred to dikes, water controls, roads, buildings, and other facilities. Control of undesirable vegetation lagged. The overall effectiveness of many areas was reduced. Because of continued difficulties in obtaining adequate appropriations, the refuge system has not yet fully recovered from that setback.

Ironically, it was crop depredations by waterfowl that enabled the Bureau to resume land acquisition for refuge purposes. To alleviate damage to rice and other crops and disperse large concentrations of wintering waterfowl, the Congress in 1948 passed the Lea Act. It authorized the purchase of wildlife management areas on which crops could be grown and on which waterfowl could feed, rather than

in the farmers' fields. The Lea Act also provided that hunting of waterfowl could be permitted at the discretion of the Secretary of the Interior. A total of 6,900 acres, in four areas, was purchased under this plan and created the Colusa, Sutter, Merced, and Salton Sea National Wildlife Refuges.

The Duck Stamp Act in 1949 was amended to increase the cost of the duck stamp to 2 dollars to provide more funds for land acquisition. It also provided for the first time that up to 25 percent of most refuges could be opened to public hunting when the wildlife population levels permitted. The Duck Stamp Act was again amended in 1958, this time to increase the cost of a duck stamp to 3 dollars and provided that up to 40 percent of a refuge could be opened to public shooting. It also earmarked all such funds for land acquisition, especially for purchase of areas that produce waterfowl. This legislation specified the basic responsibility of the Government to be the preservation and perpetuation of the waterfowl resource but it also recognized responsibilities to sportsmen.

The years from 1948 through 1958 were sorry ones because of an agricultural progam that subsidized the drainage of potholes in the Prairie States. The amended Duck Stamp Act and legislation making drainage less attractive have eased the situation to some degree, but not enough, we think; we believe the preservation of more areas through purchase or easement is essential if waterfowling is to survive—as we now know it.

THE RESULT of all efforts from the turn of the century to 1963 has been the creation of some 289 national wildlife refuges, comprising approximately 28,560,000 acres.

They include all categories of refuges—waterfowl, colonial birds, and big game. Refuges that are managed primarily for waterfowl number 220 and include 2,589,292 acres of marsh and water. In addition, there are some 66 thousand acres of potholes and marshes, the waterfowl production areas, acquired in scattered locations in 57 counties of North Dakota, South Dakota, Minnesota, and Nebraska.

AS TO THE CONTRIBUTIONS the refuges make to the preservation of waterfowl and other wildlife: In each of the four administrative flyways are populations of birds that use refuges almost exclusively during a part of their life cycle. In the Atlantic Flyway, the entire greater snow goose population winters chiefly on four national wildlife refuges—Pea Island, Back Bay, Mackay Island, and Chincoteague.

The Mississippi Valley flock of Canada geese utilizes principally the Horicon, Crab Orchard, Reelfoot, and Tennessee Refuges and the state-owned management areas in southern Illinois and Kentucky. The large Eastern Prairie Canada goose flock concentrates on the Squaw Creek and Swan Lake Refuges in Missouri. Intensive management efforts have been started to restore a more southerly migration to such areas as the Holla Bend, Wapanocca, White River, and Yazoo Refuges in Arkansas and Mississippi.

Geese feeding on grain grown especially for them at Tule Lake National Wildlife Refuge, California.

National Wildlife Refuges in the United States are identified by the sign of the flying Canada goose.

The Canada geese of the Central Flyway utilize heavily the Lower Souris, Sand Lake, Tewaukon, Salt Plains, and Tishomingo Refuges.

In the Pacific Flyway, up to 90 percent of all waterfowl concentrates on such refuges as Bear River, the Tule Lake-Klamath Basin Refuge complex, Sacramento, Colusa, Sutter, Merced, and Delevan. The diminutive Ross' goose is especially dependent on the west coast refuges for its winter home.

ONE OF THE BEST known purposes of refuges is to save birds that have faced extinction.

The Aransas National Wildlife Refuge in Texas is the winter home of the rare whooping crane. Only 14 birds were known to exist in 1938. Their numbers have fluctuated over the years, but in 1964 there are 33 of these magnificent birds. The Canadian Government has provided protection to the whoopers on their breeding grounds. Without such refuge areas, the whooping crane would undoubtedly have disappeared. While the breeding and wintering grounds are safeguarded, the long migration route between is the most vulnerable to the whoopers' existence. Since it would be impractical to acquire all intervening areas used by these birds, the sportsmen of the United States and Canada have a vital responsibility in providing the protection needed.

The trumpeter swan in 1934 was near extinction in the United States. Only 73 birds lived in the Centennial Valley and nearby Yellowstone National Park. The Red Rock Lakes National Wildlife Refuge, established in 1935, did much to foster the comeback of the trumpeters in Montana and adjacent States. The protection and breeding habitat provided there have been so effective that we had nearly 700 trumpeters in the conterminous United States in 1964. Many public zoos throughout the country can display birds of this species through a loan program of the Bureau of Sport Fisheries and Wildlife. A transplant program, in which a small flock of swans has been moved to the Lacreek Refuge in South Dakota, provided the means whereby trumpeter swans have nested successfully east of the Rocky Mountains for the first time since pioneer days.

THE TOTAL PRODUCTION of waterfowl on national wildlife refuges is but a small part of the entire continental production, but it is a significant part. It is all the more noteworthy because much of the production is on restored tracts that ill-advised drainage and other intensified activities had removed from use by birds.

On lands that now comprise the Souris Loop Refuges in North Dakota—Upper and Lower Souris—drainage and intensive land use had destroyed highly productive marshes. After the land was acquired by the Federal Government and dikes and water control structures were built and grassland habitat restored, the refuges have been able to produce about 30 thousand ducks a year. Other examples are the Horicon

Refuge in Wisconsin, about 17 thousand; Agassiz Refuge in Minnesota, 30 thousand; Bear River in Utah, 50 thousand; Bowdoin in Montana, 25 thousand; Lower Klamath in Oregon, 40 thousand; Malheur in Oregon, 40 thousand; Tule Lake in California, 30 thousand.

WATER MANAGEMENT is an essential phase of refuge management. The national system of wildlife refuges contributes significantly toward the conservation of water resources. The management of water for ducks and geese has required the construction of hundreds of miles of dikes and canals and hundreds of water-control structures. The purpose of water manipulation is to provide the best possible nesting, feeding, and resting habitat. Closely

This brood of gadwalls on Agassiz National Wildlife Refuge, Minnesota, have not seen much of the world, but they appreciate the security of the Refuge.

allied with it is grassland management to provide nesting cover for dryland nesting duck species and secondarily for upland game birds. In managing grasslands, the refuge system provides grazing opportunities for many neighboring farmers and ranchers. The grass resource provides economic benefit to the local community; the regulated removal of grass benefits waterfowl.

Similar practices apply to timber management and to agriculture. In the case of farming, the operation is usually carried out on a share basis with cooperating neighbor farmers. Again the local economy benefits, and the refuge benefits— the latter through supplemental foods for ducks and geese. Other land use programs include sales of gravel, hay in limited quantities, harvest of furs, and so on.

Since charges are made for disposal of products from the land, the Government receives considerable revenue. A share of this revenue, 25 percent, is returned to local counties for roads and schools to offset the loss in taxes that resulted when the land was taken out of private ownership.

While the national wildlife refuges provide habitat for large numbers of the continental waterfowl, they also afford hunting for thousands of sportsmen. The 58 refuges that are open to waterfowl hunting make nearly 600 thousand acres of public shooting grounds. Fifty-nine refuges are open to big-game hunting and 50 to upland game hunting. These figures are for August 1964.

Actually, the entire refuge system is based on the precept that the wildlife on refuges is for the enjoyment of the American public. It follows, therefore, that refuges should provide for some public use. The Congress recognized the need for recreational use on refuges when it passed Public Law 87–714 (1962), the Refuge Recreational Act. It also recognized that recreation must be limited in type and scope so as not to destroy the very purpose for which the refuges were created. The Congress was so emphatic in this regard that 9 times in the Act it is stated that recreation permitted must be compatible with the primary purpose for which a refuge was established.

Recreational activities on refuges, therefore, are oriented to the enjoyment of wildlife through visitor centers, nature trails, picnic areas, hunting, and fishing. Only on a relatively few areas are swimming and boating permitted. Fewer yet are areas where camping is permitted. Since the Recreation Act is new, few changes have occurred since its passage. Plans have been made, however, for further recreational features when funds become available.

Successes, such as the saving of endangered species, saving habitat, and achieving greater production of waterfowl, point up the need for expanding the system of refuges. Expansion of the refuge system will provide better production and distribution of waterfowl, more hunting for more hunters, and more ways for Americans who are not hunters to enjoy our wildlife resources.

J. CLARK SALYER II and
FRANCIS G. GILLETT.

WOOD DUCKS

State Areas

FIGURES tell something of the great efforts of the States in managing and conserving waterfowl—the number of management areas they have (1,360 in 1961) and the acreage under their control (about 4.5 million).

Figures, though, do not disclose several essentials: The effective cooperation of State fish and game departments with other public agencies, including Uncle Sam, and private organizations and persons; their dedication and spirit; and the States' record of leadership and achievement.

As to the reservation or dedication of State land for waterfowl preservation, that record goes back to 1870, when California established the first such refuge at Lake Merritt in Oakland. This winter concentration area was the site of much of the early banding of ducks in the United States.

Other States followed suit. Connecticut established Nell's Island Refuge (now Charles E. Wheeler Refuge) in 1877. Wisconsin took action in 1891, when a part of Horicon Marsh was set aside as a duck refuge. The area, so dedicated, was marked by a boundary wire, and the closure of hunting at sunset on surrounding lands was ordered. Artificial feeding was practiced to help make the refuge more effective. Michigan gave protection to some Great Lakes marshes and other marshes along its rivers in 1891. Back Bay Refuge near Portland, Maine, was established in 1909.

Louisiana established Louisiana State Wildlife Refuge and Vermillion Parish Refuge in 1911. Minnesota gave protection in 1913 to waterfowl areas within the Superior National Forest. The acquisition of land at Sandbar Refuge was started by Vermont in 1920.

In Utah the Corinne Refuge was created in 1923. Iowa in 1925 gave protection to Round Lake. Horseshoe Lake was acquired by Illinois in 1927. Between 1929 and 1932, California set up Los Banos, Gray Lodge, Suisun, and Imperial Refuges, all vitally important wintering areas in the Pacific Flyway.

Great Island and Lord's Cove were established by Connecticut in 1931. New York created a refuge at Howlands' Island in 1932, the same year in which Rhode Island's Watchaug Refuge was started. The Tuckahoe Marshes in New Jersey were made a refuge in 1933.

IN THE BEGINNING, as the States began to concern themselves with waterfowl, emphasis was placed on protection, mostly from hunting.

The bullfrog may at times be a predator on ducklings, but it is also an important marsh resource in many Southern States.

Areas were closed to shooting for various reasons. Some were reserved as refuges to offer unmolested resting sites, others to provide supplementary foods, and some to delay migration for the improvement of local hunting. Some lands were set aside mainly to furnish enjoyment for nonhunting groups. Others were closed to shooting so as to reduce the possibility of overharvest. One or more of those objectives may have been attained on each refuge acquired.

Some of these basic objectives are still held, but the trend since 1935 has been toward the creation and management of combination refuges and public shooting grounds. This principle grew from an increased concentration of waterfowl on State and Federal refuges that were closed to hunting and an increased demand for public hunting opportunities. Under our system of public ownership of wildlife, the growth of public shooting grounds is a logical and natural development.

States and the Federal Government provide hunting opportunity on lands and waters coming under their respective jurisdictions. It is not a competitive thing. Federal areas were established primarily to assure preservation of waterfowl habitat and breeding stock, although many are opened to hunting on part of their acreage as warranted by waterfowl populations. It is clear, however, that the States have taken leadership in promoting hunting opportunity.

Even in places where hunting is done on Federal refuges, it is often managed by the State in close co-operation with Federal authorities. This role of the States is a service to hunters who pay part of the bill for restoring, preserving, and managing game in the States. Through the purchase of hunting licenses and payment of Federal excise taxes on sporting arms and ammunition, they make substantial contributions to the financing of State fish and game departments, which consequently are interested in providing opportunities to hunt on most waterfowl management areas. Without such access, thousands would have no place to hunt.

THE CONGRESS had a major part in making it possible for the States to acquire and develop areas for waterfowl. The Congress sensed the urgent need for action when it enacted the Federal Aid in Wildlife Restoration Act in 1937. This Act, commonly known as the Pittman-Robertson Act—or P.R.—provided financial help and enabled many States for the first time to finance significant wildlife restoration work.

Under authority of this legislation, the 11-percent Federal excise tax on the manufacturers' price of sporting arms and ammunition is apportioned to State fish and game departments. Funds are provided to each State on the basis of area and the number of paid license holders in relation to the total for all States.

During the first 15 years of the Pittman-Robertson program, from 1939 to 1953, 38 States acquired and improved habitat for waterfowl. Important purchases were initiated, such as Butte Lake Refuge in Colorado, Ogden Bay in Utah,

512

WATERFOWL TOMORROW

Cheyenne Bottoms in Kansas, La Joya in New Mexico, Summer Lake in Oregon, Danbury Bog in New Hampshire, Assawoman Bay in Delaware, Bayou Meto in Arkansas, Egg Island in New Jersey, Sauvie Island in Oregon, Fountain Grove and Duck Creek in Missouri, Horicon Marsh in Wisconsin, the giant Roseau Marsh in Minnesota, Stillwater in Nevada, Willow Slough in Indiana, Crex Meadows in Wisconsin, Hog Island in Virginia, Bear Island in South Carolina, Sweet Marsh in Iowa, Shiawassee in Michigan, and Little Otter Creek in Vermont. These projects, a few among many, covered large acreages. Some were developed jointly with the Bureau of Sport Fisheries and Wildlife when national wildlife refuges were established on adjacent lands.

Between 1938 and 1961, the P.R. land program moved at a rapid pace; 912,739 acres were acquired and developed by States for waterfowl.

The States have made great progress in reserving lands for waterfowl. At the end of 1961, 1,360 separate waterfowl areas, embracing more than 4,558,252 acres of land and water, were under State control.

Of this total, about 2,361,178 acres were owned, and about 2,197,074 acres were under long-term lease, easement, or agreement.

These management areas were subject to handling in various ways. Some were designated as refuges where no hunting was permitted. Some were public hunting grounds. Others were a combination of both. Over half of the total (2,471,807 acres) were open to waterfowl and other game hunting. About 44 percent (1,983,927 acres) of the total project acreage provided some waterfowl habitat, chiefly in the form of open waters, wet meadows, swamps, flooded timber, marshes, cropland, and pastureland.

The 14 states in the Mississippi Flyway led in the acquisition of management areas; 772 of them totaled 2,339,158 acres. Many were small marshes acquired primarily for production. Two-thirds of the areas (1,754,629 acres) were owned and one-third (584,529 acres) were leased. The Atlantic Flyway States had 137 areas totaling 1,023,015 acres; the Pacific Flyway States, 71 areas and 635,649 acres; and the Central Flyway States, 380 areas and 560,430 acres.

Florida has the greatest acreage of management lands with 740,300 acres under its control, but most of the land was under long-term lease and only a part of it was valuable to waterfowl.

Louisiana with 562,410 acres, more than half of it owned in fee, was in second place. Minnesota had the largest number of management areas, 360. Based on actual State ownership, Michigan held the greatest area, 370,926 acres; followed by Wisconsin, 332,572 acres; Louisiana, 264,310 acres; Minnesota, 256,144 acres; and Arkansas, 177,705 acres. These States are in the Mississippi Flyway.

Some State waterfowl projects have been superimposed on other projects, such as those built to control floods, store water, or produce hydroelectric power. Long-term lease or license arrangements with construction agencies have permitted State fish and game departments to build waterfowl habitat on such projects as subsidiary developments. These included construction of satellite areas or subimpoundments, and the planting of food crops in or adjacent to the impoundment basin.

The Congress opened the door to this progressive approach for gaining multiple benefits from public projects by passing the Fish and Wildlife Coordination Act of 1934. Water projects sponsored by the Corps of Engineers, the U.S. Bureau of Reclamation, and other Federal agencies will henceforth include, where practicable, consideration for migratory waterfowl and other wildlife values.

Since the Act was passed, 557 thousand acres of public waters have been brought under limited State management to help ducks and geese. Not all State waterfowl projects are of large acreage. Opportunities to acquire tracts of several thousand acres are becoming scarce, and high prices discourage action on those still available.

Many States, especially those in the North, are giving increasing attention to small projects. Iowa, South Dakota, Minnesota, Wisconsin, Maine, New York, New Hampshire, Vermont, Connecticut, and Rhode Island have made notable progress. Minnesota, up to 1961,

A waste piece of swampy land in Michigan is converted into a productive area for waterfowl by building a dam and a water control structure.

had acquired more than 100 thousand acres of small wetlands on more than 360 management areas. The purchases were made so that the land would not be drained and to provide hunting opportunities.

IN DEVELOPING some tracts, States have used more than conventional engineering to create habitat of great value for waterfowl. For example, maximum use was made of a limited water supply at Ogden Bay Refuge in Utah by the construction of dams, canals, and water controls. Before development, the water was shallow and the refuge had serious outbreaks of botulism, a virulent disease of ducks. After development, the deeper water produced an abundance of food plants, attracted ducks, geese, and swans, and provided good hunting. Botulism hazard was greatly reduced, and tens of thousands of ducks were saved. The key improvement in the Cheyenne Bottoms in Kansas provided supplemental water to a 19-thousand acre marsh by way of a diversion canal from Walnut Creek and the Arkansas River. It is now an important area in the Central Flyway.

Another State waterfowl project came into being through international cooperation. Roseau Marsh in Minnesota was watered by digging a diversion ditch from Pine Creek in the adjacent Canadian Province of Manitoba. At Summer Lake in Oregon a dwindling lake level was restored by means of diversions, canals, and low dikes to make 6,500 acres of marsh highly productive for waterfowl.

THE ABILITY of land and waters to produce and support waterfowl is a changeable thing, and the development and management of habitat are a large part of State waterfowl programs.

Brackish or saline marshes often are extensive, but they may be of low quality. Diking to hold fresher water along the upland edge has greatly improved productivity of both Atlantic coastal marshes and western alkaline sump areas.

Many States in the Midwest and Northeast have created large numbers of small, shallow waterfowl marshes. In most of them, provision has been made to control water levels to permit maximum production of waterfowl food and cover. In the Northeast, most of the small projects are on private land under long lease to the State. New York has built nearly a thousand small marshes.

Throughout the country, State-sponsored research and experiments have helped show the way for improving and maintaining waterfowl habitat. Improving low-quality wetlands has been a major objective of research in some States. Northern bogs and marshes that have a high water table but little or no permanent open water to attract waterfowl can be improved by level ditching and making potholes. Channels with gently sloping sides have been dug on such sites; open water and food-growing ability have

Ducks produced in the Nebraska sandhills join their migrating cousins for the flight to warmer areas to the South.

been provided thereby. Wisconsin has pioneered in this type of effort. The technique has been applied by North Central and Northeastern States.

REHABILITATION of marshes and water areas is a feature of activities in some States. The control of pest plants, such as waterchestnut and water-hyacinth, and the planting of waterfowl foods are examples. Extensive clearing to develop goose pastures and aerial sowing of rye-grass on mud flats has helped geese in numerous places. Ducks have benefited from numerous plantings of aquatics and farm crops.

Shoreline fencing on hundreds of management areas has protected nesting grounds from trampling by cattle and has added greatly to production of young ducks. Artificial nesting platforms for geese and nesting boxes for wood ducks have enhanced the reproduction of these species.

State projects have benefited wildlife besides ducks and geese. Northern marshes provide excellent winter cover and sanctuary for pheasants and rabbits. Some southern areas shelter more localized forms of wildlife, such as alligators. Many areas support abundant sport fish and add to the prime fishing grounds for public enjoyment. These side benefits promise to grow in value as demands for outdoor recreation increase.

Action by the States to help preserve waterfowl as an important recreational resource has come none too soon. Habitat has been lost as high prices for crops and new

methods and machines have stimulated drainage of marshes. Hunting clubs have removed tracts from public use. The acquisition and development programs of States have helped reserve lands for public hunting.

THE STATE ACTIVITIES we have described do not fit into a master plan, a prescribed program. Although much of the effort has been directed at preservation, it is natural for a State to consider first the hunting interests of its own residents. Therein lies a problem in national management of waterfowl.

The States must share with Canada and Mexico (with whom the United States has treaties pertaining to migratory birds) a migratory waterfowl resource that is produced largely in Canada and winters chiefly in the United States and Mexico. What one State does in acquiring and developing areas for waterfowl hunting may profoundly affect hunting in a neighboring State. Because only so many birds come down the flyways, the duration of their stay in any State depends largely on the quality and quantity of the habitat available to them. Managed land and water projects can change ancestral patterns of waterfowl distribution. Several millions of acres of State lands are now managed specifically for hunting waterfowl and there are more to come. The result is a growing interstate problem on how best to share the waterfowl resources.

An illustration of the effect of activities in one place on other States: During the forties, management of

Maryland Game and Inland Fish Commission men on waterchestnut control operation, Upper Chesapeake Bay. Control of this pest plant requires perpetual vigilance.

This "gut plug" on Deal Island in Maryland controls the level of water on a tidal marsh when the tide is out.

Horseshoe Lake Refuge in southern Illinois resulted in a large portion of the Canada geese in the Mississippi Flyway stopping there. Excessive harvest reduced the flyway population to a point that the season had to be closed in 1946. During the fifties, Horicon Refuge in Wisconsin was intensively managed for geese, and by the late fifties many of the Mississippi Flyway flock stopped there for a longer period than usual during the fall. An effective system of harvesting the birds at Horicon was developed by manipulating habitat, adjusting the location of hunting sites, and establishing rest periods. Beginning in 1960, area kill quotas were established on the hunting areas around Horicon and Horseshoe Lake Refuges to control the harvest of Canada geese so as to maintain desired population levels.

In short, the distribution of many species of waterfowl, including the mallard, can be manipulated to a marked degree by acquiring and managing habitat, and setting rules or regulations for hunting. What is needed is a high degree of cooperative effort to synchronize, in all parts of a flyway, various management plans so that the distribution of birds will be more equitable. We need forbearance, also. That should not be overly difficult for the men and women in the States who by cooperation, leadership, and plain hard work already have done so much in managing waterfowl and conserving habitat for waterfowl tomorrow. Beyond that, how well the needs of waterfowl and the wishes of sportsmen are met will depend in large measure on the funds and manpower resources that the States and Federal Government can muster for the purpose.—SAMUEL E. JORGENSEN, J. THOMAS STEINER, and DONALD F. LA POINTE.

AMERICAN COOTS

Private Duck Clubs

WATERFOWL in quest of living space can often find it on private marshland. While seeking it, some get shot. The number killed in relation to the benefit received by the overall population is a rough measure of the value of such marshlands to waterfowl.

Duck clubs vary in this respect. Some are out-and-out drains on the resource and contribute nothing. At the other extreme, some clubs, due to geographic location, physical features, and interest on the part of the club members, are veritable refuges; providing wintering, breeding, resting, and feeding habitat.

Six thousand private duck clubs in 48 States manage 3 million acres and have 130 thousand acres in refuges. The figures are estimates, because they vary somewhat from year to year, but we can say as fact, not estimate, that they perform functions not possible under governmental ownership.

One is to provide habitat, and that is being done in a notable way by clubs in Florida, Ohio, Illinois, Arkansas, Louisiana, Texas, and California. Another is to limit the number of guns per acre and with it the kill.

An example is the western Lake Erie marshes, which are largely privately owned. Reducing the bag limit from 4 to 2 there cut the total harvest practically in half. No such reduction in kill occurred along the Ohio River or its tributaries, where public hunting is prevalent. Nor did reducing the bag limit have much effect on the kill at the State-owned marshes. If this is generally true over all the flyways, then the effect of regulations on total kill is influenced by the proportion of marshlands under club management.

Two excellent waterfowl marshes on Lake Erie became public shooting areas near the close of the Second World War. At the Pointe Mouillee Marsh in Michigan, the increased shooting pressure resulted in a higher kill in the first 2 days than at private clubs during the entire season. Despite added restrictions on shooting hours and other control, furthermore, public shooting at Magee Marsh in Ohio accounts for more waterfowl in a season than the combined kill of three neighboring clubs of similar or larger size. We have indications that management of species may be more practical on private than on public shooting grounds because, for one reason, the members very likely can identify fowl more accurately than the generality of hunters.

THE BEST DUCK HUNTING is usually on wintering grounds. The birds are available longer, and the hunter is less dependent on the uncertainties of weather and migration than

he is in other sections of a flyway. Duck clubs therefore are most numerous on the wintering grounds.

An example is California, the main wintering ground for waterfowl in the Pacific Flyway. We estimate that the 5 million acres of wetlands California once had have dwindled because of agriculture, industry, and urbanization to about 500 thousand acres, of which about 300 thousand acres are in private ownership (mostly duck clubs). The rest is in State and Federal waterfowl areas.

Because these private lands are a large part of the wintering grounds, their importance to waterfowl is apparent. Their accomplishments parallel those of State and Federal waterfowl areas. They preserve habitat, control depredations on agricultural crops, and provide hunting.

Pintails find the club grounds especially attractive, because the grounds, when flooded, float up abundant seeds and insects. During the fifties, before there were enough public areas to accommodate depredating ducks, artificial feeding of grain was done on public and private lands. Now, with more public waterfowl areas, and more food raised on duck clubs, the depredation problem is being controlled by natural means.

At the start of the hunting season, clubs use management practices that improve hunting and benefit the resource at the same time. Larger clubs that can spare the acreage, set aside refuges where the birds are not molested. Surveys of waterfowl population in fall and winter show that some duck clubs

The stock accessories of a well-equipped midwestern duck hunter are a punt, a pole, decoys, shotgun, and retriever. With a pocketful of shells this hunter is prepared for a full day of hunting.

in the Butte Sink of the Sacramento Valley consistently hold more birds than State or Federal waterfowl preserves. Nearly all duck clubs hunt only on traditional shooting days of Wednesday, Saturday, and Sunday; many shoot only on weekends. During nonshooting days, waterfowl make good use of the entire duck club.

Clubs perform a salient function after the hunting season closes. Waterfowl then spread out from refuges and rest areas to take advantage of all habitats. Usually winter rains have provided additional water, and the wintering grounds reach their peak condition. Some clubs also furnish nesting habitat, but the number of nesting ducks is small compared to the millions of wintering birds.

Most clubs want to improve habitat but lack of water for large-scale developments. Nearly all of the rain in California comes in winter, and plant growth depends on irrigation the rest of the year. In some parts of the State, water becomes available to duck clubs at a reduced price after agricultural crops are harvested. In other localities, clubs may obtain irrigation drain water. Still others depend on wells, but usually pumping costs are so high that water is impounded only during the hunting season.

The designation of water specifically for the use of wildlife is a new development. An example of how duck clubs have prevented the

destruction of valuable waterfowl habitat is the effort of duck clubs of the Grasslands Water District in California. When Friant Dam was built to hold back waters of the San Joaquin River, the Bureau of Reclamation bought water rights below the dam. Such action threatened the existence of the clubs, which depend on the San Joaquin for their water. Considerable negotiation preceded the introduction of the Grasslands Bill, which Congress enacted in 1954 as Public Law 674. It reauthorized the Central Valley project with consideration for fish and wildlife and, of most importance to the Grasslands Duck Clubs, provided water for waterfowl purposes.

Provisions for fish and wildlife are also a part of the California water plan. As water is distributed into new districts of the State, plans are made to use the drainwater for wildlife. Drainwater that has be-

A good retriever, like this Labrador, brings birds to the hunter that might otherwise be lost in the marsh. Watching a well-trained hunting dog work is an important part of the sport of waterfowling.

come too alkaline for further agricultural use will still grow plants for waterfowl food. Such water can be a boon to duck clubs that can ill afford to buy high-priced well water.

Duck clubs preserve and maintain valuable habitat, but the primary purpose is to furnish hunting. Without the incentives of reasonable seasons and bag limits, many would quit operating. Their lands lose their high value and are then converted to other uses. More waterfowl habitat is thus lost. Because State and Federal agencies can never hope to own and manage enough habitat to insure waterfowl populations adequate for hunting or bird-watching, private landowners must be encouraged in every practical way, short of overharvesting, to preserve their waterfowl habitat.

Our figures on the numbers and acreages of clubs are based on questionnaires sent to the States in 1963. Relatively few States have made detailed inventories of such private holdings and statistics which follow are estimates in many instances.

CLUBS IN THE PACIFIC FLYWAY manage a significant proportion of the habitat. In California, a thousand clubs manage 300 thousand acres, and have 15 thousand acres in refuges. In Washington, 500 clubs control about 20 thousand acres. In Oregon, 500 clubs manage 15 thousand acres. Four clubs in Arizona control about 200 acres. In Utah, 40 clubs have about 37 thousand acres, about 10 percent of it in refuges. Nevada has 15 clubs

which manage 55 thousand acres. Four clubs in Idaho manage 1,500 acres.

IN THE CENTRAL FLYWAY, Texas has about 500 clubs, which control about 500 thousand acres; 50 thousand acres are in refuges. Colorado's estimates are 350 clubs, 30 thousand acres, a thousand in refuge. Others are Kansas, 60 clubs, 4,800 acres; Oklahoma, 25 clubs, 6 thousand acres; Montana, 20 clubs, 2 thousand acres; and Wyoming, 20 clubs, 2 thousand acres. North Dakota, South Dakota, Nebraska, and New Mexico have few clubs.

IN THE ATLANTIC FLYWAY, New York has about 90 clubs, with 25 thousand acres. Clubs in New Jersey number about 60 and own about 10 thousand acres. Maryland leads the flyway in number of clubs, with about 380, which control 55 thousand acres. Virginia has 100 clubs, with 30 thousand acres in duck marsh and 10 thousand in goose management. In Pennsylvania, about 25 clubs control 20 thousand acres. Clubs in North Carolina number between 75 and 100 and manage 150 thousand acres, with at least 5 thousand in refuge. In South Carolina, 14 clubs cover 70 thousand acres, and set aside 10 thousand acres for refuge. Florida has about 20 clubs, with 2,800 acres and 300 in refuges.

IN THE MISSISSIPPI FLYWAY, Louisiana leads the Nation with about a thousand clubs and 1.5 million acres. About 600 Illinois duck clubs manage 100 thousand acres, with 20

Fact-finding on waterfowl involves cooperation on a broad front. Here an Ohio Game Management agent consults about waterfowl problems with a private duck club manager.

thousand acres in refuge. About 150 goose clubs in Illinois maintain 15 thousand acres of wintering habitat. Culture of domestic rice has brought significant changes to the wintering habitat in Arkansas. Many duck clubs in the Grande Prairie region also serve as reservoirs from which water may be drawn for rice production. Some 350 clubs manage more than 100 thousand acres of marsh. They all pump water and in dry years often have an advantage over nonclub hunters. In average years, however, there is enough overflow to furnish hunting for those who do not belong to clubs. In fact, the open hunting often is better than on club lands,

mainly because of the available food in the hardwood bottoms.

More than a dozen clubs in Michigan have about 9 thousand acres. Estimates for other States are: Indiana, 7 clubs, 7 thousand acres, a thousand in refuge; Mississippi, 25 clubs, 25 thousand acres, 10 percent in refuge; and Ohio, 20 clubs, 30 thousand acres, 4 thousand in refuge.

Few clubs have holdings in Wisconsin. Some of the finest marshes in Minnesota would have been drained long ago were it not for the interest of private individuals. About 400 clubs in Minnesota manage 40 thousand acres, all of which provide fine places for breeding and spring migration. No estimates are available for Iowa, Kentucky, Missouri, and Alabama. In Tennessee, 28 duck clubs manage 10,624 acres of marsh; 8 clubs have 900 acres of goose areas.

WE THINK the contribution that duck clubs make and can make has not been appreciated fully by the Federal Government, the States, and the clubs themselves.

One reason may be the occasional violations of bag limits or ban on baiting—something that may happen elsewhere as well. In fact, among well-established clubs in Minnesota, Illinois, Ohio, and California, some of which have existed for a century or more, a constitution, by-laws, or unwritten laws demand the members adhere to the letter to regulations, which may be more restrictive than Government regulations.

On the other hand, individuals or groups sometimes acquire and exploit properties near a public or private refuge. Baiting and other violations may occur there, and the resource would be better off without them. They usually are fly-by-night operations, but the public may consider them to be clubs.

Sometimes a reason for less than full cooperation between duck clubs and professional waterfowl managers has been the Government's preoccupation with acquiring its own wildfowl management areas, conducting its own research programs, and developing and enforcing regulations. All that may tax Government personnel to the utmost.

In California, State game technicians and Federal conservation workers encourage duck clubs to improve the habitat by properly regulating the use of water, raising aquatic foods, and controlling undesirable cattails and tules. Clubs are also informed by these advisory groups as to the type of plantings most likely to succeed in California. In two Soil Conservation districts, nearly every member is a duck club owner. Another district is being formed in an area dominated by duck clubs. State and Federal technicians stand ready to help marsh managers who request it. We suggest that waterfowl managers would do well to observe the accomplishments of modern scientific farming—whether on farms, on the land-grant college campus, or the laboratory—and the programs of information and extension to encourage better land management and conservation. The management of aquatic environments offers many of these same opportunities, even though the basic knowledge is not nearly so complete as for farmland.

The lack of technical guidance in wildlife programs on private lands is not a fault alone of public technicians and scientists and other professional people. It is, rather that people who entrust the health and education of their families to specialists in medicine and education and employ lawyers, accountants, and engineers in their business, for guidance on the management of wildlife, turn to guides who have never been out of their county of residence or to hunters and amateurs of wide hunting experience but no knowledge of the food habits, breeding requirements, disease, and other factors by which ducks live and die.

Some duck clubs have an investment of nearly a million dollars, with annual maintenance budgets of 50 thousand dollars. An enterprise of that magnitude certainly warrants professional consultation and management. It is gratifying that in recent years biologists have become established as private consultants specializing in waterfowl management.

We know of many examples of privately held land that have been developed or improved for waterfowl under professional guidance. Examples are the King Ranch and the Welder Wildlife Foundation lands in Texas; Lake Scugog in Ontario; Kenneth Sather's project at Round Lake in Minnesota; the Valente Club in California, the Winous Point and Ottawa Clubs in

Ohio, and the Erie Club in Michigan. There are others.

Most management efforts have been aimed at improving the carrying capacity during hunting season. Clubs in the northern row of States have begun to place more emphasis on production. One, for instance, is the Winous Point Club, where research has been done on methods of increasing production through artificial nesting structures and introducing new breeding colonies of ducks and geese.

As waterfowl habitat continues to yield to the runaway growth of human populations, the preservation of high-quality areas becomes of increasing importance. Most private club properties are basically top grade. They are capable of improvement even beyond their present good status—not only as maintenance areas during the hunting season but over most of the year. And some could function effectively as production areas as well. Public agencies would do well to encourage the holding and intensive development of private lands. The needs of waterfowl are great and growing; the problem is bigger than can be met by public agencies working alone.—JOHN M. ANDERSON and FRANK M. KOZLIK.

Have no doubt about it, the time has arrived when we must manage specifically for anything we want from the land. Every acre is being watched by someone with a single interest. Our renewable resources will be renewed only if we understand their requirements and plan it that way.
—DURWARD L. ALLEN.

SNOW GEESE

They Also Serve

OUT OF THEIR LOVE for living things, American citizens and public-spirited organizations over the years have created private sanctuaries for wildlife.

Many are no larger than fair-sized backyards. Others rival in size the biggest national wildlife refuges. Some seek to protect only one or a few species, although usually they provide food and living quarters for many others. Some, mostly the early ones that antedated the creation of the national wildlife refuges, have only incidental values for waterfowl. Many established later, have considerable value to ducks and geese and preserve important local blocks of wetland habitat. Many provide transitory benefits. Others have great national significance and are

as old and as secure as any State or national wildlife refuge.

How many there are we do not know. Their number changes constantly. Many, by their nature and purpose, do not enter public records or seek publicity.

We do know their great public value. Some are well-planned centers for research that can be conducted nowhere else. Some provide community demonstrations of the effectiveness of intelligent protection of living things and their habitat. Some serve to educate and interest students and citizens of the neighborhood and give satisfaction to their sponsors and friends.

Some, particularly the smaller ones, are little more than inviolate sanctuaries—areas posted against

527

trespass and hunting and permitted to remain in a natural state. Others may be managed intensively.

Many farms and ranches are waterfowl sanctuaries in fact if not in name. Some owners permit no hunting at all. Others restrict hunting privileges to a few individuals or to a small part of their property. Even some of the duck hunting clubs so limit the hunting on their properties that most of their lands are essentially refuges. Some maintain inviolate sanctuaries on their holdings as attractants to ducks and geese.

Of this diversity of kinds and purposes, we mention, as examples, a few of the areas that we ourselves know.

The National Audubon Society, whose offices are at 1130 Fifth Avenue, New York, has an ambitious program of refuges, which include many waterfowl sanctuaries. Scattered over the United States, they protect valuable wetlands vital to wildlife preservation. Audubon sanctuaries with warden protection extend over more than 1 million acres of land and water. Some are crucial to the survival of rare birds. Others protect attractive wild environments and serve to help educate the public to the value of natural areas.

The Society maintains four Audubon Centers—in Greenwich, Conn.; Sharon, Conn.; Dayton, Ohio; and El Monte, Calif. The centers are used to train teachers and youth leaders through personal experiences with Nature. A more recent program, the Nature Centers Program, promotes the creation of community-owned-and-operated areas for nature study by school children and youth organizations. The Society provides technical assistance in planning and organizing the centers.

The Society's Richardson's Bay Sanctuary in Marin County and the sanctuaries near Redwood City and Newark in the San Francisco Bay area of California provide havens and food for thousands of ducks and geese each year.

The 26-thousand-acre Rainey Refuge near Abbeville in Louisiana is administered as a sanctuary for all forms of wildlife. It lies in the heart of a major wintering ground for ducks and geese of many species and has great value for waterfowl.

A number of Audubon refuges in Florida, especially those of Kissimmee Prairie, Lake Okeechobee, and a number of small units in the Tampa Bay district, were established primarily to protect ibises, storks, herons, egrets, and rare species like the limpkin, or threatened birds of prey like the everglades kite. They also furnish winter homes for large numbers of teal, wood ducks, and other northern waterfowl.

Some Audubon refuges are owned in fee simple. Others are controlled under lease for varying periods.

The Nature Conservancy vigorously promotes the survey and protection of natural areas with various objectives in view. This nonprofit membership corporation cooperates with colleges, universities, and public and private organizations to acquire natural areas for scientific and educational purposes. Many of the tracts protected by it are in forest or grassland. Some have great value for waterfowl.

One of the most important is the

Buena Vista Lagoon in California, between Oceanside and Carlsbad. The widespread destruction of marshes in southern California has increased the value of this remaining bit of habitat. The area is still threatened by real estate and development promoters of the sort who think primarily in terms of quick profit.

At least eight other tracts containing potholes, marshes, or other lands of value to waterfowl have been saved by this group. The Nature Conservancy has fought to preserve a number of natural areas that highways, real estate developments, and ill-advised zoning in the name of "progress" have tried to obliterate forever.

Offices of the Nature Conservancy are at 2039 K Street, N.W., Washington, D.C.

AMONG THE BETTER KNOWN private refuge areas is the Jack Miner Sanctuary in Kingsville, Ontario, near the north shore of Lake Erie.

Something to honk about! Family scenes, like this one on Remington Farms near Chestertown, Maryland, are becoming increasingly common as interest in establishing free-flying goose flocks grows.

Jack Miner was a self-educated naturalist who began life as a farmer, trapper, and hunter. Soon after the turn of the century, he developed an interest in protecting waterfowl and converted his family farm into a sanctuary for ducks. Later, geese were attracted to the artificial ponds that he constructed on his property. In 1909, he scratched his name and address on a scrap of aluminum and placed it on the leg of a wild black duck. The band was returned by a hunter in North Carolina the following year.

This was the beginning of an extensive private banding program. Mr. Miner began trapping waterfowl in earnest on his ponds and releasing them with bands bearing his name and a verse of scripture. By the time of his death in 1944 the Jack Miner Sanctuary was attracting thousands of visitors and bird students, who came to observe the flocks of Canada geese and other waterfowl which congregate there in spectacular numbers.

Since the death of its founder, the sanctuary has been administered by the Jack Miner Foundation under the direction of his sons, Manly and Jasper. It is supported by private contributions. The sanctuary furnishes an important haven for many of the Canada geese that travel the Atlantic and Mississippi Flyways.

Lockhart Gaddy was another hunter who, like Jack Miner, developed an interest in waterfowl that transcended his love for shooting. In 1934, when live decoys were outlawed, Mr. Gaddy released his six pinioned callers on a one-acre pond newly constructed on his large farm near Ansonville, North Carolina. As wild geese began to join the domesticated birds on his pond, Gaddy began feeding them as a hobby. Four years later there were hundreds. By the time of his death in 1953, he had extended the size of his pond to 4 acres and was feeding between 10 thousand and 12 thousand Canada geese and several thousand ducks of many species each winter. Occasional blue snow, and white-fronted geese visit the area.

Since the death of Mr. Gaddy Gaddy Pond, the heart of the Lockhart Gaddy Refuge, has been maintained by Mrs. Gaddy.

A. B. Williams founded a similar refuge for geese on the James River below Richmond, Va., in 1924. He maintained it for many years and willed it to the Fish and Wildlife Service. It is now Presquile National Wildlife Refuge. As a fine example of private initiative in providing food, cover, and sanctuary, Mr. Williams built up a flock of more than 3 thousand Canada geese and a large population of mallards, pintails, black ducks, and wood ducks. Since his death, the area has continued to grow in value to waterfowl. It now furnishes winter habitat for about three times the number of ducks and geese that used it before it came under Federal management.

A major part of Troy Meadows in New Jersey is owned by Wildlife Preserves, Inc., a private organization, and until 1963 was operated under an agreement with the Fish and Wildlife Service. It is one of the most valuable pieces of marsh-land still remaining in the State.

Just south of Troy Meadows in Morristown is the Great Swamp, an area of about 5 thousand acres within 25 miles of New York. Citizens, through the North American Wildlife Foundation of Washington, D.C., have purchased more than 2,500 acres. The land has been deeded to the Fish and Wildlife Service as a perpetual wildlife area. The rest remains to be acquired and added to this unit. Considerable numbers of wood ducks, black ducks, and other waterfowl use it. Its location, in one of the most densely populated sections of America, may make it one of the great conservation-education centers of the country. That is the hope of the public-spirited Americans who have contributed nearly a million dollars to preserve it.

The King Ranch in southern Texas is not considered a wildlife refuge, but we mention it as an example of wildlife values that can accrue to the public from a private area. Many species of game and nongame birds, mammals, and other vertebrate life exist there because of its location and its varied habitat. The variety and high populations of the different species are a source of pleasure to the public as well as to workers on the King Ranch and to conservationists.

Some of the largest concentrations of ducks and geese in the Southwest are there. When rainfall is normal, Laguna Largo is one of the finest waterfowl wintering areas in the country. Deer, wild turkey, sandhill cranes, javelinas, quail, and

a great variety of nongame species abound. Innumerable shore birds and wading birds inhabit the long lagoons and mudflats on the shore of the Gulf and Laguna Madre and the peripheries of the many ponds and lakes of the million-acre King Ranch. It is indeed a paradise for wildlife.

Many other large ranches of the Southwest and West have great value as private wildlife sanctuaries, although few are managed under the scientific principles of wildlife conservation practiced on the King Ranch. Millions of acres of private holdings, however, provide almost complete protection for wildlife because of management policies. Wherever they contain marshes or water, they offer resting and feeding areas and breeding and wintering habitat for waterfowl.

JAMAICA BAY has about 12 thousand acres of shallow-water marsh and small islands. It is on the doorstep of metropolitan New York. It furnishes habitat and sanctuary to many kinds of wildlife, principally shore birds and waterfowl. During the fall, early winter, and spring, there are large concentrations of brant, black ducks, mallards, and green-winged teal. The deeper waters harbor large rafts of scaup and other diving ducks. It is adjacent to John F. Kennedy International Airport and is operated by the New York City Park Department. Its accessibility makes it of major educational value, and many local nature clubs, schools, and youth groups conduct tours there.

Tinicum Wildlife Refuge in Philadelphia is another important sanctuary for waterfowl that is administered as part of a metropolitan park system. It was saved from destruction through the efforts of a public-spirited group of local citizens organized as Philadelphia Conservationists, Incorporated. The 200-acre freshwater marsh is heavily used by black ducks, teal, and mallards, and attracts many species of shore birds. A resident manager encourages public visits and conducts tours of the area.

Lake Merritt, a tiny waterfowl refuge in the heart of Oakland, Calif., is the oldest wildlife sanctuary in North America. One Samuel Merritt is said to have bought the land soon after the Gold Rush and to have enlarged the small slough that then existed on it by damming a stream. The California legislature around 1869 passed a bill making Lake Merritt a State Refuge. The city later acquired it and has maintained it ever since.

Lake Merritt is a stopping place for thousands of pintails, canvasback, widgeon, geese, and other wintering migratory waterfowl. Banding operations have been carried out there for many years.

The Andrew Clark Refuge in Santa Barbara, Calif., comprises 45 acres. Originally established in 1928 as a private sanctuary by Mr. Clark

A manmade marsh on a private ranch in California. Excellent growths of marsh and aquatic vegetation useful to waterfowl are produced here.

it was later acquired by the city, which now administers it. It is near the ocean and attracts a large number and variety of water birds. To many persons it gives great educational benefits and enjoyment, and to the rest of us an example of two facts—that an area rich in wildlife, regardless of size, can be a place of great public value and that it can be developed and maintained at a modest cost.

A growing number of small cities and towns are making their communities into bird sanctuaries. Many furnish habitat for small birds and, if they contain water areas, for waterfowl at times.

Some cities and coastal towns in Florida and North Carolina have considerable areas of water and make a point of attracting waterfowl during the winter season.

THE DELTA Waterfowl Research Station at the south end of Lake Manitoba in Canada provides nesting habitat and feeding grounds for many migratory birds, although it is operated primarily as a waterfowl research center.

The Delta Station was started in 1931 when James Ford Bell, Minneapolis industrialist, established facilities for waterfowl research at the edge of the famous Delta Marsh, 75 miles northwest of Winnipeg. A few years later, Mr. Bell drew up a plan of cooperation with the North American Wildlife Foundation and subsequently donated the original buildings and land to the Foundation, which has greatly expanded and improved the facilities. Many people have contributed funds with which to erect additional buildings and purchase more land since that time and to help finance the research studies that are carried on there each year. Although the station is owned by the North American Wildlife Foundation of Washington, D.C., it is operated cooperatively by the Wildlife Management Institute.

The Delta Station is in one of the largest pristine marshes in the Canadian Wheat Belt. The marsh covers about 95 square miles and is one of the finest waterfowl breeding areas on the Canadian prairies.

Ten species of ducks—mallard, gadwall, blue-winged teal, shoveler, pintail, redhead, canvasback, lesser scaup, white-winged scoter, and ruddy duck—breed there regularly. A few American widgeon, green-winged teal, and common goldeneye nest there, and also are present as migrants. During the autumn months nearly all species of ducks, geese, and swans of North America may be seen passing through the Delta Marshes on migration. Fair-sized local populations of Canada geese have been re-established through the release of birds propagated in the Station hatchery.

Remington Farms is an outstanding wildlife management demonstration area near Chestertown, in Kent County, Maryland. It comprises some 3 thousand acress of farmland on a peninsula. It has about 5 miles of tidewater frontage from two tributaries of Chesapeake Bay. The adjacent tidal waters and 20 freshwater ponds and lakes, appropriate plantings, and good land management create an excellent habitat for waterfowl. It exemplifiies what can be done by intelligent leadership

*The scene is at Remington Farms in Maryland where a dike is being built that will
impound water for ducks.*

and planning and the use of simple
and relatively inexpensive, but
sound, wildlife management techniques.

The property is a wildlife demonstration area, but its administrative
personnel are involved in many activities. It shows that good land management, which builds up soil,
increases fertility, prevents erosion,
and preserves ground water, is a
sound procedure for building agricultural and wildlife production. All
land use on the farms is based on
soil capabilities determined by scientific studies.

The project renders a great public
service through its demonstrations,
research, and educational programs,
and by providing highly productive
wildlife habitat. The wildlife pro-

gram at Remington Farms started in
1956 and already has made valuable
contributions. Its educational work
consists of demonstrations of successful and economic land-management
procedures, public lectures, training
of youth groups, and publications.

The Rob and Bessie Welder Wildlife Foundation and Refuge were
established by a devise in the will
of the late Rob Welder which provided that a "small" part of his
extensive cattle ranch be dedicated
to "wildlife research and education." The Refuge has some 7,800
acres and is 30 miles north of
Corpus Christi, Tex. Welder's will
provided that the income of the
property be used to support the
Refuge and its program. From 400
to 500 head of cattle regularly

graze the property. The area also contains a few oil wells whose royalties finance the operations of the Foundation.

The soils are fertile. Because of variations in soil types and topography, the Refuge supports a rich flora and fauna. Deer, wild turkey, quail, waterfowl, javelina, coyotes, bobcats, and a great variety of nongame birds, mammals, and other vertebrates are abundant.

Unique research on wildlife and related fields of land use is conducted by a small staff of scientists and a few graduate students who are working for higher degrees at several universities and have fellowships that permit them to spend part of their time at Welder.

Important educational work is carried on by lectures, publications, and visits of groups of university and other students and pupils, Scouts, and groups of citizens, who observe wildlife in its natural habitat.

The 500-acre Kellogg Bird Sanctuary near Battle Creek, Mich., owned and operated as a research station and educational center by Michigan State University, was established in 1927 by W. H. Kellogg, a manufacturer of breakfast cereals. It is used extensively for important research in wildlife problems by the staff and students of the University. Its ponds and lakes are heavily used by wood ducks, black ducks, and other waterfowl.

Sapsucker Woods, the Cornell University Laboratory of Ornithology at Ithaca, N.Y., is comparable in principles and objectives. It has many species of land birds and waterfowl. The laboratory is known for its research on bird songs, photography, and physiological relations of birds.

THERE ARE dozens of other private wildlife sanctuaries that we might have mentioned. Many of the State Audubon Societies, like those of Massachusetts and Connecticut, maintain excellent areas which are outstanding educational units that provide permanent refuge values for waterfowl. The Erie and Winous Point Shooting Clubs of Ohio are conducting outstanding research programs on parts of their extensive holdings on the shores of Lake Erie. Private sanctuaries of varying size. are found throughout North America. Some have significance and value only to local communities. Others make a major contribution to the preservation of waterfowl flights of the entire continent.

Wherever they are, on the seashores of Florida, the shores of the Great Lakes, the marshes of New England, or the lakes of the Northwest, these private sanctuaries are precious assets. What they do is silver. The spirit out of which they grew is gold.—CLARENCE COTTAM and IRA N. GABRIELSON.

COMMON GOLDENEYE
HEN AND BROOD

Survival of the Species
In Canada

TWO THOUGHTS lie behind the modern concept of wildlife refuges; the first is the idea of sanctuary. Any creature much sought after by hunters must have areas where it is safe and undisturbed. The purposes of sanctuaries are to limit the harvest of the species concerned and thus promote their long-term welfare, and to serve as reservoirs from which surplus stocks may emerge. The second idea is that of the preserve. The environment of the species is necessary for its survival; the essential elements of the environment must therefore be preserved.

The sanctuary idea is an old one. It sprang from the belief that hunting is one of the most important factors influencing the numbers of game. The concept is not always valid. Sanctuaries are required when hunting pressure reaches the point where it has a continuing adverse effect upon local populations.

The need for habitat preserves has been less readily recognized. Only since man began intensive exploitation and modification of his environment has it become clear that many species of wildlife can exist only within a rather narrow range of conditions. If we are to preserve waterfowl, we need waterfowl habitat preserves.

To SURVIVE, wildlife has to contend with man both as predator and competitor. Roughly speaking

537

the more numerous people become and the more intensively they use the land, the more likely is wildlife to have problems of survival.

In much of North America, particularly in Canada, the pioneer phase of our culture is still a vivid memory. Only now are people coming to realize that some of our wildlife species may not survive the changes of this age unless we take specific action to maintain their habitat and regulate their use. We now face the problem of survival of waterfowl in numbers sufficient to provide for continuing human use in recreation.

What is the situation in Canada in regard to the survival of these important species? Before answering that question, we should consider some Canadian facts.

CANADA IS DIFFERENT from the United States in many ways. Canada has 3,852,000 square miles; the United States, 3,615,000. Canada has an average density of population of about 4.7 the square mile; the United States, 49.8.

Those differences, like anything based on averages, can be a bit misleading. The density of human settlement in the St. Lawrence Lowlands of Ontario and Quebec is not unlike that in upstate New York, for example. The average density of population in the Prairie Provinces, the heart of the duck breeding area, is close to 15 persons the square mile, including the persons in urban centers. In all of Canada, 90 percent of the people live on 10 percent of the land. The population of Canada is growing rapidly, at a rate of about 3 per-

cent a year. Yet most of the growth is taking place in and around urban centers and in localities where settlement has long been established.

CANADA has a great deal of waterfowl habitat. More than 7.6 percent of Canada is covered by inland waters. Not all its lake-splattered landscape, however, is particularly useful to waterfowl. The vast Canadian Shield, largely underlain by crystalline rocks and comprising most of the country east of the Mackenzie, is relatively unproductive. The Hudson Bay Lowlands and the Mackenzie Valley are much more attractive to waterfowl. But the best broad expanse of waterfowl habitat in Canada is the prairie country of southern Alberta, Saskatchewan, and Manitoba.

That area is the key to production of ducks important to hunters in North America. Much of the prairie is also good agricultural land, privately owned, and there waterfowl must contend with man and his works. In the St. Lawrence Lowlands and in parts of the Maritimes and British Columbia, waterfowl habitat is patchy. Some excellent marshes, favored resting places for migrant ducks and geese, are adjacent to valuable agricultural lands and in the path of residential and industrial expansion.

Although we expect little change in or loss of waterfowl habitat in a large part of Canada, the situation in the southern agricultural zone is not unlike that in the United States. To maintain waterfowl populations at a desirable level surely will require more habitat preserves and perhaps more sanctuaries than we now have in southern Canada.

MOST PUBLIC LANDS in Canada are administered by the Provinces. Exceptions include the Territories, national parks, and military and naval reserves.

The Federal Government, however, has been empowered to establish migratory bird sanctuaries—in which migratory birds may not be hunted. Sanctuaries may be established on Crown (that is, public) or private lands. Control over land use in sanctuaries is limited to lands owned by the Crown. To date there has been no management of land to benefit wildlife in migratory bird sanctuaries. There is no effective control over the use of private lands within a sanctuary. In many instances, particularly in southern Canada, the lands within a sanctuary are privately owned.

Migratory bird sanctuaries in Canada date from 1887, when the islands and shores of the north end of Last Mountain Lake, in what was then the Northwest Territories and is now Saskatchewan, were set aside by Federal Order in Council. Since the area was then in the Northwest Territories, the lands were administered by the Federal Government. In fact, lands in Alberta and Saskatchewan remained under Federal administration until 1930. Sanctuaries created in those Provinces before 1930 were primarily land reserves—that is, areas where the lands could not be alienated or used for any other purpose. For some years many sanctuaries were at least partly open to hunting, although none is now.

During the latter part of the period of Federal administration of lands in Alberta and Saskatchewan, there also were 44 areas reserved as public shooting grounds in these two Provinces. Six public shooting grounds were established by the Federal Government in Manitoba and one in British Columbia.

In the Migratory Bird Regulations for 1925 (the year public shooting grounds were established) the following words appear: "As it is recognized in the interest of sportsmanship and recreation that areas offering shooting facilities are now limited, steps have been taken to set apart and reserve suitable areas which shall be freely available to the public for shooting purposes."

The public shooting grounds in Alberta and Saskatchewan were abolished after the transfer of lands to those Provinces in 1930.

CANADA in 1964 had 108 migratory bird sanctuaries, whose area exceeded 39 thousand square miles. An area of more than 38 thousand square miles is accounted for by 10 large sanctuaries on Crown land in the Northwest Territories. They were established to provide some control over mineral exploration and exploitation in the major breeding areas of arctic geese.

The relatively small areas of sanctuary for migratory birds in southern Canada are fairly well distributed. Many of them are complemented by Provincially administered sanctuaries. Several in southern Canada were established primarily for the protection of rare species. Vaseaux Lake in British Columbia was for some years the

Just checking! Here Richard C. Passmore is showing his hunting license to officer Norman Ross, a member of the Royal Canadian Mounted Police. A special squad of officers is given the responsibility of enforcing regulations authorized by the Migratory Birds Convention Act.

A Canadian Wildlife Service Bird Sanctuary sign being installed by officer Norman Ross.

wintering area for a flock of trumpeter swans. Richardson Lake in northeastern Alberta is a favored nesting place for migrant Ross' geese.

All the Provinces except Prince Edward Island have Provincial sanctuaries or game preserves, many of which, like some of the Federal sanctuaries, are established on privately owned land. The areas in many Provinces are quite large. In Saskatchewan, for instance, all community pastures, totaling more than 2,500 square miles, are game preserves. Some are open to hunting; others are not. In Alberta, shooting of waterfowl is prohibited on 24 lakes and within one-half mile of their shores. Waterfowl hunting is prohibited also within 100 yards of all major rivers. On 15 game preserves and 40 Provincial parks hunting is not allowed. Ontario has more than 50 Crown game preserves. In most Provinces, in fact, the provision of sanctuary areas seems adequate, although minor adjustments may be desirable from time to time.

The major difficulty in Canada is the lack of reserved areas within the settled agricultural zones.

GAME DEPARTMENTS of five of the ten Provinces administer lands that are managed or reserved primarily as waterfowl habitat. These are Nova Scotia, 7 thousand acres; Ontario, 10 thousand acres; Manitoba, 160 thousand acres; Saskatchewan, 2,840 acres; and British Columbia, 3,034 acres.

In four other Provinces, New foundland, Prince Edward Island, New Brunswick, and Alberta, the game departments, singly or in co-operation with other branches of the Government, administer lands that are useful to waterfowl but are not reserved primarily as waterfowl habitat. Their extent is difficult to define. The chief game officer of Alberta considers that more than 60 thousand acres of such lands in Alberta can be considered as waterfowl-producing areas. It is hard to say whether these lands are securely designated for waterfowl use.

THE PROCEDURE in reserving lands for particular purposes may be administrative or statutory. In British Columbia, for example, the Comptroller of Lands may declare that a certain tract is reserved from alienation (that is, cannot be sold or otherwise disposed of) for the purposes of wildlife conservation. Such reserves have been created so far in response to requests by the governmental game agency, often as a result of pressure from sportsmen's organizations.

Reserves created by administrative orders may be dissolved in the same way. Public support is the only guarantee that reserves will be maintained in the face of pressures for other uses.

Reserves may be created also by Order in Council, an executive process that involves the Sovereign and has the force of law. This process is a bit more complicated, and the dissolution of reserves created by Order in Council is correspondingly less easy. Nevertheless, what is done by Order in Council can be undone by the same means. Again, public opinion is the best safeguard of governmental reserves.

ONLY RECENTLY have lands in Canada been bought and reserved specifically for waterfowl. The total area brought into that category by 1964 was small. But a start has been made, and several Provincial game departments have active programs to increase the acreage of waterfowl habitat under their control. The Canadian Wildlife Service has begun a pilot program of concluding agreements with landowners for the preservation of prairie potholes.

In all Provinces, except the Maritimes, there are large areas of Crown land. Their administration varies. In Newfoundland, Nova Scotia, New Brunswick, Ontario, Manitoba, and Alberta, the wildlife agencies and the lands agencies are in the same department of government. Their game agencies have an excellent opportunity to influence the administration of Crown lands so that it is beneficial to waterfowl. In British Columbia, Saskatchewan, and Quebec, the lands agencies and the wildlife agencies are in different departments.

THE MOST INTENSIVE management of public lands for waterfowl and waterfowl hunting has developed in the most densely populated districts.

In Ontario, where it is the stated policy of the Department of Lands and Forests to retain marshes on Crown lands for use by wildlife, the Ontario Fish and Wildlife Branch controls shooting hours, numbers of hunters, and locations of blinds within its managed hunting areas. The Ontario Fish and Wildlife Branch operates a 1,700-acre public shooting area at Long

Point, Lake Erie. Along the shore from Long Point west to the Detroit River are public marshes at Rondeau Point, Point Pelee, and near the mouth of Cedar Creek. Waterfowl and waterfowl habitat are managed primarily for enjoyment of the public in the St. Lawrence Seaway Park. The Ontario Fish and Wildlife Branch expects an increase in the extent of waterfowl management areas and sanctuaries in the coming years.

In places where hunting pressure has been substantial for some time and waterfowl habitat has come to be at a premium, clubs and individuals have bought or leased wetlands to assure access to hunting. That has taken place in Quebec, along the Ottawa and St. Lawrence Rivers; in Ontario, along the shores of Lake Erie and Lake St. Clair and along the southern tip of the Canadian Shield; and in British Columbia, in the lower Fraser Valley. Some of the duck clubs in southwestern Ontario were established more than 100 years ago.

A well-known private organization, Ducks Unlimited, has contributed a great deal to the welfare of waterfowl in the Prairie Provinces of Canada, not through land acquisition but by more than 600 water conservation and marsh management works under agreements with landowners—in many instances the Crown.

ON THE CANADIAN SHORES of Lake St. Clair, across from Detroit, duck clubs control about 30 thousand acres. In the Long Point area, on the north shore of Lake Erie, there are close to 40 thousand acres of good duck marsh. Most of the area is controlled by private clubs. In all, about 85 percent of the wetlands bordering Lakes Erie and St. Clair are believed to be privately owned. They and other private tracts are used primarily for waterfowl hunting. Undoubtedly, therefore, the occurrence of waterfowl in southwestern Ontario depends largely on private lands.

A large proportion of those lands is controlled by hunters who live in the United States.

Most private hunting clubs limit shooting times so as to provide better sport. Often, for example, shooting may be allowed only on Wednesdays and weekends. Some clubs provide food for ducks in "refuge" areas within their limits. Some have been known to bend the law in their interpretation of the regulations that limit the use of bait. Except in southwestern Ontario, few clubs in Canada practice habitat management.

Some of the marshes in southwestern Ontario are well equipped to maintain waters at the level most conducive to the growth of desirable aquatic plants. At least one, the Bradley Marsh, in the southwestern corner of Lake St. Clair, for years has used pumps, dikes, and ditches to create conditions favorable to ducks and muskrats. Once reclaimed but found relatively unprofitable as an agricultural enterprise, the Bradley property was reconverted to marshland in 1929. The production of muskrats and the rental of shooting privileges provide the main income from the land.

Elsewhere in Ontario, marshes

are maintained for waterfowl in Prince Edward County, on the north shore of Lake Ontario; on Lake Scugog (where some valuable banding of large numbers of migrant ducks was done more than 30 years ago); and along the St. Lawrence River. A public marsh, part sanctuary, part public shooting ground, was established on the shores of Lake St. Lawrence (created by construction of the Seaway) in 1957.

GOOSE HUNTING CLUBS, including the famous Cap Tourmente Club, control extensive areas of tidal marsh on the St. Lawrence River just downstream from Quebec, on lands leased from Laval University. Duck clubs control small tracts of marsh on the St. Lawrence River between Quebec and Montreal and on the Ottawa River between Hull and Grenville.

In Manitoba, some 10 thousand acres of privately owned marshland, mostly at the south end of Lake Manitoba, are retained for waterfowl. About half of the tract is a private goose sanctuary at Marshy Point. The owner, in cooperation with the Delta Research Station and the Manitoba Game Branch, has established a substantial breeding population of Canada geese there. Several thousand migrant Canada geese use the area in the autumn. At the Alf Hole Sanctuary in eastern Manitoba the numbers of breeding Canada geese also have been increased by management.

The well-known Delta Waterfowl Research Station also is at the south end of Lake Manitoba. Among many useful research projects carried out there, have been some

concerned with manipulation of water levels and edge cover, designed to yield information basic to better marsh management.

A number of duck hunting lodges on other parts of the large Manitoba lakes control shore access to marshes and provide guides and outfits to hunters, but they do not own the marshes.

In the lower Fraser Valley of southwestern British Columbia, several thousand acres of privately owned land are used primarily for duck hunting. These include tracts on the tidal foreshores and upstream. Apart from the foreshores, shooting clubs control probably more than half of the waterfowl habitat in that region. One club, which controls about 16 thousand acres, has 15 members who pay an average annual fee of 300 dollars. The yearly assessment on members has been as high as 1,500 dollars when special management procedures were undertaken.

The British Columbia Government recently reserved 11 thousand acres of very valuable waterfowl habitat in the Duck Lake area which is located in the Southeastern part of the Province.

THERE ARE A NUMBER of private and municipal areas in Canada to which waterfowl are attracted primarily for the spectacle they provide. One well-known place is the Jack Miner Sanctuary at Kingsville, Ontario. The Miner property, with its decoy flock, artificial pond, and well-managed pasture, attracts some 25 thousand Canada geese each spring and fall. It is an out-

This incubating black brant was reluctant to leave its down-lined nest.

standing tourist attraction in the Windsor-Detroit region.

The Harvey Moore homestead in eastern Prince Edward Island is another locally important sanctuary. The creation of two ponds by damming a small stream and the provision of grain as winter feed have resulted in the buildup of a winter population of more than 2 thousand ducks.

Municipal parks in a number of Canadian cities attract large numbers of ducks and geese at various times of year. They provide safe refuge for the birds and are particularly important in that they give large numbers of city dwellers the chance to become familiar with waterfowl. Among areas of this sort are Beacon Hill in Victoria, Stanley Park in Vancouver, St. George's Island in Calgary, Wascana Park in Regina, and Toronto Island Park.

THE PATTERN OF LANDS reserved for waterfowl in Canada is a patchy one. It has developed in response to irregular and uncoordinated pressures. Certainly, the need now is for a comprehensive plan for reservation of lands for waterfowl.

To execute such a plan would require the cooperation of both Federal and Provincial Governments and the provision of adequate funds. But first, as the content of this chapter should suggest, we must define more precisely what we have in the way of wetlands and decide where additional reservations are needed.

This is the immediate task in Canada. It will be pursued as a part of the National Land Inventory, for which procedures are now being developed, and which will get underway in 1965.—

DAVID A. MUNRO.

CANVASBACKS

Ducks Unlimited

DUCKS UNLIMITED is a private, non-profit organization dedicated to perpetuating and increasing the North American waterfowl resources by preserving and developing their breeding habitat on the prairies of western Canada. The background and reasons for its formation are somewhat different from those of other conservation agencies.

Severe drought during the early thirties across the prairies of western Canada depleted the continent's waterfowl supply. Normally this area produces a large part of the total duck population.

Investigations during that critical period were made by an organization known as More Game Birds of America. The findings were plain and ominous: The breeding grounds of the birds had to be restored and developed or duck populations would decline permanently.

Canada had no legislation that provided for the use of tax money for this type of endeavour. The laws of the United States forbade the spending of public funds in a foreign country for such purposes. The solution therefore depended on the formation of a sportsmen's organization that would be able to

545

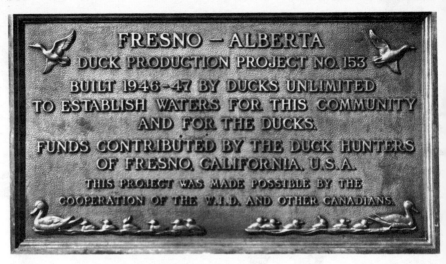

FRESNO – ALBERTA
DUCK PRODUCTION PROJECT NO. 153
BUILT 1946-47 BY DUCKS UNLIMITED
TO ESTABLISH WATERS FOR THIS COMMUNITY
AND FOR THE DUCKS.
FUNDS CONTRIBUTED BY THE DUCK HUNTERS
OF FRESNO, CALIFORNIA, U.S.A.
THIS PROJECT WAS MADE POSSIBLE BY THE
COOPERATION OF THE W.I.D. AND OTHER CANADIANS.

*California sportsmen provided the money, Alberta, Canada, the place, and Ducks Unlimited,
the technology to produce more ducks.*

operate in Canada and be financed by private funds. Support was immediately forthcoming. Backed by businessmen and dedicated conservationists, Ducks Unlimited was incorporated in the United States on January 29, 1937, and the drive for funds began.

The organization of Ducks Unlimited (Canada) was completed in 1938. The first field work was undertaken that year.

At the beginning, Ducks Unlimited considered drought on the Canadian prairies the most serious threat to waterfowl. The company therefore set water storage in suitable areas for waterfowl production as the major objective. This basic approach has remained largely unchanged, although it is now recognized that in the long-term view agricultural expansion and drainage are a more serious threat to waterfowl than drought.

More emphasis, therefore, is being placed on a program to inform the public and governments of the basic needs of wildlife in the hope that a multipurpose approach to the use of lands and waters will be undertaken.

Periods of drought and heavy rainfall alternate on the Canadian prairies, and waterfowl populations fluctuate with them. Cultivation, drainage, overgrazing, and other agricultural activities reduce the amount of prime habitat and work against maximum productivity. Good management, however, helps offset such destruction. The work of Ducks Unlimited is designed to further such management.

THE THREE PRAIRIE Provinces of Manitoba, Saskatchewan, and Alberta cover about 735 thousand square miles. The prairies and aspen parklands, which comprise the prime waterfowl breeding habitat, however, are only 166 thousand square miles (106,496,000 acres) in extent. To the north, the Northwest Territories and the Yukon total 1.5 million square miles. If you look at a map of western Canada and consider the wide distribution of nesting waterfowl, you may be astonished that so small a part of this expanse could have such an effect on the numbers of waterfowl. The myriad lakes of the northern part of the three Prairie Provinces, the Northwest Territories, and the Yukon seem to offer unlimited habitat well beyond the influence of man. This northern habitat is marginal, though, possibly because of climate or food— or there may be other reasons. The fact is that it has never been able to maintain waterfowl when drought eliminates the prairie habitat, as it did in the thirties, 1946, 1949, and 1959–1962.

In years of good water on the prairies, distribution of several important duck species clearly shows their preference for prairie habitat. In the midfifties, a wet period on the prairies, the average waterfowl breeding population in the settled areas of Saskatchewan and Alberta was about 30 pairs the square mile. Densities ranged from almost zero in the intensively cultivated flat lands to 185 breeding pairs in the old potholes associated with the old

A successful Ducks Unlimited waterfowl project on Lake Manitoba, Canada.

glacial moraines of the last ice age. Except for local concentrations in river deltas, the northern populations were well below one pair the square mile.

Efforts by Ducks Unlimited have been concentrated therefore on the development of habitat in this vital southern region. Many engineering and biological techniques are employed in the development of areas suitable for waterfowl. Water, food, and cover, the three essentials for good production, are the elements D.U. tries to incorporate in building and developing its projects.

On the prairies—except in exceptional years and then usually just locally—creeks and streams carry water (from the melting snow) only in the spring. It is necessary therefore to design projects to catch and hold this runoff. Staff biologists determine the depth of the area, and the necessary structures or controls are designed accordingly.

Because funds are limited, first to be considered is how to use the money to best advantage for waterfowl. As many projects are built on private land, the owners' permission must be obtained to flood the selected area. Long-term easements, signed on all projects built to date, are given free; all taxes and any incumbrances are carried by the owner.

Much the same situation applies to lands owned by Provincial and Federal Governments. Their cooperation in giving long-term leases on extensive tracts, on which some of the larger projects have been built, has been helpful.

Leases received in 1960 from the Saskatchewan Government cover 340 thousand acres in the Cumberland area in the eastern part of the Province. Another lease for 150 thousand acres, received in 1962 from the Manitoba Government, covers the Carrot River Triangle just west of The Pas. The Alberta Government also has been unstinting in its support of the program.

When it is sure that there will be no land complications on a proposed project, staff engineers proceed to run the necessary surveys, which include contouring the area and cross-sectioning the suggested dam or control site. That done, a detailed map is drawn to show all elevations and controls necessary to hold the water level that will be best suited for the production of waterfowl. The map and the easements from all farmers or landowners are then sent to the Water Rights Control Board in the Province in which the project is to be built. Plans and easements are inspected; if they are satisfactory as to design and other details, a license to construct is issued.

THE SUITABILITY of places for building waterfowl projects can be determined in several ways. Engineers make ground reconnaissance. Surveys sometimes are made from the air during spring runoff. Aerial photographs are taken and studied.

The size of a tract under consideration for a project is less important than the potential production that may come from it. Small projects sometimes are much more productive than larger ones.

Types of projects are varied and

reflect the purpose, whether to maintain the permanency of existing marshes or develop new ones. Simple earth dams on the outlet of shallow marshes store additional water to outlast drought. Restriction of evaporation areas is also effective: Dikes built across shallow marshes or lakes that frequently are dry confine the water to half or less of

Too wet for the truck, too dry for the boat! Ted Burkell, Ducks Unlimited (Canada) manager in Alberta, on a duck banding expedition.

Ducks Unlimited field men run a level for a new waterfowl project in southern Alberta, Canada.

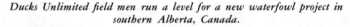

the former area. The result is a smaller but deeper and more secure breeding area.

Many large, shallow, prairie lakes too saline to be of much value to breeding waterfowl often have inflowing creeks through shallow bays of lower salinity. A dam across the neck of the bay where it joins the lake develops the bay into good habitat. An inflowing creek can also be diverted through a series of natural basins en route to the lake. Creeks and other flowages, less well defined, also can be diverted into marshes and shallow lakes.

NEW MARSHES can be created by diverting water into natural depressions through the use of dams and other controls. Many fine areas have been developed in southern Alberta by using waste irrigation waters. This type of project is valuable and productive, because a steady and assured water supply is always available.

The improvement of potholes has proved extremely valuable during the past drought years. This type of project has been built in terrain where there are many shallow potholes in the spring. These are always very attractive to birds looking for nesting areas. In years of low runoff, these areas go dry before broods can fly. Heavy losses result.

Pothole improvement is quite simple: An area where many of these shallow ponds are located is selected and the deepest depression in the area is then used as the main pond. This must be deep enough to hold at least three or four feet of water. The procedure then is to channel all surplus water to the main pond; this provides a permanent area where young birds can go when the outlying shallow ponds dry up.

In building and developing the many types of projects which Ducks Unlimited now has scattered across the prairies, a skilled and competent engineering staff has been most essential. Each project calls for its own type of structure or control. These have ranged from small earth-fill dams, through a range of many different types of concrete controls, up to large ten-bay structures with complete stoplog and gate control and costing tens of thousands of dollars.

PARALLEL TO THE EFFORTS of Ducks Unlimited is the work administered under the authority of the Prairie Farm Rehabilitation Act, by a Dominion Government agency that deals with drought and its effect on agriculture. The agency encourages the development of surface water resources and better land uses. The thousands of stock watering ponds and the many irrigation reservoirs it has built across western Canada have added much to the well-being of waterfowl.

In 25 years of work on the Canadian prairies, Ducks Unlimited has built more than 600 projects. These control water on more than 1 million acres with a shoreline in excess of 5 thousand miles. Since 1938, a total of 8.3 million dollars

Young pintails on a Ducks Unlimited project in Alberta, Canada.

has been spent on conservation work in Canada. The major part has been used for building and developing waterfowl projects.

COSTS HAVE VARIED according to size of the area and the type of structures needed for proper control. Initial costs have averaged about 6.5 dollars per acre flooded. Upkeep and repairs have been very low, averaging less than five cents an acre per annum for the past 25 years.

In southern Alberta, where surplus irrigation water is used to supply many projects, the costs of upkeep have averaged somewhat higher than other prairie projects designed to catch and hold runoff. The fact that the former have an assured water supply makes them somewhat more valuable, however, as production from them is assured even during long droughts.

Cooperation of both the Eastern and Western Irrigation Districts in Alberta has helped in keeping the costs down, as there is no charge to D.U. for the water used. In many instances, the Government of Alberta has also shared the cost of building the projects in that Province, particularly when the project benefits the community as a whole.

It is cooperation like this that has helped make Ducks Unlimited successful. Much work has been done that would have been impossible without the support of farmers, landowners, and the various governments.

As yet, many of the projects are not intensively managed, except in irrigation districts where operation of the structures and controls to distribute water requires supervision. However, Ducks Unlimited has been active in the management field.

Fencing has been done to protect nesting cover and emergent plants from livestock. Sago pondweed, a valuable prairie food plant, has been introduced into many projects by seed and tubers. Emergent cover has been introduced by planting the rootstocks of hardstem and softstem bulrushes. In some shallow areas that have become too overgrown with emergent plants, particularly cattail, the plants have been removed by burning, mowing, and sometimes spraying with chemicals. Controlled spring burning of many miles of lake and marsh edge is undertaken in Manitoba in cooperation with farmers and municipalities. Before this program was organized, burning of marsh edge to encourage hay growth was done throughout most of the nesting season. It caused heavy losses to waterfowl. Under controlled burning, all areas are burned off before the birds start to nest in the spring.

As PART OF an overall management program, Ducks Unlimited has surveyed all important waterfowl areas in Saskatchewan. The purpose is to establish a waterfowl priority as a safeguard against ill-considered drainage. Data on the areas have been gathered for use by the Provincial Government and other agencies if and when a land acquisition program is undertaken. Areas in excess of 640 acres were catalogued first because they are the ones under most pressure. A start has been made on smaller areas. Initial steps of the same type program have been started in Manitoba. Plans have been made to survey the northern part of Alberta, where new lands have been opened for farming.

For the information of its directors and contributors, Ducks Unlimited makes an annual survey of the waterfowl populations in its sphere of activity. It covers the number of breeding pairs in spring, brood counts on projects and special-study areas, a water and production survey in late July, and aerial surveys in early September of waterfowl concentration points in the northern parts of the three Prairie Provinces.

About 350 volunteer observers report three times a year on waterfowl and habitat conditions. Their data are compiled, analyzed, and published monthly in summer and fall in a leaflet titled "Duckological," which is prepared in Canada and distributed to D.U. contributors.

DUCKS UNLIMITED does not consider itself a research organization, but it has cooperated in many research programs whose findings may have application to its work. It has also participated in programs to control damage to cereal crops by waterfowl.

One intensive research program was the banding of waterfowl to determine distribution and flyway patterns. Through December 1962, 126,800 ducks and 2,600 Canada geese had been banded. An analysis of returns up to 1956 was published in a booklet. Several other pamphlets have been published, mostly for educational purposes. Among them are "Hawks of Western Canada," "Saskatchewan Marsh Plants," and "Prairie Ducks and Geese." Information concerning these may be obtained by writing to Ducks Unlimited, Winnipeg, Manitoba, Canada.

The operations of Ducks Unlimited (Canada) are administered from a head office in Winnipeg. Provincial offices are in Regina, Saskatchewan, and Edmonton, Alberta. The permanent staff totals 27 engineers, biologists, technicians, administrators, and clerks. Up to 100 persons may be employed during the construction season. Most construction work is done by contract, although some equipment and employees are available to make repairs to existing structures and controls and to build small projects.

The overall operations and policies are guided by a board of 30 directors, who are Canadians and Americans in about equal numbers. They are unpaid. They give time and money freely so that money from contributors may be spent wisely and well in the cause of waterfowl conservation.

—ANGUS GAVIN.

A Helping Hand

BLUE-WINGED TEAL

Water Off and On

IT WAS a sight and sound to remember. Thousands of mallards and pintails flushed with a roar from the Batchtown Unit of the Mark Twain National Wildlife Refuge in Illinois. Even more impressive than the flight were the birds that stayed behind—more than a million ducks close together on an area of nearly 2 thousand acres.

Never, before or since, has Batchtown, good as it is for waterfowl, had a concentration like that of the fall of 1953. The birds were there for a reason, and the reason came about by accident.

Streamflow on the Mississippi River was high in the summer of 1953—so high that the gates on Lock and Dam 25 were operated partly open. This lowered water levels above the dam, including the area of the Batchtown Unit. When water levels dropped, expanses of mudflats were exposed. Smartweed and millet from natural seeding densely covered the flats. Streamflow lessened late in the summer and the gates were closed after a seed crop was assured. This again flooded the Batchtown Unit, including nearly 2 thousand acres of prime duck food. Food and cover conditions were excellent. Vast numbers of migrating mallards and pintails stopped to feed on the abundant seed. Some pintails actually became so gorged from eating smartweed seeds that they had to taxi like a diving duck in order to become airborne.

In all the years that Batchtown Unit has been in existence, it has had enough water—sometimes too much—but, except for the summer of 1953, it has not been possible to get enough water off the land at the right time. Future management plans are pointed in that direction, and some day it may be possible to achieve by design what Nature and circumstances so vividly demonstrated in 1953.

This points out one thing. Water—even good, clean water—is often of reduced value to waterfowl if the level is constantly stable or if water levels change at the wrong time. Water must be managed if it is to be most useful to ducks and geese. It must be *off* and *on* at the right time.

MANAGEMENT of water requires some sort of structure or control or both to permit raising, lowering, or keeping water in or out of an area at will.

Water management on a nesting area may differ from that on feeding, hunting, or wintering areas. Each type of management may call for a different type of structure. Some types require elaborate control devices with gates and spillways. Others may utilize simple controls, such as a flap-gate. Still others may be designed with no control struc-

tures at all, being merely a series of low overflow dikes in which water levels are controlled by pumps, siphons, or tidal influx. Information as to the type of control needed may be obtained from the Bureau of Sport Fisheries and Wildlife, State game departments, the Soil Conservation Service, or through county agents.

Waterfowl management gained new emphasis when drought was severe in the early thirties. It was then thought that impoundments should be designed to insure a constant supply of water and that stable levels were of prime importance so that on refuges, at least, a future water shortage might be averted.

The initial development of food and cover plants may be spectacular on newly flooded areas. Experience has shown, however, that if the water level is constant, conditions may deteriorate as new vegetation appears in the normal course of plant succession. Many impoundments constructed in the early thirties prospered for several years before retrogression set in and their use by waterfowl declined. Nevertheless, many people believed in "water at any cost" and stoutly opposed any lowering of water level on a waterfowl marsh.

Occasionally, however, impoundments were lowered for repair of structures or for flood control, for instance, and the impoundments were dried out for a month or two. When reflooding brought a more vigorous plant growth and increased waterfowl usage, refuge managers decided that perhaps it was good management to do by design what formerly occurred only by accident.

Marsh managers began to experiment, and the theory of water manipulation was born. Now we recognize that manipulation of water is much more important than the maintenance of stabilized levels in the proper management of most waterfowl habitat.

NATURE has demonstrated the advantages, as well as disadvantages, of cyclic fluctuations in water levels and can tell us a great deal about them. In depressions among upland prairies and on flood plains of many rivers, seasonal recession of water levels followed by submergence due to autumn rains and melting snow, is responsible for the sustained usefulness of many of our most valuable waterfowl habitats. This natural process produces large amounts of useful duck foods (such as millets, cyperuses, and smartweeds) on shallow lakes and sloughs that dry up in summer.

In like manner, nutrients that would remain bound up in submerged, undecayed plant materials are quickly converted and released by the processes of decomposition. Organic decomposition also retards the gradual filling of shallow, upland lakes by the accumulation of submerged vegetation. Seasonal flooding then makes the newly produced feed accessible for the use of waterfowl.

Now we get these benefits in many new places by using various kinds of water-control structures to control drawdowns carefully.

An impoundment requires an adequate supply of water. Sources of water include surface runoff, streamflow, springs, industrial and previously used water free from harmful wastes, diversions from streams or rivers, wells, and tidal influx. Satisfactory impoundments have been developed with fresh and even brackish and saline waters.

The possibility of severe flood conditions often adds to construction and maintenance costs of an impoundment, because major spillways of large capacities may be needed and because structures may be damaged during periods of high water. Places that regularly have low waterflows, however, often may fail to maintain enough food and cover for young waterfowl, and conditions may arise that favor outbreaks of disease, such as botulism.

Topography often determines the feasibility of a project and the most suitable type of structure. Natural basins of low gradient, having gently sloping banks, provide excellent locations for waterfowl impoundments. On such a site, a large water area can be impounded which will produce shallow, marshy edges at low cost.

By contrast, areas that are canyonlike, with steep sides or a streambed with a steep gradient, are not desirable, because a high, costly dam is necessary to obtain adequate water surface, and the resulting impoundment often is deficient in the shallow areas and marshy edges most waterfowl like.

Wetlands for waterfowl need not be deep. Shallow, marshy tracts are preferred by dabbling ducks, such as mallards and blue-winged teal.

A dense stand of spikerush growing in an area from which water was withdrawn at Mattamuskeet National Wildlife Refuge. The area was flooded in the fall to provide feed for ducks.

It is desirable that water depth vary within an impoundment. A suggested range is from 6 inches to 18 inches in at least half the basin. Diving ducks, such as canvasbacks, use deeper water for feeding but prefer shallow water for nesting sites.

The usefulness of impoundments, constructed primarily for the development of feeding grounds, often can be greatly increased by subdividing them into units by cross dikes equipped with water gates to permit independent control of water levels.

Water control structures should be designed to allow one to control water levels as completely as possible. It is essential to have enough control capacity to permit rapid lowering of water within an impoundment. It is also desirable to design the structure to permit complete drainage. Dikes and water gates should also be adequate to permit increasing water depths above normal operating levels wherever possible.

Many impoundments provide spillways as protection against flooding and control structures to provide drainage, but they are not designed so that the water depths can be raised above the anticipated normal operating level. New impoundments should have such provision, because undesirable emergent and shoreline plant species often can be controlled best by flooding.

ON SALT MARSHES, flooded impoundments are a way to control saltmarsh mosquitoes. They cover sites where mosquitoes deposit eggs and aid fish and other natural agents to control mosquitoes. Furthermore, the impounded water offers satisfactory habitat for many species of wetland wildlife.

Dikes on tidal marshes and other exposed sites occasionally are subject to erosion by tidal currents or waves. Low-level dikes, about 18 inches high and well sodded, have resisted such action better than larger structures. The low-level types, designed to be overtopped by high water, utilize small, simple water-control structures of the flapgate or drop-log type. The structures should be built with wide wings that extend into the dike to prevent cutting and erosion. Such impoundments usually are not operated on the drawdown principle but where possible are maintained at a fairly constant water depth of 6 to 10 inches at all times.

Diked impoundments are not practical on all types of salt marshes. Water surface sometimes can be created by excavating ponds to a depth of about 24 inches. Another way to improve salt marshes is to install permanent check dams in fresh-water streams that flow through the salt marsh. Fresh water distributed over the salt marsh will change the ecology and usually create better waterfowl habitat.

CONTROL OF WATER levels is essential for the most intensive and economical management of impoundments for waterfowl. The erection and maintenance of waterfowl nesting and loafing structures can be facilitated greatly by temporary drainage, particularly in impound-ments developed mainly for such species as wood ducks and Canada geese. Clearing of semiwet woodlands, where trees cannot be removed by machines, or such operations cost too much, can be accomplished gradually by flooding the trees for 2 to 3 years to kill them. To speed their decay, a biennial summer drawdown for 8 to 10 years should follow the flooding.

In regions where it is not feasible to increase marsh fertility by the use of commercial fertilizers, the burning of woody debris—dead standing timber or slash—is an effective way to improve habitats.

Studies at the Patuxent Wildlife Research Center have shown that woody debris burned on temporarily drained impoundments and along adjacent watersheds is an excellent source of plant nutrients, including exchangeable potassium and readily available phosphorus. The amount of exchangeable calcium is often greatly increased and helps correct acid conditions that stimulate excessive growth of such pest plants as the bladderworts.

Carbonic acid, created when submerged vegetation decays, can precipitate suspended clay, thereby clearing excessively cloudy water. Enough moist soil vegetation can usually be produced by exposing about one-half to two-thirds of the bed of a turbid impoundment to supply the necessary amount of carbon dioxide to precipitate suspended materials when it is reflooded.

When a suitable water supply is available, a circulating flow can be used to replace objectionable matter, such as algae blooms, acid, humic stains, or alkali, with water of better quality. At Seney National Wildlife Refuge in Michigan, flushing to remove humic stain is considered a good management practice on the impoundments. It improves the penetration of light and contributes to better growth of submerged aquatic plants.

MANIPULATION of the water level often makes it easier to control various troublesome animals such as muskrats, snapping turtles, and carp. Outbreaks of certain types of duck diseases, such as botulism and algae poisoning, sometimes can be averted by judicious use of drawdowns. The control of undesirable emergent plants also sometimes can be effected by a drawdown or reflooding if local conditions are favorable.

Drawdowns may permit the control of emergents by drying the beds to such an extent that mowing, crushing, disking, burning, and the like can be done. Marsh managers in California have found that water removal simplifies the control of cattails and bulrushes. After draining, the impoundment is permitted to dry, and the heavy emergent growth is mowed and burned. The ground is then plowed or disked to bring the roots to the surface, where they are killed by drying during the summer months. While this method is effective, it is not always possible in places where the beds cannot be dried out. Phragmites, a problem plant in many areas, can sometimes be controlled on dewatered sites and elsewhere by crushing with a roller equipped with angle iron cleats.

Where drawdowns occasionally result in heavy stands of such undesirable species as cattail and willow, it may be possible to control them by reflooding to a depth that stops their growth. The control structures would have to hold the water levels higher than normal or to a depth that will kill the plants.

Solid stands of emergents in a marsh are not desirable. Most wildlife in a marsh prefer the "edge effect," or interspersion of various types of vegetation. When dense, solid stands of emergents do occur, flooding may provide a means of changing the stands and create this interspersion so desirable in habitat management.

Waterfowl use of stands of emergent vegetation varies in a number of ways. On nesting areas, for example, some diving ducks will nest only where they can build in emergent vegetation, but they prefer emergents that are not too dense. On dense, solid stands, they may nest only on the outer edge. Thus the nesting potential is limited. Duck broods make less use of dense stands than they do of stands that are either thin or interspersed with open water areas.

When water is drawn down on permanent impoundments in the Midwest in summer, undesirable stands of cattails, willows, beggarticks, and bulrushes may grow up, especially when summer drawdowns are made in consecutive years. Properly managed drawdowns in alternate years, followed by the maintenance of water depths of about 3 feet the following year, may prevent such encroachment.

Cattail may be a slow invader when it spreads by roots alone, but it takes over rapidly when its seeds reach exposed mudflats. Once established, cattails will grow well in water up to 3 feet deep. Stands thin out gradually in deeper water. Cattails are valuable in a well-balanced waterfowl marsh, but they are a problem when dense, solid stands of them dominate the vegetation pattern.

An example: A unit of the Lower Souris National Wildlife Refuge in North Dakota was drawn down in the summer of 1955 to permit rehabilitation and construction of nesting islands. By fall, seedlings of cattail and softstem bulrush were apparent. The scattered plants had spread into fairly extensive stands in 1957. To control botulism, the same unit was drawn down in 1960 in stages, and complete drainage continued through September. In June 1961, rapid drainage was again necessary when evidence of botulism appeared. By August of that year, cattail and softstem seedlings were present over much of the area in densities up to 25 or more plants to the square yard, a much higher density than desired. Disking and other control measures were started that fall and were continued into 1963. The pool has since been reflooded. Thus, as a result of this experience at Lower Souris, no future drawdowns are planned earlier than mid-September unless botulism or other factors so dictate.

A similar situation occurred at

The water in this pond can be controlled at will. Flexibility in managing water levels pays dividends by increasing pond productivity.

Sand Lake National Wildlife Refuge in South Dakota. In the summer of 1959, one of the pools was almost dry because of limited rainfall and a lack of water in the James River. Its margins soon became a solid stand of cattail, although places cultivated in 1959 had little or no cattail in succeeding years. Heavy grazing of dry marsh aided greatly in reducing growth of cattails once the area could be reflooded. When water 3 feet deep flooded the cattail stands, a gradual thinning occurred in about 2 years.

When cattail, or any other emergent, occurs in solid stands, waterfowl usually use the area less. Before planning a summer drawdown, it would be well to consider the danger of encroachment of undesirable emergents and weigh the benefits expected from the development of moist-soil plants. Often the creation of a situation that is temporarily beneficial may lead to undesirable conditions later and to problems that did not exist before.

THE CHARACTERISTICS of each site determine the extent, frequency, and the most desirable periods for drawdowns and reflooding. Partial exposure of the bottom usually is preferred to complete drainage. It often is desirable to maintain full-pool water levels in one impoundment and to lower the levels of neighboring impoundments, especially if water is not available for reflooding before the expected time of use by waterfowl. Exposure of about half the bottom for at least 3 months during the growing season every 2 or 3 years is a common practice.

Gradual reflooding of emergent beds of food plants should be started at the end of the growing season to permit full utilization of newly submerged foods by dabbling ducks and diving ducks. If the water supply is ample for rapid reflooding, it is best to reflood in stages of 1 or 2 feet every 4 to 8 weeks.

Nesting areas allow less latitude for water level manipulation than nonnesting areas. In spring and early summer, some water must be left in nesting areas so that nests of diving ducks particularly will not be left high and dry and broods will have a place to develop. It is important also to guard against an increase in water levels that will flood out established nests.

THE SEEDS of many useful marsh plants germinate better when water levels are lowered until only a moist bed remains. Then better aeration and higher temperatures stimulate germination of seeds of many duck food plants that are difficult to establish when the land is covered with water. Once established, the emergents tolerate fluctuating levels pretty well if the water is not too high over the beds. Growth can be obtained from natural seeding once the bottoms are exposed. Complete drying is not desirable, however.

Where wildrice is grown in nontidal sites the maintenance of stable water is essential during the time the first leaves are floating. The first leaves drown out easily by prolonged flooding before they stand erect. For a few weeks management of wildrice on such sites therefore requires that no flooding occur during this interval. That is one reason why wildrice usually does not do well on uncontrolled streams, rivers, or lakes, especially if late spring rises are common.

STABILIZED WATER LEVELS during the growing season sometimes are preferable in impoundments that are suitable for the continued production of submerged food plants, unless a heavy layer of undecayed vegetation has accumulated on the bottom. Impoundments that have been held at a stable level for too long, however, often tend to produce fewer and fewer aquatics as time goes on. Drawdowns are important in improving production of valuable submerged plants, such as sago pondweed. Such drawdowns, either by evaporation or control structures, account for the high productivity of many western lakes. In Michigan, where summer drawdowns were made, some kinds of submerged and floating-leaved plants diminished in numbers during the first year of reflooding. Stands of water smartweed and northern naiad were luxuriant after flooding, apparently in response to greater supplies of nutrients.

Winter drawdowns apparently improve the germination of seeds and encourage submerged aquatics to come back with new vigor. On the Upper Mississippi River, levels were held low during the winters of the early forties, because enough water had to be made available on the lower pools of the river to aid in floating ships downstream and for hydroelectric generation at Keokuk, Iowa. Those drawdowns at the outset were viewed as potentially detrimental to waterfowl by sportsmen and conservationists, but it turned out that the aquatic growths that developed were among the best ever recorded. Seed production increased markedly.

Late fall and overwinter drawdowns for improved production of submerged aquatics have been successful at Bear River National Wildlife Refuge in Utah and the Lower Souris Refuge in North Dakota. Carp and other unwanted fish were removed during such periods. Absence of bottom-disturbing fish may have permitted the consolidation of bottom soils and contributed to improved light penetration during the following growing season.

Drawdowns to encourage aquatic growth should be started late enough in the fall so that seed germination of emergent plants is inhibited but early enough to permit drying of the top soil layer so as to stimulate germination of aquatic seeds the following spring.

ONE OF THE more remarkable aspects of water management is its use to spur the growth of annual moist-soil plants. That was what happened at the Batchtown Unit.

If water is drawn off an area in spring or summer so that shallow marginal areas are exposed, good stands of annuals usually come in from natural seeding. Exposing only the margins is effective, but disking or otherwise disturbing the soil can increase greatly natural production of millets, chufa, certain smartweeds, and similar plants. Biologists in Ohio get best results from drawdowns in May. They recommend partial reduction of water levels rather than a complete drying of the soil.

Refuge managers in Michigan also found that complete drying of the soil is not desirable. Complete drying fostered abundant growth of sedges and woolgrass but limited growth of more desirable annuals. Anyone who tries this type of management should irrigate or flood slightly so as to maintain a moist condition for plant growth.

This principle is popular in California, where areas set off by low dikes are seeded to wild millet as feed for ducks. Average yields of 1,500 pounds of seed an acre are produced. Yields of more than 3 thousand pounds have been reported. That amounts to 30 to 60 bushels an acre.

In places where the slope is suitable, only small border checks are needed to irrigate the crop. The shallower parts—if deep places occur—usually are diked off for planting to millet. The deeper places are kept for the development of such aquatics as sago pondweed and as a possible source of irrigation water.

Usually no seedbed has to be prepared on newly formed ponds. If emergent vegetation is present,

Pumping water is the most efficient way to flood some marshes. This stream can flood an acre to a depth of a foot in an hour.

however, the ground should be disked to break up the sod before seeding. Seeding can be done then by broadcasting by hand or from airplanes on dry or flooded ground.

Millet that is sown on flooded areas should be soaked beforehand so it will sink. After seeding, the impounded places are irrigated several times during the summer as needed or as the water supply permits. Keeping the field wet fosters lush growth and gradual maturing of the seed. Drawing the water off and permitting the fields to dry out make for a rapid, uniform development of seed. In the fall, when ducks return to the region, the impoundments are flooded to make the seed more readily available to them. Large numbers of ducks are drawn to the rich feeding grounds, and hunting is good.

Somewhat the same principle is used in States on the Pacific coast to develop areas of alkali bulrush. Water in the impoundments is drawn down to a mudflat stage to allow the bulrush seedlings to establish roots. Water is returned then and held at 1 to 3 inches until the crop matures. After the crop matures, the impoundment can be kept dry until it is flooded just before the hunting season.

In the Illinois River Valley, duck clubs develop moist-soil areas as a way to attract ducks. The clubs build low, overflow-type levees, which are overtopped by flood waters each spring. As river levels recede, the diked-off areas are drained as far as possible by gravity flow through various types of control structures in order to expose as much land as possible. Often pump-ing is done in places where the slope is too gentle to permit sufficient drawdown.

When the water is drawn off, the tracts are left to grow up to millets, chufa, and smartweeds from natural seeding or are seeded to wild millet, Walter millet, and Japanese millet by aerial seeding. The low levees keep water out of the diked-off areas, except when the water is unusually high in summer. Moist-soil plants thus can develop a seed supply before the waterfowl return on their fall flights.

After the seed crop is matured, water again is introduced by gravity flow whenever possible or by pumping. Flooding is done gradually, so that new areas of moist-soil plants are being flooded over a long period, thus making the seeds available to waterfowl—usually the puddle ducks, such as mallards, pintails, baldpate, and teal. Excessive shooting prevents desirable utilization of food supplies. Most clubs set aside a part of their property as an inviolate sanctuary to assure that there will be ducks over the land on which hunting is permitted.

At Swan Lake Refuge in Missouri, water manipulation is used to provide moist-soil plants for Canada geese. Feeding grounds are flooded by siphoning water into them from adjacent impoundments in early spring to retard weed growth. Water is removed in late May to permit seed of smartweeds, millets, chufa, and others to germinate. The areas are irrigated during the summer by siphoning water into them as needed. All impoundments are flooded in the fall, again by siphoning, so that the seed crop is available and the area is attractive to ducks and geese.

Roosts for wood ducks can be created sometimes by flooding standing timber in late summer or early fall. This was done by Maryland on a strip next to the old Chesapeake and Ohio Canal near Washington, D.C. The roost thus made proved to be an excellent wood duck banding site.

Flooding is sometimes used in Louisiana to attract large numbers of ducks to harvested ricefields. Their feeding helps to control red rice and other weeds that infest these fields.

What it all amounts to is that waterfowl management is habitat management and that, in turn, is mainly plant management. Waterfowl require water. Even more, they require plants—not just any kind, but particular species. Uniform water levels, if maintained too long, tend to encourage many plants of low value to waterfowl and some that may even interfere with the use of a water area by ducks and geese.

Some of the most desirable food plants are annuals, which cannot maintain themselves on permanently flooded sites. They require moist or dry ground to grow and produce a good crop. Later they must be flooded to be attractive to waterfowl. Sometimes Nature provides those conditions through summer drought, fall rains, and flooding. But Nature often accomplishes the least when the most is needed.

Water off the land and on the land makes possible the planned production of valuable waterfowl food plants, facilitates the control of noxious plants, creates nesting and brood habitat, and contributes to the recreational potential of the waterfowl resource. It is an economical means of improving on Nature and increasing the productivity of habitat for waterfowl.

In short, it is a way to grow two where only one grew before. In these days of diminishing habitat, that's important.

—WILLIAM E. GREEN,
L. G. MacNAMARA, and
FRANCIS M. UHLER.

Better Living for Ducks—
Through Chemistry

NORTH AMERICAN water-
fowl and Siberian farmers
have much in common—government philosophies and the weather
often work against them. Yet they
both persist—in a marginal fashion.

In the "good old days" waterfowl was a surplus crop; agricultural production was sparingly adequate. Now the reverse situation
plagues us. Why?

Agricultural scientists have learned
how to treat soils, both physically
and chemically, so that super-

abundant harvests are commonplace. For many self-evident reasons
the agronomic scientist has been
especially favored in his quest for
knowledge over his counterpart in
wetland soils.

The investigator of wet soils has
not kept pace with the vigorous
and increasing demand for ducks.
Those of us concerned with the
plight of waterfowl may do well to
take a page from the agronomists'
book to the end that we may learn
to produce more and more ducks

from less and less acreage. Such is our challenge if waterfowl and wild-fowling are to be perpetuated.

We may learn how to produce more ducks on fewer acres if we learn how to regulate the chemistry of flooded soils. We would then be doing for ducks what agronomists and soil scientists have done to help farmers achieve superabundant harvests through chemical and physical management of soils.

Men who till the earth have cast covetous eyes on the soils of swamps and marshes for centuries. When drained, such soils may become among the most productive on earth. Others, who have used water as a growth medium, learned hundreds of years ago that the yield of fishes could be strongly stimulated by periodic drainage. Natural water areas which dry out once in a while are frequently more attractive to waterfowl than those permanently watered. Builders of lakes, ponds, and marshes have noted exceptionally high yields of plants and animals for a brief interval—4 or 5 years—following their development. These observations suggest that continuous submergence depresses the yield of aquatic environments.

▸ What are some of the events that occur in flooded soils to debase their ability to yield abundantly? One that has been suggested is that the life produced by submerged soils exhausts available, essential nutrients. This concept, because of its widespread acceptance, is worthy of consideration.

Low-lying soils that are flooded receive the wash water that falls as rain or snow on upland soils of the watershed. Such water, as it flows over and through the soil, picks up a variety of materials. Of special concern is the amount of dissolved, essential nutrients it may carry and their fate after they reach basin soils.

To appreciate the chemistry of bottom lands we might examine some of them in New York State before they were flooded, shortly after submergence, and after they have been under water for several years. A distinction should be noted between the terms "available" or "soluble," (which I use interchangeably) and "total," which includes available and unavailable primary foods.

In central New York, the soluble, essential nutrients in soils to be flooded were compared with those in nearby upland soils (drainage area soils). The bottom-land soils rated as follows: Phosphorus, twice as great; nitrogen, the same; calcium and magnesium, an increase of two and one-half times; potassium, the same; manganese, essentially the same; iron, an increase of fourfold.

Comparisons in the chemistry of soils before they were flooded and after a year under water indicate the direction and magnitude of change: Phosphorus, approximately unchanged; NO_3 nitrogen, a modest drop in concentration; NH_3 nitrogen, an increase of about two and one-half times; available calcium and magnesium, a drop of about one-third in the concentration, a loss represented in part by increased concentrations of them in the water; potassium remained unchanged.

A sharp increase was noted in soluble manganese, and increases in soluble iron ranged from twofold to more than ninefold. Despite the decrease in soluble calcium and magnesium following submergence, the reaction of the soil was slightly more alkaline. After flooding, conversion of sulfates to sulfides would account fully for observed trends in soil reaction. It is likely that most Temperate Zone soils that can be flooded contain a higher concentration of available essential nutrients than do upland soils.

THE AMOUNT of organic matter in various stages of decomposition was much greater in an agronomic soil that had been submerged continuously for about 20 years than in the adjacent upland soil. Extremely high—and probably toxic—concentrations of soluble iron also were noted. A high level of divalent manganese was recorded. It may have inhibited the productive character of the marsh. Available concentrations of other primary essential nutrients, save for NO_3 nitrogen, which was depressed, remained unchanged or increased over that of the dry, adjacent soils.

The chemical analysis of soils in six central New York marshes suggests that life produced by them

A plastic indoor pond at Cornell University used in studies of aquatic plant growth under controlled conditions.

A battery of one-tenth-acre ponds at Cornell University used as an outdoor laboratory to study water and soil chemistry and other factors affecting aquatic plant growth.

does not exhaust their fertility. Rather, a more logical conclusion would be that flooded soils serve as banks for nutrient elements. By producing life—organic matter— efficient vaults are developed for storage of chemicals or for their release as the marsh community manifests a need. (An anomaly of organic soil is its high exchange capacity.) Marsh soils, studied to date in central New York, are "rich" soils or soils that contain higher concentrations of essential mineral nutrients than would be encountered in most agronomic soils.

RICH SOILS are not necessarily fertile soils. Does flooding result in too much of a good thing? The search for causes of curtailed productivity may well turn to an evaluation of nutrient imbalance.

To this end we relate the observation that newly flooded soils are usually highly productive and that depressed production appears to be related to the length of time the impoundment has existed.

Drainage of soils submerged for two decades resulted in chemical changes that shed light on some of the causes for curtailed production with continuous submergence. Within 4 to 7 days after removal of the surface water by drainage, seed germination was noted. Growth of plants was not evident until the soils dried enough to allow surface aeration. Following soil aeration, growth was spectacular. Exposed, but water-saturated soils, remained barren of rooted plants throughout the growing season. Following drainage, soluble, essential nutrient levels were depressed save for NO_3 nitrogen which increased. The content of organic matter in the soil dropped sharply, and a modest depression was noted in soil reaction.

WITH SOIL AERATION there was a sharp reduction in the concentration of soluble iron and manganese. Plant growth (nodding smartweed and sedges) was not spectacular until divalent iron levels receded to around 20 parts per million (p.p.m.). In the barren, water-saturated soils, iron concentrations remained in excess of 275 p.p.m. for the growing season. Other nutrients remained in adequate supply to produce abundant growth, yet none was recorded.

Poorly colored (yellowish), slender, slow-growing aquatic plants acquire a healthy green and become robust when transferred early in the growing season from an iron-rich soil (more than 200 p.p.m.) to an iron-poor soil (less than 100 p.p.m.). Lowland rice production is curtailed when soluble iron exceeds 25 p.p.m. In the Northeast, the greatest change in soil chemistry following soil aeration is in the amount of soluble iron. Other changes in the chemical composition of the soils following soil aeration, save for changes in soluble manganese, would be unlikely to suppress productivity. Soluble iron, while an essential nutrient, is known to be toxic to plants when available in surplus amounts. For these reasons, excessive concentrations (more than 100 p.p.m.) are thought to be the primary limiting factor for fresh-water marshes on acid soils in temperate regions.

Several research workers have defined conditions that change insoluble (ferric) to soluble (ferrous) iron. They are: Dissolved oxygen at or below 0.5 p.p.m., high concentration of carbon dioxide, the presence of organic matter, and a soil reaction near pH 6.5.

THE SHALLOW WATER of marshes usually is thought to be mixed by wind action throughout its depth during the growing season. Yet topography and vegetation in the marsh can reduce the effectiveness of air movement, and stagnant—stratified, or unmixed—water is commonplace.

Because of the shallow water in marshes, flooded soils warm appreciably. Chemical activity therefore is pronounced at the mud-water interface. Intense biochemical oxygen demand exhausts the supply of dissolved oxygen in the bottom water almost at once. Because of stagnation, the bottom few inches of the water may remain free of dissolved oxygen for much of the growing season. The intense breakdown of organic matter generates a great deal of carbon dioxide. Organic matter, a powerful force in the conversion of insoluble iron to soluble iron, is ever present in marshes.

The reaction of acid soils frequently is near pH 6.5 or slightly below in shallow-water areas of temperate regions. Acid-soil marshes, therefore, are active producers of soluble iron.

German scientists have demonstrated that the production of soluble iron is held to a minimum in submerged, alkaline soils under natural conditions. Further, it may be noted that agronomic crops may suffer from iron starvation when the pH of the soil is especially high. Thus a lack of soluble iron possibly could reduce the effectiveness of alkaline-soil marshes for waterfowl.

IN COASTAL MARSHES, a consideration of the influence of sulfides must supersede that of soluble iron as a critical limiting factor.

Sulfides tend to accumulate in the soils of coastal marshes, but in this respect clay soils are especially susceptible. In the management of salt marshes for waterfowl, periodic drainage and soil aeration may be indicated. Concurrent with soil aeration, sulfides would be transformed to sulfuric acid. Accompanying such a change would be a drastic increase in soil acidity, and plant growth would be strongly suppressed or prevented, possibly for a considerable length of time.

MARSH MANAGEMENT implies, in part, a chemical regulation of the soil to insure production of crops attractive to waterfowl. Marsh management includes also the selection of sites to be flooded, the installation of structures to control the water level, and sometimes the planting of desirable aquatic plants.

The effectiveness of marsh management on acid soils, where water levels cannot be controlled, is open to question. Aeration of the soils so as to precipitate excess iron, and in some instances manganese, is impractical. Usually the surface soils of such marshes are composed almost wholly of organic debris and so usually are acid and strongly buffered to resist change in reac-

tion. The amount of bases (ground limestone) normally required to effect a pH of 7.5 or above is generally so great as to make costs prohibitive. Because most such marshes are associated with lake or river systems, a large part of the bases, or other chemicals that might be added, very likely, would be moved from where they were applied and dispersed so thinly as to be ineffective.

Perhaps most permanent, natural water areas surrounded by alkaline soils could be improved for waterfowl. In such environments, high pH may prevent the formation of soluble iron in concentrations needed to produce attractive amounts of food and cover. The addition of industrial wastes containing ferrous iron and sulfuric acid would help alleviate problems that arise from a deficiency of iron.

In selecting coastal marshes for waterfowl management, clays should be avoided in favor of loam or sandy soils. In addition, salt water marshes, especially those on organic soils, are apt to evidence a shortage in copper, a trace element, and magnesium.

MANMADE MARSHES can be developed in almost every part of the continent.

The site to be flooded should be nearly level. Marginal contours should be widely spaced. Level sites usually cost less to develop and remain more attractive to waterfowl. Waves that break directly on the shoreline cause finer soil fractions to be sorted and transported from the part of the marsh usually considered to be most important to waterfowl. The shoreline soils of marshes with well-defined margins are soon depleted of their growth-producing fractions. Such marshes soon lose much of their important edge.

Woody sites are especially attractive to waterfowl for a few years after flooding, and the development of such areas has found favor with some waterfowl managers. Available evidence, however, emphasizes the need for a more critical appraisal of such a practice.

The longer term effect of flooding woody vegetation, when it is killed by a change in water level, is to hasten the deterioration of the productive character of marsh soils. Humic stains, resulting from the decomposition of woody materials, give the water the color of coffee. More solar radiation is trapped in the surface portion of stained water, and the water has an early and marked thermal stratification.

An increase in soil acids is commonplace with the increase in organic matter and the production of organic acids. Conditions required for dissolving iron are intensified. Numerous branches and trunks of trees on the floor of the impoundment reduce the area available for the growth of desirable, rooted aquatic plants. And the tangle of emergent dead trees complicates maintenance work from a boat in summer or on the ice in winter.

All told, the difficulties in managing soils of flooded, woody sites are especially onerous. In the development of production units for waterfowl, the selection of such areas for flooding is generally to be discouraged whenever better sites are available. This is not to deprecate the great value of woodlands where seasonal flooding preserves the forest while making available a rich bounty of mast. Neither does it mean that impoundments on woodlands should not be fairly considered where land values or other considerations rule out more desirable sites.

THE QUALITY OF THE SOILS surrounding a potential marsh is indicated in a practical way by the success of agriculture. This is the best indicator we have for assessing the potential attractiveness of the marsh for waterfowl after it has been developed. Manmade marshes in localities where annual evaporation and transpiration losses remove a large part of the stored water generally will be more productive of waterfowl than those in which one can maintain a uniformly high water level. Water removed by these processes does not carry with it dissolved nutrients from the marsh.

Flooding soils with more than 2 feet of water reduces the production of food and cover for waterfowl. Structures for impounding water in marshes should be designed so that no more than 25 percent of the area can be flooded to a depth greater than 2 feet. When features for holding more water are provided or can be improvised, the landowner, the general public, and sometimes the marsh manager can find excuses for holding an additional supply. In New York, except for the northwestern part of the

State, most of the several hundred manmade marshes developed to date have water depths in excess of 3 feet over much of their flooded basins. Most of them more clearly fill the needs of fish ponds than marshes.

The concentration of dissolved nutrients within the water increases with depth. Therefore a structure designed to remove surplus water from the surface, as opposed to the bottom, would preserve fertility.

One of the least expensive and most promising management techniques for marshes is a well-planned drainage program that will make adequate soil aeration possible. To effect such drainage, the base of the water-control structure should be at least 1 foot lower than 75 percent of the area to be submerged.

The physical requirements of marsh management are accomplished with relative ease. Chemical needs are less easily detected, and adverse nutritive balances are often difficult to correct.

CHEMICAL SOIL TESTS often leave much to be desired, because they mainly reveal conditions prevailing only at the time of sampling. When marsh soils are sampled thoroughly in July or August, however, and when samples are treated to prevent change before analysis, analytical results are of value and prerequisite to the chemical management of marsh soils. Measurement of temperature fluctuations, dissolved oxygen, and total alkalinities of the water are valuable supplements to analytical data obtained from soil samples.

When it is evident that the productivity of a marsh has been lowered and soil tests indicate that soluble iron concentrations exceed 100 p.p.m., drainage is indicated.

Removal of water just before ice forms in the fall is the least costly in terms of nutrient loss. Then plant and animal life within the water is at a minimum. Most of the dissolved nutrients would be precipitated on the soils, and the release of nutrients from decomposition of organic matter would be at a low ebb. Conversely, drainage during the growing season or in winter, when the marsh is covered with ice, is especially costly in the loss of dissolved and organically combined essentials. In fact, drainage at any time other than late fall is to be discouraged.

Water should be withheld from the marsh soil during winter and spring and into the summer until the concentration of dissolved iron has dropped to less than 20 p.p.m. If soils are reflooded then and given no further treatment, nothing will have been accomplished by drainage and soil aeration to prevent an early return to a low level of productivity. But the addition of a material such as ground limestone to produce an alkaline soil reaction (a pH of at least 7.5) appears to be of singular value in suppressing development of toxic concentrations of soluble iron. There is little danger from adding too much lime, but it is possible to worsen conditions by adding too little, as the soil reaction may be raised to pH 6.5—the optimum for bringing iron into solution. In determining lime requirements for a marsh, the reaction of the dried and aerated soil should be used in the calculation.

LIMING to improve flooded soils has been criticized because calcium and magnesium, the more valuable components of limestone, remove (through the phenomenon of base exchange) other and often scarcer essential nutrients from the colloidal fraction of the soil. The assumption is that the nutrients released from their colloidal bond would be lost to the environment in much the same manner as they might be lost to agronomic soils. This assumption is valid only when ill-advised, frequent drainage is practiced.

Often a marsh manager may hesitate to add lime because it may tie up phosphorus as an insoluble calcium phosphate. That may occur in a dry soil, but the forces in dry soil are not comparable to those in waterlogged soil. During the growing season, dissolved oxygen is generally absent from the mud-water interface. Conversely, carbon dioxide concentrations usually are high. Thus it is to be expected that phosphorus would be released from its calcium bond in such an oxygen-free environment by the action of carbonic acid (carbon dioxide and water) on calcium.

The costs of liming marsh soils are high because of the amount of lime usually needed, transportation, and labor expense. Yet it is likely that one adequate application would suffice for a long period. New demands to satisfy an increase in organic matter should be more than supplied by the yield from the drainage area. Surpluses received from the surrounding soils would replace lime lost in normal overflow water and whatever is carried into the mineral subsoil. When overall costs of chemical management of acid-soil marshes are considered, an investment in an application of the proper amount of lime may be the best one and the least costly in terms of benefits to waterfowl.

Management of marshes for waterfowl must consider always the need for desirable plant and animal food. Breeding waterfowl have a high protein requirement. In fact, wood ducks deprived of a high protein diet fail to reproduce. Grain consumption by wild, captive waterfowl falls sharply with the onset of the breeding season, and domestic waterfowl are benefited in breeding by a food rich in protein.

Breeding birds and broods of ducks therefore are apt to reject marshes with a dearth of animal foods and select those that have a wealth of small crustaceans and other animal life. Marshes whose soils are put in condition to produce attractive amounts and kinds of vegetation also produce an abundance of aquatic animals. Sites poor in plants are short on production of animal foods.

ATTEMPTS TO ESTABLISH plants from seeds, transplants, root cuttings, and so on generally fail unless the flooded soils have been prepared for them. Even at a time when ferrous iron concentrations are below 20 p.p.m. and favorable soil reaction has been established, test plantings are advisable instead of an all-inclusive planting program.

The need for stocking animal foods has not been proved as desirable forms have appeared naturally following flooding at sites where studies have been made.

Management of wetlands with more ducks as the purpose is far from being an exact science. We know well enough what waterfowl need for a good and productive life; yet providing these things in the variety and quantity needed brings problems galore.

One thing is certain. Living entities—all of them—originate in the soil. And soil is as variable as the life forms it will produce. This variability is measurable; it relates to the kinds, quantities, and relationships of the chemicals—the basic components of soil and the building blocks of living substance.

As surely as nylon, gasoline, and DDT can result only from the right chemicals in the right combination, so must the production of waterfowl depend ultimately on a chemical medium capable of supporting the chain of plant and animal life leading to ducks. So it is that the regulation of the chemistry of flooded soils is the precursor of ducks on the pond.

—ARTHUR H. COOK.

AMERICAN BITTERN

Planting and Misplanting

DEVELOPING HABITATS for waterfowl is similar to managing agricultural lands for livestock. Both deal with water, soil, good and bad plants, and specific kinds of animals. But there is one big difference. With wild waterfowl you are not dealing with a captive resource—they come to you by their own choice—they must be attracted to your area because of the food or protection you provide.

An essential element of the marsh or pond is its vegetation which provides both food and protective cover. Getting the right plants to grow in the right places in your marsh is not easy. The ones you do not want—let's call them weeds— may seem to appear out of nowhere and quickly take over ponds or marshes, clog waterways, choke lakes, and infest meadows. They may shed showers of viable seed or spread aggressively by rootstocks, rhizomes, or rosettes. They flourish in good years, thrive in adversity, and seem to have no enemies.

The plants you want seem to be fewer; overly sensitive to drought, diseases, drowning; easily crowded out by other growth; short lived. Getting them to grow and last may be costly. Weather, water, and soil

579

conditions often thwart your best efforts to keep the choice species productive.

But here is the first of several principles I should like to have you think about before we take up more specific details of planting nonagricultural types that need little or no tillage and that improve waterfowl habitat: We have no universal standards by which we can separate plants throughout their ranges into truly good or bad groups, even if we limit our discussion to those that are important to waterfowl.

Species that provide food or cover in one region may be a liability elsewhere. The usefulness of a plant may be altered by its abundance or the form in which it occurs. Hardstem bulrush, for example, may be preferred nesting cover for certain diving ducks, especially when it is in clumps or belts interspersed with open water. In large, unbroken stands, however, its average value, acre for acre, drops or disappears. Ducks, no less than doves, quail, turkeys, and pheasants, find variety to their liking. So, a balance of open water and useful plants in a suitable pattern, with more ducks, is our goal.

We have several ways to induce specific types of plants to occupy the right space. You can manipulate water, soil, or use by wildlife in one situation. In another situation, your tools to bring the birds back when feed and ducks disappear are plants themselves.

Planting for ducks is a relatively modern development. In the United States, at least, it goes back only to Model T days. The first United States Government publication on duck food was printed in 1911. But how did this art with a scientific flare get started?

The pattern of events comes naturally. Much of civilization has been built on the results of man's planting ability. His green thumb has meant the difference between oblivion and survival. So why not plant for ducks? When the feed disappears, and along with it, duck hunting opportunities, planting comes to mind as the most logical way to bring the birds back.

Like any land manager, you may expect to get out of your project about what you put into it in sweat, toil, and planning. You are well on the way if you have a fair knowledge of waterfowl food and cover plants and the needs of the birds. If you do not, your best first move is to talk to an expert, preferably one who knows the area where you think planting may be advisable. Later I suggest several sources of help.

Another general principle was made clear during the accelerated land acquisition program by Federal and State conservation agencies in the thirties and early forties, when much pond and marsh acreage was acquired and maintained or restored. People wanted to get new marshes quickly into production and improve old ones. The tendency was to create large impoundments and make extensive plantings with species of known value to waterfowl and for such special purposes as preventing the erosion of dikes. Many plantings were made without full regard for

Waterfowl biologist Francis M. Uhler planting Olney threesquare in brackish water at Blackwater National Wildlife Refuge, Maryland.

the needs of the plants or the consequences of their spread beyond control. As a result, plants often were taken out of their geographic range, and little thought was given to their adaptability to local conditions.

The rate of success of early planting efforts was low, but they pointed up the importance of careful planning. In deciding what to do consideration should be given the type of vegetation already growing on the site, the nature of the pond or marsh, food preferences of ducks using the tract, and the need for followup maintenance. Two points you need especially to remember in trying to reach a decision on the need for food and cover plantings.

First: Each type of plant has definite requirements that limit its occurrence. The alkalinity, salinity, wave action, clarity, or depth of water may be unsuitable. The soil may be too hard or too mucky. The growing season may be too short. Plants already growing on the site may compete too aggressively.

Second: Many plants of value to waterfowl can spread rapidly and become established in new areas or survive periods of adversity until conditions are more suitable for growth. If all factors are favorable for the growth of certain plants, many of them will become established eventually. But competition or other factors may retard their appearance. Here you can give a helping hand. Plantings are especially important on newly created ponds and marshes. There you may steal a march on Nature and prevent or at least delay invasion of unwanted plants by planting the ones you do want.

Even without plantings, new ponds almost always become covered with vegetation, some good, some bad. Special adaptations such as size, weight, durability, and special structures enable seeds and other propagules to be carried by wind and water or to hitchhike with birds and other animals to new locations. Once there, hard or waterproof seed coatings, special germination requirements, slow growth or rates of development, and ample stored food enable seeds or plants to survive adversity until favorable conditions return.

So, if the plants you desire are not present in waters that have been around for several years, look for limiting factors that might make planting them wasted effort.

BEFORE YOU PLANT, you will want to make an inventory of physical features of the pond or marsh you want to create or improve.

Start out by sketching a base map that shows as accurately as possible the depth contours, bottom types (rock, sand, loam, clay, peat, muck), water clarity, and kinds of plants already present. This diagram helps you judge whether plantings are needed, the species and quantity of planting stock to get, and the locations where the stock should be sown or set out.

Examine the soil carefully for evidence of present or past growth that may still be viable and producing food and cover for ducks or which may crowd out the plants you want to grow. Because the visible growth of aquatic plants often dies back in the fall or winter, leaving little or no superficial evidence of persisting seeds, stems, roots or tubers, the site may appear barren all winter and in the spring before growth commences. Later, as water and warm weather return, spores, seeds, stolons, bulbs, and fruits break dormancy and become productive. It is, therefore, best to visit the site several times during the growing season, including the periods when the plants are flowering, to get a true picture of actual conditions.

Watch the birds that use nearby habitats similar to the one you intend to develop. See what they are feeding on. Then doublecheck by trying to identify the contents of the gizzards of ducks taken during the hunting season. Compare them with seeds and tubers growing in the wild or as pictured in publications about duck foods. If you cannot puzzle them out, send them to your State agricultural college or visit one of the specialists I mention later. Some knowledge of the items being used by the birds will guide you in gathering planting materials or in ordering them from commercial sources. While collecting them you also will find out how and where the plants grow best.

PLANTS ALREADY THRIVING in your pond or marsh may not be the best for your purposes. If they are weedy types, you may have to eliminate them before you can hope to establish the ones that waterfowl will use.

You can do so by various methods that eradicate them or lessen their vitality. One is by direct control through hand-pulling, plowing, mowing, or using chemical herbicides.

Another method, usually preferred because it is safer and cheaper, is to change the water levels by deep flooding to drown out the undesirable plants, for example, or draining the pond to eliminate growth by drying them out.

Drastic measures, such as draining, may take the pond out of production for a time, but, like major surgery, it may be the only solution to some problems. While the pond bottom is exposed, desirable plants may volunteer or seeding can be carried out, as I describe later. Gradually restoring the water levels will permit the growth to continue so that it is available to ducks in the fall. You must watch these developments closely, because unwanted pest plants may become established while the water level is low. The best time to control them is before you start planting.

When you have the problems of weed control out of the way and know what plants you want to grow and where you want each species, sketch their locations on your map. Next, drive stakes to show the exterior limits of each planting. These markers will help you avoid overlapping in your sowing and should give you a much better idea of the eventual appearance of your pond or marsh vegetation pattern, assuming that most of your plantings are successful. The stakes will also pinpoint the unsuccessful ones if replanting is necessary. It will be easy to modify the pattern you previously diagramed on your map, as it actually appears, lifesize, on the ground.

As a general rule of thumb, in water deeper than 2 feet do not make plantings of cattails, bulrushes, sedges, wildrice, and other plants that rise well above the surface. Submergent species, such as pondweeds, wildcelery, naiads, and widgeongrass, which grow under water, are most productive in clear water at depths less than 6 feet. In turbid water, where much of the available light is absorbed by suspended materials or stains, there is little purpose in planting submergent food plants at depths beyond which a white china saucer is visible on a clear day. Under such conditions, plants may survive, but their production of edible parts is lessened.

Turbidity in a new pond or one in an eroded watershed may be considerable, but the pond water may gradually become clear as the plant growth increases unless carp, grazing livestock, or other factors continue to keep soil particles in suspension.

Fertility of the water also can be a problem. It may encourage algal bloom and obscure sunlight, but the algae or pondscums may disappear gradually as the higher plants use up the dissolved nutrients or substances which favor algae. As light penetration improves, it may be possible to make more productive plantings.

MOST OF THE aquatic plants you will want in your pond or marsh reproduce both by seed and vegetative structures, such as roots, bulbs, stolons, or even the upper plant parts. The materials you will use ordinarily will depend upon their availability, the planting location and conditions, and the purposes the plants are intended to serve.

Because plants are products of their environments, local strains usually do best under growing conditions similar to those in which they developed. With certain species, such as wildrice, seed gathered in the Northern States and planted at more southerly locations may not germinate, because temperatures may not be low enough to cause them to become properly conditioned. The planting stock should be from the same region and preferably from waters and soils like those at the planting site. Other advantages in obtaining materials nearby are lower transportation and storage costs and less deterioration of stock, especially if it is planted shortly after harvesting. Some companies that sell planting materials have representatives who can collect and ship stock from points near you.

Very likely you will find it enjoyable and instructive to harvest planting stock. You can do this at almost any season, but collections usually are made most easily in the late summer or fall when seed is ripe, or in late fall when the plants become dormant.

Seed often is preferred because of the ease of harvesting, drying, storing, transporting, and planting. Seed may be gathered by hand or with simple equipment. With a stick, ripened seed heads are rapped until they fall on a canvas or other cloth spread on the ground to catch them. This method is frequently used with annual plants, especially with such grasses as wild millets and tidemarsh waterhemp, as well as many kinds of smartweeds.

The seed heads of some plants, such as many of the bulrushes, sedges, and others that have more firmly attached seeds or fruiting structures, are plucked by hand or sheared off with a pocket knife, hedge trimmer, or scythe and left in the sun to dry. The chaff is removed easily by flailing and winnowing. Actually, if much seed is needed and ground or ice conditions are suitable for the use of powered equipment, tractor-drawn mowers and even self-propelled harvesting combines specially adjusted to collect and separate the seed are efficient.

Seeds of submerged plants often may be gathered where they lie windrowed along the margins of ponds, lakes, and rivers. They should be planted immediately or dried and then sifted through hardware cloth of suitable mesh. Many of the seeds obtained by this method may not sprout because of prolonged wetting and drying, but the ease of collection compensates for the reduced rate of germination. You should take all possible care to avoid collecting seeds of undesirable plants.

A few plants, such as native wildrice, require special handling to insure germination. With this species, keeping seed continuously immersed in cool, fresh water is a good precaution against spoilage before planting time.

The use of vegetative parts sometimes has a number of advantages over seed. Complete plants usually are easier to identify than seed, so there is less chance of accidentally introducing unwanted species. Perennials started from vegetative materials, being more robust and rapid growing because of abundant reserves of plant food, can be planted in temporarily deep and turbid water, where seeds of the same species may not germinate or survive.

You can use rakes and pitchforks to gather flexuous plants. Dislodge entire plants or parts of them, such as roots and tubers, stems, and leaves, all of which may produce new plants. They may be gathered and planted throughout the growing season. Some species may be gathered and planted anytime. One free-floating group, the duckweeds, can be skimmed off or screened from the water with sieves or sheets of hardware cloth.

You can harvest a large variety of perennial marsh plants most easily in late fall. Among them are certain grasses, bulrushes, spikerushes, sedges, arrowheads, cattails, smartweeds, and burreeds, and such pad-leaved species as waterlilies and watershield. The plants become dormant in late fall and may be removed and planted or stored with the least danger of injury. Many of them can be pulled by hand or dug from the ground with a spade. When soil conditions are suitable, some plants without taproots are removed in large quantities with a moldboard plow or homemade device set to shear the soil just below the main root level. The plants can then be removed individually or as small clumps or sods.

If planting stocks are not available locally or if you have no time or inclination to gather them, commercial nurseries that specialize in aquatic plants may be able to fill most of your needs. The companies advertise their products and services in sports magazines and provide descriptive pamphlets if you ask for them. The pamphlets usually include lists of plants suited to specific areas, brief comments on their value to wildlife, prices for quantities and planting suggestions. When you order, send a copy of your base map and any other information that may help the nursery to judge whether the plants you have ordered are suitable for your area. The nursery will send the propagules at the best planting time.

A word of caution, though: The pamphlets may oversimplify the problem, exaggerate desirable features, and not mention the undesirable aspects of some species. One company, for example, has recommended the planting of phragmites for developing hunting blinds and mentioned its value to ducks for cover but did not say it is a troublesome pest in many waterfowl habitats throughout the United

Plants "tie down" sand. Prevention of drifting sand is one of the major problems in maintaining waterfowl habitat along the Atlantic coast. Biologists here are planting sand-tolerant vegetation on a new dike to hold it in place.

States. All in all, however, these companies provide a useful service. In view of the difficulties in harvesting and storing the materials, the prices are reasonable and usually include shipping costs.

PLANTING IMMEDIATELY, regardless of whether you have harvested or purchased the stock, is preferable to storage, because you save money and effort and because the chances of loss or deterioration of the propagules are less. Storage may require considerable space and special equipment or controlled conditions. Some species can with-

stand adversity in storage, but most stock so handled will not give best results when planted.

Tubers, bulbs, and rootstocks should be stored in moist sand, Spanish moss, sphagnum moss, or other similar packing at temperatures low enough to prevent growth or spoilage. They also may be buried outdoors in late fall in shaded, moist soil; their prospects of surviving winter temperatures are good. In northern States, propagative materials can be arranged in loose layers in screened crates and then immersed in cold lakes or streams throughout the winter until planting time early in spring. The stored materials must be placed out of reach of flood damage or ice action, yet water must circulate freely through the crates.

Plant parts that are not dormant or that must be transported a considerable distance in warm weather should be packed in ice or kept cool and moist by other means and planted or stored as soon as possible after arriving.

A word of warning: The transporting of certain aquatic plant pests is restricted or forbidden by Federal and State laws. Among the more serious pests mentioned by existing and proposed legislation are alligatorweed and water-hyacinth in the South and Southeast, waterchestnut in the Northeast, and Eurasian watermilfoil and parrotfeather in various parts of the country. County agricultural extension agents can provide or help you obtain information on quarantined plant species.

Ornamental water-loving plants used by the aquarium or horticultural trade, including water-hyacinth, watermilfoil, lotus, and saltcedar, eventually may be discarded or intentionally planted in natural waters from which they spread. Such "foreign" weeds then may become especially troublesome because their natural enemies are absent and because you have improved conditions for all plants — the problem species as well as the desired ones.

Other plants that have value in certain parts of their range, but elsewhere may occupy space needed for more useful species, include

bladderwort, water-starwort, maidencane, phragmites, needlerush, leatherleaf, and the mints.

THERE IS NO CLOSED SEASON on planting—you can do it any time. Most planting, however, is best done in the fall or spring.

Fall planting is preferable since it allows you to collect and set out materials when water levels ordinarily are lowest. There is no overwinter storage problem, plants are more easily identified, and they will have a long rest period at low temperatures on the site where they are to germinate and grow in the spring.

The only important drawback with fall plantings is the possibility that they may float away or be destroyed or removed by muskrats, waterfowl, and other animals, or by ice action and water currents.

At planting time, you should study the plans you prepared earlier. Seeds, bulbs, roots, and cuttings are soaked in water for at least a day before setting them out. Soaking reduces their buoyancy and speeds up sprouting. Larger items, which tend to float or drift, may be weighted with a stone or a piece of metal, such as a nail, bolt, or nut, or they may be imbedded in clay or mud balls. Cheesecloth is good wrapping material for plants and the weights.

If you can wade in the water, push bulbs and roots into the bottom soil with your foot, hand, or a pole. Planting is easier if the water level of the pond or marsh can be lowered temporarily. Start in the deeper parts and work into the shallows, while restoring the water level gradually.

To avoid overlapping and to insure complete coverage where desirable, mark the limits of each planting site with stakes if you have not done so already. Deploy tubers and rootstocks in groups to create clumps of vegetation that eventually may measure from 6 to 12 feet in diameter. They will help to reduce wind and wave action against dikes or islands. At the same time they will provide nesting situations and materials for certain waterfowl and other marsh birds that build nests on or over water. Later the clumps can serve as hunting blinds.

Usually it is inadvisable to plant coarse, emergent plant species, such as cattails or the tall bulrushes, including hardstem and river bulrushes, in waters that are so shallow and expansive that large areas can become choked by such plants. The margins of dikes and small islands, which ducks use when they leave the water to preen or rest, attract them less when growth is rank. Only low-growing plants, such as spikerushes, should be encouraged therefore along the shore.

Seed intended to produce submergent plants can be broadcast where the bottom is suitable in water 2 to 6 feet deep. A bushel of medium-sized seeds (such as sago pondweed) will sow an acre if you broadcast a handful of them about every third step.

You should avoid plantings in established stands of vegetation unless you change management practices to favor the plant you are introducing. Scattering sago pondweed, wildrice, or bulrush seed into unbroken growths of rushes or cattails is fruitless, but this has been done when no inventory of the plants already present had been made. If plantings are to be made in such situations, the existing vegetation must first be eliminated or weakened by the methods I mentioned so that the new seedlings will have more favorable conditions for growth and spread.

WITH PLANTINGS COMPLETED, followup care usually is necessary to assure their survival. Immediate protection against wave action, excessive water depths, overuse by wildlife and livestock, and competition of other plants may be necessary.

Holding the water so that it barely covers the plantings until growth appears, and then gradually increasing the depth to optimum levels, will reduce wave action and stimulate plant growth, especially where you want seeds to germinate. This is a useful method for new ponds, but it involves some hazard with pest plants on the exposed bottoms of older wetlands.

It may be necessary to improvise temporary protection for the planted tubers and rootstocks from muskrats, livestock, and other animals that find them palatable. Muskrats can be removed by trapping. Carp can be eliminated by seining, trapping, or draining. Livestock can be kept out by fencing only the planted plots or the entire ponds and marshes, although controlled grazing may be necessary eventually to keep the areas open enough to be attractive to ducks.

Do not judge the success of most food and cover plantings solely on growth during the first season. Some plants require several years for good establishment. Others grow well initially, then decline, or disappear entirely the second season.

Of 1231 plantings of 16 aquatic species made in Maine during the thirties, and re-evaluated by the Maine Department of Inland Fisheries and Game in 1948, about 90 percent did not survive in significant quantity. Most of the failures were in waters that fluctuated widely or even became dry part of the time.

This apparently low rate of success may not be as poor as the percentage suggests and actually may be equal to or better than most other comparable efforts of that time. The few records that have been kept rarely have included preplanting inventories of the sites or experimental control plots to show what was present or might have occurred if no plantings had been made. Thus usually we have no standards by which to judge the success of older plantings.

On the other hand, plantings of hardstem bulrush by the Civilian Conservation Corps during the thirties in Federal refuge impoundments in North Dakota, Nebraska, Oregon, and many other States, have persisted. Many have spread excessively. In fact, willow cuttings originally planted to reduce erosion of dikes produced thickets that attracted beavers. The animals plugged culverts and headgates with branches

Wildrice being inspected by Bureau of Sport Fisheries and Wildlife biologist Clark Webster. This native grain provides valuable fall food for ducks, but it does not last into the winter.

and tunneled into the dikes, thereby complicating problems of water manipulation. Extensive work was needed later to control the willows and the beavers.

Planted stock, especially roots, tubers, and some large seeds, have food reserves that support thrifty initial growth. The plants may flower well and even set seed. Unless their continuing needs are met, however, limiting factors at any stage may curtail their development or eliminate them entirely.

Annuals, which ordinarily do not live from one season to another but rely on seed production and germination for replacement, may not last beyond the year that the planting is made if their seeds fail to sprout or the plants do not produce seed.

Francis M. Uhler, biologist at the Patuxent Wildlife Research Center in Maryland, has devoted many years to observing and experimenting with growth responses of food plantings for waterfowl in

Honkers on the rise.

many situations. He advises great care in choosing planting stock because of the variation in the seed production or vegetative growth of strains of plants under seemingly identical situations. He recognizes experimental values of the trial-and-error approach, but he believes that a sound understanding of the requirements of any plant is more apt to assure success.

This advice is all the more pertinent because we have few complete records of past operations in planting waterfowl food; probably they would list more failures than successes. That is normal in a field so complex and new and is a reason for further experiments and research. One thing is certain—there is a place for planting in waterfowl habitat management of tomorrow. By knowing what that place is and how to plant effectively, we can save effort, time, and money and attract ducks.

THE DO-IT-YOURSELF marsh manager will do well, first of all, to gain some basic understanding of plants important to waterfowl, of planting techniques, and of weed control. Here are a few of the better publications on these subjects: *Wildfowl Food Plants: Their Value, Propagation, and Management* by W. L. McAtee; *Michigan Waterfowl Management* by M. D. Pirnie; *Food of Game Ducks in the United States and Canada* by A. C. Martin and F. M. Uhler; and *Improving Duck Marshes by Weed Control* by A. C. Martin and others. The last two are circulars available for a small charge from the Superintendent of Documents, United States Government Printing Office, Washington, D.C., 20402.

FINALLY, let me point out some sources of more information. Conservation departments of the States and Canadian Provinces have technical personnel trained to find answers to your habitat management problems.

The Bureau of Sport Fisheries and Wildlife has five regional offices in the contiguous States and local representatives as refuge managers, wildlife management biologists, and game management agents. The Bureau has cooperative wildlife research units at 18 universities and wildlife research stations at several locations. In Canada, the Canadian Wildlife Service and Provincial agencies also have trained personnel to help you.

The Soil Conservation Service of the United States Department of Agriculture has biologists throughout the country, particularly in States where agriculture is prominent. That agency has undertaken a program to import and test various wetland food and cover plants with potential value to waterfowl.

A telephone call or letter or visit to the agriculture extension agent—the county agent—in your county seat, or to your State conservation department, may be a productive first step in getting the information you want. Their services are free and are gladly offered.

Another possibility is to employ a private wildlife management consultant. You may find that the dollars you pay him will be money well spent.—RAY C. ERICKSON.

Weedkillers and Waterfowl

IN THE FINAL analysis, the kind and distribution of plants largely determine the value of a marsh. Many marshes are choked with weeds of little use to waterfowl. Replacing them with useful plants is a challenge and a worthy enterprise.

A weed is a plant that is growing out of place. A plant may be a weed in one situation but not in another. Weedy plants, as we consider them here, are plants that reduce the usefulness of wetlands to waterfowl because of their low food and cover value; growth in dense, inpenetrable stands; or aggressiveness in competing with more useful plants.

Some wetland weeds are native species. Others come from other countries. Some infestations have worsened because of activities that have altered water levels or changed the fertility of water and bottom soil. Some undisturbed natural marshes are dominated by plants of low value to waterfowl. When they take over, the use of the marsh is limited.

PEOPLE CONTROL MARSH WEEDS by cultivating, mowing, burning, flooding, dewatering, and other means. The use of chemical weedkillers in waterfowl marshes is a newer way, a technique of management that can retard the downgrading of marshes, and produce favorable changes that result in greater use by waterfowl.

Downgrading may be an aspect

of plant succession—the replacement of one plant or a group of plants by another—which goes on all the time. If species of low value replace preferred food and cover plants, the use of the marsh by waterfowl is reduced. A good waterfowl marsh is a temporary stage in Nature's process of filling open water areas and gradually converting them to swamps and finally to uplands. Many wetlands are in advanced stages of conversion to wet meadows and uplands and offer little for waterfowl.

Research starting in the thirties on wetlands throughout the country disclosed that herbicides are a means of controlling cattail, water-hyacinth, sedges, phragmites, and various moist-soil grasses, which seal over the shallow open water and make the marshes unattractive to waterfowl. Setting plant succession back gives natural volunteer foods (such as millet and smartweed) a chance to become established. It also enhances the successful seeding of food plants.

A GOOD WATERFOWL MARSH contains an abundance of different food plants intermixed with enough emergent vegetation to protect the birds against rough weather and natural enemies. The birds will use water that is choked with sago pondweed and other submergent

Experimental control of alligatorweed with an herbicide near Cape Fear, North Carolina. This obnoxious plant crowds out desirable waterfowl food plants, eliminates open water, and clogs boat trails.

food plants, but the density and total area of the emergents are critical factors.

The amount of open water needed varies with the season and species of ducks and geese. Emergent plant growth should be scattered about in islands and strips intermixed with areas of open water. Small open patches are acceptable on northern breeding grounds. On migration areas and wintering grounds, the open water areas should be larger and should occupy up to 80 percent of the total marsh. A marsh that is choked with cattails, phragmites, or bulrushes is seldom used by waterfowl.

An edge, or line of change in habitat, exists in places where open water borders emergent vegetation or the shoreline. It offers the basic requirements of food, cover, and protection within a short distance. The marsh with the largest amount of edge generally supports the most waterfowl. Crooked shorelines or scattered patches of emergent vegetation increase the amount of edge.

An essential feature of a territory claimed and defended by each breeding pair of waterfowl during the nesting season is a loafing spot, which the male may use for preening, resting, and sunbathing while the female is at the nest. Drakes of many species prefer a stretch of beach or shoreline bare of vegetation yet protected from strong winds by cover plants nearby.

Each species of ducks and geese has different requirements for food and cover plants. The requirements change with the season and with daily changes in weather. The best waterfowl marsh must meet the varied food and cover requirements of many species during the time the birds are present.

A MARSH COMPLETELY COVERED by one or a few rank-growing, emergent plants, such as phragmites or cattail, provides little waterfowl food and lacks necessary variety of food and cover. As the density of emergent vegetation builds up in these marsh jungles, desirable features of the marsh are blotted out. The edge effect is gone. Shorelines are obliterated. Feeding and loafing areas are eliminated. Valuable food and cover plants are crowded out. Activities of the birds, particularly the movements of young broods, are restricted.

Algae sometimes is a problem. The stringy, filamentous type may cover the water surface with a floating mat and cut off necessary light for valuable submerged aquatic food plants. If such marshes are dewatered, mats of algae may dry into hard crusts on the exposed bottom soil and prevent growth of millet and other moist-soil food plants that normally would develop.

SALT, SMELTER WASTES, petroleum oils, and other common materials have been used for centuries to kill unwanted plant growth.

Since the discovery of the herbicidal properties of 2,4-D in the forties, a number of highly effective weedkillers have been discovered. Among them are chemical relatives of 2,4-D, TCA, dalapon, several triazines, substituted ureas, and amitrole.

Many wildlife biologists have done considerable research on the herbicidal control of marsh weeds, particularly cattail, alligatorweed, water-hyacinth, phragmites, needle-rush, waterchestnut, Eurasian water-milfoil, and saltcedar.

Wetland weeds differ in their susceptibility to herbicides. Seldom is a herbicide fully effective against undesirable species yet nontoxic to desirable plants. A selective herbicide is one that will kill or control one species but will not harm others. As research continues, more is being learned of the selective weedkilling capabilities of some chemicals and how to use them in managing waterfowl habitat.

The materials we discuss are a few of the better ones that have been used to control various types of marsh vegetation.

SILVEX, 2,4-D, and 2,4,5-T are related chemicals that are used in agriculture. One or more of them will control a high percentage of the broad-leaved plants in wetlands. They generally do not kill grasslike plants. In waterfowl marshes they are used primarily on woody plants and broad-leaved weeds, like water-hyacinth, waterlilies, and water-chestnut. These herbicides are available as granules for dry application or as liquids for spraying.

Dalapon and TCA are used on farms and industrial tracts against annual and perennial grasses and grasslike plants. In wetlands they are used also to control cattails, rushes, phragmites, and other grasses. Dalapon is primarily effective when it is applied to green

active growth. TCA is most effective when it is absorbed by roots. Dalapon is effective on vegetation in shallow water, but TCA is not.

Amitrole alone and in combination with ammonium thiocyanate is primarily a nonselective control agent for many annual and perennial plants in waterfowl habitat. It is used on cattail, phragmites, and other perennial grasses and some broad-leaved weeds. In Florida, amitrole-T for control of water-hyacinth is reported safer than 2,4-D from the standpoint of damage to desirable food plants and crops to which it may drift. Combinations of amitrole-T and fenac likewise are reported to be superior to other treatments. Amitrole must be applied to green, actively growing foliage. Amitrole and dalapon together are effective on cattail and phragmites, even in shallow water.

SOIL STERILANTS are weedkilling compounds that remain active in soil for long periods. Treated areas are bare of vegetation up to several years. The sterilants include boron compounds, sodium chlorate, Monuron, diuron, TBA, erbon, atrazine, and simazine. They are used in marshes mostly to create small openings and loafing spots in beachline vegetation.

Atrazine and simazine are toxic to many plants. Corn and a few others are tolerant. The use of delapon or amitrole, either alone or with 2,4-D, will remove vegetation and facilitate the production of corn in patches, even where plantings are made directly on uncultivated soil.

BEST RESULTS are had when herbicides are applied at the proper rate and time. The stage of plant growth, temperature of the water, and the prospect of rain also should be taken into account.

Equipment for application ranges from small hand sprayers and broadcasters to large ground-spray rigs and aircraft sprayers. The proper type to use is determined by size and location of the marsh to be treated and the chemical used.

Application from aircraft is especially efficient in areas difficult to reach with other equipment. Experienced pilots can do an excellent job on small as well as large tracts. For example, a series of small openings can be created in dense vegetation simply by starting and stopping the sprayer on a straight line course of flight.

Surface applicators are better than aircraft if the amount of material to be applied per unit area is high and placement requirements are exact—especially if small areas are to be treated.

SPRAYING MARSH WEEDS with herbicides generally causes no obvious, direct damage to waterfowl if the proper material is used in a prescribed manner.

The herbicides we named for use in marshes were selected for their low toxicity to animals as well as for their effect upon marsh weeds.

Some products are extremely hazardous to aquatic animal life, particularly fish and other animals that live in a closed environment. Among them are arsenic compounds, chlorinated benzenes, dinitro compounds, aromatic oils, and acrolein. Herbicides known to be toxic to wildlife should not be used on waterfowl habitat.

Hazards to waterfowl from herbicides used to control marsh and aquatic vegetation are negligible when those of low toxicity to animals are selected, when directions are carefully followed, and when care is taken to avoid overdosing and spillage.

The oil carriers used with some herbicides can have a toxic effect on aquatic animal life but are not toxic at the low volumes used. Amitrole, 2,4-D, dalapon, simazine, silvex, and certain others have a low toxicity to waterfowl.

Permits for spraying are required in some States. Anyone considering the use of herbicides in marsh management should consult local authorities regarding State regulations and specific directions for use. The following precautions are vital when one uses herbicides in marsh management:

Use only in specific places where the need is established, where herbicides can do the job best, and where benefits outweigh potential hazards.

Select the safest weedkiller.

Treat the smallest possible area needed to accomplish the objective.

Spray when any potential hazard to the birds is low.

Do not apply at rates higher than those recommended.

Use water-based sprays in preference to oil solutions or water-oil emulsions.

Read and follow directions on the labels of the herbicide container.

When the same or some other

undesirable plant species invades treated areas, it is usually necessary and desirable to follow herbicidal treatment with other management techniques, such as grazing, mowing, flooding, or the use of a different herbicide, depending on the situation.

For example: Duckweed is a tiny, floating, aquatic plant acceptable as duck food. It often invades openings following removal of cattail with dalapon if the treated spots are reflooded to a depth of more than a foot. Increasing the depth of the water after applications of herbicides generally retards invasion by low-value emergent species. Different species require varying depths of water to prevent reinvasion.

To delay regrowth of treated plants or invasion of other trash species, treated areas may be seeded to valuable food or cover plants, such as millet or smartweed, if the treated area can be dewatered and soil conditions are suitable. These desirable species compete for space, moisture, light, and plant nutrients and thus retard or prevent the entry of less desirable plants.

LARGE-SCALE CONTROL of marsh plants may be accomplished most effectively and economically by burning, flooding, dewatering, mowing, cultivation, or grazing by livestock, or by such wildlife species as muskrats and nutria. Where those methods fail, herbicides may be especially useful. Costs of materials range from 1.5 dollars to 20 dollars an acre, depending on the rate of application and kind of weeds to be controlled. Soil sterilants are more expensive and are generally used only in creating small openings for loafing sites along shorelines.

Cost of application will be as low as 1.50 dollars an acre for large-area, low-volume treatments by aircraft or field sprayers. Higher application costs will be encountered where it is necessary to use other equipment.

We list six typical situations in which herbicides may be used to advantage:

Creating open-water places in dense, emergent vegetation for nesting by diving ducks and coots and for general use by all waterfowl.

Making openings in shoreline vegetation for loafing spots used by breeding ducks.

Controlling brush and tall herbaceous plants on nesting islands and inaccessible sandbars used by geese and ducks as loafing and resting spots.

Controlling algae to reduce the hazard of algal poisoning and to improve growth of food plants by increasing penetration of light.

Destroying emergent vegetation used as travel lanes by predators to reach nesting islands from the mainland.

Controlling woody vegetation on dikes, ditches, and canals and around water-control structures to facilitate maintenance.

All bear on the point we started with: It is the kind and distribution of plants that largely determine the value of a marsh. Herbicides are one of the tools available for controlling vegetation and keeping the marsh attractive to waterfowl.

—CLAIR T. ROLLINGS
and ROBERT L. WARDEN.

Farming for Waterfowl

THE USE OF farm crops in the management of waterfowl is new, but the use of grain by waterfowl is not.

North American Indians patch-farmed long before white men came. Chroniclers of the Ponce de Leon, Narvaez, and DeSoto expeditions in the 16th century mentioned the extensive agriculture the Southeastern tribes practiced. Corn was a major crop, and when their fields in river bottoms were flooded, the corn that grew there and the ducks that visited them were brought together. Writers in the late 17th century told how ducks flocked to the ricefields of early settlers in South Carolina.

The face of North America has changed since the days of the Indians and the colonial rice planters.

Much of our best natural waterfowl habitat is gone. Ponds and marshes have been filled to create new sites for housing and industry. Drainage for agriculture and mosquito control has dried up others. Overgrazing and improper farming practices have allowed dust and silt to fill others. Canals have drained fresh-water marshes that once supported a wealth of food plants for waterfowl. Pollution has ruined additional thousands of acres of the Nation's best underwater feeding areas. Straightening stream channels to control floods has prevented winter overflows that once shallowly flooded thousands of acres of hardwood bottoms and made tons of mast available to feeding ducks. Still more thousands of acres of bottomland hardwoods have been cleared for river reservoirs, which may furnish ample water but no food for waterfowl.

This destruction of natural habitat has been offset partly by the construction of many great impoundments, including irrigation pools of the Bureau of Reclamation, reservoirs of the Tennessee Valley Authority, navigation, power, and flood control impoundments of the Corps of Engineers, and hydroelectric reservoirs of power companies. In some of the manmade lakes, clear water and relatively stable levels permit the growth of some aquatic plants. In most of them, however, deep water and drastic fluctuation prevent the growth of aquatic vegetation. If these areas are to hold waterfowl and help offset the loss of natural habitat it is necessary that a supplemental food supply be available. This can be residues from agricultural crops, providing the birds normally arrive after harvest is essentially complete. In some areas, where standing or swathed grain is available when the birds arrive, it may be necessary to provide crops grown specifically for the birds if a depredation problem is to be avoided.

THE SUCCESS of early experiments on farming for waterfowl opened a new field of management opportunities and possibilities.

Good natural foods grow only in specialized wetland sites, but farm crops can grow on most open, arable land. Modern farming methods, including the use of chemical fertilizers where needed, can make an acre produce thousands of pounds of highly nutritious food—as much or more than can be had from the best natural production.

We can grow regular farm crops around reservoirs and so convert them into first-class waterfowl concentration areas. A farming program also can be used to supplement natural foods at places where they are insufficient to support the birds for long periods.

Farm crops also help solve special problems. In the Sacramento Valley of California, a scarcity of natural food forced ducks into irrigated fields, where they fed heavily on rice and other crops. Intensive farming on the Sacramento, Colusa, and Sutter National Wildlife Refuges held the ducks there and reduced depredations on private land. On St. Marks National Wildlife Refuge in northern Florida, Canada geese had abandoned their ancestral feeding grounds on the tidal flats and turned to nearby peanutfields. The result was excessive kills during hunting seasons. Farming on the refuge attracted the birds back into the closed area. At other times, food plantings have brought about better distribution of the birds and created new hunting opportunities.

Farming for waterfowl has limitations. Only shallow-water ducks feed on upland fields; mallards, black ducks, American widgeon, and pintails use them regularly and heavily. Practically all geese, particularly Canada geese, however, take readily to upland crops. In many places they subsist almost entirely on corn and pasture mixtures and return to water only for drink and sanctuary. Upland farming for

Plowing at Savannah National Wildlife Refuge in Georgia to control pest weeds and prepare the ground for planting waterfowl food plants.

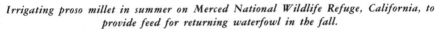

Irrigating proso millet in summer on Merced National Wildlife Refuge, California, to provide feed for returning waterfowl in the fall.

Refuge manager and permittees on the Squaw Creek National Wildlife Refuge, Missouri, examine the crop before dividing it on a share basis. The Government's share will be left standing to provide food for waterfowl and other wildlife.

A sprinkler system is used to irrigate a crop of millet planted for waterfowl at McNary National Wildlife Refuge in Washington.

waterfowl has critics as well as supporters. Some speak disdainfully of "dry land ducks." Others see in it a hope for maintaining waterfowl for tomorrow.

Waterfowl feeding in fields tend to decoy other waterfowl, including species that we do not customarily regard as field feeders. In places where farming programs have been in progress for some years, we have noted more field use by widgeons, wood ducks, and teal.

MANAGEMENT OF UPLANDS brings corresponding changes in the feeding habits of waterfowl. Geese usually discover food in fields quickly, but ducks are more reluctant, in some localities, to use uplands. Sometimes it is necessary to "train" ducks to feed in fields by leaving only small amounts of crops in the choicest locations at first and gradually expanding the program as the birds become accustomed to field feeding. The human activity that normally occurs on open land during daylight hours sometimes has led ducks to change from day to night feeding. Geese likewise have adjusted themselves to a greater degree of night use.

Some blue and snow geese, which normally are marsh feeders, have abandoned their ancestral wintering ground along the Louisiana coast and now winter nearly 500 miles to the north on cornfields of the Wheeler National Wildlife Refuge in Alabama. At Sand Lake National Wildlife Refuge in South Dakota and Squaw Creek National Wildlife Refuge in Missouri, usage by these species often exceeds that of Canada geese.

Do WATERFOWL PREFER cultivated crops to the natural foods that have supported them for countless years, or does necessity force them into the fields?

How important is farming in feeding the migratory waterfowl resource?

The first question: An experience at the Wheeler National Wildlife Refuge during 1961 and early 1962 gives something of an answer. The collapse of a lock wall at Wheeler Dam of the Tennessee Valley Authority almost drained that reservoir and left thousands of acres of moist mudflats, which produced rank stands of smartweeds, wild millet, and other natural food plants. Tons of seed were produced.

Although ducks for years had fed in the agricultural fields of the refuge, not a single instance of ducks using fields was noted during the fall and winter of 1961–1962. The refuge winters some 45 thousand Canada geese, but even they seemed to prefer the natural food, and their use of uplands was sharply reduced. In this instance the birds had a choice of natural food on mudflats—often covered or partly submerged by winter floodings— and food in agricultural fields.

As to the second question: We know that farming for waterfowl is important in some localities. States with good natural habitat have avoided this costly method of assuring food for the birds because the need for a supplemental food supply was not critical. Louisiana, for example, has vast, valuable coastal marshes, but only a fraction of 1 percent of the waterfowl on refuge and management areas use cultivated crops. But in Kentucky, where habitat is limited, 16 percent of the waterfowl use natural foods; 84 percent depend on crops. In Wisconsin, usage is divided about equally between natural and cultivated foods.

Farming is used extensively on national wildlife refuges to provide food for migrating and wintering waterfowl and to lessen depredations. Surveys at several refuges in 1961–1962 showed that about one-third of all feeding by waterfowl was on cultivated crops. Seventy-five percent of the geese and 30 percent of the ducks using national wildlife refuges in the Southwestern States are harbored on refuges, where farming for waterfowl is practiced. Three million birds were maintained for several weeks in California on three small, farm-type refuges totaling 17 thousand acres.

MANY FARM CROPS are used by waterfowl. Several are useful in a wide range of soil and climatic conditions. They are corn, the grain sorghums, rice, millets, wheat, oats, barley, rye, ryegrass, alfalfa, certain clovers, soybeans, some pea species, and buckwheat. Their many strains and varieties make it necessary to select the ones that are suited to a locality.

Food crops grown for waterfowl are essentially of two types: Those that produce seed and those that produce green forage.

Seed crops are summer annuals that have hard fruits—seeds. Forage crops are annual or perennial grasses and legumes that provide green food for geese and, to a lesser degree, for ducks.

Occasionally the same crop may be used by waterfowl both as seed and green forage. Wheat and barley are eaten in the seed stage in the Northwestern States and western Canada. Farther south the seeds of those plants mature in June and July and usually sprout or rot before waterfowl arrive, and the crops are useful only as green forage.

The matter of food preferences is complex, mainly because of the many species of waterfowl. Wheat is a preferred forage in all localities. Legumes, especially alfalfa and ladino clover, are more nutritious than the grain forages. The preferred seeds are corn, rice, and grain sorghum. Millet, barley, and wheat are almost as good. Soybeans and other legume seeds usually rank below grain in acceptability. A greater competition for food, however, means that preferences for various seed and forage crops are less well defined.

ECONOMICS may determine the type of crops in any farming program for waterfowl. Broadcast crops are produced more cheaply than row crops, and several good waterfowl foods, including the millets, grain sorghum, buckwheat, and various forage species, grow well in broadcast stands. Corn must be planted in rows and well fertilized and cultivated. Soybeans, for best yields, also must be row cropped. Other factors that bear on crops and planting methods include the competition from pest plants and the possibility that mature crops can be flooded or must be fed upon dry

Corn is the most satisfactory of all agricultural feeds eaten by waterfowl, and varieties are suited to growth in practically all States. Ducks and geese relish corn. It produces good yields of a highly nutritious feed except it is low in protein.

Waterfowl are surprisingly adept at extracting the kernels from ears of standing corn, but corn that is leveled or flooded is more readily available to them.

(Note: Manipulation of standing crops [other than by flooding] constitutes baiting under Federal regulation, and it is illegal to take birds attracted to such feed. One should know the Federal regulations on the handling of domestic crops where hunting is to occur.)

The amount of corn that birds eat varies according to the species and conditions. In Kansas, a 100-acre field, estimated to contain 25 bushels an acre, was mowed, and the corn was consumed in a week by 85 thousand ducks and 15 thousand geese. The average consumption was calculated to be 3 to 4 ounces a bird per day.

The grain sorghums—milo maize, kafir corn, hegari, feterita, and other varieties—are accepted readily by geese and ducks. They are suited to a variety of soil and moisture conditions in a wide geographic range. They are more drought resistant than corn and produce well in broadcast stands. The sorghums are susceptible to more damage by small birds, insects, and disease, and the grains sprout or rot rather quickly in wet weather.

Low-growing varieties are used most easily by waterfowl. Flooding, mowing, or "railing down" the crop encourage consumption. A 25-acre field in southern Kansas was estimated to produce 23 bushels of grain an acre—a total of about 35 thousand pounds. The total crop was consumed by 10 thousand white-fronted geese in 3 weeks. Two hundred acres of milo, supplemented by 700 acres of young wheat in southern Texas, held 20 thousand geese and ducks for 5 months.

Rice is one of the best of all waterfowl food crops. It is particularly attractive to mallards and pintails. Geese feed upon the seed and graze the green stubble. White-fronted and snow geese may even consume the straw. Ducks maintain themselves on 3 or 4 ounces of seed daily, but they may take 8 ounces or more a day. Rice for waterfowl is used mainly in Arkansas, Louisiana, Texas, and California. In places, especially in California, it is grown so as to draw ducks away from other crops. Rice is eagerly consumed by ducks and produces a good yield, but it is expensive to grow, has special soil requirements, requires an ample water supply, and is subject to heavy damage by small birds, especially blackbirds.

Millet includes a number of annual grasses of many species and varieties. All are used by waterfowl, especially ducks. Adaptability to local soil and moisture conditions determines which variety to plant, but wild millet, Japanese millet, and browntop millet usually have proved best.

The millets are cheaply produced in broadcast stands and mature in a short season. They also may be damaged heavily by small birds and require shallow flooding for best use by waterfowl.

Wheat and barley are dual-purpose crops. They provide green forage wherever planted and grain in the Western and Northwestern States and Western Canada. Wheat and barley planted there in spring mature in early fall. The seed is eagerly taken by ducks and geese. In southern Colorado, 100 acres of good barley are required to sustain 10 thousand mallards through 3 winter months. Five to six ounces per bird per day maintains mallards in good condition through severe weather. In the West, the grains are taken standing or swathed, but in the more humid East, they can be used only for forage. Fall-planted wheat and barley mature in early summer and rot before migrant waterfowl arrive.

Barley is consumed as green forage, but its recovery from grazing is slow. Wheat, however, is one of the best forage crops for waterfowl. It is so attractive and is grazed so heavily in some places that the less desirable oats and rye are added in planting to extend the period of use.

One hundred acres of wheat should be planted for each thousand wintering geese—an appropriate ratio—to avoid overgrazing and permit a normal wheat harvest. On a refuge in northern Oklahoma, 1,500 acres of wheat were barely enough to sustain 25 thousand to 30 thousand Canada geese through 4 to 5 months of cold weather. One 200-acre stand of young wheat was consumed completely by 3 thousand geese in 4 days.

Young oats also provide good forage for geese. The crop is well adapted to certain soil and climatic conditions, particularly in the South-east. Care must be used to time the planting so the stand is not over-rank when geese begin to use it. Oats less than 4 inches in height are almost as palatable as young wheat.

Italian or annual ryegrass provides fine forage and has characteristics that make it especially desirable. It is more resistant to silting and flooding than any of the small grains. It survives flooding for periods up to 2 weeks. Even when it is planted early, it does not become too coarse for good usage. It can tolerate a wide range of soil, moisture, and climatic conditions. The seed requires little soil coverage for germination and is well adapted to overseeding in fields that have grown corn and other summer crops. Such fields provide an ideal combination of hard food and green forage. It is suitable for planting on sandy locations along the Atlantic coast and will withstand salt spray and high wind.

Several legumes, notably alfalfa and the clovers, provide good green forage. Alfalfa is expensive to establish, is subject to insect damage, and requires specialized soil conditions, but it furnishes excellent grazing for geese in some parts of the country and often is consumed heavily by some ducks, especially American widgeon. In northern sections, it is subject to freezing and dormancy.

Ladino, white dutch, crimson, red, and alsike are the clovers most frequently used in waterfowl management. Mixed with perennial grasses, ladino and white dutch clovers form fine goose pastures that do not require annual planting

Millet is grown as a waterfowl food crop in Utah. Millet seed makes excellent duck feed if it matures by the time birds arrive in the fall.

Millet seeded by airplane on Lower Souris National Wildlife Refuge in South Dakota provides food in the fall for migrating waterfowl.

To keep growth succulent, stands should be mowed or grazed low before their use by waterfowl begins. If extremely heavy use is expected, rank stands are less subject to damage if they are left as they are. All legume forages are more nutritious than the grasses and may substitute for seed foods to some extent.

Two legumes, soybeans and field peas, are seed foods of some importance, although neither is preferred to the grains and grasses, and consumption is lower.

Soybeans and peas produce fairly well in broadcast stands, but soybeans should be row cropped, well fertilized, and clean cultivated for maximum production. The large-seeded oil varieties usually are best for waterfowl planting.

Sometimes when geese feed on soybeans their crops become distended and impacted. A few to hundreds of such afflicted birds die from time to time. The condition is triggered by a combination of factors, especially parasite infections and lead poisoning.

Field peas are best adapted to light, sandy soil. Ducks and geese usually favor them above soybeans. The seed decomposes quickly after contact with soil.

Buckwheat has the advantages of good acceptability by waterfowl, a short growing season, and ability to produce fair yields when broadcast. Normally considered a northern crop, buckwheat can be grown southward to southern Florida. It does best, however, in moist soil and a cool growing season. Seed should be planted about 65 days before the date of expected frost.

CERTAIN MODIFICATIONS of normal agricultural practices are involved

Preparing ground on the Lower Klamath National Wildlife Refuge on the California-Oregon border for the planting of crops to feed migratory waterfowl.

in producing crops for waterfowl; most of them reduce the efficiency of operation.

Federal and State wildlife agencies that want to attract and hold waterfowl may farm certain public lands for this purpose themselves. In other instances, public lands are farmed under a lease or share-crop arrangement.

Depending on the degree of interest and the returns from commercial hunting, individuals and private groups will sustain programs of various size and cost. Some hunting clubs make heavy investments in crops and in the aggregate they make a great deal of food available to waterfowl. Individuals, obliged to make a living from agricultural crops, may limit farming for waterfowl to a few unpicked rows of corn near a farm pond. In any event, the aim is to attract birds and improve hunting. The method can be effective, but costly, when it is on a large scale. Paul Scheffer, of the United States Soil Conservation Service, found in California that farmers could profitably develop their marginal agricultural lands for waterfowl hunting. On three areas in the Central Valley initial development costs were 95 dollars an acre; fixed annual maintenance and operating costs were 36 dollars.

THE AVERAGE COST of producing corn or other solid foods varies with the locality but usually ranges from 18 dollars to 25 dollars an acre. If irrigation is needed, the cost of row-crop production often approaches 50 dollars an acre. Drilled or broadcast crops can be produced for about 15 dollars an acre on

nonirrigated land or 25 dollars an acre when irrigated. It costs 10 to 15 dollars an acre to establish forage crops.

Although waterfowl may fly 10 to 20 miles for food, fields near water are most desirable, especially those on islands, peninsulas, and shores. Only the better locations should be farmed in the early stages of management. As numbers and competition for food increase, the birds seem less sensitive to the size and location of fields, to the nearness of cover, and to disturbance. Proper cultivation, high yields, and good land management are the aims in farming for waterfowl, just as they are in cash farming.

TIMING IS VITAL. Crops must be available when needed, of the proper type, and in adequate quantity. In northern areas, food is produced primarily for migrant fowl. A large volume therefore must be available for a short period, usually from early September through November. Further south, where birds spend the entire cold-weather period, the use period is longer, and crops must be available from mid-October through mid-February. During spring migration hunting pressure does not limit their feeding range. The birds have many fields to choose from and usually are not dependent on waterfowl management areas.

Crops maturing too soon in summer or early fall may be wasted, as weeds come on to hide the food. The seed may shatter and sprout or be consumed by hordes of small birds. Crops maturing too late will be bypassed by migrating birds;

610 WATERFOWL TOMORROW

then the efforts of the entire year are wasted.

Cropping should aim for a proper balance of solid seed and green forage in amounts to satisfy the number and species of waterfowl expected. Provision should be made for suitable resting areas on water, mudflats, or sandbars, preferably those that have no screens of timber to separate them from adjoining fields. Resting areas must offer reasonable security from disturbance.

FARMING FOR WATERFOWL is not without problems.

Crows, starlings, and blackbirds often make serious inroads on many plantings. They are attracted especially to grain sorghums and other small-seeded crops.

Deer, if they are numerous, can destroy sizable acreages of corn, soybeans, peas, and other legumes.

As with any other agricultural operation, insects, diseases, pest plants, and unfavorable weather are always hazards.

Once accustomed to using farm crops, waterfowl may engage in undue depredation, because they do not distinguish between crops on managed areas and crops on other lands. Birds, normally, are welcome by most landholders while hunting seasons are open; these same persons bemoan crop losses as soon as seasons close.

Occasionally some well-intentioned individual creates a private sanctuary by feeding a small flock of visiting geese, only to find, a few years later, that he is swamped by thousands of these birds that are beyond his means to support.

Farming for waterfowl is a method of proved effectiveness in reducing the number harvested by hunters; yet in other ways it can be equally effective in increasing the hunting take. It can concentrate large numbers of ducks and geese where that may be desirable or disperse them over wide areas to meet other objectives.

Farming for waterfowl can be done legally or illegally so it behooves the farm managers to know the difference.

The growing demands for land may well lead to shortages of suitable feeding areas for waterfowl. The growing numbers of people complicate the problem of providing a reasonable distribution of this cherished natural resource. Domestic crops, intensively managed, offer the prospect for producing great quantities of waterfowl food on a limited acreage. And in their eager acceptance of dryland crops, waterfowl lend themselves to management in many ways. The plow, disk, and drill are not likely to solve all the problems of waterfowl management, but this new technique, refined and better understood, is sure to find a place among intensive methods for managing waterfowl in the years ahead.—LAWRENCE S. GIVENS, MARCUS C. NELSON and VERNON EKEDAHL.

MALLARDS

Green Trees and Greenheads

ACORNS are a staff of life of many species of wildlife that live in woodlands. Deer relish them, and the knowing hunter seeks out stands of oak as the place to hunt when the acorns fall. Grouse gorge on them, as do raccoons and wild turkeys. Squirrels grow fat on the bounteous crops of mast.

And later, when fall and winter rains soak the ground and push creeks and rivers out of their banks, the extensive hardwood bottom lands of the South become overnight the feeding grounds of millions of mallards and wood ducks and a magnet that draws hunters from the breadth of the continent.

Some years the fall rains do not come or are too little or too late. Then the ducks, finding no water, go elsewhere to feed. And duck hunters, denied their sport, try to find a way to improve on Nature.

They found a way in the late thirties near Stuttgart in eastern Arkansas, a section already famous for mallards attracted by the Grand Prairie ricefields and seasonally flooded pin oak flats. Their idea was to flood the timberland artificially and so attract ducks on schedule. Such timberlands they

611

call "green tree reservoirs." Dead tree reservoirs preceded them; they were caused by irrigation reservoirs, which had been built to provide a water supply for rice production and had killed trees by submerging them during their growing season. Green tree reservoirs thus came into being for a double reason: They attracted ducks but they did not interfere with proper management of the timber resource.

Many of the 160-odd duck clubs, which control more than 53 thousand acres—primarily forested lowlands—in the Grand Prairie-Bayou Meto district near Stuttgart, depend on green tree reservoirs, because natural overflows generally occur late in the waterfowl season or do not flood the forestlands. It is a strategic location for green tree development, for it is in the mallard-rich Mississippi Flyway, and has extensive hardwood bottoms, an abundance of oaks, and good terrain. It is not uncommon around Stuttgart for timbered tracts of 100–200 acres to hold 25 thousand to 50 thousand mallards. Sometimes 250 thousand ducks may be temporarily concentrated on a few hundred acres. When both the developed areas and the overflow bottoms are watered-up by man and Nature, this type of habitat may winter the bulk of the mallards in the Mississippi Flyway.

GREEN TREE RESERVOIRS for a few years were unique to eastern Arkansas and helped to support Stuttgart's claim to be the mallard capital of the world. Word of their success began to spread. The Arkansas Game and Fish Commission took an early lead in green tree development in conjunction with a vigorous land-acquisition program. Green tree reservoirs were in operation by the midfifties in a number of States in the lower Mississippi Valley.

The Missouri Conservation Commission developed a 600-acre green tree reservoir for public hunting on its Duck Creek Wildlife Area in southeastern Missouri in 1956.

Most States in the lower Mississippi Flyway had green tree reservoirs in operation by 1963. Several States in the Atlantic Flyway as far north as Maryland had small projects planned or in operation. Noxubee National Wildlife Refuge, near Starkville, in Mississippi, exemplifies what green tree development can do in an area previously considered of minor importance to ducks. Before its first green tree reservoir of some 400 acres was developed in 1955, the refuge had a peak duck population of 21 thousand. With initial operation of the reservoir during the 1955–1956 season, the number rose to 46 thousand. Since completion in 1958 of a second green tree reservoir of 340 acres, the peak duck population at Noxubee has twice exceeded 100 thousand.

A good gauge of green tree reservoirs as winter habitat is their total use by waterfowl. Before the developments at Noxubee, the maximum number of use-days recorded during any one season was 1.8 million. With 740 acres of green tree habitat in operation, the maximum number of use-days during a single season has been more than 6 million. This three-fold increase took place during a period of declining mallard numbers in the flyway as a whole.

Green tree reservoirs need not be on such a large scale to be effective. Even small reservoirs containing desirable oak mast and properly flooded will attract both greenheads and woodies if they are anywhere in the neighborhood.

THE KINDS OF DUCKS that use green tree reservoirs are much the same in different parts of the country. The mallard is the major species on green tree reservoirs in the Mississippi Flyway. In Arkansas, mallards comprise about 90 percent of the ducks in flooded green timber, and wood ducks, most of the remaining 10 percent.

Mallards account for about 75 percent and wood ducks about 15 percent of the total use by ducks in the green tree reservoirs at the Noxubee Refuge. The remaining use is primarily by ring-necked ducks, black ducks, hooded mergansers, and green-winged teal, but all species wintering at Noxubee, except canvasback, have been seen in the flooded green timber.

On the basis of known use on existing reservoirs and the general wintering distribution of mast-feeding ducks, it is not difficult to predict which species might use green tree developments. King mallard will reign in most sections of the Mississippi Flyway, but local and migrant wood ducks will often monopolize these reservoirs in October or early November before the main flights of mallards arrive.

No one species will dominate the use of the reservoirs in the Atlantic Flyway. Green tree developments in the southern end of the Atlantic Flyway can be expected to attract wood ducks primarily, along with smaller numbers of mallards, ring-necked ducks, and blacks. A flooded stand of good oaks anywhere between South Carolina and Maryland is almost sure to attract woodies, blacks, and mallards, any one of which may be the dominant species.

Mast-producing trees, suitable terrain and soils, water, and ducks—these are the basic components of a successful green tree reservoir. The finished product can be large or small, cheap or expensive, good or bad, depending on the quality and quantity of the components and how they are mixed.

FEW SECTIONS can hope to match the success of green tree developments in eastern Arkansas, where pin oak flats occur on impervious clay soils of terrace lands almost as flat as a table top. Low levees, relatively inexpensive to construct under such conditions, can impound several inches of water over large tracts. Natural streams and rice irrigation systems provide a dependable water supply. The mallard, like other puddle ducks, is inclined to be lazy about his feeding, and in the pin oak flats it is often unnecessary for him to tip-up to fill his crop with bite-size acorns.

In the selection of a site for a green tree reservoir, the basic requirements—mast, suitable terrain and soils, and water—should be given almost equal consideration.

The quality and quantity of each may vary, but they are all essential if the reservoir is to be successful in attracting ducks.

Few studies of food habits have been directed specifically toward ducks on green tree developments. Crop and stomach contents of 20 mallards and 9 wood ducks collected at Noxubee Refuge showed that acorns made up almost 100 percent of the food taken. Acorns were a major food item of mallards, pintails, ring-necked ducks, and wood ducks in Missouri one fall. An examination of the crops of 583 mallards killed by hunters near Stuttgart revealed that acorns comprised 29 percent by volume of the total foods taken. This will vary each year, however, depending on availability of feed in ricefields and other factors.

OAKS HEAD THE LIST of mast species that are desirable in a green tree reservoir managed primarily for waterfowl. Bottom land oaks with small acorns are the best source of feed, but little research has been done to determine which species are preferred.

In Missouri, the pin oak seemed to be the main species used by ducks, presumably because of its widespread occurrence as pure stands in areas close to water or subject to flooding. At Noxubee Refuge, both mallards and wood ducks preferred acorns of cherrybark oak over water oak or willow oak, although all three species were abundant.

The more desirable bottom land oaks for waterfowl include pin oak, water oak, willow oak, cherrybark oak, Nuttall oak and Shumard oak. Pin oak is a local term used in Arkansas to include all species of oaks that have small acorns. Many other oaks with small and large acorns are utilized by ducks to some extent and may be important in some localities.

While the oaks we mentioned are most desirable, most areas considered for development will contain a mixed stand of these and other species. A number, notably blackgum, sweetgum, baldcypress, and hickory, are taken by woodland ducks and may be of value in supplementing oak mast, particularly in years when few acorns are produced.

Another supplemental source of food may be herbaceous plants on the forest floor. Various smartweeds, grasses, and sedges of recognized value to ducks are common in forest openings and may be of significance after logging operations, when soil disturbance and increased sunlight improve conditions for their germination and growth.

THE TOPOGRAPHY of a green tree site should be such that a large area can be flooded to a small depth at reasonable cost. The lack of such an ideal site need not discourage the prospective developer, however, for successful reservoirs can be developed in a variety of situations, depending on the landowner's interest and resources.

Dikes may be of the simple type of contour levees used for ricefields. They are spaced to provide a series of small impoundments. Or, the dikes may be substantial, permanent ones engineered to impound hundreds of acres. An important consideration in bottoms subject to natural overflows is to design the dikes low and wide to avoid or reduce damage when flood waters overtop them.

The type and size of the water-control structures will depend primarily on the size of the reservoir and the volume of water that must be handled. Structures may be of any type that will permit impoundment at the desired level as well as complete drainage.

To protect the dikes, spillways should be provided for the automatic release of water above the desired level. Spillways may be low sections of the dike, riprapped to withstand erosion, or natural elevations at the ends of the dike to prevent overtopping.

ANY OF SEVERAL methods may be used to flood green tree developments. A dependable and adequate water supply is desirable but is not always possible. Storage reservoirs from which water can be released by gravity flow into green tree areas are the ideal arrangement.

At the Duck Creek Wildlife Area, the Missouri Conservation Commission developed an 1,800-acre permanent reservoir, which is a source of water for flooding the adjacent 600-acre green tree reservoir managed for public hunting.

At Noxubee National Wildlife Refuge, an ample water supply was assured by developing green tree reservoirs downstream from an existing thousand-acre lake.

Many of the commercial green tree developments near Stuttgart get their water from the sources used for rice irrigation. A less convenient water supply generally is available in other places.

Permanent streams sometimes can be diverted to provide a dependable water supply. This method is particularly adaptable where small streams enter terraces and well-drained forest bottoms. It involves the placement of a gate or stop-log structure in the streambed. Closing the structure permits diversion of the streamflow into the reservoir. A diversion ditch usually is necessary. Excellent water control is obtained, but the cost of the control structure may be rather high, except on very small streams.

Pumping is another method that allows complete water control. The source may be a well, stream, or lake. Because the annual cost of operating the pump may be prohibitive on large acreages, pumping sometimes is used as a supplemental or emergency method of obtaining water.

If a more dependable source is not available, rainfall and runoff sometimes are stored. In much of the Southeast, however, precipitation in the fall normally is low and not dependable. The watershed must be relatively large in relation to the size of the reservoir if one is to make the most of fall rains.

UNDER NATURAL CONDITIONS, most bottom-land hardwoods are flooded irregularly for brief periods during the winter and spring. Since the development of the green tree idea, a major matter of concern has been the possible effects that prolonged fall and winter flooding may have on the survival and vigor of trees, mast production, and regeneration. Although some dead tree reservoirs testify to the hazards of early trials and errors, general guidelines for the management of water levels have been developed.

Flooding can be started safely in the fall just as the leaves begin to turn color. The woods still look green, but dormancy is beginning. In early spring, when the buds begin to swell and the twigs start to brighten in color, it is time to start draining. The period of safe flooding extends from early October to February in most of the South.

The ideal depth of flooding is 1 to 18 inches. Mast in deeper water will not be easily available to puddle ducks. It is not necessary, however, that the ground be completely covered, for slight ridges supporting good mast species may remain dry and still be utilized. Sometimes, particularly in the larger reservoirs, where excessive depths occur at the maximum level, it is desirable to flood gradually, so that the water creeps over new territory each day. Ducks are attracted to the feather edge, and maximum utilization of mast crops can be achieved. There is some indication in Arkansas that a drop in water levels may cause ducks to leave a reservoir—possibly because of a lessened food supply in the flooded zone.

Manipulation of water levels may help prevent depletion of the acorn crop by grackles, squirrels, and other

Controlled flooding of mast-producing timber provides excellent habitat for mallards and wood ducks. After the ducks leave such winter quarters, the flooded timber must be drained or the trees will die.

animals before ducks arrive in the fall. On refuges and hunting areas managed primarily for waterfowl, competition for acorns by these other species may be serious; complete initial flooding early in the fall will eliminate much of it. Periodic lowering of water levels during the fall and winter may prove necessary to obtain full use of the acorns by ducks.

COMPLETE DRAINAGE before the growing season is important, for summer flooding can damage or kill desirable mast species. Sites for green tree reservoirs, because of their flat terrain and heavy soils, are difficult to drain. Complete drainage may be further complicated by beaver activity. At Noxubee Refuge, beaver seem to be attracted by flooding of the green tree impoundments. They do no particular damage in the fall and winter but cause trouble when they attempt to impede drainage in the spring. Their ponds may kill desirable mast trees in one season.

Several studies to determine the effects of reservoir management have shown that flooding, when properly done, not only is harmless but actually is beneficial to timber production. W. M. Broadfoot, of the Delta Branch Experiment Station in Stoneville, Miss., studied 16 timbered impoundments in Arkansas and Mississippi, representing a variety of flooding conditions. He found that hardwoods in bottom lands can be flooded from September or early October to April without damage to trees.

Mr. Broadfoot emphasized the adverse effects of delayed drawdowns and summer flooding, but he concluded that winter flooding increases the amount of soil moisture carried over into the summer and enhances growth rates and the production of acorns. Another benefit is the complete fire protection afforded during the impounded period, which coincides with the time of greatest fire hazard.

R. E. McDermott and Leon S. Minckler carried out a 4-year study of stand and mast characteristics of pin oak on the Duck Creek Wildlife Area and Mingo National Wildlife Refuge in southeastern Missouri. They concluded that stands of pin oak were not adversely affected by 4 consecutive years of flooding from early October to February. Fall and winter flooding brought greater yields of sound acorns and less insect infestation.

The average stand of hardwoods in the South contains a high percentage of cull trees and inferior species, the result of many years of fire, irresponsible cutting, and other abuses. The stand must be improved if such tracts are to have maximum value for green tree reservoirs or for timber production. The aims in improving a hardwood stand for ducks and timber production are essentially the same. The goal for waterfowl management is to achieve a forest with a preponderance of vigorous, large-crowned, mast-producing species.

The desirable commercial hardwood species include a large number of important producers of mast. Cherrybark oak, water oak, willow oak, Nuttall oak, and Shumard oak are species that may be given high priority in timber management and waterfowl management. Numerous other species of high to moderate commercial value are also of value to ducks and other wildlife. In mixed stands with the more preferred oaks, they provide a well-balanced wildlife habitat. In this group are sweetgum, baldcypress, swamp chestnut oak, overcup oak, white oak, and yellow-poplar.

Practices helpful in improving hardwood stands in bottom lands for waterfowl include several of basic importance in timber management. Cull trees which are not needed for mast production or nesting wood ducks should be removed. Stagnated and slow-growing stands of desirable trees should be thinned to give the crowns a chance to grow. The canopy should be opened up. Inferior or unwanted species may be eradicated by chemicals

If waterfowl management is the primary aim, preferred mast species will be favored. If commercial production of hardwood is the primary objective, the species of greatest commercial value will be favored. In either case, the broad overlap of desirable mast species and commercial species permits the development of effective green tree reservoirs.

The alluvial valleys of the lower Mississippi and its tributaries, with their extensive hardwood bottoms, offer notable opportunities for green tree development. Similar but less extensive opportunities exist on any number of Southeastern river systems—the Pearl, Pascagoula, Tombigbee, Alabama, Altamaha, Ogeechee, Combahee, Cape Fear, and Roanoke, to name a few. Tributaries extending well into the upper Coastal Plain and the Piedmont have many suitable sites. If only a portion of these hardwood bottoms were developed as green tree reservoirs, their capacity for attracting and holding ducks would be enormous.

Federal and State agencies, large timber companies, and private landowners have shown more and more interest in green tree reservoirs to attract waterfowl. State game departments see them as opportunities for providing public hunting. Private landowners use them for recreation and as a source of income through the sale or lease of hunting rights. To timber companies they are opportunities for increasing timber production, developing multiple use, and providing recreation to employees and customers. The Bureau of Sport Fisheries and Wildlife recognizes their value as quality wintering habitat for an important segment of the migratory waterfowl resource. Without a doubt, green tree reservoirs will do much to advance the distribution, utilization, and preservation of wintering woodland ducks.

—ROYSTON R. RUDOLPH and
CARL G. HUNTER.

Matches and Marshes

FIRE, a destroyer, is also a helper, when it is wisely employed to keep waterfowl marshes from becoming brushy bogs or wooded swamps. It is a destroying angel, whose ecological mission is to cleanse.

Cleansing is often necessary, sometimes to keep plants from killing themselves by their own vigorous growth. Marsh grasses and sedges are low-growing plants, whose bladelike foliage can dominate a marsh. Nevertheless, they are in constant danger of being overwhelmed by taller vegetation. Potential competitors, such as broad-leaved or woody plants, have difficulty gaining a foothold in strong stands of grasses. But in marshes this dense, lush growth may accumulate until the grasses and sedges themselves can no longer grow through their own mat of old foliage.

This accumulation in northern marshlands is disposed of each year by ice, spring floods, grazing animals, and other forms of natural cleansing. In the southern marshes, however, where long growing seasons leave heavy masses of old, matted growth, drastic measures are needed to keep the plants from being smothered in their own exuberance. Hurricanes make quick work of clearing away these accumulations. Fire, usually started by

619

Controlled burning in winter to produce goose food on Mattamuskeet National Wildlife Refuge in North Carolina.   Green shoots beneath the burn are used almost immediately by grazing geese.

lightning, can also do the cleanup job effectively.

The Indians knew that. In the annals of early American explorations are many references to seasonal burning of marshes and other grasslands. White settlers, according to some chronicals, became enthusiastic firebrands who set fire to everything that would burn, although more thoughtful historians point out that this burning helped trapping, hunting, and travel, and improved grazing for livestock.

Marsh burning as an instrument of game management was practiced by early explorers and settlers. One, John Lawson, wrote in his *History of North Carolina* in 1714: "They [snow geese] eat the Roots of Sedge and Grass in the Marshes and Savannas, which they tear up like Hogs. The best way to kill these Fowl, is to burn a piece of Marsh or Savanna, and as soon as it is burnt they will come in great flocks to get the roots, where you will kill what you please of them."

MARSH BURNING in North America gradually came into common use in many places, notably in the fresh, brackish, and salt marshes in the southern Atlantic seaboard and along the Gulf of Mexico. Now, in Louisiana alone, nearly a million acres of coastal marshes are burned annually. This is purposeful burning, done by landowners to improve marshes for fur animals and cattle as well as waterfowl.

Throughout the history of marsh

fires and down to the present time, some burning was capricious. Some was malicious. Some had no explanation other than the psychological. Economics as well as conscience now discourage the reckless use of fire. Once it was learned that its proper use paid dividends, and its improper use often was costly, there was less inclination to misuse this two-edged tool.

BRACKISH MARSHES along the Gulf of Mexico are fertilized by ash deposits left by fire. Marshes usually have a healthier appearance during regrowth following fire, partly because of the release of nutrients by burning. Potassium, calcium, phosphorus, magnesium, and chlorides are among the plant nutrients in ash deposits. Nitrogen is presumed to be volatilized into the atmosphere.

Some plants in brackish marshes take up certain substances from salt water by an osmotic process in their cell walls. The concentrations of nutrients that result are deposited in the soil as ash when the plants burn. As the fertilization process begins, soil acidity drops. The warm temperatures characteristic of Gulf coast marshes, even in the winter, stimulate new plant growth soon after a fire.

When people saw that proper burning helped to "cultivate" the marshlands, they came to realize that fire is a good servant but a headstrong one. Marsh managers began to speak of controlled fires, and it became apparent to men experienced in marsh burning that control of fire was like the control one exerts over dynamite: The best

time to "control" an explosion or a fire is before, rather than after, it is touched off.

Experience and later research on burning has disclosed that many factors must be considered before fire is turned loose in a marsh. First, we must have a clear understanding of the goals the fire is supposed to accomplish. We must be aware of possible side effects and willing to accept bad features in order to gain desirable ends. We must give serious attention to those factors that determine the progress of fire, such as amount and condition of fuel, direction and velocity of wind, amount of water in the marsh, and the presence of firebreaks to contain the conflagration.

A marsh that has been unburned for many years accumulates a huge store of fuel, in which any fire, be it manmade or natural, may culmi-

Uncontrolled burning often destroys duck nests. This one belonged to a mallard in Saskatchewan, Canada.

nate in a terrifying fire storm. Yet fire itself is the best way to keep the supply of fuel from reaching dangerous proportions. A marsh that has been burned regularly does not offer much fuel for any given fire. When it is burned in a light wind, the fire travels rather slowly and with comparatively little heat. The hotter fires do have a special place in marsh management but are not used as a regular practice.

Specific objectives should always be understood before a marsh is fired. Normally the aims would be one or more of the following: To set back plant succession from an undesirable climax (or a near-climax) to a subclimax plant com-munity that will be more productive of food for waterfowl; to remove or open up dense growths of vegeta-tion to a degree suitable for use as feeding areas by waterfowl; and to create ponds and open water areas in a dense marsh by burning into the marsh floor.

BEFORE FIRE IS USED, a careful study should be made of vegetative types, soil characteristics, water levels, salinities, and tidal conditions.

Consideration should be given to the season of the year as well as to winds and humidity at the time of burning.

It should be remembered that burning techniques to provide food

A peat fire in a dry period created this marsh pond in Louisiana, which obviously is attractive to a host of pintails.

for geese will differ substantially from those used to benefit ducks. It is generally a poor practice to burn during or just before the waterfowl nesting season. This normally rules out burning from February through August, unless long-range gains in improved habitat outweigh an immediate loss of nests and young birds.

Heavy marsh cover tends to reduce battering and eroding effects of rushing storm tides. Also, mature plant communities are more resistant to damage from flooding by salt tides than are freshly burned marshes. Consequently, burning should be avoided in places where erosion is a problem unless a denser and more protective plant cover will be produced thereby. In coastal marshes subject to hurricanes, burning should be delayed until the peak of the storm season has passed, about October 15.

COVER BURN is one of the three categories of fire. This comparatively cool and nonspectacular fire is employed when water levels are at or above ground level and root horizons.

Cover burn usually is done in the fall and winter to remove rank growths that are too dense for waterfowl. Such burns produce an immediate change in habitat because they remove all standing vegetation. Seldom, however, do marked changes in vegetative types result from a cover fire. As this superficial fire moves across a marsh, vapor zones that develop from the accompanying steam protect the exposed stubble for 2 or 3 inches above water level.

Snow geese, of both blue and white color phases, are particularly attracted to fresh burns, which often are created for this very purpose. These birds feed heavily on roots, rhizomes, and the young shoots of vegetation that are thereby made available. Along the Gulf coast, the geese frequently move in while the burned-over marsh is still smoking. Blue and snow geese use a burned marsh less and less as the new plant growth becomes tall and rank.

Burning a marsh, section by section, at intervals of 2 or 3 weeks throughout the fall and winter, is one way to hold a flock of blue and snow geese in a general area. It also reduces the chances of marsh damage from large concentrations of these birds in one locality. These geese are gregarious, and large flocks can eat out a part of freshly burned marsh by consuming or otherwise destroying the root system of plants. Ponds sometimes are created in soft marshes in this manner. Such open water favors use by ducks, but it is not desirable in the management of goose range.

On their wintering grounds, blue and snow geese frequently cause damage to cattle pastures and fur-producing marshes. Burning of publicly owned marshes to attract geese away from privately owned lands tends to relieve what otherwise might become a serious wildlife depredation problem.

Healthy, shallow-water marshes in the final stages of plant succession sometimes produce vegetative cover too dense for winter use by ducks. A clean cover burn in fall or winter quickly alters this condition, and the marsh then can be

readily used. Several species of puddle ducks use freshly burned and flooded marshes as feeding areas, particularly if puddles and ponds are present.

ROOT BURNS are made when the marsh floor is dry and the water table is well below ground level. Such fire damages roots of plants and can change the types of vegetation.

A "hot" root burn can reduce or remove climax vegetation, which generally is useless to waterfowl. A substantial setback in plant succession usually brings on new food plants that are more attractive to ducks. In dry marshes occupied by several perennial plant species, a fire normally can be expected to have its greatest effect on the plants with the shallowest root system. Careful consideration should be given to this factor, as well as soil moisture levels, because the plants with the deeper root systems likely will be favored by such a burn.

A root burn has a more permanent effect on a marsh than a cover burn, and more care should be exercised in its use. Regardless of water levels or vegetative composition, however, a burn will not always eliminate unwanted climax species and allow a desirable subclimax type to flourish indefinitely. An undesirable species may be favored by burning under certain conditions, particularly if it is fire resistant

THE THIRD TYPE of burn involves an extremely dry marsh growing on a layer of dry peat. Marsh soils comprised mainly of organic materials from decaying plants will burn when dry enough, if sufficiently free of salt. Small potholes, ponds, and even large lakes can be created by means of peat burns.

Fires of this type should not be set unless some means exist for flooding the marsh and extinguishing the remaining smoldering peat.

A peat burn normally reaches mineral soil or the subsurface water before it burns out. Opportunities to use such a burn usually exist only in long-established freshwater marshes, because tidewater coastal marsh soils often contain too little organic material and too much salt.

Peat fires are possible only during very dry seasons. That is most of the year in arid regions. The aim should be to create a series of shallow ponds of one-half to 2 acres, rather than a large lake. Small marsh ponds generally are much more productive of food for ducks than are large ponds or lakes. This point is important, because extensive peatbog burns in the North tend to remain sterile.

Peat fires in 1946 created a series of marsh ponds and lakes in a dense freshwater marsh in the northeastern part of Cameron Parish in Louisiana. Its use by wintering waterfowl increased greatly. During November 1962, about 175 thousand puddle ducks, 100 thousand coots, and 30 thousand snow geese were observed on the 25 thousand acres. Heavy usage by geese is uncommon, however, in a marsh of this type—an indication that deep

After being "burned off," this Louisiana coastal marsh attracted large flocks of snow geese.

To be helpful to waterfowl, burning must be done by skilled workers.

peat burns are not recommended on the wintering grounds for geese.

As a WATERFOWL management practice, fire serves best in a marsh over which water control can be exercised. In opening up or eliminating marsh cover, a hot root burn followed by complete flooding suppresses sprouting and regrowth. It also induces production of submerged aquatics for 2 or 3 years. Afterwards, an annual or biennial summer drawdown of the water level will encourage seed-producing annual grasses in fresh marshes.

Sparsely vegetated marshes cannot be successfully burned. Healthy marshes with heavy growths of vegetative cover can be burned every year, or at least every 2 or 3 years. Clean burns can best be made under conditions of low humidity

and with winds of less than 6 miles an hour. Late afternoon and evening, with increased humidity and reduced air movement, are favored in arid regions, or burning may be delayed until the ground is frozen and perhaps has a light snow cover. The size of a burned area is normally controlled by the presence of roads, waterways, or other barriers. Protection can also be obtained by igniting the downwind portion first.

Whenever any burning is done in marshes, great care should be exercised when burning around buildings, water-control structures, and equipment.

All possible consequences of a marsh burn should be carefully considered *before* a fire is started.

Local fire laws and ordinances must be observed.

The indiscriminate use of fire in marshes is apt to brand the incendiary as a knave or fool, or both.

PRESCRIBED BURNING is the term now given generally to marsh fires that are set, deliberately but carefully, to accomplish some desirable goal. The older term "controlled burning" is recognized as just a little bit unrealistic, for control of such conflagration really ends the instant fire is started.

Like any weapon, fire is always loaded, and the novice at marsh burning would do well to treat it accordingly. The well-singed (and therefore very cautious) experienced marsh manager sees in every box of matches a Pandora's box of good and evil. The task is to coax out of the box the benefits of fire without setting loose any of its diabolical consequences.—RICHARD K. YANCEY.

GADWALL

Cows and Cutter Bars

GRAZING AND MOWING marsh, meadow, and upland vegetation can do much to improve and maintain waterfowl habitat. Grazing and mowing also can do more harm than good.

Excessive grazing in the droughty thirties temporarily ruined many duck breeding areas in the North Central States and the Prairie Provinces. Meadow and shoreline vegetation was cropped to the ground in places. Emergent aquatic vegetation was clipped to the surface of the water, and the sites were muddied and despoiled. Nesting cover for ducks was ruined. Brood cover was lacking. Shorelines and shallow-water feeding areas were uninviting to waterfowl. All who saw it might well believe that cattle and ducks are incompatible.

So, when several national wildlife refuges were established in the late thirties and early forties in the North Central States, the plan for lands near water was one of nonuse. Ducks could do best, it was thought, in lush surroundings, and many marshes deserved a respite from the harsh treatment they had undergone.

Then a different view took hold. Many shorelines and meadows had grown up to dense, tall stands of vegetation, little used by ducks. It was evident that most duck marshes would benefit from some degree of use by livestock. Furthermore, the fact that ducks and wild grazers—bison, elk, and antelope—once had

627

lived together on the grasslands in apparent harmony suggested that ducks and grazing were compatible.

Today we know that regulated grazing by cattle improves and maintains breeding habitat, which otherwise becomes overgrown with low-value, space-consuming vegetation. In actual practice, however, many pastures are severely overgrazed, and waterfowl find them less attractive than if they were subjected to no grazing at all.

Only when grazing pressure is regulated is it a constructive measure in the management of waterfowl production areas. Other means for regulating plant growth and development are mowing, burning, treatment with chemical weedkillers, cultivation, and crushing with heavy implements. Grazing has the advantage of being economical, effective, and in agreement with good land use practices in some of the best duck breeding areas on the continent.

The false idea persists in places that marsh-edge environments, free of agricultural use, make the best duck breeding areas. Another erroneous belief is that all ducks have the same needs. People generally understand that dabbling ducks differ from diving ducks, but do not realize that each of many species of dabbling ducks—mallard, pintail, blue-winged teal, shoveler, gadwall, and the others—has its own requirements. The same applies to the canvasback, redhead, lesser scaup, and other species of diving ducks. These differences make it difficult to generalize about grazing and mowing as tools for the management of waterfowl habitat.

What is good for one kind of duck may be unnecessary for a second species and harmful to a third.

THE VALUES of the marsh to waterfowl, other than as breeding habitat, must be considered when a grazing program is being developed. Marshes, especially the larger ones, serve many needs of waterfowl, not the least of which is to provide food. Grazing to improve breeding habitat may have to be sacrificed in the interest of food production where cattle may damage food plants, such as wild millet and smartweeds. Plans for wildlife on a specific area also must take into account the needs of a varied animal population. Deer, grouse, pheasants, muskrats, and mink may use waterfowl habitat. Sometimes the needs of these groups will necessitate modification in the ideal grazing plan for waterfowl.

MODERATE GRAZING is recommended for marsh edges that have solid stands of tall, rank vegetation, such as cattails, phragmites, river bulrush, hardstem bulrush, cordgrasses, and willows. Trampling and grazing by cattle usually will open these stands and improve their composition. Nesting cover on the drier sites is thinned by grazing, and landing spots and travel lanes are created. Shoreline cover of the sort preferred by resting ducks is produced. Adjacent cover in shallow water is improved for adult ducks and broods. Some benefits also accrue from the effects of fertilization by stock.

Light grazing in upland nesting

cover helps reduce destruction of nests by predators. The environment for bull snakes, which destroy many eggs in Nebraska, is made less suitable when some grass cover is removed. Other predators, such as skunks, raccoons, and badgers, also are less inclined to inhabit areas grazed by cattle. Grazing also reduces the hazard of grass fires.

More caution with grazing has to be exercised around large lakes and marshes than around small ponds and potholes. Large bodies of water whose shores are windswept, wavewashed, and unsheltered by reeds or rushes are used only sparingly by dabbling ducks in the breeding season.

Protective emergent cover is less important on ponds—the basins themselves generally provide adequate safeguard from the elements for both ducks and shallow-water aquatic foods. This tolerance by breeding dabbling ducks to complete removal of tall vegetation around small water bodies was noted during a study of stock watering ponds on the short-grass prairie in west-central South Dakota. Grazing that removed tall and rank vegetation but left the shorelines covered with grass did not lower the use of the ponds by adults and broods. This use dropped sharply only when excessive grazing created shorelines of bare mud.

In another way, however, small water areas are more vulnerable to the adverse effects of cattle than are large marshes. Emergent vegetation, essential to many diving ducks for the construction of nest platforms, is more easily damaged by wading

cattle on small, shallow ponds. This problem merits special attention in pothole regions where canvasbacks, redheads, and ruddy ducks breed.

Waterfowl authorities are becoming increasingly convinced that sound range management is good waterfowl management. Some biologists do not accept the maximum recommended stocking rates of range managers, but it is gratifying to note how much the gap on this point has narrowed. An example of the agreement between range and waterfowl specialists is that grazing schedules on several national wildlife refuges in the North Central States were established by technicians of the Soil Conservation Service. The greatest conflict today between waterfowl interests and livestock interests involves serious overgrazing by operators who are unaware of or indifferent to the evils of overpasturing.

As a GENERAL RULE, cattle and ducks can live together reasonably well on the same sites when grazing is sufficient to remove half the average amount of the primary forage plants produced annually. Many stockmen believe this practice wastes forage, especially in years of above average rainfall. The range specialist, however, knows that a large average carryover (the amount of grass left when the grazing season ends) insures a good, long-term relationship between yield of cattle products and grazing capacity of the land.

Allowable grazing pressure for good range management and good waterfowl management varies from site to site and depends on geographic location, plant cover, past use of the range, soil type, topography, and moisture conditions. If a heavy cover of grass is desired on special wildlife areas, carrying capacities recommended by range managers may have to be reduced. Rotation grazing among different units and periodic protection from grazing also may be helpful adjuncts to some land-use practices for wildlife.

On national wildlife refuges, these summer stocking rates leave ample nesting cover for ducks: One cow to 2–4 acres of grass in Iowa, Wisconsin, and Minnesota; one to 8–12 acres in the eastern parts of the Dakotas; and one to 12–15 acres in western North and South Dakota and central Nebraska. The figures agree closely with those recommended by the Canada Department of Agriculture for adjoining native grasslands in the Prairie Provinces. For west-central South Dakota, range specialists recommend a grazing pressure of 27 acres per cow on a continuous, year-round grazing basis. This intensity of grazing was found to be acceptable by waterfowl managers, providing the pastures contained a suitable number of water areas. Even at prescribed grazing rates, if too few water areas are present the ponds and immediate surroundings will be overgrazed while portions of the pasture far from water will be little used.

Grazing pressure of about one cow to 5 acres should be tested where control is desired over tall, rank, wet-meadow vegetation on the prairies. Fencing should be employed to prevent over-use of adjacent cover types. The well-being of the cattle on the moister soil types also must be considered and, in this respect, advice of local animal husbandry experts should be sought.

Moderate grazing is part of a wildlife land management plan devised by wildlife biologists of the University of Minnesota for tall grass prairie of northwestern Minnesota. In this project, they faced the problem of maintaining habitat for greater prairie chickens and breeding waterfowl. Persistent invasion of aspen and willow had to be controlled, nesting cover for the two wildlife groups had to be maintained, and pothole shorelines had to be kept attractive to ducks. From a study on the effects of spring burning, fall burning, various degrees of grazing, and mowing on the several components of the environment, it was concluded the best management plan should have a 4-year sequence as follows: First year, spring burning; second year, no treatment; third year, moderate grazing; fourth year, no treatment.

RANGE MANAGERS and waterfowl ecologists agree quite well on the time when grazing should begin in the spring. To maintain a strong stand of grass, grazing should be deferred until the leaves are manufacturing and storing food, but longer delay may be wasteful and harmful. For one thing, if grazing does not begin early enough, cool-season grasses tend to crowd out the warm-season species.

Grazing, when first introduced into land use plans of national wildlife refuges, was not permitted before July 1 to avoid disturbing breeding waterfowl. It has been found since then that disturbance of breeding ducks and trampling of nests, two popularly held fears, practically never become important as long as cattle numbers are not excessive. Recommended cattle turn-in dates for waterfowl refuges are planned for the time when new growth is 3 to 6 inches tall. In the Northern States, this usually occurs about May 15, and in southern Canada, about late May or early June.

Coarse species of lowland plants that make up the bulk of unwanted vegetation in waterfowl breeding areas are generally most palatable early in spring. To graze at this time may conflict with the recommended turn-in date for upland pastures. This problem can be resolved by separating the two areas with fencing. If this is not practical, the welfare of the upland areas should receive first consideration. Placement of salt and other means of getting better grazing use of the marsh vegetation should be tried if forced grazing with fencing is not employed.

Stock removal dates are not important from a range- or wildlife-management viewpoint on conservatively grazed pastures. October 15–30 is the period when most stock leave grazing units on the Lower Souris National Wildlife Refuge in north-central North Dakota. On areas open to hunting, it is sometimes advisable to remove cattle before the season opens to avoid conflict with hunters.

On national wildlife refuges in waterfowl migration and wintering areas, one of the chief uses of grazing is to maintain pastures in a condition favored by geese, widgeon, and coots, which feed readily on weeds and closely clipped grass shoots on heavily grazed cattle pastures. Holding fields in the right condition for this purpose sometimes conflicts with the more conservative recommendations of range specialists, because geese prefer a pasture that is kept closely mowed by cattle and has neither old nor tall growth.

HAYING OPERATIONS in duck breeding areas are usually harmful to waterfowl. The mower, rake, baler, and other associated implements destroy nests. The cutter bar on the mower kills and maims nesting ducks. As a tool for improving wildlife habitat, the mower has limited value; even then, some of the indirect effects of hay removal may be undesirable. In short, haying and nesting waterfowl are basically incompatible, and the problem mainly concerns finding ways to reduce the harmful effects of haying rather than in learning ways of making it a constructive device for improving habitat.

Haying on uplands and meadows used to be a general practice on national wildlife refuges in the North Central States. The policy existed because haying was more easily controlled than grazing, and it provided some economic use of waterfowl lands with nominal disturbance to natural conditions. Hay harvest, it was reasoned, would also open up rank cover to nesting waterfowl and lessen the threat of fire.

The hazards of haying to ground-nesting birds have been carefully appraised. The normal period of haying on the Northern Plains is June 15 to August 1. This period overlaps the height of the duck nesting season. Losses on hayed areas usually approach 100 percent of the active nests. Substantial numbers of hens are killed or injured.

Deferment of haying is the most worthwhile adjustment that can be made for nesting waterfowl. August 1 is the earliest that mowing should begin on any refuge in the Great Plains if late nests are to be spared. An additional postponement of a week or two is suggested during exceptionally late seasons. Hay cutting before July 20 in places where dabbling ducks breed in North Dakota usually will destroy a significant portion of the nests.

SHORT OF deferred haying, all efforts to find a practical and worthwhile solution to the conflict between hay harvest and waterfowl nesting have met with failure. Attachments to the tractor or mower for flushing hens have proved unsuccessful. Besides, they do not prevent damage to the nests, and nests with hens temporarily absent do not come to the operator's attention so that he may take protective action.

When small islands of vegetation are left unmowed around nests, predators apparently are attracted to the clumps, and high losses result. Leaving larger uncut patches (25-feet square or more) reduces

hazards to the nests, and hatching success increases. This provides only partial protection, at best, however, and hardly justifies the reduced economy of the haying operation.

Some success in saving nests, which later hatched in alfalfa, clover, and bromegrass hayfields, was observed in a study by the Delta Waterfowl Research Station in Manitoba. Farmers were asked to leave as little cover as possible around each nest or merely to raise the cutting bar as it passed over the nest. Cutting in this manner did not produce conspicuous islands of cover, and better than average results were reported.

When mowing is done on national wildlife refuges, a strip from the water's edge to 400 feet above the spring shoreline is often left uncut. This practice benefits nesting ducks, but unfortunately predators take advantage of the cover, too.

DEFERRED HAYING helps nesting ducks and their nests to survive, but there is another item that must be considered in adjusting haying to benefit waterfowl. Dead vegetation sought as nesting cover in the spring is lacking on areas hayed the previous year. Also lacking on regularly hayed lands is the layer of ground litter essential for raising nests above moist ground and above the level of minor flooding.

Haying in one year reduces the acreage suitable for nesting the following year. As a consequence, heavier concentrations of nests will be located on unhayed sites, and the rate of nest losses usually is higher in such situations. The highest nesting success generally occurs where nests are well dispersed.

ONE RECOMMENDED USE of mowing for management of breeding habitat is based on the fact that ducks avoid bare areas when they select nesting sites. Nesting areas susceptible to heavy predation losses or flooding may be made unattractive to nesting ducks if the vegetation is closely mowed in late summer or fall.

Meadows choked with rank vegetation and unused by nesting ducks may be restored temporarily by cutting early in summer. Adequate second growth thus can develop before freezeup, and nesting cover for the next spring will be ideal.

Mowing also can be used to create openings in dense, unbroken stands of marsh vegetation, thereby making them available for loafing, courting, and feeding. It is done in late summer or fall after natural or controlled lowering of water levels has permitted the drying of ground normally inundated in spring.

Mowing can help remove undesirable or excess marsh vegetation. Successful and enduring control of annual plants and certain perennial plants, notably cattails, can be obtained by systematic cutting. The key to cattail control is to mow the stand when pistillate spikes are well formed and at least two-thirds full size but not mature enough to scatter viable seeds. A second cutting is required about a month later after regrowth has reached a height of about 2 feet; somewhat better success can be expected if water is present to cover the cut stem bases.

Cutting over ice has been tested as a measure to control cattails in Canada. Openings created by this means remain virtually free of cattails during the first summer. New growth gradually fills the openings until the fourth summer, when the area again resembles untreated sites. Mowing should be done close to the ice, so that spring floodwater covers the stubble.

Underwater cutting of phragmites during the flowering season is effective in Delaware and Maryland, but the method has limited practicability. Woody plants, such as willows, may be controlled by cutting on the ice or after drawdown and then flooding the stumps for one growing season.

Mowing to produce upland waterfowl pasture has been used at the Patuxent Wildlife Research Center in Maryland. Low-grade woodlands there have been converted to meadow by clearing and planting. The meadow is mowed in summer for hay, and again in September with a rotary mower which pulverizes the cut material. A new tender growth develops before the autumn flight of geese arrives. The shredded material is left on the meadows to improve the soil.

COWS AND CUTTER BARS can be either a liability to waterfowl or serve their needs as can few other tools in the game manager's kit. Ducks of many species nest on uplands and along pond margins in the shadow of grazing cattle. Here, they seek out vegetation-of-a-type—not too thick, not too sparse, but just right. Without use by cattle, many grazing areas are too dense for the liking of nesting ducks. On the other hand, if the use by cattle is excessive, the vegetative cover is too sparse to serve well the needs of waterfowl.

IN SUM, it is a matter of multiple use—the principle of utilizing a resource in several compatible, harmonious ways at the same time, just as a forest, say, is managed to yield timber, wildlife, recreation, water, and miscellaneous forest products at the same time. Thus, pastures, meadows, and grasslands can be managed wisely to produce livestock, hay, grazing, and ducks to the benefit of all.

—EUGENE F. BOSSENMAIER.

CARP
RED-WINGED BLACKBIRD

Carp, a Sometimes Villain

THE CARP WAS brought to America from Europe more than a century ago as a hero of great promise and has stayed and multiplied to become something of a villain. In the waters they like, carp have destroyed waterfowl habitat and food plants, muddied the water, and crowded out more desirable game fish. Millions of pounds have been removed from lakes and rivers each year by seining and trapping. Many more have been poisoned, stoned, destroyed on spawning beds, speared, and shot with arrows. But carp, like starlings and crabgrass and rats, have a strong

survival factor; they thrive and remain with us.

The German carp is really a giant minnow, whose original home was eastern Asia. It was introduced into Europe as a food fish in the 15th century. It is still esteemed and extensively raised in ponds, in Europe and Asia where carp culture is an ancient and well-developed art. There are many cultivated strains—scaled, scaleless, and partly scaled. Much time and study have been devoted to its requirements, care, and diseases. In Europe it long has had a good reputation as an angling fish. Izaak

635

Walton called the carp the "queen of the rivers." Where food is scarce, the carp is hard to beat as a protein producer, and some ponds yield more than a thousand pounds an acre each year.

The carp is prolific, hardy, and fast-growing. It is an efficient and omnivorous feeder. That is the problem. It is too efficient, too prolific, too healthy, and too pushing. It is a superanimal that, like man, can dominate its habitat.

CARP PROBABLY WERE first transported from Europe to America in the 1830's by private persons. Robert J. Pell of Pelham, New York, in 1857 "had carp in great numbers" from stock he had obtained from a Captain Robinson of Newburgh, New York. Scaled carp were privately introduced in California in 1872. The early introductions seem not to have established carp in natural waters.

Wide distribution came in 1877, when the Bureau of Fisheries imported scaled and mirror (partly scaled) carp. The reason, wrote Spencer F. Baird, then United States Commissioner of Fish and Fisheries, was: "Their instinct for domestication has already been established—and there is no reason why time should be lost with less proven species." So carp were brought here, propagated, distributed, and planted with care.

The carp were obtained from Germany. Distribution to several States began in 1879; it ended in 1897. It was at a peak around 1883, when 260 thousand were distributed to 298 of the 301 Congressional Districts. Thousands of requests for the fish came from enthusiastic sportsmen. Care was taken to obtain disease-free stock. They were amazingly healthy and prolific. (Large females may lay 500 thousand to 3 million eggs, and they begin spawning in their second year.) Stephen A. Forbes reported 1.5 billion eggs on a 600-acre spawning area along the Illinois River in 1912.

Not long after the first releases, reports questioned the wisdom of introducing this alien. The carp were thriving vigorously, and they were causing damage. As early as 1883, the increase in carp was accompanied by a great decrease in wildcelery and wildrice in the shallower water of Lake Erie, which is warmer and shallower than the other Great Lakes and is well suited to carp. Milton Trautman in his *Fishes of Ohio* wrote that in 1899, two decades after carp were planted in Lake Erie, 3.6 million pounds were taken by commercial fishermen.

A similar explosive increase occurred in the Illinois River, where the commercial catch was 1 million pounds of buffalo-fish in 1880, but 22 million pounds of carp in 1896.

About 15 years after carp had been stocked in central Canada, Edward Prince, a Canadian, warned: "German carp are nomadic in their habits and wander apparently aimlessly into all accessible waters, hence if introduced into any streams will spread rapidly over the whole system. . . . Like undesirable weeds they have spread everywhere and it is practically impossible to limit their progress or to effect their extirpation."

Furthermore, American anglers showed no enthusiasm for carp. They had tastier and more sporting fish to catch.

THOSE WHO RATE the canvasback as the king of all ducks had a special reason to despise the carp because it ruined some of the best "can" lakes in the country. Take for example Lake Koshkonong on the Rock River in Wisconsin. About this lake Augie Kumlien Main wrote this interesting account: "Governor Hoard told me that once in the fall of the early 1870's Thure Kumlien invited him to go to the lake with him before daylight to watch the migration of the famous canvasback ducks. When morning broke the water was covered with these beautiful birds as far as the eye could see. They had come here to feed on the wild celery buds and on nutlets from the pondweeds. . . . In 1880 carp were introduced into Lake Koshkonong, unfortunately successfully, for they cleaned out the wild celery and pondweeds— consequently the myriads of waterfowl which once haunted its waters are now becoming a memory." Other famous canvasback lakes like Pomme de Terre in Minnesota suffered a similar fate due primarily to carp.

The adverse reports prompted the United States Fish Commission to assign Leon J. Cole to investigate. He reported in 1905: "As to the relation of carp to aquatic vegetation, the evidence seems to be pretty strong that in general they are very destructive, and are probably, in large part at least, responsible for the great reduction of *wild celery* and *wild rice* that has been noted in many of our inland marshes in the last few years. . . . It must be admitted that where there are a comparatively large number of carp in a pond the water is in an almost constant state of roiliness. . . . The only practical remedy is removal of the fish."

He was right. Carp rapidly became the dominant fish in many lakes and rivers. They did best in fertile, limy waters and warm, shallow, nonstratified lakes, where they browse over the whole bottom. Estimates of the standing crop of fish in such shallow, fertile lakes in the Midwest often include 200 to 400 pounds of carp to the acre, plus about 100 pounds of game fishes.

Such fertile waters also are most valuable for waterfowl.

C. W. Threinen, in an analysis of the problem in Wisconsin, noted that the greatest production of carp, in terms of seining results, was from waters 10 to 20 feet deep and that lakes fertilized with domestic sewage had high yields of carp. In three such lakes, the average annual removal was 130.3 to 439 pounds an acre. Deep, cool lakes, however, often have small populations of large carp, which do little damage to aquatic vegetation, except in shallow bays.

Carp have been in the Midwest for 75 years, but they have not established themselves in most waters of the northern coniferous zone— roughly the northern half of Minnesota and Wisconsin. A part of the reason may be that barriers, such as high dams, may prevent migration. A likelier reason may be that carp require a water temperature in spring of about 62° F. to spawn successfully. The main northern limit of their range nearly coincides with the May isotherm of 55° and the June isotherm of 65°. The quality and basic fertility of the water also may be a factor, since the waters of the northern coniferous area are generally less fertile than those of the hardwood and prairie regions to the south and west. It was noted in 1959 that carp were still advancing at the rate of 20 to 40 miles a year in Manitoba, where the 60° July isotherm may be the northern range limit.

The greatest concentrations of carp now are in the Mississippi River drainage, where 19.7 million pounds of carp were taken and sold in 1958, and the eastern Great Lakes region, where 8.3 million pounds were caught. Carp are salable but are not of great commercial value. The total catch for the United States in 1948 sold for about 1.5 million dollars, an average price of about 4.6 cents a pound. The commercial take in the United States has averaged about 30 million pounds a year since 1955.

THE OBVIOUS DAMAGE they cause to water plants may lead one to think that carp feed mostly on vegetation. That is only partly true. Also, feeding on plants represents only part of the damage done. Carp feed on nearly anything edible except live fish. Aquatic invertebrates make up a large part of their diet. To get them and plant parts, carp do much rooting of the bottom. Often the uprooted water plants float ashore.

Some kinds of water plants—among them sago pondweed, curly pondweed, and coontail—are more resistant than others to damage by carp. Sago has both tubers and a rather extensive system of rhizomes. Curly pondweed grows from a thick winterbud that can reanchor the stem when loosened. Coontail has no true roots but is anchored by the bottom of the plant.

In lakes in southern Minnesota, the feeding habits vary with the size of the fish. Stomachs of carp of all sizes often contain 30 to 40 percent vegetable matter and 15 to 30 percent aquatic insects. Fish smaller than 5 inches feed mainly on waterfleas and scuds. Fish between 5 and 11 inches seem to prefer aquatic insects. Both of these groups of invertebrates are important sources of protein in the diet of waterfowl and game fishes.

Roiling of the water also is associated with large populations of carp. Penetration of light is thereby reduced, and the growth of submerged plants is limited. Carp often are associated with heavy blooms of blue-green algae. The stirring of the bottom by carp and fishes of similar habits may keep nutrients in the lake bottom in circulation and may promote algal growths. The amount of roiling depends somewhat on the kind of bottom soil and is of least consequence where the soil is fibrous.

CHANGES IN AQUATIC habitat come quickly as a carp population builds up. As the fish multiply, weed beds decline. Thick growths of pond-weeds, watermilfoil, coontail, and other plants are replaced by bare mud. Water that used to be clear becomes cloudy with silt. Fenced exclosures have been used to demonstrate the consequences of carp activity. The results are plain. Inside the fence, vegetation thrives; outside, the plants are consumed, rooted-up, and destroyed as the carp burrow, root, and churn. As long as they are present, water remains turbid, and recovery of vegetation is slow. Their removal often brings a spectacular clearing of the water and improvement for waterfowl.

LAKE MATTAMUSKEET in North Carolina, which has 30 thousand acres of open water, for many years has been a major wintering area for Canada geese in the Atlantic Flyway. It was plagued with a high population of carp in the forties. Aquatic plants were sparse. Few

Carp clogging Blitzen River at Malheur Lake, Oregon, after treatment with rotenone. These fish, 640 tons of them, average 8½ pounds each.

On the way home with a load of carp. The commercial utilization of these fish is not sufficient to keep their numbers under control.

ducks used the lake. Attempts to remove the carp with fyke and pound nets were unsuccessful. A program of carp removal was begun in 1949 by seining areas baited with corn and other material. Between 1945 and 1960, 2.4 million pounds of carp and 244 thousand pounds of catfish were taken. Most of them were sold to owners of upland fishponds in North Carolina. Plant recovery was evident in 1951 and 1952 and ducks began to use the area. The refuge has supported a wintering population of 75 thousand geese and 90 thousand ducks since 1948. The pintail is the most abundant duck.

Removal of carp from Lake Mattamuskeet reduced its turbidity tremendously and let desirable food plants grow on 15 thousand acres

of previously bare bottom. Aquatic vegetation now covers 17 thousand to 20 thousand acres of the lakebed

Many instances of rapid return of vegetation, especially sago pond weed, have been noted in the Mid west after carp have been eliminated by toxicants or winterkill.

CONTROL OF CARP has taxed the ingenuity and finances of conserva tion agencies for more than 50 years. Many States have engaged in seining and netting carp and trap ping them during spawning runs.

The physical removal of carp from waters has been successful in reducing populations and benefiting the habitat and numbers of game fish in some places—usually in lakes that can be intensively and heavily seined over a period of years. Many lakes are difficult to seine, however, and fewer carp may be removed than will grow up to fill the void in a year, so that little or no permanent effect on the carp population is achieved. In shallow, fertile lakes such potential growth of carp populations is high—often more than 100 pounds per acre a year.

In heavily seined lakes, there may be a change in the age and size of the carp population. In one instance, the composition of the catch following heavy seining changed from 13 percent to 93 percent juveniles. This is important, for it is the younger fish that feed most heavily on aquatic invertebrates that are important in the diet of young ducks and game fish.

Screens and barriers to prevent carp from migrating upstream and infesting new waters or waters from which carp have been eliminated have been effective sometimes. Floating screen barriers installed in conjunction with dams often are used. Carp lay eggs usually in the shallow waters of sloughs; exposing them to the air is an effective control if water levels can be lowered rapidly. This method has been used successfully on the Fort Randall Reservoir of the Missouri River in South Dakota.

Several kinds of toxicants have been used. Toxaphene and rotenone have proved to be effective, but they are costly to apply and they kill fish of all kinds and many aquatic invertebrates.

Toxaphene and similar compounds must be used with great care on waterfowl areas, especially if applied from the air, since they can also kill birds if used unwisely. Also, experience has shown that it is difficult to obtain a complete fish kill with a toxicant. If two carp—male and female—are left, it is too many.

What is needed is a selective toxicant that will kill only carp—a toxicant similar in action to that used for the control of the sea lamprey. Research to that end has been started by fisheries scientists of the Fish and Wildlife Service.

CARP HAVE SOME redeeming qualities. Many shallow fishing lakes would soon become choked with aquatic vegetation were it not for their activities. In the South-Central States they provide considerable sport fishing. Commercial fisheries each year take carp worth 1.5 million dollars.

Carp have gained such a bad reputation that there is a tendency to blame them, sometimes unjustly, for any and all damage to aquatic habitats. Other fish or even human activities may sometimes be to blame.

Furthermore, some kinds of fish that resemble carp may be blamed but are quite innocent. Feeding habits of different kinds of rough fish often are quite different, as is their effect on the habitat. Buffalo-fish are large, native fish of the sucker family that superficially resemble carp, but they feed largely on plankton crustacea. Sheepshead, or freshwater drum, is a common rough fish of the Midwest that feeds mostly on small fish and insect larvae. The black bullhead, however, is a bottom feeder and may produce effects on the habitat—

especially high turbidity—much like the effects caused by carp. The bullhead often is abundant in fertile, shallow lakes and can survive low levels of oxygen in winter that kill all game fish, as well as carp, buffalo, and sheepshead.

Any program for improvement of waterfowl habitat involving removal of fish or installation of fish barriers therefore should take into account rough fish other than carp. The carp is a villian, but he may have associates in his crimes against waterfowl habitat.—JOHN B. MOYLE and JEROME H. KUEHN.

WOOD DUCKS

Bonus From Waste Places

I REMEMBER the marsh-dotted prairies of my boyhood in southern Minnesota, the teal and mallards I got on the back forty and in shallow lakes not far from home, the mink and muskrats I trapped in the sloughs, and a farm boy's felt, but inexpressible, intimations of immortality: Earth has no fairer place than this, where people and meadow flowers and God's other creatures thrive side by side. ·

I have seen what has happened. Wild meadows and billowing wheatfields have given way to fields of corn and soybeans. With them went the prairie chickens. The bulldozer, dragline, and power-shovel ditched the countryside. Marshes and shallow lakes began to disappear, and with them the canvasback, redhead, and ruddy duck. The bittern, coot, and grebe no longer call across the pastures at sundown from the wetlands I recollect so well.

I know what can be done to save, before it is too late, the meadows and marshes and odd corners where that other part of life can thrive and where we need not obstruct the path of expanding industry and agriculture. We are a prosperous people and can certainly afford to save at least some choice marshes. And we can create new nesting and feeding grounds for waterfowl on sites of low value, waste places, little-

643

used lands that can be developed as waterfowl habitats. Many such exist in Minnesota and in other parts of the United States. It is about these second rate sites that this chapter is concerned.

Suitable topography for creating water a few inches to 3 feet deep, a source of supply to maintain the desired depths, and soils on which useful marsh and aquatic plants can flourish are everywhere: Highway borrow pits and lowlands that can be flooded by using highway fills; bogs or seepage swamps; soggy woodlands; abandoned gravel, sand, and clay pits; certain types of abandoned strip mines; effluent basins next to sewage lagoons or sewage filter beds; submarginal farmlands and poorly drained depressions too wet for crop production; coastal flats; alkaline sinks in the West. All are useful.

They can be productive, attractive, and suitable for many kinds of water birds, although there will be problems such as disturbance and predation on the smaller tracts.

An example of how they may be used is the 20 shallow ponds and small marshes that are being developed for waterfowl on various types of low-grade sites near Laurel, Md., a heavily populated district. These marshy ponds have attracted more than 70 kinds of waterfowl and marsh or shore birds that did not previously occur there. Breeding populations of wood ducks, mallards, hooded mergansers, black ducks, and Canada geese have lived there. Pied-billed grebes, king rails, American and least bitterns, and black-crowned night herons are among the birds that have nested there. They are a bonus of interest and beauty for birdwatchers and hunters.

HIGHWAYS DESTROY wildlife habitat. They also can create breeding grounds and resting places for waterfowl. Aquatic birds make extensive use of highway ditches. In the Prairie States many species rear young in such unintentionally created habitats. Simple water-control structures can be installed at the heads of secondary road culverts in many places to create small marshes and shallow ponds.

Borrow-pits along highways and fills made across broad basins and shallow swales are readymade sites for new habitats for waterfowl. It is not hard to slope their edges, add islands to give waterfowl seclusion and concealment, and erect predator-proof nesting structures to make borrow-pit ponds attractive and productive.

Highway departments have helped transform such places into habitats for aquatic wildlife at the Moosehorn National Wildlife Refuge in Washington County in Maine, the Thousand Acre Marsh in New Castle County in Delaware, White's Creek Impoundment in Marlboro County in South Carolina, and many other points. A study of topographic maps and aerial photographs will disclose other possibilities in every State.

BOGS AND SWAMPS are available for making waterfowl habitats. Their high water tables and gradual slopes favor such usage, but topography may make the construction of dikes or diversion terraces costly. One should study the watershed and its relation to natural depressions to determine their practicability. Perhaps road fills can be used as dikes for impoundments. Suck dikes have been used to convert low-grade shrub swamps into productive waterfowl impoundments at the Patuxent Wildlife Research Center in Maryland and elsewhere. The removal of woody vegetation and breaking the mattress of roots in surface soils usually will expedite the development of impoundments in bogs and swamps.

Nutrients can be added to the ponds by burning felled trees and brush in the basins, thus making them more productive. The alka-line ashes of burned woody debris aid in reducing acidity and help minimize competition from undesirable growths of bladderworts that are stimulated by organic acids produced when large amounts of decaying wood are submerged.

The softness of the subsoil may make clearing swampy or boggy sites a chore. In warm, humid climates, good habitat can be created gradually by flooding shrubs and trees for 2 or 3 years deep enough to kill them. Decay can then be hastened by aeration of the beds through periodic summer draw-downs. Acid-tolerant food plants grow well in such impoundments.

LARGE NUMBERS of abandoned gravel, sand, and clay pits and

"Here we come, World!"   A nestful of wood ducks 1 day old.

many types of strip mines—otherwise sad relics of "progress"—exist throughout the country. Their potential for waterfowl habitats varies. Many are worthless or low in value, but many are worth developing; their suitability depends on the kind of bottom materials, type and amount of water available for flooding, and depth and topography of the basins. Runoff waters can be diverted into them if they are reasonably fertile. Drainage from farmlands usually is well suited for such purposes. Gravel, sand, or clay produce food and cover plants if the bottom materials are not excessively firm.

Shallow depths that insure good light penetration to the bottom are important. Major portions of the basins preferably should be a few inches to 3 feet deep and usually not more than 5 feet. Irregular shorelines and numerous low islands are an advantage. Bulldozing can make them and maybe fill in excessively deep sections. Hard bottoms occasionally can be covered with nearby materials that are better suited for plant growth if earthmoving costs are not excessive. Converting eyesores into attractive wildlife sites often enhances community values.

Suitability of food and cover plants depends on the sites: On saturated soil and water less than a foot deep, buttonbush, winterberry, rice cutgrass, bluntscale bulrush, common threesquare, and squarestem spikerush; in waters 1 to 4 feet deep, southern smartweed, watershield, spatterdock, floating pondweed, and snailseed pondweed;

in dark-stained or highly acid sites, white waterlily.

SEWAGE LAGOONS, or oxidation ponds, particularly in the prairies and plains, are an effective and economical means for towns to handle sewage disposal. Most of them are built on diked, level land a mile or so outside the communities they serve. The individual units usually are constructed in series and may cover a few acres to about 40 acres.

Many of these ponds have become useful replacements for disappearing waterfowl habitats. Their waters are rich in phosphorus and nitrogen and soon produce large numbers of snails, midge larvae, and other aquatic invertebrates important as food for waterfowl and shorebirds. An abundance of algae and suspended organic matter usually prevents the growth of submerged food plants, however. Sanitary engineers recommend that these ponds be designed to prevent the growth of emergent vegetation, because some may encourage mosquitoes. The highly fertile effluent from sewage ponds often can be diverted into natural or manmade basins, where it stimulates a vigorous growth of many plants for waterfowl.

I estimate that more than 650 such ponds were in operation in the United States in 1964, and at least 140 were in the Canadian Prairie Provinces, where they handle sewage from towns with populations of from 600 to 3 thousand. They are fairly common in southern Minnesota cities of about 7 thousand population. Sewage lagoons for cities of that size have a combined area of about 150 acres and are divided by dikes into connected units of 30 to 40 acres.

Missouri has more than 100 sewage ponds. North Dakota had at least that many—an increase from only 7 in 1952.

The first sewage lagoon in North Dakota was developed by the town of Fessenden in 1928. When I saw the unit some years ago, it had more waterfowl than any area of comparable size I visited in that part of the State. W. Van Heu-

velen, Director of Water Pollution Control for the North Dakota Department of Health, discussed the Fessenden sewage lagoon, after it had been in use for 24 years. In a report in the Official Bulletin of the North Dakota Water and Sewage Works Conference, he wrote:

"This particular lagoon has operated satisfactorily from its installation, and has never been a nuisance or a hazard to the community. . . . Waterfowl and shore birds find abundant food supplies in and around the lagoon. One observer had noted that a sewage lagoon

The fence makes the difference!   These geese could not be successful without it.   This nesting pair of Canada geese is part of a free-flying flock at Remington Farms in Maryland.

becomes a very fine wildlife habitat. He estimated that in the vicinity of the 10-acre Maddock (N. Dak.) lagoon this summer about 1 thousand birds are making their home. Because of the rich food supply that is found in and about the lagoons, birds will be attracted to a sewage lagoon and choose this in preference to a natural pothole where the food supply is much more limited. A sewage lagoon, in all its appearances, looks like a pothole area. The observer can walk around the dikes and note no nuisance conditions and certainly would not recognize this area as being fed by raw sewage."

FEW REGIONS in North America offer more opportunities for creating new habitats for waterfowl than the little-used flatlands along the Atlantic, Pacific, and Gulf coasts and the alkaline basins in the West. On the delta of the Bear River in Utah, sun-baked alkali flats have been converted into productive marshes of the famous Bear River National Wildlife Refuge, which supports peak populations of more than a million waterfowl.

The use of wasteland for waterfowl feeding and nesting grounds has had high priority in the national wildlife refuge program of the Bureau of Sport Fisheries and Wildlife for more than 30 years. Thousands of acres of alkali flats have become highly productive habitats.

Among such developments is the 10,500-acre Monte Vista National Wildlife Refuge in southern Colorado. There, on greasewood flats,

more than 220 ponds, lakes, and marshy meadows have been fashioned since 1953. Within 8 years, mallards, gadwalls, pintails, blue-winged teal, green-winged teal, cinnamon teal, and redheads, the avocet, Wilson's phalarope, common snipe, American bittern, and black-crowned night heron nested there. The wintering population is 70 thousand. Sandhill cranes are there in spring and fall.

At Brigantine National Wildlife Refuge in New Jersey, 16 hundred acres of salt marsh have been diked to form fresh-water habitat. Drawdown management of the pools brought 50 thousand waterfowl in 1961; only a few came before that.

Low-grade needlerush flats of the St. Marks Refuge in Florida were diked to form shallow, fresh-water feeding grounds. Now they are an important part of the only major wintering area for Canada geese in Florida. Shallow, fresh-water impoundments were made on mixed shrub and cordgrass flats at Pea Island Refuge along the coast of North Carolina. It is part of the principal wintering grounds of the greater snow geese, which nest in Greenland, North Baffin, and Ellsmere Islands.

A number of water-control structures can be used in new impoundments. Types that permit drainage and stabilization at any desired level should be used if feasible so as to make it easier to maintain the best balance between food and cover plants and to aid in the economical control of undesired plants and animals. Properly prepared concrete culverts often are the most economical in the long run if the water is acid. In most places, though, asphalt-coated, galvanized sheet-iron risers and culverts are satisfactory and are easier to transport, install, and operate.

WATER FROM SPRINGS, small streams, and artesian wells or water pumped or flowing from large bodies of water nearby may be used to supply manmade habitats. In the Eastern States, where annual precipitation is 30 to 60 inches, runoff from fertilized farmlands is preferred. During times of normal rainfall, an open watershed of 10 to 20 acres is considered enough to supply water for a 1-acre impoundment on compact soils. Too much water from an infertile watershed is undesirable because it carries away dissolved nutrients. The best impoundments, if other things are equally favorable, are so located that excess water can be diverted away from the basin rather than through it.

Of the numerous aids for improving habitat for waterfowl, I discuss a few of special significance in the development of breeding and feeding grounds on small waste spots.

In particular, predator-proof and starling-deterrent nesting structures have considerable value.

Snapping turtles should be removed periodically. One can do that by means of setpoles, equipped with sturdy fish hooks attached to strong chalk line, 4 to 5 feet long. Hooks with a bow diameter of three-fourths to seven-eighths inch are preferable. Pieces of fish, meat scraps, or 3-inch lengths of water snakes are suitable bait. The line should be attached by means of a slip noose. It can then be slipped to the bottom of the pointed pole, which should be pushed firmly into the pond bed in water 1 to 3 feet deep.

Disturbance by stray dogs and people must be prevented, particularly during the nesting season. Low, cross-shaped islands aid greatly in supplying concealment and freedom from disturbance for ducks and geese in open impoundments.

Turbidity created by carp and by the brown bullhead and other bottom-feeding catfishes can destroy submerged vegetation. Such fish must be removed to permit the necessary penetration of sunlight.

Topminnows should be introduced to control mosquitoes in nearly all marshy fresh ponds in the South. They also are a source of food for many waterfowl and larger fish. Several species of sunfishes have similar value, even when these are stunted in overstocked ponds.

Deficiencies of grit and lime should be remedied. Oyster-shell grit, of the type used by the poultry industry, should be placed along the pond borders where it is accessible to ducks and geese. Concrete rubble partly submerged in shallow waters in acid sites often enhances the production of snails, which are important in the diet of many ducks.

Hard seeds of such plants as squarestem spikerush, sawgrass, twig-rush, and burreeds often substitute for mineral grit in silt regions and serve both as food and grit.

Development of meadows along borders of most small impoundments is helpful in increasing use by many species of waterfowl. Lime and fertilizer, applied for hay production on such sites, serve a double purpose when they later leach into submerged basins and add fertility.

THE FEEDING ACTIVITY of muskrats often is a problem. They—and waterfowl—like plants with starchy rootstocks or tubers, such as the bulrushes, arrowheads, and sago pondweed and wildcelery. Wildrice

also suffers damage from muskrats and snapping turtles. These two vertebrates should be kept under control in many waterfowl habitats, and plants resistant to feeding by them should be used in the early stages of habitat development.

Water depth and light penetration are important to the success of submerged plants. Dark-stained waters of many acid ponds frequently are a major handicap. Planting of submerged species should be confined to sites in which the bottom is visible in midday sunlight. Several aquatic species, useful as waterfowl food and not seriously damaged by muskrats, may be grown in clear acid waters

Small islands provide nesting and resting sites in ponds and greatly enhance their value for waterfowl.

more than 15 inches deep and down to depths of 5 or 6 feet. Among them are floating pondweed, ribbonleaf pondweed, snailseed pondweed, slender pondweed, southern smartweed, water smartweed, watershield, and spatterdock. White waterlily will grow in turbid or extremely acid waters.

In acid waters less than 15 inches deep, several other species are useful for both food and cover. They include eastern burreed, hairy arrowhead, squarestem spikerush, mermaidweed, and buttonbush. Their abundance can be increased by lowering water levels or reduced by adding to the water depth. Sometimes rice cutgrass, warty panicum, redtop panicum, bluntscale bulrush, dotted smartweed, and winterberry furnish excellent food for ducks along the slightly submerged margins.

The tuberlike winter buds of paint-root are good food for shoalwater ducks on deep peat and acid sands of the Southeast and on sites that can be kept moist during the growing season and shallowly submerged during autumn and winter. Torrey threesquare and water bulrush are well adapted for shallow, acid impoundments in States on the Canadian border. Both produce tubers and seeds that ducks and geese relish.

Soft rush is a valuable cover plant for use on saturated soils and in water less than a foot deep. It grows well throughout the eastern half of the United States and eastern Canada. It is durable in the face of muskrats and wintry weather. Its tussocky habit permits inter-spersion of food plants and easy entry by waterfowl or marsh birds.

Outstanding plants for food production on recently disturbed soils include wild millet, fall panicum, and bigseed smartweed. They are well suited for impoundment basins that are drained during the summer and flooded during the autumn and winter. Disking the drained bed early in the summer increases their seed production.

BRACKISH AND ALKALINE habitats occur in depressions along tidal channels, on alkali flats, in the shrub and weed sandflats behind coastal lagoons, and in extensive cordgrass and needlerush meadows. They vary from a few acres to hundreds of acres. The carefully planned use of water-control structures is the key to their successful development. Within their proper ranges, the following salt-tolerant plants are of special value: For clear, brackish, coastal or inland impoundments 1 to 5 feet deep, muskgrasses, sago pondweed, widgeongrass, horned-pondweed, and spiny naiad; for moist or saturated, moderately brackish coastal or inland soils subject to flooding during the dormant season and for similar coastal soils flooded by high tides, seaside arrowgrass, saltgrass, and Walter millet; for moderately brackish tidal margins, gulf spikerush, dwarf spikerush, saltmarsh bulrush, alkali bulrush, glassworts, and tidemarsh waterhemp.

WATERFOWL usually can be attracted to newly created nesting

The area behind this sluicebox was low quality swamp timber. When flooded it provided useful waterfowl habitat.

grounds without resorting to stocking if suitable cover, food, and nesting sites are developed. How soon that happens depends on such factors as disturbance, predation, mortality during the hunting season, and the abundance of breeding birds in the region. When native breeding birds are scarce, several kinds of waterfowl may be released. Suitable predator-proof nesting structures for certain species can be helpful in developing breeding populations.

When they are selecting their first nesting territory, many young ducks and geese return to the area in which they learned to fly. The type of nest site they choose often is influenced by the type in which they hatched. This phenomenon, sometimes called "imprinting," can lead to the increased use of unusual, but safe, nesting structures. Methods are not known for large-scale imprinting of ducklings to encourage their use of safe nesting structures, but the release of immature birds in suitable habitats, at the age of 5 to 6 weeks, seems to offer the best chance of success in stocking programs.

Breeding populations have been established in habitats created on former wastelands by stocking semi-domesticated adult birds of varying age. At the Seney National Wildlife Refuge, Mich., a 400-acre goose pasture and nesting area was developed by carefully regulating the water levels. The unit was stocked with about 300 captive-bred, pinioned Canada geese in 1936. By 1962, the breeding population had increased to nearly 3 thousand birds, which were using manmade ponds and islands of the refuge. The young were permitted to migrate and have spread widely as nesting birds in the surrounding region.

ON A SMALLER SCALE, Canada geese have been established on a series of small ponds on and near the Patuxent Wildlife Research Center in Prince Georges County in Maryland. Complete protection from hunting and disturbance is afforded there. The releases were made in 5 small groups of 6 to 12 between 1945 and 1955. The geese, trapped from wild flocks in Maryland and North Carolina, included only one known mated pair. All were of unknown age. The releases totaled 20 pinioned and 31 wing-clipped birds. Nearly all of the wing-clipped birds left the area when they developed new flight feathers. The remaining geese have increased to more than a hundred birds, all of which are full-winged and migrate during severe winters. In 1963, at least 18 pairs nested on seven ponds, ranging in size from about 3 to 53 acres. Similar success has been reported from many other areas across the country.

The Patuxent Center is an example of what can be done to convert unsightly wastelands into picturesque ponds and marshes to provide greater opportunities for the enjoyment of Nature. It is a Bureau of Sport Fisheries and Wildlife installation midway between Baltimore and Washington, within 20 miles of the busy capital city and in an area populated by more than 3 million people. There one can see flocks of wild geese feeding contentedly in manmade marshes 9 months of the year. In the spring, you hear the dovelike mating call of the least bittern and the mysterious notes of king rails from the tangles of rushes and sweetbells at dawn. Often, on a summer evening, you can stand quietly among the flowering buttonbushes at the edge of a shallow pond and admire a doe wading among the lily pads with her spotted fawns or watch a wood duck leading her brood through the spatterdock bonnets.

This I often do, and so do many visitors from Washington, Baltimore, and other places, for we who work at Patuxent welcome our fellow citizens. We like to tell them about what we are doing—and what can be done with little effort and expense in many other localities—to redeem waste places, to reconstruct what is destroyed, and to prove that people and God's other creatures can thrive side by side.—FRANCIS M. UHLER.

MALLARD
CANADA GEESE

Instant Nesting Habitat

WHEN THE GREAT flocks of Canada geese move north, their voices heralding spring, some birds stay behind. Free-winged, but bound by instinct to the place of their hatching, they will perform the rites of spring amid unusual surroundings, in unlikely locations. Honkers will nest in wash tubs in Missouri and in treetop platforms in Montana. They will incubate in old tractor tires in Maryland, watched by placid, cud-chewing Holsteins.

These are not rare, freak accidents. The establishment of flocks of free-winged Canadas in many States is a growing, planned endeavor, that uses what we call instant nesting habitat to raise our production of waterfowl.

An upsurge in the making of impoundments—public and private, large and small—has provided many farm ponds, lakes, and floodings, which sometime may rival the potholes of Canada in total acreage, if not in localized density or overall quality. Many of these manmade impoundments and a number of natural waters lack suitable nesting habitat or lie outside the natural nesting range of desirable species. They serve well as wintering areas. Manmade nesting places may bring a number of these waters into greater productivity.

Artificial nest sites can replace in

part natural cover that was eliminated by grazing and other factors. They can reduce predator raids on nests; this is often a limiting factor. They can serve as inducements to the nesting of wing-clipped mated pairs used to originate flocks in new range.

EUROPEAN CONCEPTS and models, including pitcher-shaped wicker baskets from the Netherlands and woven-reed wigwams from Denmark, sparked the first experiments with artificial nests in the United States and Canada.

For example, the Dutch woven basket, first introduced at the Delta Waterfowl Research Station in Manitoba by former decoyman Nan Mulder, inspired Francis M.

Uhler's work with crow-proof mallard nest structures at the Patuxent Wildlife Research Center. An array of manmade nests adapted to American species and needs evolved from such early modifications of European styles. Several basic rules were followed in designing them: The use of inexpensive, readily available material; simplicity of construction; durability; and ease of maintenance.

THE WOOD DUCK was the subject of the first large-scale efforts—in Illinois in 1936—to increase numbers of American waterfowl by means of artificial nest structures. After 27 years of experimentation, three satisfactory styles of boxes for wood ducks have been developed.

New housing project in Montana. Canada geese use elevated nesting structures like this one being erected by employees of Montana State Fish and Game Commission.

Various materials are used in their construction—wood, sheet metal, and wire mesh and roofing paper.

The best wooden nest boxes are made of durable cypress. Pine may be used, but should be pressure or surface treated with a preservative to delay rotting. Creosote and similar preservatives that darken lumber appreciably or may harm nesting ducks should not be used. Boxes with minimum interior measurements of 9 by 10 inches and 20 inches deep provide enough space and seclusion to keep the woodies contented.

Boxes of galvanized sheet steel or sheet aluminum, developed by Frank C. Bellrose, Jr., of the Illinois Natural History Survey, last longer and usually cost less than wooden boxes. Ideal metal units are 10–12 inches in diameter and 24 inches high, with wood or metal bottoms. When dulled by exposure, galvanized boxes absorb considerably more heat from direct sunlight than wooden structures. A coat of aluminum paint helps avoid overheating eggs and increases durability.

Wooden and metal nest boxes arc mounted vertically. So they can be cleaned easily, they have lids that are easily removable yet so attached that they will not blow away in strong winds. Placing the entrance hole near the top darkens the nest area and helps protect the eggs from "long-armed" raccoons. A 3-inch strip of hardware cloth on the inside of the box, leading from the bottom to the entrance hole, helps the young to reach the outside world. All wood duck boxes have one-fourth-inch drainage holes in the bottom. Three inches or so of sawdust and wood shavings should be supplied as nesting litter.

Starlings often set up housekeeping in wood duck boxes. Noting that these pests do not tolerate as much light at the nest as do woodies, Francis M. Uhler developed a horizontal box at Patuxent. Construction is simple and inexpensive: A cylinder of heavy-gauge, mesh wire, about 12 inches in diameter and 24 inches long, covered with heavy-duty, graveled roofing paper. Circular boards, of the same diameter as the cylinder, form the ends; one has an entrance hole and the other has an adjustable opening to regulate inside lighting and discourage starling competition. Galvanized wire holds the roofing paper in place and attaches the cylinder to a post.

Boxes should be erected over or within one-fourth mile of water. They should be conspicuous. Wood ducks accept bright, new houses more readily than weathered, old ones, probably because the new ones are more easily seen. Carefully camouflaged boxes, tucked away in secluded, natural settings, may never be found.

WILD MALLARDS, normally ground nesters, will use open or well-lighted nests on or near ground or water, but mallards usually use elevated, darkened, boxlike nests only in places where artificially propagated birds have been released. The possible significance of this point is discussed later.

Mallards as a rule are less demanding than wood ducks as regards nest-box styles and materials. One

Canada goose finds "mileage" left in this old tire.

popular design is an open-end cylinder, about 24 inches in length and 12 inches in diameter. The material may be furnace pipe, one-eighth-inch marine plywood or wire netting and roofing paper. Modified metal grease drums are readily accepted. In these cylindrical nest structures one end normally is completely open; the other usually is two-thirds closed. A low wooden partition, near the middle, defines (with the partially closed end) a nest space some 12 to 14 inches long. Such nests frequently are placed 2 or 3 feet above water, either side-lashed to a post or mounted on 1-inch pipe. In the latter, holes are drilled in the top and bottom of the cylinder; the structure is slipped over the pipe and rests on a large washer welded (or held by a cotter pin) about 14 inches from the top. The open end will swing away from the wind if it protrudes off center a few inches.

Rectangular boxes of similar dimensions and materials are equally useable. Dressing cylinders and boxes with grass or reeds on the top and sides, to provide shade, camouflage, or a natural look probably is neither effective nor necessary.

Wooden nest structures, made from raw materials or modified from crates or boxes, make satisfactory nest sites for mallards. Acceptable interior measurements are 10 by 12 inches and at least 10 inches high. The entrance opening should be at least 8 inches wide and 8 to 10 inches high; it should have a projecting landing strip about 8 inches square or larger. These boxes are mounted on posts over or near water.

At Remington Farms, near Chestertown, Md., it was found that mallard ducks made simultaneous, successful use of as many as four box or cylinder nests mounted on a single post. The population of nesting mallards in the neighborhood is dominated by artificially propagated birds, which are more tolerant of crowding than a wild population. Besides these multiple nests, poultry-type row nests were tested. They were roofed over and mounted in two rows of 9 to 18 nests each on platforms and inverted barges. Hen mallards accepted these cavities readily and laid eggs in nearly all of the nests—but strife developed. They stole each other's eggs and nest material, swapped nests, and left home to a degree that greatly reduced nesting success. Individual units, even when grouped close together, proved to be much more efficient.

Mallard nest structures ranging from topless boxes to roofed, compartmented units, and mounted on floating rafts, have been tried in several localities. Most rafts are wooden, about 4 feet square, buoyed by truck tire innertubes, and anchored with chain or slack wire. Mallards take to these nest sites

Explosives are an economical means to building ponds in some situations. In this Maryland area a wood duck pond is being created. Note the rocket-shaped metal nesting box already in place.

readily, but so do raccoons, and such nests are more difficult to guard from 'coons than structures mounted on poles.

Nest materials must be provided. Cylindrical or rectangular boxes in exposed sites may be swept clear of material by wind—a major reason for partitioning off the nest area in these structures. A heavy base layer of wood chips, topped with hay or coarse, dry grasses makes a satisfactory, reasonably wind-resistant nest.

Temperature and humidity are critical to the hatchability of duck eggs. As yet, however, we know very little of the actual range of these factors in mallard nest boxes, other than that they vary with style. The minimum and maximum tolerances and ideal conditions for incubation likewise are not known. Mallards normally nest on the ground, but dew and soil moisture are not available in nest boxes.

Does the hen, returning from a dabbling excursion, carry enough water on her feathers to maintain satisfactory humidity in the nest? Should we cut holes in the box roof to let rainwater in, or in the bottom, to let it out? These and similar questions are yet to be answered.

ON CHESAPEAKE BAY, booby blinds—large, offshore duck blinds— are erected on pilings several feet above the water. They are partly roofed. Just before the hunting season, they are covered with switch-grass or pine or cedar boughs. Vernon Stotts, a biologist of the Maryland Game and Inland Fish Commission, found black ducks and

A simple nest box for wood ducks. It is protected from the egg-hunting raccoon, does not attract starlings, does not overheat, and it is readily accepted by wood ducks.

some mallards nesting on about 10 percent of these blinds. He located 134 clutches over a 5-year period.

Hatching success was good, probably because of the distance of the blinds from land-bound predators— 100 yards or more in some cases— but also because ospreys shared some blinds with ducks. The ospreys inadvertently protected the duck nests in driving crows away from their own eggs.

Noting that the location, type, and density of roofing material apparently influenced the use by ducks, Mr. Stotts suggested steps that builders of blinds could take to convert from duck hunting in winter to duck production in summer. His experience also reveals that black ducks will use artificial nest sites. Common goldeneyes and hooded mergansers likewise are adaptable to nesting in manmade structures. Both species have nested in boxes erected in Northern States. In Minnesota, goldeneyes have accepted boxes at rates equal to those of woodies.

Captive redheads, canvasbacks, and pintails used nest boxes successfully at the Howlands Island Game Management Area in New York, as did common mergansers and Barrow's goldeneyes in Oregon.

Hobbyists have employed manmade structures for still other waterfowl in captivity. The adaptation of the structures to wild birds could be important in future attempts to extend nesting ranges and increase production of many species.

NEST BOXES can be death traps if visited regularly by predators. No nest box program should be initiated without incorporating adequate safeguards against predation.

Elevating nests keeps out non-climbing terrestrial predators. Climbing nest-robbers—the raccoon chief among them in most regions—can be excluded by guards placed on the post or tree below the nest box. A 30-inch truncated metal cone, fitted snugly around the post, will do the job. It must be placed high enough on the post to prevent a big 'coon from jumping or climbing directly onto it from the ground but far enough below the box to keep him from reaching around it to gain a foothold.

Metal cylinders, 36–40 inches long, make useful guards around wooden nest box posts. They must be perfectly smooth, and at least 8 inches in diameter—raccoons have been observed climbing new 3-inch diameter downspouting. Tight-fitting cones and cylinders will frustrate nest-robbing snakes as well as raccoons. When used on trees, however, allowance should be made for growth. Nests mounted on metal posts at Patuxent have been protected by sandwiching each post tightly between two 9-inch-wide, 38-inch-long sheets of aluminum, 0.2 inch thick. The edges are bolted tightly together with brass machine screws to eliminate toeholds.

WOOD DUCK BOXES attached to large trees can be protected from squirrels by a steep, conical lid; from 'coons, by a metal bracket holding the box 2 feet out from the trunk. Specially designed oval and tunnel-guarded entrances exclude raccoons from wood duck boxes in Illinois and Massachusetts, respectively, but do not deter the smaller 'coons of Maryland.

Water often is overrated as a shield against nest predators. Nest structures on rafts or on unguarded posts over water are easily raided by swimming 'coons and snakes.

Crows are a serious threat to nests in structures with large entrances, such as those designed for mallards. In experiments at Remington Farms and elsewhere, recessed, darkened nests—achieved by tunnel entrances or mazelike interior designs—discouraged crows for a year or so but were eventually raided. We know as yet of no completely crowproof box that mallards will use.

Predators may ignore newly erected, unguarded nest structures. Sooner or later, however, they become aware of the contents, probably by accident. Once this happens, such knowledgeable forms as crows and raccoons will seek out every box and may even learn from this experience to raid nests guarded by devices that have been effective predator deterrents for years.

Learning occurs most rapidly where predators are common and the nest-box program is intensive. Consequently, protective devices and box styles that are labeled "predator proof" after a season or two in one locale may be vulnerable in later years or in other places. Small-scale nest-box projects in sites where predators are few (as, for example, on farm ponds in clean-farmed landscapes) may never require the extensive and expensive protection necessary to major projects in localities supporting dense populations of predators.

Localized predation of nest boxes frequently is traceable to one or a few individual predators, rather than to the entire population. Selective trapping may eliminate them. The fact remains, however, that if predators learn to associate nesting structures with pleasant experiences, they also could be taught to shy away from such structures if suitable repellents could be found.

CANADA GEESE along the Okanogan River in Washington have a habit of nesting in osprey nests. Members of the Oroville Sportsmen's Association decided to capitalize on this habit and erected straw-lined baskets of willow twigs in trees. Geese nested in 12 of 18 baskets one spring. The sportsmen set up more willow baskets, baskets of chicken wire, and old galvanized washtubs. Charles Yocom, of Humboldt State College, estimated that more than 600 goslings hatched in the homemade nests the first 6 years they were in use.

Successful in itself, this program in Washington was only a beginning. It inspired projects in several States. In Colorado, nesting honkers use platforms topped with baled straw and mounted on metal fenceposts. On the Patuxent area, they take readily to 30- by 30-inch baskets, 9 inches deep, formed from heavy wire mesh, and fastened to a reinforcing-rod frame. Lined with roofing paper perforated for drainage, the nests are mounted 2 feet over water on metal posts and filled with compacted dead grass. An introduced colony of Canadas hatched 15 broods in these baskets and on small, manmade islands in 1962.

The Missouri Conservation Commission provided elevated washtubs as nests for introduced breeding geese on the Trimble Wildlife Area. For 2 years, the birds showed little interest in the artificial nests, but in 1959 the first brood of goslings tumbled from a tub. By 1962, 52 Canadas—74 percent of the nesting population—were using these unlikely nest sites, and produced more than 150 goslings. Ground-nesting geese, harassed by bank fishermen and predators, had less success. In fact the greater productivity of the tub nesters has made the difference between a project which was faltering and one which is now highly successful.

In the Flathead Valley in Montana, John Craighead, of the Bureau of Sport Fisheries and Wildlife, and Dwight Stockstad, of the Montana Fish and Game Department, tested elevated platforms as nesting sites for local geese. They erected 83 boxlike, soil- and duff-filled platforms, 30 by 25 inches by 6 inches deep, at heights of 4 to 44 feet. The number of nesting geese in the vicinity did not seem to increase. Some ground-nesting birds shifted to the platforms, however, and had a higher hatching success and a greater percentage of successful nests than the ground nesters.

Artificial nests for geese differ in certain respects from those designed for ducks. Given the advantage of an elevated nest and an offshore site, a pair of aroused honkers can put up a formidable battle, making predator guards less necessary. But, unlike mallards, geese object to being crowded and are seldom tolerant of disturbance by people.

That means that the spacing and location of nest sites are critical for geese. Biologists on the Trimble Area in Missouri were able to reduce territorial demands by building "ganderstands"—artificial loafing sites for male geese—10 feet from the nest tubs.

Artificial nest structures must be acceptable to important ground-nesting species, including mallards and geese, if they are to play an important role in the production of wild waterfowl. If artificial structures are placed on or near the ground and resemble natural nest sites, then use by ground nesters has been good. The response to elevated nests is erratic, however; some populations use them readily from the start, but others largely ignore them.

Why this difference? It may relate to the background of the birds themselves. Biologists know that some species of birds are subconsciously imprinted with associations encountered during a limited period, often a few hours, after hatching. Waterfowl hatched and imprinted in elevated, natural nests may take more readily to elevated artificial nests than their ground-hatched counterparts. This would explain the ready acceptance of artificial aerial platforms by geese in Washington and Montana that already were accustomed to osprey nests. In time, local populations of normally ground-nesting species may actually come to prefer elevated nests, as does the *hoogbroedeenden* (high-breeding) mallard strain in the Netherlands. The acceptance of nest structures by artificially propa-

gated mallards, previously mentioned, may stem from some imprint
left by hatching in incubators.

Learning certainly is involved in
the use of nest boxes, as demonstrated by the accelerating acceptance
of washtubs by Canada geese in
Missouri. Box-nesting mallards at
Remington Farms result from
hatches in nest boxes, incubators,
and ground nests. The nucleus of
imprinted users of nest boxes may
provide the example from which
the others learn similar behavior.

It seems clear that ground-nesting
waterfowl can be induced to use
artificial nest sites and that acceptance can be accelerated by using

birds naturally or artificially adapted
to elevated nests. The degree and
nature of the influence of imprinting,
learning, or some factor yet unknown
on this process offer a fertile field
for further research.

FOLLOWING THE ESTABLISHMENT
of the 5,808-acre Pea Island National Wildlife Refuge on the Outer
Banks of North Carolina in 1938,
gadwall and blue-winged teal joined
black ducks already present to form
the southernmost nesting population
of these species on the Atlantic
coast. James Parnell, of North Carolina State College, in 1959, estimated
a combined hatch of nearly 700

Bureau of Sport Fisheries and Wildlife biologists inspect a wood duck nest box at Patuxent Wildlife Research Center in Maryland. The bracket attachment is designed to prevent access by raccoons.

ducklings, an impressive figure for the south Atlantic coast. One factor probably had an important bearing on the success of this colony—there are no raccoons on Pea Island.

Studies in many regions show that natural islands may aid nesting waterfowl by providing increased "edge" for nest sites and concealment of young, plus protection from ground predators. Following this cue, waterfowl managers now construct manmade islands to provide instant nest sites. They include bulldozed push-ups of small mounds for geese in Oregon and elaborate structures, as on the Lower Souris National Wildlife Refuge in North Dakota. There, M. C. Hammond and G. E. Mann recommended islands of 0.3 to 1 acre and described island nesting densities of 20–80 nests to the acre.

All is not ideal with nest islands, however. The very fact that they may hold heavy concentrations of nesting ducks makes them a prime attraction for predators. Unless protected, as by a wide expanse of deep water on all sides, islands may only increase the vulnerability of nests to predation.

Islands, whether formed by bulldozers or draglines or from dumped fill, must be protected from erosion. Riprapping, breakwaters of stone or emergent vegetation, a good vegetative cover on the crown, and close spacing of several islands to provide protection against waves are effective safeguards. Adequately protected, bulldozed islands at Lower Souris cost 1.82 dollars a running foot in 1955. With life expectancy of 100 years for islands, the cost

totaled only 20 cents a goose and 5 cents a duck expected to be produced.

MANY LOWLAND AREAS receive little waterfowl use for nesting or any other purpose, because they have silted in or become overgrown with vegetation to the exclusion of essential patches of open water. In these situations, instant habitat often can be created by blasting.

Blasting as a waterfowl management technique has for some time been limited by the cost of dynamite. Recently, however, an inexpensive, new explosive agent has gained wide acceptance. This is ammonium nitrate (AN), a well-known commercial fertilizer, sensitized by soaking with fuel oil (FO), and exploded by using a small quantity of dynamite as a primer.

The advantages of AN–FO, as this mixture is commonly called, are low cost, ready availability of ingredients, and relative safety. As with any blasting agent, of course, full safety precautions must be observed, and work must be supervised by an experienced explosives handler.

Tests by the U.S. Forest Service and the conservation departments of such States as Minnesota, Wisconsin, and Michigan underscore the value of AN–FO for improving and creating waterfowl habitat. Two 50-pound charges placed in heavy clay soil in Minnesota, for example, produced a pothole 25 by 35 feet by 7 feet deep, at a cost of 11 dollars including labor. Two 8-pound charges in a Michigan peat marsh resulted in a hole 14 by 19 feet, 4 feet deep, for 4 dollars. Results varied with soil type, and AN–FO had to be packaged in waterproof containers for satisfactory use in wet soils.

These are minor limitations, however, in view of the many tests showing that for comparable results, AN–FO blasting costs were one-fifth to one-third those of dynamite. With this increased economy, blasting should be more useful in creating instant habitat for waterfowl in the future.

AN ATTRACTIVE total environment is important when attempting to establish or build a population of nesting waterfowl. Suitable submerged, emergent, and shoreline vegetation provides food and cover to enhance the appeal of new impoundments. Fencing against grazing, where feasible, encourages natural cover. Periodic drawdowns improve established, manmade waters.

Adequate loafing sites are important, too. They can be provided with anchored rafts, islands, or protruding logs. Supplemental feeding of pelletized commercial breeder rations in late winter, for example, has helped maintain high nesting populations of semiwild mallards on impoundments where natural foods are scarce.

IT IS NOT ENOUGH to provide nest boxes from which tiny woodies, greenheads, and honkers tumble.

Instant—artificial—nests normally are used where no natural nest sites or cover exist. Frequently this means that escape and loafing cover for ducklings also is nonexistent. In some habitats without cover, new broods are literally sitting ducklings to inclement weather and predators. Protection can be had by planting and encouraging such emergent aquatic plants as buttonbush, spatterdock, and certain rushes. As a bonus, these emergents provide a variety of insects for feeding ducklings.

Snapping turtles, bass, pike, and gar go after ducklings, and should be removed from small impoundments that are designed primarily for waterfowl production.

When an adequate breeding population of waterfowl gains good production levels on properly developed impoundments, sheer duckling numbers may overwhelm the effects of predation with a minimum of artificial "assists." Francis M. Uhler believes this to be a factor at the Patuxent Wildlife Research Center, one of the best examples of instant nesting habitat at work. Here, waterfowl of species never before nesting locally are producing thriving broods in natural-looking pond and marsh habitat. Impoundments, built, planted, and provided with nesting structures by man, have made the difference.

—GEORGE V. BURGER and
CLARK G. WEBSTER.

RING-NECKED DUCKS

Research, Key to Progress

"RESEARCH IS THE KEY to tomorrow" is more than a slogan, it is undeniable fact. Without research the outlook for waterfowl would indeed be bleak, for all the cards seem stacked against them.

Waterfowl require living spaces of special kinds. People have found many uses for these same spaces. The outcome of this competition seems inevitable—waterfowl must stand aside for what we humans term "progress."

Fortunately, there always have been people with inquiring minds unwilling to accept the "inevitable." They are the researchers, and their miraculous findings are all around us—moon shots, wireless transmission of image and sound, medical cures for scourges of yesterday. The list is endless. When people make up their minds to find a better way, they usually do through painstaking, time-consuming, and often expensive research.

As for waterfowl, a storehouse of knowledge met most management needs until recently. Biologists have delineated the range of most species and they can count the birds accurately enough to forecast the size of the fall flight into each flyway. Thousands of band recoveries have

667

removed much of the mystery of travel routes, longevity, mortality due to gunning, and other characteristics of waterfowl. Much has been learned about the hunter, too. In the United States his annual take is carefully measured and his reaction to various types of regulations is better understood by the biologist than by the hunter himself.

Much is already known about the habitat requirements for many kinds of waterfowl. For instance, we have learned that good duck crops occur only when prairie potholes number several million. Ducks flock together in fall and winter but during the breeding season they demand some solitude. This is provided best by innumerable potholes, so when they are in short supply duck populations slump.

While much is known about waterfowl, it's but a pinpoint of light compared to the needs in times ahead. By the year 2000, our population may reach 300 million. Our food and cropland surplusages of today will gradually fade until some day, perhaps the year 2000, additional acreage must be brought into production if our present standard of living is to continue. What about waterfowl and their habitat then? Certainly we do not have the answers now to many of the problems sure to arise. It will take deep digging to get them and failure to do so may mean that the sport of waterfowling will be only a memory by the turn of the century.

RESEARCH is never at its best in a crisis. It is most productive and economical when planned with attention to priority needs. The first job—spelling these out in order of importance—has been done in a document entitled "Statement of Needs for Waterfowl Research and Management Investigations by Agencies and Organizations in the United States."

Waterfowl are for the enjoyment of people, and to satisfy this general objective, the waterfowl must be both abundant and widely distributed. Management has set some specific goals—waterfowl populations equal to those of the early 1950's and hunting opportunity for some 3 million people in the United States, Canada, and Mexico. Research—and it's a big job—must find ways to maintain waterfowl abundance and hunting opportunity at these levels, despite heavy inroads on the greatest controlling influence—wetland habitat.

Abundance alone can prove a liability rather than an asset. Great flocks of mallards may play havoc on swathed wheat and cause the farmer involved and all his neighbors to declare war on these "pests." A refuge may play host to many thousands of waterfowl but add little or nothing to recreational opportunity. Research can help management bring about better distribution, always keeping in mind that abundance and wide distribution are not ends in themselves. The true test is the welfare of the birds and the amount of genuine pleasure and satisfaction afforded the public.

MANAGEMENT has two primary tools for influencing waterfowl populations and distribution: hunting regulations and habitat manipulation. It is up to research to sharpen these tools.

Research must find the most efficient and most accurate ways to determine the stock on hand and to measure changes in its status. The problem is complicated by the large number of species involved, the great expanse of territory which they frequent, and the different kinds of habitat which they choose. Already, remarkable progress has been made in devising ways of measuring these populations but as management becomes more intensive the need for more precise measurements increases.

Good inventories open other management doors. They provide a basis for sound regulations and permit maximum harvests consistent with a reasonable carryover of breeding stock. They also provide a measure of habitat utilization so that its relative importance can be assessed. Keeping track of several dozen kinds of waterfowl over a range measured in millions of square miles is a sizable chore. Yet it's being done with commendable accuracy and the system devised stands as a major triumph of research.

Breeding ground surveys in May and June determine the distribution and size of the adult duck population. In these months most species are easiest to count. In July an-

Dyeing of wings of this pintail with a harmless solution will help biologists trace the bird's daily movements.

Chemical analysis of soil, water, and feeds can demonstrate the presence of pollutants hazardous to migratory waterfowl. This scene is a chemical laboratory of the Bureau of Sport Fisheries and Wildlife.

The modern chemical laboratory with its well-trained staff and precision equipment serves as the analytical arm of the waterfowl research team.

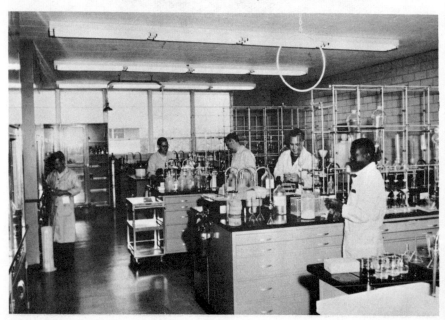

other survey measures the relative success of the breeding season. The method used is to fly strips or "transects" across the vast breeding grounds at predetermined intervals. Flying 150 feet above the ground, the pilot and observer record on a dictating machine all the waterfowl seen along a path ⅛-mile wide on each side of the plane. Every 4 lineal miles flown gives a one-square-mile sample and for each habitat unit the results finally taken from the recording machine are expressed in terms of ducks (by species) per square mile. Simple enough, yet the procedure took several years in development and involved hazards aplenty.

A head count of the birds is only half the problem. Hunters and their success must be reduced to figures, too, if the effects of various regulations are to be appraised. It's being done. One mail survey yields statistics on kill, distribution of hunting effort by time and place, and other information. Another mail survey yields wings of ducks and tails of geese. In the hands of experts they tell a story on the species composition of the kill and age ratios.

A lot of work has gone into establishing criteria for determining the age of birds by their feathers; more research is needed before this technique can be applied to all species. Age ratios obtained in autumn and winter are a good measure of breeding success.

In conjunction with information from banding and kill surveys they can be used to help reconstruct the population level prior to the hunting season. This technique also serves as a check on the accuracy

of the breeding ground survey. With techniques such as this, research is taking much of the guesswork out of waterfowl management and in its place a scientific basis is evolving.

SPECIES MANAGEMENT is a promising refinement of waterfowl management which will demand more attention from research people in the future. Some species of ducks in some years are being overhunted; more are being killed than are replaced by reproduction. We know this from the percentage of bands returned. At the same time, other species are being underutilized; gunners could take more without lowering the population level. Precise measurement of these differences in rate of harvest would mean increased hunting opportunity, provided there is a practical way of accomplishing it.

If hunters were skilled in duck identification, the problem would be greatly simplified. Suppose, for example, that there is an excess of bluewings. In southern areas at least, hunters could enjoy a September outing, bag a few prime bluewings (while other ducks are still scrawny and full of pinfeathers), and everyone would be happy. But present-day hunters are not adept in distinguishing one duck from another and conservation agency officials are fearful, with reason, that a special teal season might be damaging to other ducks in the same area. Thus, research can go only so far; beyond that it is up to the hunter.

Canada geese are fine subjects for species management. Identification is no problem and they faithfully use the same areas year after year. They respond to management better than any other waterfowl species. Their breeding grounds are not subject to many of the hazards confronting the prairie ducks. They are extremely popular among hunters and nonhunters alike. Waterfowl managers have capitalized on these traits and the harvest of some flocks of Canadas is controlled almost as precisely as would be possible with a flock of tame turkeys. A quota is set on the number to be taken and enough breeders are retained to permit a full replacement in the following year.

Canada goose management represents a pinnacle of achievement to date in handling waterfowl. In 1946 these birds had become so scarce in the Mississippi Flyway that a closed season was declared. Something had to be done promptly. It was. Monies were made available for acquisition, management, and research. Results were spectacular. The population started to climb almost immediately. It continued to climb while the duck population was nosediving, and the trend continues upward.

Paradoxically, management of Canada geese also represents one of management's greatest failures. As we said earlier, abundance is not the only goal of management. Abundance has been or is being achieved in this species but not good distribution. In many instances, intensive management has been at the expense of high-quality recreation.

Some northern refuges appear to have "dammed" off or "shortstopped" much of the goose flight, gradually drying up goose areas farther south.

In similar fashion, certain highly attractive areas have acted as a magnet, causing great concentrations where formerly the birds were more widely dispersed. Unfortunately, these massive assemblies bring out the worst human behavior. Commercialism in a greedy degree follows the big flocks. And some hunters, mislead by the appearance of unlimited abundance, conduct their hunting accordingly.

Research and management are seeking ways to improve the situation. Several thousand geese have been captured on concentration areas and moved by trucks to good goose habitats farther south along former important flightlanes. State-wide closures to hunting prevail around the release areas. The objective is to re-establish the traditions which once compelled these birds to use more southern wintering grounds. Various techniques are being tried to encourage wider dispersal from concentration points. These include manipulation of shooting hours, temporary closure of all or parts of certain counties, use of captive flocks, and establishment of food plantings attractive to geese.

Harvest control is not the only, or even the primary, part of species management. Meeting the habitat needs of the birds is highly important, too. It is a fertile field for research.

HABITAT MANAGEMENT, as a start, aims to save and utilize wisely what we have, especially in places where it will do the most good. We know that the prairie sections of Canada and the United States produce the bulk of our waterfowl. We also know that it is in this area that the drainage threat is greatest. Logic tells us then that here is where our efforts should be concentrated to save all we can of our prime marshes and potholes. Even in doing this, there is need for research to help do the best job at a minimum of expense.

But logic should not end there. It should also tell us that, at best, not all can be saved, and substitute measures must be taken if we are to maintain the potential for producing ducks in harvestable numbers. Some species of waterfowl breed not at all, or in low numbers, on the prairies. Most of our geese, for example, and some diving ducks are bred in the boreal forest or tundra zones; other ducks—the wood duck is one of them—find suitable nesting grounds throughout much of the wooded area of the United States and in southern Ontario and Quebec. A few species such as the mottled duck, a cousin of the black duck, prefer the Gulf coastal marshes. All told, the whole of North America outlines the breeding grounds of waterfowl, a fact frequently overlooked and one of great significance.

It means, for instance, that drought or other weather extremes can bring nesting failures to some species when other species are producing bumper crops. The drought of the late fifties and early sixties illustrates this point.

The prairie country in that period was so dry that duck production in some areas approached the zero point. Pintails and mallards declined sharply following several years of nesting failure; canvasbacks and

Ducks on the Bear River National Wildlife Refuge in Utah remain on the water as a survey plane passes over at low elevation. Hunters sometimes complain that aerial surveys drive all the ducks away.

The air boat is an essential form of transportation in shallow marshes. Here a biologist at Shiawassee National Wildlife Refuge, Michigan, is conducting a waterfowl census.

redheads were even harder hit because they depend even more heavily on prairie habitat. Finally the numbers of the last two species dwindled to a point requiring closure of hunting seasons. Meanwhile, Canada geese, wood ducks, and scaup prospered to the point that hunting regulations for them were liberalized.

All this emphasizes the point that we cannot manage waterfowl as a unit. We must consider separately the habits and habitat needs of individual species. This is what we mean by "species management." It involves all phases of waterfowl

management; it means considering the smallest common denominator, the species or even local populations of some kinds or races of waterfowl. Developing this information species by species, habitat by habitat, and flyway by flyway is the Herculean job facing the researcher in the years ahead.

ONE BRIGHT CLOUD on the horizon is the strong possibility that the birds we have could provide even more recreation than we now enjoy. Both hunters and managers are guilty of wasting birds and space. One or two birds are left at the hunting grounds for every four taken home because hunters have not made a clean kill or, for one reason or another, have been unable to find the bird they shot down.

Some hunters deliberately leave birds behind—coots used for target practice, "small" ducks, undesired or protected species, or overlimits. All hunters contribute toward seeding the feeding grounds of waterfowl with lead pellets. These, in sufficient quantity, are lethal to the ducks, geese, or swans which ingest them. Much of this wastage could be avoided and the savings used for recreation.

Managers of public hunting grounds or duck clubs may waste birds by permitting shooting where hunters are unable to retrieve the birds or by condoning "sky-busting" or other unsportsmanlike practices. They may waste space by not developing manageable sites or by unnecessarily restricting public use beyond the needs of the birds.

Lead poisoning eventually could be eliminated if research could find an acceptable substitute for lead shot. The saving in ducks would exceed the output of many thousands of acres of prime habitat. If crippling losses could be reduced by a third, we could accommodate more hunters without having to curtail hunting opportunity.

Waterfowl which die of botulism, fowl cholera, and other diseases are removed from public use as surely as though the birds had never been produced. Research has already shown how to lessen the effects of some of these diseases. Studies at Bear River Refuge in Utah have resulted in water management techniques which have saved many thousands of ducks from certain death from botulism.

Pollution is another big waster of waterfowl—how big no one knows because often its effects are subtle. Some pollution die-offs are spectacular and widely publicized, such as the chemical poisoning and detergent cases along the Detroit River in Michigan, or the soybean oil spillage case which killed some 10 thousand ducks in Minnesota during the spring of 1963. Others, like those along the Atlantic seaboard, are evidenced by a dead duck here, another there, washed up along mile after mile of beach. In the aggregate, such losses may far exceed those which make the headlines.

How can research prevent such losses? The long-term approach is to help industries, municipalities, and other polluters get rid of harmful wastes without jeopardizing the waterfowl resource. But sometimes research hands are called upon for stop-gap solutions. In October 1963, a few days before the greater snow goose population was due to arrive at its famous traditional feeding area, Cap Tourmente near Quebec City, a ship pumped an estimated 1 thousand gallons of bunker oil from its bilges. The oil spread over the feeding grounds, thickly coating the vegetation. Biologists of the Canadian Wildlife Service, promptly recognizing the danger to these North Carolina-bound geese from the eastern Arctic, conferred with chemists and enlisted the help of local residents in raking up the polluted vegetation. A chemical added to the mess permitted burning, and when the geese arrived on schedule their feeding area was safe again. In the Minnesota case, a treatment was devised for the oil-soaked birds which eventually restored to health a thousand or more and enabled them to return to the wild.

Chemical pesticide residues are found over millions of acres of habitat, both wetland and upland. These may have both direct and indirect effects on waterfowl and may be passed from adult to offspring through the eggs. When captive adult drake mallards are fed sublethal dosages of Kepone (a chlorinated hydrocarbon) they lose their secondary sexual characteristics and resemble hens. These drakes regain their green heads and other typical male coloration after being removed from the contaminated diet. We wonder whether ducks, like mosquitoes, will develop a resistance to certain pesticides and, if so, how long it may take them to do so. One thing is certain: less pollution, in fact less waste of all kinds, means more birds for recreational use.

Waste abatement is a primary goal of waterfowl management. Far too little is known about this subject at present and research must supply many of the answers. Let us heed the Mississippi Flyway's slogan, *Make haste to reduce waste;* it is a timely admonition for today and tomorrow.

ABOVE ALL ELSE a duck needs a home—in fact, two of them: one for summer, another for winter—and waystations in between. Man with his ditches and dams, his bulldozers, cement mixers, and land levelers is changing the face of the earth. Sometimes he intentionally or inadvertently creates new homes for waterfowl but more often he destroys them. The "housing" shortage for ducks is most acute on the breeding grounds and getting worse. Expecting man to shut off his face-lifting machines is wishful thinking of the highest order. How then can the waterfowl living space problem be solved?

Answers may be found among the following possibilities:

Stepping up efforts to save what we already have.

Creating new breeding grounds.

Increasing the productivity of management areas.

Transplanting birds into unoccupied habitats.

Taking advantage of opportunities presently ignored.

Telling the public that a problem exists and informing them about its possible consequences.

Research must play a key role in supplying these answers, so let's take a closer look at some of these possibilities.

Thus far, most of our efforts in saving wetlands have involved acquisition or lease. There is a limit to how much wetland can and should be transferred from private to public ownership. When this limit is reached, unacquired wetlands still will be endangered unless other approaches for saving them have been developed.

The profit motive seems to determine the landowner's decision on whether or not to save his wet areas. Studies are needed to determine the economics of converting wetlands to dryland crops. If other benefits do not provide economic justification for saving wetlands, it will be necessary to consider some form of payment to landowners for public services rendered. This, too, will require research to determine reasonable payment rates for various wetland classifications.

Creating new breeding grounds is a must if expected habitat losses are to be mitigated. Looking ahead to the time when food and fiber needs dictate, our most productive soil undoubtedly will receive first attention in any agricultural expansion plans. Therefore, it would seem illogical to concentrate the building of new waterfowl areas in highly productive agricultural regions, even though such areas also produce the best duck crops.

The extent to which second-rate waterfowl habitat can be made more productive has received some study, but more will be required before any large-scale expansion into such habitats is undertaken. Some promising results already have been achieved. A defunct drainage prospect in Minnesota, the Agassiz National Wildlife Refuge, now ranks among the best as a waterfowl-producing area. Before management, it was practically worthless, either for waterfowl or agriculture. Thousands of acres, apparently of similar type, are still available for waterfowl developments in the Lake States region. This is one of the places where research and management working together may find it possible to help offset losses of production habitat elsewhere.

A prime objective of waterfowl production refuges is to double or triple the output. This in recogni-

Machines do in minutes what would require days for a biologist to do in tabulating and analyzing statistics on waterfowl migration and hunting.

Banding flightless waterfowl in Saskatchewan. Some 1800 ducks, mostly mallards, were taken in this drive.

tion of the fact that as habitat shrinks, each remaining parcel will be required to contribute correspondingly more, if the population is to hold its own.

Difficulties stem from knowing too little about the requirements and preferences of individual species. Each kind of duck behaves differently and often a given species does not act the same in different situations. Gadwalls are a good example. On the Canadian prairies you find the nesting pairs spread out like most other ducks. But at Lower Souris Refuge in North Dakota, dozens of gadwalls are content to nest side by side on a manmade island only an acre in size. What triggered this unusual behavior? The answer, if known, might enable the refuge manager not only to double his output but to increase it manyfold.

Predators are a problem over most of the breeding grounds. In one area crows or magpies may be the culprits; in another, skunks or raccoons. These and other birds and mammals will eat eggs with great relish when they are available. The end result is that at least half the duck nests may be broken up by predators.

The answer seems obvious: get rid of the predators. This solution, however, never has proven practical in North America on any large scale. But predator control has resulted in improved nest success on certain managed areas such as Lower Souris and Agassiz National Wildlife Refuges. It is still a matter for research to determine if, where, and when such control is feasible and desirable.

AVICULTURE (artificial propagation) is a recreational end in itself, occasionally a profitable venture, and definitely a tool of management. It is in the latter connection that we consider it here. Raising waterfowl and releasing them into the wild is nothing new. Game farms preceded modern wildlife management and have flourished ever since. Recently, in fact, game-farm mallard production may have reached a new high, stimulated by the demands from tower shooting preserves and such mass release programs as those of Max McGraw in Illinois, the Pennsylvania Game Commission, and Remington Farms in Maryland. The pros and cons of such programs have been argued for years and studied in detail by the State game commissions of Wisconsin and New York. The conclusions reached depend largely on one's viewpoint. Most people agree that such programs are neither a panacea nor a substitute for habitat ills but that they can serve a useful purpose when properly applied.

It is in another connection, however, that more research is needed. An air traveler passing over mid-America on a clear day can see below him thousands of small ponds which were not there a decade or two ago. These ponds are now almost as numerous as the prairie potholes of the United States—and are increasing almost as fast as the potholes are decreasing. Herein lies the challenge. Can research in aviculture result in a duck that can reproduce in greater numbers on farm ponds? Can farm ponds themselves be modified to become more useful to waterfowl?

Another area supporting only sparse populations of breeding ducks is the coastal marshes, particularly those of the Gulf coast. To what degree can they replace lost habitat of the North in contributing toward the waterfowl crop? Experiments underway in southwestern Louisiana may find out whether aviculture can be used to solve the problem.

Homegrown Canada geese are appearing in increasing numbers in several Northern States. One such flock in Ohio produced a thousand goslings in 1963. Another at Seney, Mich., in existence for a longer time, has leveled off at about 800 goslings per year. Minnesota has several local flocks and envisions the day when breeding Canadas may again repopulate suitable habitat throughout the State. The Dakotas have similar goals. Missouri hopes eventually to equal the take by its hunters with homegrown geese, and in the Deep South, Louisiana is making an effort to establish a breeding flock.

This is an encouraging plus in waterfowl management which has gradually gained momentum. Where it will end nobody knows, but that it is worthy of research's attention seems evident.

Most of us have blindspots when it comes to taking advantage of our opportunities. Waterfowl experts are no exception. The soggy meadows of the Red Lake Indian Reservation have not changed much for many years. Officials and conservationists by the dozens had passed these flats many times not recognizing their potential for waterfowl management. Recently, biologists focused attention on the possibilities and, early in 1964, a contract was let to build a large duck marsh.

It is too early to say how much this area will contribute to waterfowl production, to the economy of the Indians through the sale of wildrice, furs, and guide services to hunters, or to recreation. If it pays off as expected, there are many similar areas waiting to be developed. Again, research and management working together as a team must evaluate such opportunities and be prepared to apply the findings as widely as possible.

OFTEN NATURE gives clues that can be invaluable in directing the job of waterfowl management. Skillful people, who can read the signs, watch changes in plant composition to determine whether the waterfowl range is improving or degenerating. They look for telltale changes in the invertebrate life and the chemical makeup of the marsh. The general condition of the birds themselves—their weights and presence or absence of certain parasites— is a reflection of possible trouble spots.

Occasionally, Nature does the whole management job herself. Her tools are droughts, hurricanes, and other drastic measures. Over the years potholes full of water become less and less productive, just as corncropping an upland field year

after year will deplete its fertility. So, periodically, Nature dries out the pothole, thus "summer-fallowing" it. Refilling again, its former productiveness returns. Noting this, managers use a similar technique on their refuges.

Hurricanes can do wonders in renovating "wornout" marshes and Hurricane Audrey was a classic example. It took the southwestern Louisiana marshes apart and put them back together again far better than they were before, so far as waterfowl are concerned. Biologists have studied the result in detail and every effort will be made to maintain this favorable stage of plant succession.

Back Bay and Currituck Sound, along the coasts of Virginia and North Carolina, provide another example. During the 1950's, it became apparent that something was drastically wrong with this famous waterfowl area. In March 1962, a violent episode in Nature helped prove the validity of conclusions reached by biologists. A storm put seawater over the area raising salinity, and precipitation of silt particles followed. The water became comparatively clear and plant growth responded phenomenally. The food supply was augmented by the appearance of multitudes of small clams which ducks relish. Ducks flocked to these improved conditions and biologists chalked up another "assist" for Nature. They also started looking around for other places to apply this new-found knowledge.

LOOKING AHEAD, business will continue to be brisk in waterfowl research. For the biologist, problems are the stock in trade and of these there is no shortage in waterfowl management. Beginning with the job of production there are problems galore, and the quest for solutions involves not only the fine details of biology but of sociology, economics, and politics as well. You expect that in working with lands and waters that serve multipurpose needs. More questions arise in planning for the support of waterfowl in their transcontinental migrations; and there are problems, too, in dealing with the proper and best utilization of the birds—people of all interests considered.

It's no job for a pessimist. But inquiring minds in search of a challenge will be well stimulated in probing the requirements of waterfowl, then providing them—economically and in harmony with other occupants of this one earth. As for satisfactions—they will compare in magnitude with the job at hand.—DANIEL L. LEEDY,
DAVID A. MUNRO, and
WALTER F. CRISSEY.

The best research comes from the scientist who keeps his head in the clouds of inquiry and his feet on solid ground. To him the world owes its future. On him rests the security of its people. May his labors never cease.
—CARL D. SHOEMAKER.

A Letter to a Hunter

DEAR SIR: We have your welcome letter of August 20, in which you urge that the duck season be closed this year because a 3-year drought has been rough on the ducks. We appreciate your statement that you "have hunted for 48 years and want to save the sport for my grandson" for it touches directly the heart of the matter: The hunting that used to be and the hunting (plus other values of waterfowl) that we all want to save for coming generations.

In the same mail delivery that brought your letter was one from a man in Arkansas, who wrote: "Why don't you give the poor duck hunter a break? We buy hunting licenses and duck stamps for what? The hunting season is over before the ducks arrive and the number of mallards a guy can shoot is too small."

As we said, we welcome all such expressions of different points of view about ways to manage waterfowl, for they express a concern we all feel about the conservation and wise use of this immeasurably valuable resource. Also they give us the opportunity to put problems like

683

Waterfowl breeding ground surveys require many hours of careful planning. Here Edward Wellein and Arthur Hawkins are plotting flight lines on a map before taking to the airways.

yours in a broad framework of the "greatest good for the greatest number in the long run."

We cannot give you a short answer, and we cannot give you a glib promise that all will be well next year or when your grandson is ready to hunt. So please bear with us as we go into the traits of populations of waterfowl that must guide us in any responsible program of management.

As YOU KNOW, living things generally reproduce in numbers far in excess of what the environment will support. The excess is surplus and disappears from the scene in one way or another—by starvation,

predation, disease, accidents, and so on. That is to say, the carrying capacity of the habitat determines the population levels of wildlife. Crops of game cannot be stockpiled beyond the capacity of the land to feed, shelter, and protect them. That is the basis of modern game management.

Experience tells us that removal by hunting of resident game, such as quail, pheasants, and rabbits, substitutes in a large measure for natural losses. In numerous instances, where hunting of a species has been prohibited for long periods, the populations have not increased very much.

Game managers have found also

that hunting is self-regulating in the case of many resident game species. Long before the animals are reduced to a low level, the effort needed to get a bag discourages further hunting. Populations of a species such as ruffed grouse become thinly sparse and harder and harder to find as the numbers are reduced during fall and winter.

But waterfowl, as you have noticed, remain bunched as the hunting season progresses. During fall migration and on the wintering ground, waterfowl are found on rather limited amounts of aquatic habitat, chiefly marshes, bays, lakes, and rivers. By reason of their tendency to flock together, they are vulnerable to hunting throughout the season.

Furthermore, seasons on the birds begin the first of September in Alaska and northern Canada and extend to March 10 in Mexico. During this period, most of the birds are subjected to a succession of opening days in various Provinces and States as they move southward. No resident game species is subjected to such a lengthy bombardment by so many guns on such limited habitat.

For these reasons and others, waterfowl can be overhunted. This is part of the problem you write about.

We analyze carefully the information from bands that are put on some birds and are returned to us by hunters. The returns indicate that when the kill of most species of waterfowl is reduced by short seasons and small bag limits, the total loss from all causes is reduced.

For example, consider the results of a study of the relationship of first-year recoveries of bands from black ducks to changes in hunting regulations. In 22 of 25 possible comparisons since 1932, modifications in the regulations and the resulting kill of banded birds changed in the same direction. In other words: When regulations were relaxed, more bands were returned— more birds were killed—and vice versa. Band recoveries 10, 15, or even 20 years after banding indicate that waterfowl can have a rather long life unless abruptly ended over some hunter's blind.

Some species, as you know, are particularly susceptible to overshooting. Returns of bands showed that 50 percent of the young canvasbacks were harvested when regulations permitted taking four or more birds a day and the season lasted 50 days or more. An average of about 40 percent of the adult canvasbacks in the fall flight were killed or crippled before the end of the shooting season. No species of game can sustain so heavy a harvest for long unless the annual replacement of young is high and the loss due to causes other than shooting is low.

We also learned that restrictions on hunting will reduce harvest rates on canvasback and that the population can maintain itself even with a low rate of production. We have evidence (which we shall be glad to send you, if you wish) that this general principle holds true also for several other species of waterfowl that are hunted heavily.

You write, of course, of the situation in your own neighborhood. We bear in mind that counties, States, and countries, as well as neighbor-hoods, are part of the broad situation. The annual range of waterfowl is international, and waterfowl are protected by treaties with Canada and Mexico. The numbers of birds that migrate through each of the four flyways are not equal, and the annual populations do not remain static. Also, more of some kinds of ducks and geese migrate to one flyway than to another. The Federal Government, therefore, must prepare regulations that reflect the relative populations of birds and hunting pressure in each flyway.

Now, to get closer to home. Several management devices are at hand to permit the maximum rec-reational use of waterfowl consistent with its perpetuation. One is the establishment of wildlife refuges, on which proper conditions can be maintained. They give us a chance to control part of the distribution of the birds and the rate of their

For the hunter—the end of a perfect day.

movement southward from their nesting places to their wintering grounds.

Another way is to set up and enforce hunting regulations. They help to keep the take within safer limits, give hunters a more even chance, and achieve a better distribution within each flyway.

Federal waterfowl regulations used to be liberal and uncomplicated. Birds were plentiful, hunters were not, and seasons and bag limits were practically unlimited. The seasons in 1918–1929, you may recall, ran for 3½ months and the bag limit was 25 ducks, 8 geese, 8 brant, and 25 coots a day. Probably no more than 500 thousand hunters were in the field then. Waterfowl habitat was still abundant and well distributed.

We now have about 2 million duck hunters, who compete for opportunities to hunt on habitat that has been reduced substantially in quantity and quality.

You and we and all hunters have been forced to accept increased restrictions on hunting as more people participate. Regulations have grown more complex in order to permit a fuller use of some species in good supply. More restrictions have been placed on the taking of species that are in short supply and require additional protection. We have come to recognize that ducks are not just ducks, but rather members of groups made up of many different species, each of which has its own requirements so variable that some may prosper while others are failing. Regulations therefore are tending

State and Federal biologists examine duck wings received from hunters randomly selected across the country. These wings reveal facts needed in waterfowl management such as rate of hunter success, species composition, and sex and age ratios.

Shooting at waterfowl out of gun range—"sky-busting," results in needless crippling and waste of birds. The true sportsman respects the limits of his gun.

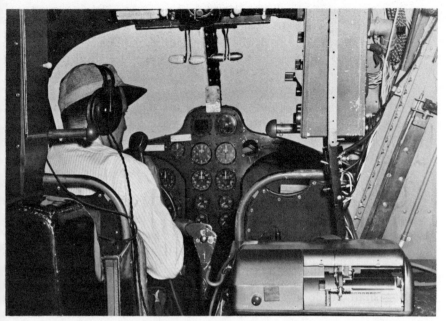

Pilot biologists in waterfowl surveys do not have time to write out their observations. Walter F. Crissey demonstrates use of a recorder to keep records as survey progresses.   In actual survey operation, he would be accompanied by a biologist observer.

toward more and more selectivity. We call it species management.

Several matters other than protection or preservation are considered carefully when regulations are being drawn up. One of them may sound strange to you. At certain times and in some places, there are too many ducks. That may seem unlikely or foolish to the rain-soaked hunter who shivers all day without firing a shot or seeing a bird. But the Saskatchewan wheat farmer, or the California rice grower, who sees greedy hordes gorging on his grain— to either of them there can very well be too many ducks. To protect their livelihood, we may need intensive methods to control depredations and sometimes special

hunting regulations to reduce locally the numbers of waterfowl.

So, we are guided by the principle of trying to make maximum recreational use of waterfowl while staying within the abilities of waterfowl to keep their numbers up. In practice, this has resulted in an increased take of underharvested species and in a reduction of bag limits or complete closure on species in danger of overharvest. It has resulted also in the establishment of four management flyways, each with individual bag limits and length of seasons based on estimated waterfowl populations and hunting pressures. Otherwise, the regulations across the country would have to be uniformly determined by the species or section in shortest supply. Obviously, such stringent regulations would mean the loss of a great deal of recreational opportunity.

THE BASIC AUTHORITY for the Federal Government to protect and manage migratory game birds is contained in treaties with Great Britain and Mexico. The Treaty of 1916 with Great Britain (for Canada) was the first entered into. It says in part:

"The High Contracting Powers agree that, as an effective means of preserving migratory birds, there shall be established the following closed seasons during which no hunting shall be done. . . . The closed season on migratory game birds shall be between March 10 and September 1. . . . The season for hunting shall be further restricted to such period not exceeding 3½ months as the High Contracting Powers may severally deem appropriate and define by law or regulation."

Similar language is contained in the 1936 treaty with Mexico. Both conventions are implemented by the Migratory Bird Treaty Act.

You and all other hunters await with keen interest the annual regulations for the taking of migratory game birds. Do you know how we go about gathering and analyzing the information that we use to formulate the regulations? If you have ever tried to count people in a crowd or apples on a tree, you may think the work of inventorying birds scattered across half a continent is impossible to do with any degree of accuracy. Not every duck

can be counted. We must rely on indices of increase or decrease that we get by sampling on a statistically sound basis. We think our yearly surveys to get up-to-the-minute information on the continent's waterfowl are the most comprehensive in the world.

We start with the breeding season. In spring, after the birds return to their nesting grounds, trained crews of the Bureau of Sport Fisheries and Wildlife conduct an aerial survey of breeding pairs, usually in May. The survey covers all important duck breeding grounds, except that of the black duck in eastern Canada. (We have started to devise ways to count them in that vast area.) Also, a tally is made of water areas and their conditions. The crews fly the same statistically randomized routes each year, and we try to have the same crews cover the same areas, year after year, to make the surveys even more accurate.

These routes are flown a second time in July to obtain data on production success. Workers of the Canadian Wildlife Service and State and Provincial game departments also cover more limited production areas within their boundaries. Usually this count begins about July 5 and is finished about July 25 in order to have the data available for use in recommending shooting regulations. By that date, only a part of the total season's production will have hatched. The production survey, therefore, consists of a measure of broods on the water at the time of the survey, plus a measure of weather, water, and other conditions that will affect or reflect production success after the count has been completed. The results of these two surveys form the base from which we develop the recommendations for the annual waterfowl hunting regulations.

Frequently we are asked why we cut off the production survey before the nesting season is completed. Two requirements make this necessary. An Administrative Procedures Act of the Federal Government requires that the public be informed of any regulatory action affecting it. Proposed hunting regulations therefore must be published in the Federal Register 30 days before the date they will take effect—in this case, the date of the earliest open season.

Further, all State fish and game departments are given an opportunity to select the time of the open season which, for them, will provide the best hunting, all things considered. The Department of the

State and Federal agents cooperate in checking hunters for compliance with migratory waterfowl regulations. This hunter was successful in bagging a pair of mallards.

Interior informs each State concerning the number of shooting days that will be allowed and prescribes a general framework of dates (October 1 to mid-January in most years) within which the selected season must occur. Many of the State game and fish departments hold public meetings or in some other way permit their sportsmen to make recommendations for the hunting seasons. The making of hunting season rules may take several weeks in the States—often it is a matter of meeting legal requirements. The inventory work on the breeding grounds therefore must be terminated in late July to give time for the steps necessary to establish hunting seasons.

A logical corollary question often asked is: Could a late hatch alter the picture? We do not think so. Biologists have found from experimental surveys conducted well into September that habitat conditions measured in July are a dependable index of the extent of the late hatch and the progress of the nesting season. Also, ducklings hatched after mid-August cannot attain flight stage before the usual freezeup. Consequently, these birds cannot influence the size of the fall flight, which is the real basis for the determination of hunting seasons.

United States game management agents do more than enforce Federal migratory bird regulations. Here one of them is helping hunters to understand the hunting regulations and to perfect their skills in identifying waterfowl.

A WINTER SURVEY is carried out immediately after the close of the hunting season in the United States. At that time, the birds are more concentrated and are comparatively sedentary. This survey involves the cooperation of about 1,600 observers and includes aerial and ground estimates. Personnel of the Bureau of Sport Fisheries and Wildlife, State and Provincial game departments, and the Canadian Wildlife Service participate. The Navy, Coast Guard, and Air Force sometimes furnish aircraft and other equipment. Bureau crews have surveyed Mexico annually, Central America occasionally, and northern parts of South America once. Most of the survey is by direct estimate, although large concentrations may be photographed and counts made from the photographs. An attempt is made to scout all important wintering grounds in ways that are consistent from year to year.

Although surveys of breeding grounds are used to determine population trends for most species of ducks, the winter survey is the only measure we have to determine the status of such species as black ducks and some geese, which cannot yet be satisfactorily estimated on the breeding grounds. Except for those species, data from winter surveys are not used in making regulations. The winter survey, however, does provide valuable information on changes of waterfowl distribution in response to changes in habitat, weather, and management measures.

But all these population surveys give us only part of the information we need to formulate sound hunting regulations. By systematic sampling since 1952, we have gathered much information concerning the size of the waterfowl harvest, the amount of hunting activity, and the effects of changing populations and regulations on harvest and hunter activity.

THE WINGS OF WATERFOWL also have a story to tell us. Each year thousands of specimens solicited from hunters are examined. From them we learn a bird's identity, age, and sex. Information provided by the hunters gives us additional facts about distribution of kill by location, time of day, and day of the season. All these bits of information help us determine the relationship between hunting regulations and harvest. The proportion of young to adults in the kill reveals production success during the current season and provides a check on the accuracy of the forecasts based on aerial surveys of production made in July.

Over the years many birds have been banded in North America, and information from this source also is useful in developing regulations. Recoveries of the bands, mostly by hunters, have provided data concerning the relationships between breeding, harvest, and wintering areas. Data from bands also provide a basis for determining mortality rates, the importance of hunting as a mortality factor, and rates of harvest in relation to changes in hunting regulations.

Waterfowl hunting regulations were promulgated on a flyway basis for the first time in 1948, with the realization that waterfowl follow four major migration routes, in which numbers of birds and hunting pressure vary. Knowledge of those two factors makes it possible to prescribe season lengths and bag limits that conform with the expected fall flight and hunting pressure in each flyway.

An additional refinement of regulations was introduced in 1959— that of managing individual populations of Canada geese. It had been recognized for several years that the geese coming into the country through Horicon Marsh in Wisconsin and wintering almost exclusively in southern Illinois were susceptible to overshooting in those two States. The continuing buildup in those areas had broken the traditional flight pattern to the south. To safeguard the Canadas, seasonal kill quotas are set each year for the areas around Horicon and Necedah

The United States Navy sometimes works in a cooperative waterfowl survey along with a training flight, to the advantage of all concerned.

refuges in Wisconsin and four counties in southwestern Illinois, which embrace the famous Horseshoe Lake-Crab Orchard-Union County concentration areas. Quotas also were established in 1962 for Canada geese at the Swan Lake National Wildlife Refuge in Missouri.

Letters like yours are in the minds of the many persons of many specialties and interests who take part each year in making the regulations. Not all of them agree, but efforts are made to solicit opinions and consider many viewpoints. To get a wide cross section of opinion, the Director of the Bureau of Sport Fisheries and Wildlife meets annually with a Waterfowl Advisory Committee, which is comprised of representatives of national conservation organizations and the four flyway councils. The committee has two representatives from each flyway council (State fish and game administrators) and one each from the National Wildlife Federation; The Izaak Walton League; the Outdoor Writers Association of America; the Wildlife Management Institute; The Wildlife Society; the International Association of Game, Fish and Conservation Commissioners; and the National Audubon Society. The Canadian Wildlife Service, the Canadian Provincial fish and game departments, and Ducks Unlimited are invited to send observers.

The advisory committee reviews the current waterfowl conditions. Proposed regulations are presented in executive session. Free discussion is encouraged. No votes are taken, but all opinions and recommendations are noted for consideration in the preparation of the final recommendations. The season recommendations are then presented to the Secretary of the Interior for his consideration and subsequent promulgation of the regulations.

Thus, the die is cast for the coming fall's recreation for about 2 million duck hunters.

TO RETURN more directly to your letter, not many persons like to forfeit personal privileges, but many citizens like you have shown a concern about the future of waterfowl. Many ardent hunters have expressed a willingness to cooperate in any program, including a temporary suspension of hunting, if that would assure perpetuation of the resource and the sport of waterfowling.

As far as most species are concerned, it is doubtful that any such drastic action is necessary now, and it is difficult to envision conditions that would warrant a total closure any time in the near future.

Nevertheless, waterfowl can be overshot and regulations do have a direct effect on the harvest and consequently on the level of breeding populations for the following spring. This means that some restraints on hunting are necessary at all times—even in the good years. And in times when numbers of birds decline, a stricter regulation of hunting is required to maintain adequate brood stock.

We think you will agree that protection from hunting is not a creative force. Short seasons, small bag limits, or even total closures do not produce birds. Habitat alone can accomplish that. Without adequate habitat, no amount of regulation will preserve waterfowl in sporting numbers.

AND SO WE CONCLUDE our long reply to your letter with these suggestions and hopes: That you and other hunters do what you can to create conditions suitable for the production and maintenance of waterfowl; accept restraints on hunting as may be required to preserve breeding stock; and bear with us as we try to make rules that will be fair to all hunters and to the birds.

Happy hunting for you and your grandson!—LANSING A. PARKER and JOHN D. FINDLAY.

MALLARDS

Waterfowl Tomorrow

PINTAILS

Viewpoint of a Naturalist

THE POPULATION explosion so many of us complain about may have redeeming features. It is forcing us to "evolve" faster, and the results may be constructive, for us and for waterfowl. This will take time, however, and the interim will be dangerous. For, surely, we must recognize that the current rapid expansion in human numbers has been abundantly destructive, and this should be a source of deep concern to us unless we set about turning it to advantage.

Our new social situation has multiplied the numbers of men and equipped them with powerful new tools of modern technology—bulldozers, draglines, airplanes, auto-

mobiles, guns. It has provided more leisure and mobility, but failed to give us a new perception into the effects of our own actions. And now we are reaping the whirlwind of our heedlessness: the senseless, government-subsidized drainage of wetlands; the penetration by roads and consequent destruction of wilderness regions; and the pollution of air, soil, and water, whether by sewage, oil, toxic chemicals, radioactive wastes, or the sportsman's deadly load of spent lead shot. All of these are evidence of our profligate use of the Earth.

And, worse evil, these destructive tendencies are currently built into the fabric of our society. It is the

699

manufacturers of earth-moving equipment, and their business associates, who lobby drainage and road building schemes, the rest of us don't need or don't want, through national and State legislatures. This is their "right to work." It is greed, shortsightedness, and ruinous economic competition that puts off solutions to the scandalous pollution of our environment.

But this need not be so. The very conditions which have produced the chaos that worries us, can, with a little more awareness and responsibility, be turned to advantage.

Part of the problem is that we are a biologically illiterate generation. So we must work at educating the people—young, middle-aged, and older—to the realities of Nature, those processes that make the Earth productive and pleasant.

This is where the population explosion comes in. For, with the growth in numbers of people, there has also been a growth in wealth and leisure, and even in knowledge. These expansions go together and are interdependent once launched. Ironically, this urban society which has provided affluence and leisure is also a tense and noisy one, and "getting away from it all" has become a necessary antidote. The increased numbers of affluent and leisured citizens—at least compared to two or three generations ago—are turning more and more to the outdoors for relaxation from the tensions of life in the new society. Waterfowl hunting was part of this surge to the outdoors during recent decades, but some interesting new changes are now evident.

SIGNIFICANTLY, the fastest-rising curves in all the charts and projections made in recent analyses of America's resources picture, including recreation needs in land, are those of travel and the recreational use of natural areas (see Marion Clawson's *Land for Americans,* 1963). Except for boating and fishing at reservoir sites, the fastest growth in outdoor recreation since World War II has been in the use of national wildlife refuges. The attendance at these refuges has grown at a rate of 12 percent annually during this period, whereas population increased at somewhat less than 2 percent per year.

Resource-oriented recreational visits (to national parks, national forests, and national wildlife refuges) totaled 183 million in 1960–61, but if present rates of increase are maintained, these will total 5 billion in the year 2000, only a generation from now.

I suggest that this is a modern version of the *return to Nature,* a pendulum swing that has always, somehow, counterbalanced excessive emphasis on urbanity. Man is of Nature and knows it deep in his bones.

We have long had a reliable, but perhaps neglected, clue to this growth of interest in the non-exploitative use of Nature in the numbers of bird guides which have sold so consistently well, going back at least to the late 1920's when E. H. Forbush's delightful volumes appeared on the *Birds of Massachusetts and Other New England States.* Roger Tory Peterson's *A Field Guide to the Birds,* in several editions which quickly became the American bird-watcher's bible, has sold well over a million copies since its apearance in 1934. The number of people who who enjoy watching birds at window-shelf feeding stations certainly runs to the millions. In 1955, Roger Barton estimated 10 million birdwatchers, based on projections of public responses to his outdoors column in a Newark, N.J., newspaper. The figure appears conservative, the more we probe it.

RECENT ECONOMIC STUDIES of the use of Horicon Marsh, a national wildlife refuge in Wisconsin, illustrate the trend. In 1961 some 44,500 goose hunting trips were made into the area, but 75,800 people came just to watch the geese from the highway which crosses a section of this marsh. Only 20 percent of

these people were regular bird-watchers. This spread between hunters and watchers continues, because in 1963 the record shows 67,367 goose hunting trips to the Marsh as compared to 202,500 visitors who came to see the geese.

The change is not merely proportional but real. There are more people deriving enjoyment from a nonconsumptive use of wildlife, but there is also a decline in the numbers of those who must consume the resource in order to derive satisfaction from it, as hunting does. Duck stamp sales and the decline of private duck clubs show this. In both Canada and the United States conservation authorities became aware of this different trend in the early 1960's. Canadian officials have suggested that the trend is even

Waiting in line at Shiawassee National Wildlife Refuge in Michigan to get a look at the large concentrations of Canada geese in spring migration.

more pronounced than the available statistics seem to indicate because many nonshooting recreationists currently masquerade as sportsmen. The rod and reel, or the gun case, are still more orthodox badges of the outdoorsman than the binocular or the natural history field guide, especially on the frontier; so the new recreationist still often carries both gun case and binocular to smooth the way.

But he won't need to masquerade for long. Already, guides and other suppliers from Florida's Everglades to the muskeg of Canada are becoming aware that nature-minded vacationers outnumber hunters, that they stay longer, help spread "the season" to year-round proportions, and are usually easier to please because so much more interests them.

THIS NEW TREND is fortunate and timely. The great increase in hunting of the 15 years immediately following World War II, since it was accompanied by a decline in waterfowl habitat, north and south, had to be short-lived. Whether hunting has cut into "capital stock"—that indispensable population nucleus which rebuilds and maintains good numbers of waterfowl on a continental basis—may be a matter of definition, as it has certainly been a matter of controversy in recent decades. The question is whether the annual "surplus," which is the allowable annual take by the gun, was based on productivity or on diminishing habitat.

Too many individual sportsmen and even State administrators have fooled themselves into believing that there were as many ducks as ever simply because the birds were being crowded onto fewer and fewer acres of migratory resting grounds or terminal wintering grounds. For those who have never learned to think in terms of a continental waterfowl supply, it has been almost impossible to recognize that a few choice areas will continue to hold maximum numbers of birds even though the total population may have been drastically reduced.

It is of course the duck hunter who has most cause to worry about the declining waterfowl supply. His sport requires sizable annual surplus populations. The times, unfortunately, may be against him. Continuing growth of the human population, even if only for another generation, and the attendant remaking of the landscape which this will continue to foster, are likely to further reduce waterfowl habitats. And, with it, duck numbers will decline—unless dollars and know-how can combine to preserve, create, and upgrade habitat and enlarge the production potential. Goose numbers will be less affected because their arctic and subarctic breeding grounds will be less drastically altered; but the numbers of geese are so much smaller that they could not maintain the hunting which could be lost with further decline of ducks.

Unless events change markedly, the hunter's take will undergo further restrictions.

IT HAS ALWAYS been true that population growth imposes competition for a place in the sun. This is evolutionary pressure, and it applies to human institutions just as it does to populations of other organisms. A crowded society will demand higher, less selfish, non-subtractive forms of recreation. Something has to give. Only one man can kill a particular duck, but thousands can enjoy that duck alive during its lifetime.

Hunting long ago became unnecessary as a form of food-getting. Hunting for sport, especially in the United States, was an outgrowth of the life of the frontier, still remarkably recent in terms of mere calendar years, but now being forgotten in the accelerating tempo of change that characterizes our new technological society. Hunting for sport, it will soon be realized, was a brief interlude in our rapid transition from the preindustrial to the scientific age.

A glance at such older, already overcrowded, societies as those of Japan or Italy, will show the alternatives that time holds out to us. In such old countries what little sport hunting there is has long been the prerogative of a handful of large landowners; there is no free hunting. But there the difference stops. The Japanese have managed to build a deep appreciation of Nature into their way of life, while the Latin peoples have turned their backs on Nature. They know birds only as something to eat or to keep in cages. Roger Tory Peterson has called my attention to the surprising fact that the most heavily patronized zoos in the world are not those of London or New York, but those of the Latin countries, a revealing clue to the separation from Nature these people have suffered.

Fortunately, like the Japanese, tomorrow's American citizen is likely to be much more perceptive of a wider range of outdoor values because he has already progressed so far in this direction. If, however, he fails, for one reason or another, to achieve that higher awareness that alone can allow him to continue enjoying the rich wildlife resources of America, he will quickly lose everything. I draw this extreme alternative because the American's mania for activity, and his power

Hunting waterfowl with binoculars and cameras affords millions of hours of recreation to citizens in all walks of life.

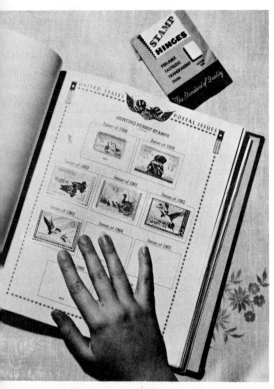

Stamp collectors help finance wetland habitat acquisition. Between 1 and 2 percent of the Migratory Bird Hunting Stamps purchased are bought by philatelists.

to exercise it against his environment, if not constrained by love of Nature, will utterly destroy wildlife within a few generations. He must commit himself to fitting his needs into the environment without robbing the latter of its naturalness. This is not at all impossible, but letting things run their unguided course will no longer do.

In this new society which is abuilding, like it or not, the sportsman can play an important role. By learning to add depth to his enjoyment of the outdoors he will, since this will also moderate his demands, extend the sport he loves. The transition can be eased by a more systematic study of the species he pursues—their identification in flight as well as in the hand, and their habits and status. The camera gun will gradually supplant the shotgun, and the trophies on film will be just as hardwon and just as prized. They will, further, last longer and be shared with a larger circle of friends and neighbors. Already, many a former duck pond has been outfitted with photographic blinds for this purpose. The spotting telescope already vies with the shotgun at every waterfowl refuge in the nation, and the "long lens" will soon do likewise.

THIS IS the first challenge: to inculcate perception. And what is that perception Aldo Leopold (in *A Sand County Almanac*) called for, except a lifelong development of awareness? Awareness, first, that we and the waterfowl and every other living thing are fellow travelers in the great evolutionary trek; and secondly, that the future success of this long adventuring of life in time—since this is what Evolution is—has become dependent on our willingness to cooperate in it. For the individual, then, hunting for sport should be a brief exercise only, a testing of reflexes and the guiles that enabled man to become the dominant species. But once we know we can, there are higher peaks to scale!

The second challenge is to rally public opinion behind a conservation program that will save the "capital stock" that once provided surpluses for the hunter, but will soon be reduced to that minimum necessary to maintain the species. A hundred thousand birds of each species can suffice to maintain the interest of the sophisticated watcher and student across the nation. But this stock must be ensured for as long as it is reasonable for men to plan. Essential breeding grounds, an augmented number of resting grounds to facilitate the migrations and give more people the opportunity of enjoying the resource, and adequate wintering grounds, well managed and unpolluted, are the basis of all waterfowl conservation programs, tomorrow as today. A broad view is needed, however. Even now our national wildlife refuges have become oases, and their unique habitats must not all be sacrificed to "management." A hundred acres of old coastal prairie in Louisiana, say, is worth more as prairie than as managed feeding ground for wintering ducks.

One of the first stumbling blocks to be overcome is that of vested interests in present ways of doing things. If the transition is disorderly, or too long put off, some species may be lost for good in the confusion. It took a long time to convince the sportsman that he had to invest in perpetuating or improving those productivity factors—land and water—that provided the ducks he wished to hunt. That his support is still a grudging one can be seen in the decline of duck stamp sales that accompanies every reduction of the daily bag. The problem now is to induce him, and everyone else, to join in insisting that provision be made in the new society for a permanent supply of wildlife of as many species as can continue to adapt to the changes that our augmented numbers must make in the landscape. If the hunter loves the waterfowl he has hunted so eagerly this past century, loves them, that is, as much as he has always claimed, he will help mold the public opinion which alone can effect this transition. He will continue to invest in wetlands even though the ducks they produce can no longer be dragged from the sky by a well-thrown shot. In the process he will learn to enjoy the flicker of their wings against the tinted sky even more keenly than his predecessors did; and he will cradle his binocular with the same sort of simple animal pleasure the sportsmen of midcentury found in cradling a 12-gauge shotgun. The habits change but the man remains.

—ROLAND C. CLEMENT.

GOLDEN RETRIEVER

Waterfowl and the Hunter

ONE OF THE standing mysteries of our well-insulated society is the urge that drives a modern man to pit himself against marsh, sleet, mud, and failure, to hunt waterfowl. No man has ever fathomed this. None is more confused by this inner drive than the hunter himself.

Ask an old duck hunter if he guns solely for the sake of killing and he will sputter with indignation. Ask him, then, why he really hunts. He'll likely stammer like a schoolboy, searching for words and making lame comments about "being out amongst 'em." And if the hour is late and company convivial, his eyes will kindle with old dreams and doings and he will soar off in long, rambling anecdotes that really convey nothing—except to another hunter.

If pressed on the subject, that old hunter would admit that killing ducks is a basic object of his hunts. But to such a man, this death-dealing is so inextricably bound with tradition, ethics, and poignant yesterdays—and so overlain by dra-

707

A beaming hunter exhibits his prize—a snow goose.

matic preliminaries—that it conveys no real sense of guilt at all. His emotions are infinitely subtle, varied, and personal, and have become fused in a sort of spiritual matrix that defies close analysis. The man cannot explain hunting's deep appeal; he only knows that it is an integral part of his world and spirit, and that neither would be whole without it.

There are, of course, the popular catchmotives for hunting: that it is a common masculine equation and a universal stamp of virility. For the synthetic hunter, these may be enough.

But they are superficial at best,

and are only loosely related to the deeper principles that will draw men afield so long as there are birds and beasts to hunt, and as long as men take pride in such things.

Modern hunting may signify an urge to escape cultural pressures and retreat back across the bridge of millennia to play once more with the old toys of our racial youth. We have existed for nearly a million years as a distinct genus, and for over 90 percent of that time we survived as hunters and gatherers. Many of us are still possessed by ancient spirits. Even when we had progressed beyond professional hunting and had entered trade and farming, we could not sever all our old bonds. We are not anachronisms, but ordinary men who have found no reason to discard proven values. In the Roman outpost of Timgad, in Algeria, a flagstone in the Forum still declares: "To hunt, to bathe, to play, to laugh, this is to live." Today, nineteen centuries later, there are about 20 million of us in North America who subscribe to that philosophy.

We've known hunters who did without the bathing but who cherished the play and laughter that embellish hunting's off-hours. To such men the wild field sports are part of their personal stake in individuality and the pride of homely skills—and something more. Dr. Murdock Head tells of watching a group of backwoodsmen dress the morning's kill in an eastern deer camp. A man standing beside Dr. Head watched the activity in silence for some time, and then turned and said simply: "These men are free." He offered no further amplification of his views, and none was needed.

Such freedom of body and spirit enables men to shed certain of their social pressures and recapitulate their racial boyhoods and walk, for however brief a time, as they believe men were meant to walk—in the company of other men, in the open, on ancient quests. Today, hunting is the one great basic adventure for millions of ordinary, town-bound men who yearn for personal participation in genuine adventure of their own making.

Yet, some nonhunters logically challenge the basic morality of this, questioning the right of a reasoning species to prey on other species—not out of any direct physical need but to satisfy a lust that perpetuates an archaic predator-prey relationship. The modern hunter is often indicted for his lack of "reverence for life," and even his morals and basic humanity may be suspect.

But with long-term exposure to the field, the genuine hunter may undergo a curious evolution. As a boy, he is solely interested in the full game bag as a token of manhood and tribal acceptance. Many men never grow beyond this. But if that boy hunts long enough, and gives honest rein to his thoughts and emotions, the old red hunting urge undergoes a subtle change and deeper values begin to emerge. He invests his quarry with character and worth. To some degree he must adapt himself to the creature he is hunting, and so acquires a measure of its freedom and sagacity. The old hunter often gains a measure of mysticism as well, for it is difficult to spend some of the best parts of one's lifetime in mountains, marshes, or plains without developing a vein of unworldliness. We have seen this occur in men who had never heard the word "transcendental," but who deeply understood its meaning. Such men may continue to hunt all their lives—not in a lust for killing, but in a growing lust for living, and freedom, and what Charles Nordoff once termed "the spirit of place."

When such a man hunts, it is difficult to regard his acts as overt offenses to the dignity and spirit of wildlife. Rather, it may be a personal testimony to the dignity and value of wildlife, and his act of hunting is not an offense but a rustic tribute. The consummate offense to wildlife is not hunting, but the extirpation of species by an indifferent technology in which wildlife is wiped out—not by man's passion—but by his single-minded devotion to a material world in which wild creatures have no place. It might be nobler for man to deliberately hunt down the last wild creature in one final declaration of

A hunter picks one of a pair in a Louisiana marsh.

value, than to sweep it away forever as an unknown and unmourned technological casualty.

THE HUNTER HIMSELF should feel more concern with such consequences of technology than with the effects of his own hunting. Biologists today are able to assess most wildlife losses, and to monitor the hunting take and hold it within safe limits. It is not so simple with

A marsh is more than a place to pursue waterfowl.   Experiences like this leave indelible imprints on the minds and hearts of men.

a runaway technology. Who can assess the full range of penalties when wildlife habitat is lost to widespread drainage? Or the land, water, and air changes wrought by a myriad of unspeakable pollutions? And, knowing the extent of such destruction, what action can be taken?

It is difficult for hunters alone to depress waterfowl populations. The decline of ducks to a point where the hunter matters has been caused by deterioration of environment. We suddenly find that sloughs no longer lie in unbroken prairie, not even in Canada. They are in farmers' fields with country roads and railway tracks beside them, and towns and cities nearby. The great northern marshes are in potential power impoundments, to be flooded and then drawn down. Many of yesterday's great, lush marshes have

Canvasback hunters like plenty of decoys. The making of decoys is an art and a unique business.

been drained to produce food of doubtful need, and our duck hunters see metal bins of surplus grain and speak angrily of "canned potholes."

The twin forces of population explosion and technology have dealt these blows, and more. Industrial science has decreed that grain should harden in swaths on the ground, thereby making the mallard an enemy of the farmer. Waterfowl may, any day, react poorly to a new combination of technical developments. They seem to have no clear right to either food or home.

We know that the arctic lichens fed on by caribou are contaminated by fallout, and that tuna from midocean have been found with near-tolerance levels of DDT. So far, it is bald eagles and bluebirds—rather than bluebills and geese—that have threatened to vanish. Yet the hunter must share, with all who depend on Nature for recreation, anxiety over the ultimate effects of massive and universal changes in the environment. His response to the new pollutions must be to know exactly what is happening to the game, and to insist that there be wiser ends than distortion of the whole environment.

In years ahead it will not be enough for hunters merely to be uncomplaining about the rationing of resources, and content with resource crumbs from our technological picnic. To do so will be to forfeit waterfowl and other wild creatures to less reluctant users of the land—users willing to place convenience and quick gain ahead of considerate and healthful use of lands and waters. Yet, we need not

A hunter steeped in the tradition of waterfowling at its best likes his hunting complete with decoys, duck calls, and plenty of elbow room.

A Maryland hunter pays three dollars to a postal clerk in exchange for a Migratory Bird Hunting Stamp. Purchase of the Stamp by those who hunt migratory waterfowl is mandatory. The revenue derived from sale of the stamps is used to purchase wetlands.

accept as inevitable the attrition of habitat that has led our waterfowl to present levels. Part of the same technology that has diminished our waterfowl production is available to serve positive ends, and to preserve and restore environments essential to waterfowl welfare.

WATERFOWL ARE NOT on the brink of extinction. Not yet. Nor is waterfowl hunting, if hunters are willing to learn and act in well-advised concert. But breast-beating is not enough, nor mourning for the halcyon days on Grandpa's duck marsh. Grandpa has drained his marsh, and his grandson must learn to blaze trails through political thickets and enforce his demands on those who so lavishly spend our resources. The hunter can be more than a muddled, harassed taxpayer; he can be a strident force with sharply-defined goals that can sway cultural and governmental policies. It is illogical that such a man should permit physical and spiritual resources to be squandered in a planless spiral whose vague goal is a better life, but which is utterly incapable of synthesizing any values as rich as those it destroys.

There is little real doubt that it is the hunter's responsibility. As a consumptive user of the resource, he must be the wheelhorse of wildlife conservation as he has always been. He has already underwritten the salvation of the elk, pronghorn antelope, wild turkey, and other game and nongame species whose decline was not his doing, but whose resurrection was managed by his affection and support. He is the most logical agent to underwrite the salvation of waterfowl because, in the most realistic sense, he is apparently the only agent who really cares. This is the man who must ramrod legislation to abate pollution, urge for research that leads to increased waterfowl production, and work for solutions to the national embarrassment of subsidized land drainage in the face of crop surpluses and duck shortages.

First he must be assured that his kill will not push waterfowl over the brink. Then he must try to halt deterioration of the environment, and reverse the trend towards destruction. These two things mesh at the level of the land itself. Shooting grounds, breeding grounds, wintering grounds, refuges—all wetlands that must be saved—are part and parcel of one scheme of waterfowl management. In all of this the interests of the hunter and naturalist complement each other, as they did when the Migratory Bird Treaty was drawn up to commonly include ducks and songbirds, the one as game and the other totally protected.

THE HUNTER HIMSELF can spoil all hunting, or he can achieve fulfillment by kindling the renewal of an ancient bond with Nature. All hunters, however indifferent, strive for this, however aimlessly. Yet, they find that fulfillment cannot be bought, nor conjured up by laws or regulations. True hunting is a personal bond with Nature that is born out of respect for the world of Nature, for the game, and for one's fellows. It is heightened and enhanced by knowledge.

Such knowledge, impelled by sympathy and conscience, can help shape a future that is really worth occupying.

It is impressive how much primitive hunters such as Eskimos and Congo pygmies actually know about their environments. This gives them very authentic traditions, and a profound reverence for the land, its plants, and animals, none of which they either control or modify seriously. But we, as civilized hunters, come from groups that dominate the environment. Whether man, muskrat, or white-tailed deer, this is a very dangerous position for any animal to be in. Any overwhelmingly dominant animal may alter its environment to the detriment of many species, including itself. We are in such a position today, and to hunt responsibly requires a much more sophisticated knowledge than that of an Eskimo. Yet it is the hunter, more than anyone else, who should be the agent most capable of maintaining man's awareness of his continued dependence on Nature—a dependence which man cannot afford to lose. It is the hunter who must cushion the impact of modern culture on ancient environment, using the most effective political and scientific tools at his disposal.

When you get down to it, the only world worth living in is one with a wholesome society meshing harmoniously with Nature—a world in which all values relating to Nature are recognized and nothing is sacrificed needlessly. This, likewise, is the kind of world most worth hunting in.

We would not have all men hunt. Most men never will. But we would have the level of hunting so raised and the responsibility of hunters so obvious as to confound their critics, and make others who are equally aware of the disintegration of the landscape turn to hunters as leaders and allies in maintaining it.

—JOHN MADSON and
C. H. D. CLARKE.

MOOSE
BUFFLEHEADS

Beyond National Boundaries

THE INTERNATIONALISM of waterfowl was simply and effectively stated by United States Supreme Court Justice Oliver Wendell Holmes more than a generation ago.

In delivering the opinion of the Court establishing the validity and constitutionality of the Migratory Bird Treaty Act in the case of *Missouri* v. *Holland,* 252 U.S. 416 (1920), Justice Holmes said: "The whole foundation of the State's rights is the presence within their jurisdiction of birds that yesterday had not arrived, tomorrow may be in another State, and in a week a thousand miles away. If we are to be accurate we cannot put the case of the State upon higher ground than that the treaty deals with creatures that for the moment are within the State borders. . . ."

We can say the same of the passage of waterfowl from one country to another. In Canada one day, they may be in Mexico or Central America a week later. Relying on the northern parts of their range for production and on the middle and southern portions for wintering, their movement from one to the other may be swift indeed. Migration records, banding studies,

717

and State-by-State surveys document this wide range and swift movement of waterfowl.

In *Missouri* v. *Holland,* the State was claiming title to waterfowl and with it exclusive authority to regulate the killing and sale of this resource. Again as Justice Holmes stated it, "To put the claim of the State upon title is to lean upon a slender reed."

As a result of the opinion, title to migratory birds remained in the Federal Governments of Great Britain (acting for Canada) and the United States. Later Mexico became an interested third party and signed a treaty with the United States similar to the one between the United States and Great Britain.

These treaties cover only regulations relative to protection of migratory birds. Their most important or best known aspect is that of regulating the hunting of migratory waterfowl. Other phases of management, not considered critical in the early 1900's, are not incorporated in the terms of the treaties or the enabling legislation. Under the treaties, most species of migratory birds are afforded protection in the three countries, with provisions for hunting seasons on those species warranting such seasons.

Unlike resident game, waterfowl are subjected to gunning pressures throughout their migratory travels, from the northernmost breeding grounds to the southern terminus of their wintering grounds. Gunning seasons, because of weather and presence of the birds, could and originally did extend around the calendar. Hunting occurred in spring

as well as during fall migration. The constantly increasing army of hunters made it apparent that the resource could not long sustain the natural hazards and the growing toll from hunting on a year-round basis.

ALTHOUGH the Migratory Bird Treaties provide a base for some international management, it became evident to the States that more coordinated management within the United States was essential. Regulations for hunting and their enforcement could do only so much. More important were coordinated management and research programs that would maintain production; prevent unnecessary losses outside of hunting; preserve adequate, high-quality wintering grounds; and obtain answers to many problems of management.

The earliest step toward the development of such programs was the organization by waterfowl biologists in 1946–1948 of flyway committees in all four flyways to discuss flyway-wide problems; develop flyway management plans; and facilitate exchange of ideas, data, and research findings.

State administrators also began to consider organization to handle management on a flyway basis. After many conferences and discussions, the International Association of Game, Fish and Conservation Commissioners adopted a resolution in 1951 calling for establishment of waterfowl flyway councils.

The resolution set forth five objectives:

Increased participation by the

States in nesting and wintering inventories of waterfowl.

Increased participation by the States in recommending waterfowl regulations to the United States Fish and Wildlife Service.

Organization of Flyway Councils to be made up of technical and administrative personnel of the official wildlife agencies in the four flyways.

Organization of a National Council to be composed of two representatives from each of the four Flyway Councils.

Appointment by the Fish and Wildlife Service of waterfowl coordinators in each flyway, whose duties would be to serve as advisers to the States and to aid in coordinating waterfowl surveys and other investigations pertaining to waterfowl management.

States in all flyways acted quickly. All four councils and the National Flyway Council were established by the end of 1952. The first meeting of the National Council and the Waterfowl Advisory Committee, created by the Secretary of the Interior, was held in Washington, D.C., in August 1952.

Membership and participation in work of the councils were not restricted to United States agencies. Both the Federal Government and the Provincial Governments of Canada are official participants to the extent they consider appropriate. In much of the work of individual councils and all deliberations of the National Council that have to do with annual harvest regulations in the United States, Canadian representatives take little part in recommendations on regulations. The councils make no recommendations as to regulations in Canada. They meet twice a year.

Great progress has been made in coordinating annual regulations on an international basis and resolving other problems. Through the councils, for example, regulations have been developed in Canada and the United States to protect certain endangered species and to liberalize the sport hunting of species that can be harvested safely at higher rates.

FLYWAY COUNCILS have had a beneficial effect on other aspects of waterfowl management. With the help of technical sections comprising State, Federal, and private waterfowl biologists and various committees, the councils explore all aspects of management and have revised State and Federal programs. Notable achievements include the development of a continental banding program, cooperative research projects, cooperative studies of control of crop depredations in Canada, and a coordinated program for acquisition of wetlands, for which the councils prepare priority lists for each flyway.

The steps to develop comprehensive, coordinated management programs are to some degree international in scope. Some believe, however, that we need an expanded, more active, and fully international program if we are to maintain adequate numbers of waterfowl. One segment with which an enlarged program could deal effectively is habitat.

AVERAGE DISTRIBUTION OF NORTH AMERICAN
BREEDING AND WINTERING DUCKS

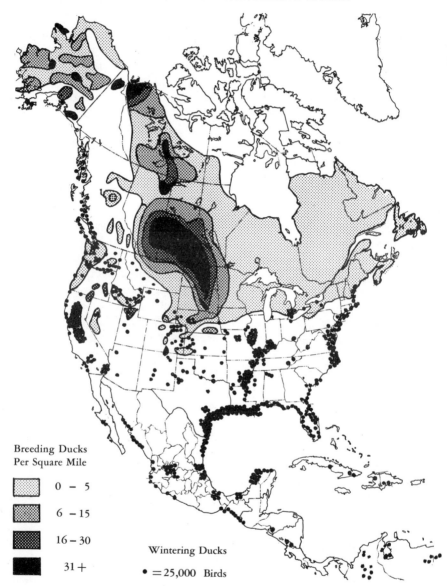

Breeding Ducks
Per Square Mile

	0 – 5
	6 – 15
	16 – 30
	31 +

Wintering Ducks

• = 25,000 Birds

As we all know, a pressing problem is the preservation of habitat. It is most urgent in the breeding grounds in the North and the wintering grounds in the South The draining of wetlands for agricultural and industrial uses has been destroying habitat. A few years ago it was an urgent problem in the United States. It is rapidly becoming serious in Canada and is beginning to be in Mexico. Thus it is of international concern: the waterfowl we see one day in Iowa may have been in the tundra a week ago and may be in the tropics a week hence. Sometimes we forget the difference between where ducks are produced and where they are utilized most heavily.

The greatest production of waterfowl occurs in Canada—at least 85 percent of the continental population, according to many estimates. Utilization, however, has been greater in the United States; perhaps up to three-quarters of the harvest takes place in the United States or is participated in by United States hunters.

A good share of the problem of keeping up the production of waterfowl, therefore, is in Canada. That United States hunters should pay a part of the cost of safeguarding the breeding grounds from which their waterfowl come seems logical enough.

The matter has had the attention of special committees of the International Association of Game, Fish and Conservation Commissioners for a long time. I give some excerpts of recommendations of the committees.

THE ONE OBJECTIVE has been to try to determine the need for and the desirability and feasibility of establishing an international waterfowl commission to help solve some of the most perplexing waterfowl management problems in both Canada and the United States. The proposal is that such a commission would receive funds from both Governments, determine waterfowl needs, and dispense or spend the funds for management work in both countries.

The Committee on American Game Policy, whose chairman was Aldo Leopold, reported to the North American Game Conference in 1930: "There is an even greater need, as yet unfilled, for international action in preserving and restoring and improving habitats. Land purchases to prevent drainage of Canadian breeding grounds, and control of nesting mortality on them, are international betterments deserving of international financing and support."

The 25th Convention of the International Association of Game, Fish and Conservation Commissioners endorsed as long ago as 1931 closer cooperation with Canada. In that year the Convention approved this far-reaching recommendation: "Provide that any part of this fund may be expended in the establishment of migratory bird breeding grounds in Canada under a workable plan to be evolved by the officials in charge, or by an International Migratory Bird Commission established for that purpose."

The Mississippi Flyway Council, in its first report on a program to acquire lands with Duck Stamp funds, recommended that 80 percent of the funds should be used to acquire production habitat; that ways and means should be found to preserve the prime waterfowl production habitat in Canada and to solve the associated problem of crop depredations; and that consideration should be given to the establishment of a Migratory Bird

Commission to handle problems of waterfowl population and habitat within the entire range of the birds.

Those suggestions and proposals emphasize that habitat must be preserved in Canada and that associated problems, such as crop depredations, must be dealt with. That means buying or leasing land and aiding landowners to solve the problem of crop depredations. United States dollars provided by the hunters who harvest the greatest share of the duck crop should pay some of the bill.

A RECENT DEVELOPMENT in further internationalizing the management of waterfowl is the establishment of a government-sponsored International Migratory Bird Committee. Its members include two representatives each of the Canadian Departments of Agriculture, and Northern Affairs and National Resources and two each from the United States Departments of Agriculture, and Interior. The establishment of the Committee indicates the concern of both Governments for greater international cooperation. Mexico also has participated in discussions of the problem. The Committee has met several times.

Those of us whose work and interests have to do with waterfowl management hope for a well-financed, internationally coordinated action program built on a solid foundation. Executive agreements and exchanges of notes are useful, but they lack the stability of a treaty. We want to remain in the waterfowl management business for a long time to come, and the program should be established with adequate guarantees of permanency.
—THOMAS R. EVANS.

RUDDY DUCKS

A Canadian Looks at the Future

PROBLEMS MAY ARISE when two or more persons have to share something. Countries run into this problem with any resource that does not stay put. Waters that flow from one country to another and fish that live and move freely in them are resources that Canada and the United States share. So it is with migratory birds, and here a third nation, Mexico, and, to a lesser extent, a number of countries in the Caribbean area and Central and South America also are involved. The future of waterfowl lies with all our countries, collectively and individually.

Pressures on our migratory waterfowl have been building up ever since settlement and hunting began. But only at the turn of the century did conservationists begin to realize that the States and Provinces could not provide through individual action for continued use of a resource that was within their confines for only parts of the year.

People soon came to appreciate that the same consideration applied among nations. Ever since the signing in 1916 of the Migratory Birds Convention Act, which provides guidelines for the protection of migratory birds in Canada and the

723

United States, responsible officials in the two countries have exchanged information, discussed changing conditions, and planned joint investigations.

Without loss of sovereignty or responsibility, cooperation in management has grown to meet the urgent needs of a heavily utilized resource. And today, perhaps more than ever before, the challenge remains. We must continue ahead along the path we chose years ago.

This story has been told many times, but it still carries a useful lesson. Between the responsible Governments there must be full and free exchange of information; frank expression of opinion; and the will to compromise when necessary for the continuing welfare of the resource and all the people who use it. Indeed, management objectives can hardly differ in principle from one country to another. We must maintain a partnership that allows for the complete responsibility of each partner and at the same time provides a whole program, a unity in fulfillment.

We consider that ducks cannot be allowed to become less numerous than they were during the early fifties. If they become so, they will make no significant contribution to public recreation. Our prime objective, then, can be simply stated: To maintain a waterfowl population comparable to that which was present in the early part of that decade.

CANADA NOW has some 350 thousand duck hunters. During the years after the Second World War, their numbers grew more quickly than the population of the country as a whole, presumably in response to a rising standard of living and a growing demand for recreation. Very likely the population of Canada will double in 25 years.

Will there then be twice as many duck hunters? More than that? Or less? Simple arithmetic will not give the answer. If the European experience is any guide, the proportion of duck hunters in the population is likely to decline. But the total number may well continue to rise, and we would be negligent if we did not plan for three-quarters of a million duck hunters in Canada by the year 2000.

In the midfifties, hunters in the Canadian Prairie Provinces were generally allowed to shoot 10 ducks a day. Limits were even higher in Saskatchewan for a couple of years. If the number of Canadian hunters doubles and if the army of United States sportsmen also grows, what sort of limits will govern their sport? I'm afraid that Nature alone will not rise to the occasion and provide more birds. Even if we maintain waterfowl numbers at the level of the midfifties, we must probably learn to be content with daily bag limits of less than half a dozen.

The problem of meeting the recreational demand would be simplified greatly if we could manage ducks and their habitat so skillfully that we could maintain average stocks at a level even higher than that of the midfifties. But that would not be an unmixed blessing, because prairie ducks, mallards particularly, have become unwelcome guests in the farmers' grainfields. There is an upper limit to waterfowl numbers if the risk of excessive crop damage on the prairie breeding grounds is to be avoided.

Progress has been made in the development and use of automatic scaring devices. Demonstrations of their use among farmers and the use of lure crops in strategic locations also have great promise. Finally, and of primary importance, are the prospects of environmental change. A long-range program of adjustment in land use, now in the planning stage, opens the prospect of removal from cereal production of large acreages, which are marginal for raising grain and are especially plagued by depredations.

The depredation problem has to be brought within reasonable bounds so that we can devote full attention to means of increasing duck stocks. We need a vigorous and positive program, which may be costlier than past efforts but which must be so effective that the users of the resource will be prepared to pay their fair share.

EVERYTHING WE MANAGE we must value. How do you value a duck? It has been said that beauty is in the eye of the beholder. Certainly the value we place on waterfowl arises from the pleasure we have in seeing, hearing, and hunting them. If, then, they are to be of greatest value to the country, they should be used by the greatest number of people compatible with maintaining high quality of use.

We in Canada therefore will follow policies of management with the objective of distributing the resource as fairly as possible within the limits imposed by Nature.

We in Canada have a special objective in migratory bird management that will be with us for some years yet, despite the onward march of technological development. Indians and Eskimos have a special position in our society. Many of those Canadians have not yet chosen wholly to forsake the way of life of the hunter living off the land. As long as that is their stated choice, it is our responsibility to ensure that they have first call on such wild food as may be necessary for their welfare. Application of this principle gives rise to complex problems, particularly since many groups of Indians and Eskimos are in a stage of social and cultural transition.

Besides our growing number of sport hunters are many more thousands of Canadians who simply enjoy waterfowl without reducing them to possession. What is the true value of waterfowl to Canadians? Some economists believe that what is not used is not a resource—all resources have a tangible value. Can this be true for resources that are used but not consumed?

I have arrived at a conceptual barrier against which many assaults have been mounted, but none, to my knowledge, successfully. What is the value of a duck to shoot, a goose to see, a tree to view, a creek to paddle? A dollar a pound? Five dollars for a morning's contemplation?

To ask these questions is to beg them, and I leave them there, but not without saying that this question of values is critical. There is literally no equally effective touchstone for decisions in our society. We may regret it or rejoice in it, but the marketplace is our measuring place.

Ducks (and their pursuers) must compete for land and water with all the other users of those basic resources, but their claim cannot be accurately measured in monetary terms. Is there some way out of this dilemma?

I believe we can make some progress by maximizing the economic return from wildlife. Convention precludes the direct sale of the product, but it takes little imagination to see that there are other ways. The taking of easements from farmers to safeguard wetlands, with moneys derived from the users of the resource, is one method. The provision of more and better goods and services to duck hunters and birders by landowners, tourist operators, and merchants is another. If we are to move in this direction, our ideas of management will have to shift a bit, and we may have to modify some of our traditional beliefs. There need be no harm in this, if we work out our ideas in advance.

IN ANY TYPE of recreation there is variation.

Fishing can be the skillful, tireless casting of a fly on the untroubled waters of a Labrador stream or the drowsy contemplation of a float idling on a sluggish backwater. It can also be a nightmarish competition between jostling contestants to see who can most quickly snag his share of several hundred lethargic, hand-raised trout just dumped into a roadside stream.

Duck hunting can be the long, patient wait in an icy blind on the St. Lawrence River, crouching behind buckbrush for the morning flight back to a Saskatchewan pothole, or paddling the cattailed edges of an Okanagan marsh. You can also shoot tin ducks at the Midway.

I shan't presume to judge which is "best," but I do know we must preserve diversity. Careful management of a marsh, with cultivated coverts and food patches and limited access to preassigned shooting points, is certainly the most efficient way to get the greatest number of man-hours of recreation from a given tract of land. Must we encourage such efficiency?

On the other hand, some of the lure of outdoor recreation is that it provides relief from the pressures of regimentation and conformity. Thus I believe we must assure the maintenance of situations where the individual has freedom of choice. Just as our National Parks must include wilderness zones, so must some of our hunting areas remain largely unmanaged.

WITH THE TREMENDOUS improvement in international travel facilities, most countries now find that the tourist industry is assuming an increasingly important role in their economies.

Canada has been favorably placed in this regard with respect to its populous southern neighbor. However, if this situation has been fortuitous, it offers great opportunities for neighbors to know and understand one another. It also makes it possible for our friends to seek in Canada a purposeful and legitimate use of that valuable renewable resource we enjoy in common.

I believe that Canada must attempt to have ducks (and places to hunt them) for those who wish to relive the hunting pleasures of the days when man did not dominate every sector of the horizon.

WHAT NOW STANDS in the way of our meeting the objectives I have discussed?

Certainly a basic obstacle is that too few people, even among those directly concerned, know the facts about waterfowl or have concerned themselves with their future. From this lack of knowledge and understanding, nearly all our problems flow.

We must do more to acquaint the public with the facts of wildlife. That we can do by the printed and spoken word and even more by our actions and attitudes.

As several writers have pointed out, those of us who are concerned with waterfowl management still have a lot to learn, too. Our research has been too much of an ad hoc affair and insufficiently coordinated.

From one viewpoint, I think the cooperation that there has been between Canada and the United States in gathering information on migratory birds has been a happy precedent in intergovernmental relations. We are indeed proud of this record.

But considering the needs of the future, the welfare of the resource, and the satisfaction of its users, we must go even further. Whether this can always be done within the existing administrative framework is a question. The formation in 1961 of the International Migratory Bird Committee indicates that progress means evolution and development of new mechanisms.

I do not know what will come next, but I do know that Canadians will keep a sharp eye on the administrative framework and be ready to consider new ways and means of getting the job done when the old ones seem no longer to suit.

IF THE PROSPECT I have attempted to reveal is obscure here and there, one aspect of it I do consider perfectly clear. We have clung tenaciously to the tradition of "free" hunting and have failed somehow to recognize that every trend in our society pushes up the costs of every activity. We have, in fact, put an artificial ceiling on the cost of duck hunting. We can hardly maintain any longer the fiction of "free" hunting.

Governments, called on to provide more and better service, must seek new sources of revenue and squeeze more tightly those they already hold. Payment for access to hunting grounds may become the rule, not the exception. I believe that we will maintain waterfowl as a part of the North American way of life for many years to come, but to accomplish that we shall have to pay our way. When we do that, both the users and the resource will benefit.—ERNEST A. CÔTÉ.

REDHEADS

Mexico and
Migratory Waterfowl Conservation

MEXICO CONTRIBUTES substantially to continental waterfowl thru its great wealth of wintering habitat. Here, thousands of square miles of lagoons, lakes, bays, and marshes, chiefly in coastal areas, are of great value to these birds.

Hunting of waterfowl in Mexico is on a very small scale compared to that in the United States and Canada, but it is increasing each year. This trend is a relatively new and important recreational development which contributes significantly to the economy of many rural areas where hunting is done. As has been the case elsewhere, the growing use of waterfowl is likely to lead to more interest and activity in Mexico in the management of these birds.

The use of waterfowl for food, especially by people in rural localities, is fully justified by economic need, as long as such utilization is not excessive. Many parts of Mexico are isolated and local food supplies are relatively of much greater importance than they are in the United States where well-developed transportation makes food and other products readily available. This is especially true of meats and other perishables. However, the commercial use of birds is specifically prohibited by law, because it can be so harmful not only to migratory species but also to resident wildlife.

There is much misunderstanding by sportsmen in the United States and Canada regarding the progress Mexico has made in reducing the illegal kill of waterfowl. Almost all armadas have been eliminated from the Valley of Mexico, the Upper Lerma Valley, and nearby localities. If any remain, they are small and their kill is negligible. The confiscation of these batteries of guns operated by market hunters was a difficult task, and its successful accomplishment was the result of active enforcement by the Department of Game and other cooperating federal agencies. But even at the peak of armada operation before 1931, the kill by these guns for any one year in Mexico probably was much less than the illegal kill throughout the United States on the opening day of the season.

A REVIEW OF THE HISTORY of wildlife legislation in Mexico shows that much progress has been made. It was 70 years ago, in 1894, that the first federal legislation for the protection of Mexican wildlife was enacted as a part of forestry legislation, but unfortunately there was no provision for its enforcement.

In 1916, a Department of Game and Fish was established, under the Secretary of Agriculture and Development, and subsequently laws for game and fish were passed. In 1918, for example, a regulation on the taking of waterfowl at lakes of the Valley of Mexico was announced. A regulatory decree of November 18,

1931, prohibited the shooting of armadas, established a fine for their use, and specified that no more than three guns, with a maximum of two barrels per gun, could legally be fired from one stand.

In 1934, the Department of Game and Fish was combined with that of Forestry and called the Departamento Autonomo Forestal y de Caza y Pesca. Two years later in 1936, the Migratory Bird Treaty with the United States was signed. This Treaty contains several regulations pertaining to waterfowl. Article II establishes a closed season for wild ducks from the 10th of March to the 1st of September, and limits hunting to 4 months of each year, as a maximum, under permits issued by the respective authorities. The act allows "a rational utilization of migratory birds for the purpose of sport as well as for food, commerce and industry."

In 1940, the Department of Game was put in the Direccion General Forestal y de Caza, and the agency for fisheries was transferred to the Secretary of the Navy. On August 28, 1940, revised regulations prohibited the commercial shooting of waterfowl. The game law of January 2, 1952, decreed that the sale, bartering, or advertising of "meats, products or remains of wild animals" were violations of the law. In 1959, the small and unimportant Game Office, until then a part of the General Department of Forestry and Game, was elevated to an independent office, the General Department of Game. This shows the interest the administration had in promoting this branch.

Although the regulations banned

the commercial hunting and sale of waterfowl, and subsequent enforcement reduced the extent of such violations, these illegal activities continue to a reduced extent in the Valley of Mexico; the Upper Lerma Valley; in the States of Sinaloa, Sonora, Tamaulipas, Veracruz, Yucatan; and in several other localities, including places near the United States border.

Much of the incentive for this illegal shooting and sale comes from the demand by foreigners for ducks and geese at restaurants and hotels in some of the tourist centers, and at the larger towns along the border. The effort to stop this commercial hunting and sale is continuing. The Mexican government would like to increase the number of tourists who come to their country for sport hunting and fishing, but, at the same time, wants to eliminate the illegal sale of waterfowl and other wildlife.

THERE HAS BEEN much progress in irrigation projects and power production, but there is urgent need for adequate consideration of fish and wildlife values in planning these projects. Probably the principal means of increasing waterfowl habitat in the interior will be through wildlife benefits included in reclamation projects. Some irrigation and power projects are so situated that relatively little, if any, management for waterfowl could be included. But there are others in locations important to waterfowl in which minor modifications in design and small expenditures of money could greatly increase wildlife and fishery values. The construction of

subimpoundments that have more stable water levels and much better food resources than the adjacent major impoundments would be one of the most effective means of adding wildlife and fishery benefits.

The most fundamental need of natural resource planning is the application of the concept of multiple use. Storage reservoirs are not only for agriculture and power production, but should serve all other logical objectives. In the initial stages of planning each project, full consideration could be given to all public benefits that might be derived. Such coordinated planning is all the more urgent in Mexico because of the lack of specific funds for wildlife and fishery projects. In the past, the benefits to wildlife, fisheries, and public recreation have often been disregarded.

Some lakes and marshes have drainage structures that needlessly reduce their value to waterfowl and fish. Study of such localities could result in a wiser program of water use, with partial restoration of waterfowl and fishery values.

The reclamation projects that have had the greatest benefit for waterfowl are those on the Yaqui, Mayo, Culiacan, and other rivers of the northwestern Pacific coastal plain. Delta land that was largely thorn forest now produces grain (chiefly rice) and other crops. Prior to these projects, there were large numbers of ducks and a few geese that wintered on the delta lakes, marshes, and coastal lagoons. But with the abundance of irrigated fields there has been an increase in the percentage of grain-feeding ducks and geese that winter there.

This has improved the hunting opportunity and brought in many hunters from California, Arizona, and other parts of the United States, much to the benefit of the local economy.

ON THE DEBIT SIDE, some grain farmers have incurred crop losses from waterfowl, and at times have had wet fields of sprouting grain so trampled or "puddled" by the birds that part of the acreage had to be replanted. One of the chief problems in these localities is that of reducing such crop losses. The encouragement of hunters to shoot in these fields would help disperse the flocks, and modifications of some farming practices to speed the grain harvest would further reduce crop losses. This is a subject that merits further study in order to develop better control methods.

For proper management of the valuable wildlife resources of Mexico, it is essential that the Department of Game, as the administering agency, have sufficient authority, personnel, and finances. Current legislative authority is satisfactory, but present financing is insufficient to provide for administrative enforcement and research needs. The constructive management of waterfowl and other wildlife resources will require additional financing. One source of this increase could be the fees paid for hunting licenses, which do not now revert to the Department.

At present there are no waterfowl refuges in Mexico. There are national parks, but these lack waterfowl habitat. In many coastal wintering grounds, the vast areas of isolated habitat serve as natural refuges, but it should not be assumed from this that there is no need for refuges in some localities.

There are unique areas in Mexico of outstanding value to waterfowl and other wildlife that merit establishment and protection as refuges. One is Scammon Lagoon, Baja California, the principal wintering ground for Alaskan black brant. It is important to many other birds and to the many gray whales that come there to calve.

Two other localities that provide excellent refuge sites are the area in northeastern Yucatan where several thousand flamingos breed, and part of the Bay of Celestun, Yucatan, where they winter. The latter is also a haven for waterfowl and other waterbirds that would benefit greatly from refuge protection. There would be adequate opportunities for waterfowl hunting elsewhere in the bay, apart from the closed area.

Some of the interior lakes and marshes might be preserved permanently for waterfowl by designating them as national wildlife refuges and providing for their management and protection. Examples are some of the remaining wetlands in and about the Valley of Mexico, such as Lake Zumpango and portions of Lake Texcoco. The preservation of outstanding localities such as these could well be the basis for joint discussions with representatives of the United States and Canada. International conservation organizations such as the World Wildlife Fund might be invited to participate in such considerations since these waters are of international importance.

Some lakes and lagoons are still heavily populated with wintering flocks of waterfowl. On a few of these the recreational value to sightseers might yield a greater financial return locally than accrues now from hunting. Good examples are Laguna Papagayo and Laguna Coyuca near Acapulco. The tropical beauty of these settings and the variety of spectacular birds are such that regular sight-seeing trips by boat should have great tourist attraction. Such development would require that waterfowl shooting be restricted to the far zone of each lagoon. Aerial and ground surveys show that waterfowl in these waters have declined greatly since hunting became more popular and widespread. The general practice of shooting ducks and coots from motorboats under power apparently caused many birds to seek safer habitat elsewhere.

IN MEXICO all wildlife is under the jurisdiction of the Federal Government. This contrasts with the situation in the United States and Canada where all wildlife except migratory birds and marine mammals are the property of the respective States and Provinces. The Department of Game is designated by the Federal government to administer the wildlife resources of the Republic, but neither personnel nor funds are provided specifically for managing waterfowl. Because of this situation it has not been possible to conduct the field investigations and to establish the management projects that are desirable. To date the chief accomplishments have been in the establishment of regulations that set seasons and bag limits, and prohibit commercial hunting and sale of waterfowl and other wildlife.

The Mexican Institute of Renewable Natural Resources (IMRNR) is much interested in the waterfowl resources of the Republic. The Department of Game cooperated with the IMRNR recently in making a survey of waterfowl habitat in many localities of the interior highlands. This project, aided by the Wildlife Management Institute, was reported in the IMRNR publication by Arellano and Rojas (1956).

The wintering grounds most in need of study are those of the highlands and the northwest coast from Sinaloa to Baja California. Those on the Gulf coast and southern half of the Pacific coast already have been studied by the U.S. Bureau of Sport Fisheries and Wildlife in cooperation with the Mexico Department of Game. Others in the highlands from the States of Mexico and Puebla northward have been investigated jointly by IMRNR and the Department of Game, as well as by the U.S. Bureau of Sport Fisheries and Wildlife.

Habitat in the interior has been more affected by human developments than it has in some localities on the coast. Accordingly more can be done in such areas to improve or restore conditions. This is a pressing reason for conducting more intensive studies in the highlands. It would appear that good opportunities exist for restoring favorable conditions so that natural foods can flourish. In many localities duck food plants will return by regrowth from roots or seeds when habitat conditions become favorable. In some places the greatest benefit would be provided by the control of pest plants that now inhibit or have eliminated desirable food plants.

Many waters of the United States and Mexico have been ruined for waterfowl by the invasion of water-hyacinths and other weed species that kill aquatic food plants by excessive shading. Unfortunately, individuals of good intent, but unaware of the consequences, have encouraged the introduction of water-hyacinths in some Mexican lakes. It would serve a useful purpose to publicize the damage caused by these pest plants and warn against their transplantation. On some waters, such as Lakes Chapala, Cuitzeo, Yuriria, and Oriental, a careful study of water supply and of the fluctuation of level may reveal ways of maintaining more stable levels and improving food conditions.

At Lake Chapala, waterfowl, fishery, and recreational values probably would justify a program to reduce or control water-hyacinths in the eastern end of the lake and in lagoons of the lake delta. This improvement would add greatly to the waterfowl-carrying capacity of this famous wintering ground, while increasing recreational and real estate values for thousands of people.

At Lake Patzcuaro, the designation of the bays and marshes near the town of Patzcuaro as refuges, and the prohibition of shooting waterfowl from motorboats under power would tend to hold more birds on this lake. This same program could be used to good advantage in several other localities.

Pollution is a major threat to some of the Mexican wintering grounds. Oil pollution has been of serious consequence in parts of the Tampico sector and in other oil fields in times past, and could be again. A well-balanced waterfowl management program should include safeguards to prevent such losses of birds and habitat. It should also include safeguards against the release into lakes and streams of chemical wastes from industrial plants. There is need likewise for periodic water sampling at all industrial locations where wildlife habitat would be affected by pollution.

A critical situation currently exists at Laguna Madre, Tamaulipas, where Boca Jesus Maria, the famous 8th Pass so well known to fishermen and hunters, is closed for the first time in many years. There is now no open channel between the Gulf and the Laguna and the resulting excessive salinity is killing fish and has killed much of the aquatic vegetation. The Laguna is being ruined as an important waterfowl wintering ground. The loss, especially to commercial fisheries, may amount to hundreds of thousands of dollars in total resource value. Dredging, to reopen the pass to the Gulf and restore these resources, is a project of concern to several federal agencies and should merit cooperative action.

As FOR THE FUTURE of waterfowl in Mexico, much will depend on an increased public awareness of the need for conserving natural resources. How rapidly this understanding and resulting action will come is open to question. Unfortunately, the world over, great foresight has never characterized conservation affairs. We can only hope that the Mexican citizenry will move rapidly enough to avoid costly errors which we in the United States and elsewhere now see so plainly.

A beginning, it would seem, might result from close governmental cooperation. The Ministry of Hydraulic Resources is in charge of the many projects involving construction of reservoirs and the control of water. It follows that close coordination between that agency and the Departments of Game and Fisheries would enhance public benefits. Maximum coordination between the Department of Game, IMRNR, and all organizations of sportsmen is also highly desirable since such mutually helpful relations will give the greatest return

for the money invested. Wildlife organizations in the United States and Canada may be able to assist in various studies of Mexico's waterfowl problems and programs. Such aid could prove of great mutual benefit.

Sportsmen, too, could assist waterfowl conservation in many ways. Because of the limited field staff of the Department of Game, conditions and incidents damaging to waterfowl sometimes occur in places where no government employees are available to report them. At such times, sportsmen can render invaluable service by reporting the needed information. The organization of sportsmen for this type of volunteer service is one element of any successful waterfowl program. The submission of water samples for pollution tests is one important aid

A pilot biologist and assistant making an aerial survey of wintering waterfowl in Laguna Madre, Mexico. Such surveys are conducted cooperatively between the United States and Mexico.

SUBSECRETARIO DE RECURSOS FORESTALES
Y DE CAZA
MEXICO

I have read critically the chapter which refers to the migratory waterfowl situation in Mexico, written by Professor A. Starker Leopold for the book, "Waterfowl Tomorrow."

I found that his information is correct, as could be expected in view of the knowledge that Professor Leopold has about the waterfowl of our country. It is very satisfactory to us that such a chapter should be inserted in this book since without it the full perspective of [waterfowl in] North America would be incomplete.

Mexico, D.F., March 31, 1964

ENRIQUE BELTRAN
Subsecretario

Original text in Spanish. Translation through courtesy Mexican Embassy, Washington, D.C.

such volunteers could offer. Information on waterfowl flights, food conditions, and the appearance of pest plants are other examples of useful assistance.

FORTUNATELY, the outlook for the waterfowl wintering grounds in Mexico is favorable along the tropical lowlands of the Republic. In coastal sectors most important to waterfowl there is little industrial expansion. The greatest losses of coastal habitat in the foreseeable future probably will be caused by the spread of pest plants such as waterhyacinths, waterlettuce, and salvinia, by silting due to upstream flooding and erosion, and by periodic drought in some localities.

In spite of these losses, there probably will continue to be a substantial carrying capacity of coastal sectors for waterfowl. As long as the northern breeding grounds are reasonably adequate and productive, and the kill of birds in the United States and Canada is not excessive, there probably will be good flights in Mexico.—A. STARKER LEOPOLD.

Waterfowl Tomorrow
in the United States

PREDICTING THE FUTURE of a national resource has become almost a national pastime. Name a resource and you can find a learned dissertation on what one can expect in year 1980 or 2000. Sometimes there is a serious need for such prognostication; sometimes it is more or less an academic exercise.

Long-range planning for waterfowl unquestionably falls in the classification of "serious need." Most students of conservation history will agree that our waterfowl resource is at a crossroad. Decisions made today might very well determine whether

or not the waterfowl resource of tomorrow will be maintained in a manner acceptable to those who are fighting for its preservation.

What do we see in the future? Can hunters expect something better than the low bag limits, short seasons, and all the other restrictions of the past few years? Will future duck and goose hunting be more and more restricted to a privileged few?

Will nonhunters have more opportunity to enjoy these birds? Will waterfowl populations continue to fluctuate, with the low in each

738

cycle getting lower and lower? Can this recreational resource really be placed on a sound basis?

These questions and many more like them are being asked with growing frequency by discouraged and apprehensive duck hunters and by many others. They are pertinent questions, and deserving of well-considered answers.

The records show that waterfowl regulations over the years have steadily become more restrictive. The correspondence files make all too clear that such restrictive regulations are irksome. Some hunters have given up hope and turned to other forms of recreation. They have good reasons for asking: "Is it worth the struggle? Can we look forward to something better?"

No one can give an unqualified answer to these questions—even for the next 20 or 30 years. But a full and frank discussion of the problem may help the interested citizen in making up his own mind as to what the answer is as far as he is personally concerned.

To begin with, we have no choice but to accept the fact that the good old days preceding the 1930's are gone. They will not return. Old-time duck hunters with fond memories might as well concede this. Even our most optimistic predictions do not contemplate that wildlife managers can regain all or even most of the waterfowl habitat lost to the advances of civilization. There is also no getting around the cold fact that in spite of low bag limits and short seasons of today we still have three times as many duck hunters crowding the marshes as we had in those "good old days."

A more practical approach would be to ask, "Can we expect to return to average duck hunting levels which existed during the midfifties, before the past several years of poor waterfowl production resulted in such stringent hunting regulations?" The answer, I believe, is "Yes." It is a practical goal, and it is the goal set for the current waterfowl preservation program of the Bureau of Sport Fisheries and Wildlife of the U.S. Department of the Interior.

Now what is the reason for our difficulties? Why do we seem to be losing ground? The problem, of course, is basically one created by man himself. We had a serious drought in the waterfowl breeding grounds in the 1930's, comparable to the one we had in the late 1950's, but at that time we had smaller numbers of hunters and much more waterfowl habitat. Duck Stamp sales, a clear indication of hunting pressure, increased from a low of 428,487 in fiscal year 1936 to a peak of 2,355,353 in fiscal year 1958—a fivefold increase during a 23-year period.

During this same period over a million acres of the finest production habitat in the United States were drained. This loss plus the additional loss of wintering and migration areas, coupled with a major increase in hunting pressure, create our most serious problem of today and our greatest concern about tomorrow.

There are other factors, of course, and some of these will be more important in the future. Land and water pollution, duck diseases, illegal kill of waterfowl, predation, and other mortality factors must also be considered in predicting the prospects for the future. But to repeat— the basic long-range problem is competition for land and water between waterfowl on the one hand and civilization with its steadily increasing human population on the other.

I do not think there is any question but that when and if waterfowl habitat—both land and water—is *needed* for producing food for our human population, waterfowl will lose out. But there is a great difference between *need* and *desire*. Much waterfowl habitat today has been lost because its reclamation for other uses was *desired* by the landowner or by a special interest public program, and not because there was a *national need* for converting the lakes and marshes to other uses. And herein lies the hope for a better planned program for the future.

The Federal government, working in close cooperation with State governments, has a good habitat preservation program underway in the United States. Congress has provided necessary authorization. Congress will also provide the funds if the public demands that the program be carried through to completion.

Why so much emphasis on a Federal wetlands acquisition program for the future? Justification for public control of a substantial acreage of waterfowl habitat is based partly on the importance of preserving the habitat itself and partly on the assumption that public preservation and development of a nucleus of wetlands will provide an incentive for private retention of additional wetlands necessary to maintain waterfowl populations at desired levels.

Only time will tell if this is a reasonable assumption, but the Bureau of Sport Fisheries and Wildlife is proceeding on this basis. Personally, I believe this approach is the proper one, but I am also convinced that a substantial part of the overall habitat goal will probably never be reached. Competition for these lands by other interests will block some acquisitions. Skyrocketing prices of some wetland areas are driving them out of reach. Some will be converted to other uses before the acquisition program can consider them. High priority demands for water in many areas bar us from securing needed water rights for waterfowl use. All of these problems are being encountered currently and will become even more serious in tomorrow's program.

Does this mean that we may not be able to provide waterfowl with the where-with-all necessary to maintain them at the 1950 levels? I don't think so. I need go back only 20 years to remember dire predictions by some agricultural experts to the effect that within 2 decades, all wetlands suitable for agriculture would be needed to provide adequate food for our rapidly increasing human population. What is the actual situation now—2 decades later? A massive government program has been designed to keep large acreages out of agricultural production because food and fiber are being produced faster than needed.

Reasons for the changed agricultural outlook can be laid directly at the door of research. Research in agriculture has found, literally, how to grow 2 bushels of grain where one grew before. In a similar manner, I believe, research should show us how to produce two ducks where one was produced before. Herein lies our hope.

What are some of the possibilities for tomorrow if research unlocks the door? Improvement of waterfowl production is one of our most critical needs. Somehow we must find ways and means of getting more breeding pairs to nest on the suitable breeding areas available to them. We must cut down the very high mortality rate of the birds at the egg and duckling stage. Only a small percentage of improvement in this area would make itself felt in a very substantial way in the numbers of waterfowl available for the duck hunter's recreation.

There are large areas of marsh and water in the United States that support very few breeding birds. Why? Birds fly over them. They have water and look good, but they lack something. We must find out exactly what—then, maybe, we can devise a cure. An additional advantage to solving this problem is that much of this unproductive acreage is also submarginal for agriculture, and agricultural competition for land would, to this degree, be avoided.

What about artificial propagation? We have fish hatcheries that raise large quantities of fish which are released in our lakes and rivers for better fishing. Why not a program to produce and raise to maturity large numbers of wild ducks in duck hatcheries and release them for duck hunters to enjoy? Would this not eliminate the most vulnerable part of a duck's life? The answer again must be determined by research. The idea has great potential and should be fully explored in the program of tomorrow.

But probably the most challenging production problem looms up in the better breeding habitat of the northern prairie. Why do certain potholes produce ducks, and others not? Why only one pair instead of two, or five, or even ten to a given marsh area? While wildlife may not be as susceptible to mass production as domestic animals, I feel sure that we have only scratched the surface on how to produce more wildlife per acre of habitat. Research and more research is the answer. If right now we were given unlimited funds for improvement and development of those marshes we still wouldn't know how to use them efficiently. We must learn, and soon, what we should do.

Assume that sufficient habitat will be dedicated to waterfowl. What about pollution? Here is a byproduct of civilization—a growing menace that we must get under control or our other problems will appear small by comparison.

POLLUTION dangerous to waterfowl assumes many forms. Oil and chemical wastes in streams, lakes and marshes, and on the coastal shallow waters can result in immediate and serious mortality. Silt may inhibit the growth of waterfowl food needed by the birds. A new form of both land and water pollution—

chemical pesticides—may prove to be even more serious than more obvious types of pollution.

All kinds of land, water, and air pollution need immediate attention for the benefit of both man and beast, but the destructive potentials of chemical pesticide pollution appear most frightening.

Research has demonstrated that some of these chemicals—currently in widespread use—can adversely affect the reproduction of birds. The implication of this is obvious. Substantial segments of our bird population could be reduced or even eliminated without the reason being apparent. Here is a pressing research problem that the United States Congress has recognized by enacting legislation authorizing much needed research. Finances to carry out the required research programs must be provided. Research in this field at the State level should be stepped up.

Another problem of the waterfowl hunters' making is duck mortality resulting from an accumulation of lead shot in waterfowl marshes. Ducks need grit to help their digestive processes, and in the course of their feeding will pick up lead shot along with grit. Only a few pellets are needed to cause death. The accumulated national loss is substantial. The solution must come from a cooperative approach between research and the ammunition companies that produce the lead shot. A disintegrating shot or one that is nontoxic must be found.

Research must also find better ways of protecting the farmer from crop losses caused by migratory waterfowl. Agricultural cooperation is essential to a successful waterfowl program, and whole-hearted cooperation will not be forthcoming if the farmer believes that more ducks mean more crop damage. Better yet, the farmer must feel that waterfowl are an asset to his operation. Finding a solution for this problem is a substantial challenge.

BUT EVEN WITH a sound habitat and an adequate research program, Mr. Duck Hunter himself has an important part to play if we are to get the most recreational mileage out of waterfowl. Keep in mind that those responsible for setting waterfowl seasons are dealing with 38 species of ducks and 8 species of geese in the huntable category. Further, keep in mind that every one of these species presents different management problems. This adds up to individual species management, and what a complicated picture this presents!

Eventually, new approaches in hunting regulations may lead to a better solution. But thus far the surest way of giving special protection to species in short supply has been through closing seasons or limiting numbers in the daily bag.

In short, duck hunters even now have to know their birds, and be able to recognize them before they are brought to bag. If game managers cannot come up with a workable alternate solution which will give the necessary protection to certain species, duck hunters are going to have to spend even more time on bird identification. Experienced hunters generally know what they are shooting at but, unfortunately, the majority of our hunters are not experienced, and many will never have the opportunity to become experts in waterfowl identification through their hunting experience alone. An effective program of hunter education is going to be essential. The duck hunter of tomorrow who cannot distinguish between certain species of ducks is going to be a badly handicapped hunter.

Duck hunters must also develop and adhere to a better code of hunting ethics. Hunting regulations serve two purposes. They help to assure the preservation of a satisfactory breeding stock and they provide "rules of the game" which tend to equalize opportunity among hunters. If the rules of basketball could be broken with impunity the sport would soon break down. So it is with duck hunting. That is why we have game wardens; they must enforce the regulations if the sport is to be preserved. The better the duck hunter of tomorrow observes the rules of the game the more legal ducks there will be for him to bag.

How ABOUT hunting opportunity for the duck hunter of the future? Duck hunting now is a "free" sport in only a few sections of the country. The duck hunter of the future will find fewer places to hunt without paying for the right of access. Many lakes and open coastal waters will probably always be open to the general public without charge, but the day is fast approaching when private landowners generally will expect compensation for the right of hunting. Based on our experience, to date, there will always be duck hunters willing to purchase duck or goose hunting rights on private land where there is a good chance of getting a bag limit.

The wetlands acquisition program of the Federal Government will provide a great deal of public hunting, since the law provides that up to 40 percent of acquired land may be open to waterfowl hunting. The States, by and large, will very likely open most of their public areas to hunting. Nevertheless, even on these publicly controlled lands the waterfowl hunter of tomorrow and other users must expect to pay some type of modest access fee. It costs a great deal to acquire, manage, and maintain these areas, and I predict that it will be the rule that he who uses shall pay.

Goose hunting of the future in the United States may be confined largely to public hunting areas and adjacent lands. These birds, generally, are susceptible to various management measures, especially protection and an adequate food supply. Their breeding grounds, to date, have not been seriously affected by civilization. Certain goose populations, such as the Mississippi Valley flock of Canada geese, have increased substantially during the past decade as a result of intensive management practices in migration and wintering areas. Opportunities for bagging a goose today are better in many parts of the country than they were 20 or 30 years ago, but it must be recognized that the quality of such hunting, based on the standards of the oldtime hunter, has deteriorated considerably. It is simply a case of having more hunters pursuing their sport in fewer places.

Concentration of most of the geese during migration and in winter on relatively few areas in the vicinity of national wildlife refuges is the reason for this.

A major goose management objective of the future will be to provide more attractive goose habitat in parts of the South formerly considered normal wintering grounds for most of the birds. This will be necessary if the southern parts of the nation are to secure a reasonable proportion of goose hunting.

IN PLANNING for the future we must not overlook the nonhunter. How can non-hunting citizens, who outnumber hunters many times, get more fun out of these birds? Part of the answer lies, I believe, in preserving or creating small areas of waterfowl habitat in heavily populated areas. Many such units do not meet the criteria for a national waterfowl refuge and they have been neglected in the national program. Yet, collectively, they are important. Such areas are a fertile field for consideration by county, municipal, and private organizations desiring to provide open spaces and outdoor recreation for heavily populated sections.

A better waterfowl interpretation program is another need. Birds which breed in the Arctic, winter in the Tropics, and make the complete year-round trip every year with an unfailing instinct have captured the imagination of a large segment of the nation's people. More recreational mileage should be gained in the future from this inherently fascinating subject.

As research unlocks life history truths about these birds they should be translated to popular language for the enjoyment of all the people. The 50 States with their periodical fish and game magazines have done an admirable job in this field as far as resident wildlife is concerned, but for various reasons the potentialities of this educational adventure in the field of migratory bird management have been sadly neglected.

In viewing the magnitude of the migratory waterfowl program, both hunters and nonhunters may very well ask: "Doesn't this all add up to a huge expense? How can we justify spending all the money necessary to manage and maintain this waterfowl resource?" The answers to these questions do require thought, but there are good answers.

First of all, we are fortunate in that the most expensive parts of the program—land acquisition and water development—provide other forms of recreation besides hunting. Many activities may be enjoyed by the public on wetlands and without interfering with the birds. Bird-watching, outdoor photography, fishing, hiking, and swimming are just a few of them. In 1962, less than 4 percent of the 10,870,500 visitors to the national wildlife refuges came there to hunt. Because of this, I feel quite strongly that duck hunters cannot properly be charged with more than a reasonable proportion of the wetlands preservation program.

Improvements designed to make life more bearable for migratory birds are of equal value to other resources and to man. Can anyone question that research or action programs designed to abate land and water pollution have high values to a very broad segment of the human population? A habitat so polluted as to be dangerous to wildlife is a habitat to be shunned by man.

In short, I think that while preservation of habitat suitable for waterfowl is expensive, it is an integral part of an essential program for preserving human habitat needed to maintain living standards at levels to which we have become accustomed. For most of us the bare essentials of food and shelter do not make for a complete life. Space for living, once available in unlimited quantities, is daily shrinking and now must be rationed when considering human needs of the future. So be it with migratory waterfowl, which also need space as a part of the whole scheme of things which make for man's better living.

If we could have been as foresighted 50 years ago as we now attempt to be, the picture, I believe, would look quite different today. It is surprising that migratory waterfowl have done as well as they have considering the treatment they and their habitat have received at the hands of white man during the relatively short period he has occupied the North American Continent.

IN CONCLUDING these observations on the future of waterfowl, I emphasize again that waterfowl management for the North American Continent is a complicated business. The governments of three nations, 10 Provinces in Canada, 50 States in the United States, and 29 States in Mexico, must all be considered in looking at the problem as a whole.

In the United States, waterfowl habitat everywhere is in direct competition with other uses. The same situation in varying degrees exists in our neighboring nations. The human population is steadily expanding; it requires more land and water to sustain itself; and at the same time it demands more birds for recreational hunting.

If we could accurately forecast human population requirements and demands, we could accurately forecast bird populations of the future. Lacking such foresight, but taking into consideration the foreseeable factors based on past trends, I believe that duck hunters and bird watchers of tomorrow can reasonably expect to enjoy their respective recreation at about the 1950–60 level, but with one proviso. They can expect this only if they want it badly enough and are willing to work and pay for it. Remember that the competing forces of yesterday and today will still be with us tomorrow.

Habitat for waterfowl tomorrow is still available; the breeding stock is adequate; and a good management program with long-range planning is underway. These are the necessary ingredients. Whether they will be dissipated through lack of interest and aggressive support is entirely up to the public. If enough citizens believe that the perpetuation of waterfowl is important, the job will be done. It is not too late.

—DANIEL H. JANZEN.

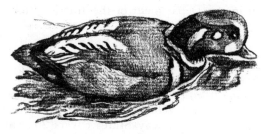

About the Contributors

THE EDITORS

JOSEPH P. LINDUSKA is Director of Public Relations and Wildlife Management for Remington Arms Company. He was formerly Chief of Game Management for the Fish and Wildlife Service, and for several years was game biologist with the Michigan Department of Conservation. Dr. Linduska received his advanced degree from Michigan State University. In 1963 the Outdoor Writers Association of America presented him the Jade of Chiefs Award for distinguished service to conservation. The Wildlife Society in the same year named him to receive its Conservation Education Award.

ARNOLD L. NELSON is Assistant to the Director, Bureau of Sport Fisheries and Wildlife. His earlier service in the Bureau includes assignments as Director of the Patuxent Research Refuge and as Assistant Chief, Branch of Wildlife Research. His training and degree in science were obtained from the University of Michigan. He is a coauthor of *American Wildlife and Plants*. In 1959 he received the United States Department of the Interior's Distinguished Service Medal.

THE ARTIST

BOB HINES, artist-illustrator in the Office of Information, U.S. Fish and Wildlife Service, Washington, D.C., was formerly with the Ohio Division of Conservation and Natural Resources. Designer of the 1946 Duck Stamp, and of the four Wildlife Conservation Postage Stamps, Mr. Hines is a self-taught artist. He is known for his illustrations in several books and maga-

zines on wildlife and conservation, and many recent Fish and Wildlife
Service publications include his art work. A number of wildlife murals
by Mr. Hines may be seen in the Department of the Interior Building in
Washington, D.C.

THE AUTHORS

C. EDWARD ADDY *(Atlantic Flyway)* is Atlantic Flyway Representative
for the Bureau of Sport Fisheries and Wildlife. His waterfowl experience
in eastern Canada and the Atlantic Flyway States covers 20 years. He
was a charter member of the Black Duck Committee, the predecessor of
the Atlantic Flyway Council. His graduate degree is from Virginia Polytechnic Institute.

JOHN M. ANDERSON *(Private Duck Clubs)* is Superintendent of the Winous
Point Club, Port Clinton, Ohio. He has had more than 20 years' water-
fowl experience, mostly in the Great Lakes area. He is a graduate of
Ohio State University.

DONALD H. BALDWIN *(Cousins by the Dozens)* is Collector and Preparator,
Department of Ornithology, Royal Ontario Museum, Toronto. Previously,
he worked for the Ontario Department of Lands and Forests at their Forest Ranger School. He is active in waterfowl and other bird banding, and
is a Vice President of the Ontario Bird Banding Association and Field
Secretary of the Long Point Bird Observatory.

WINSTON E. BANKO *(Our Native Swans)* is presently "on loan" from the
Bureau of Sport Fisheries and Wildlife to the Smithsonian Institution. He
has had 15 years' experience in waterfowl management, during which time
he completed a study of trumpeter swans, analyzing a 25-year accumulation of life history and population records. He authored North American
Fauna No. 63, *The Trumpeter Swan,* which received honorable mention by
The Wildlife Society as one of the outstanding books on terrestrial wildlife
in 1960. He is a graduate of Oregon State University.

THOMAS W. BARRY *(Brant, Ross' Goose, and Emperor Goose)* is Ornithologist
at the Northern Research Laboratory, Inuvik, Northwest Territories, for
the Canadian Wildlife Service. He has studied the Atlantic brant in the
eastern Arctic on Southampton Island. He has 9 years' field experience in
arctic waterfowl studies and holds a graduate degree from Cornell University.

FRANK C. BELLROSE *(Eastern Production Areas; Spent Shot and Lead Poisoning)*,
Wildlife Specialist, Illinois Natural History Survey, has spent 25 years in
the study of waterfowl populations, migration, and nesting in Illinois. He
has written 40 technical papers on wildlife, most of which have involved
waterfowl. He is a graduate of the University of Illinois.

DIRCK BENSON *(Eastern Production Areas)*, Senior Wildlife Biologist, New
York Conservation Department, has been engaged in wildlife research in
that State for 25 years. His field of special interest is New York waterfowl,
and for 15 years he has been in charge of waterfowl research. He is a

graduate of Pomona College and holds an advanced degree from Cornell University.

EUGENE F. BOSSENMAIER (*Cows and Cutter Bars*) is Chief of Game and Fur Management in the Wildlife Branch of the Manitoba Department of Mines and Natural Resources. Prior to his present employment, he worked as a Biologist with the South Dakota Department of Game, Fish, and Parks and the Wyoming Game and Fish Commission. He holds a graduate degree in Wildlife Management from the University of Minnesota.

FRANK P. BRIGGS (*Waterfowl in a Changing Continent*), former United States Senator from Missouri, was appointed Assistant Secretary of the Interior for Fish and Wildlife in February 1961. At that time, he was serving his third 6-year appointment as a member of the Missouri Conservation Commission. A native of Missouri, Secretary Briggs was educated at Central College and the University of Missouri, from which University he was graduated in 1915. He has twice received the University of Missouri School of Journalism's Award for Distinguished Service in Journalism. He received an Honorary Degree of Doctor of Science from Central College in 1961.

JOHN L. BUCKLEY (*Insecticides*) is Technical Assistant, Office of Science and Technology, Executive Office of the President. He was formerly Chief, Office of Pesticides Coordination, Bureau of Sport Fisheries and Wildlife, Washington, D.C. His service with the Bureau began in 1951, in Alaska. Dr. Buckley has held positions as Cooperative Wildlife Research Unit Leader; Assistant Chief, Branch of Wildlife Research; and Director, Patuxent Wildlife Research Center. His advanced degree is from the State University of New York.

The late INGALF G. BUE (*Stock Ponds and Dugouts*) was wildlife research biologist with the Bureau of Sport Fisheries and Wildlife at the time of his death, in 1963. Dr. Bue's professional wildlife experience began in 1947, as a biologist for the State of South Dakota. He was biologist, deputy commissioner, and commissioner of the State Game and Fish Dept. in North Dakota. The I. G. Bue Memorial Laboratory at Woodworth, North Dak., was named in his honor by the Bureau of Sport Fisheries and Wildlife. His advanced degree was awarded by the University of Minnesota.

RAYMOND J. BULLER (*Central Flyway*), Central Flyway Representative of the Bureau of Sport Fisheries and Wildlife, has had 20 years' experience in fish and wildlife biology, 12 of which have been concerned with the waterfowl program of the Central Flyway. His graduate degree is from Michigan State College.

GEORGE V. BURGER (*Cousins by the Dozens; Instant Nesting Habitat*) is Manager of Wildlife Management for Remington Arms Company at Chestertown, Md. He has been engaged in wildlife management on the land since 1958. Dr. Burger has a graduate degree from the University of Wisconsin.

ROBERT W. BURWELL (*Potholes—Going, Going . . . .*) is Regional Director, North Central Region, Bureau of Sport Fisheries and Wildlife, Minneapolis, Minnesota. He has had 25 years in the Federal service, 18 of which were

748

WATERFOWL TOMORROW

with the Fish and Wildlife Service. He is a graduate of the University of Michigan.

JOHN E. CHATTIN *(Pacific Flyway; Western Production Areas)* is Pacific Flyway Representative, Bureau of Sport Fisheries and Wildlife, Portland, Ore., a position he has held for 14 years. Prior to that, he was Assistant Chief of Game Conservation for the California Department of Fish and Game. He has 18 years' wildlife experience, most of which has been concerned with waterfowl. He is a graduate of the University of California.

C. H. D. CLARKE *(Mammoths and Mallards; Waterfowl and the Hunter)* is Chief, Fish and Wildlife Branch of the Ontario Department of Lands and Forests, Toronto, Canada. His experience with wildlife biology dates from 1931, and he has been with the Ontario Department of Lands and Forests since 1944. Dr. Clarke was president of The Wildlife Society in 1953. He was editor of *Canadian Field Naturalist* in 1939 and 1940. His advanced degree was awarded by the University of Toronto in 1935.

ROLAND C. CLEMENT *(Viewpoint of a Naturalist)* has been Staff Biologist, National Audubon Society (New York City) since 1958. His principal field for the past 24 years has been conservation education but he has maintained a strong interest in waterfowl. He received a National Wildlife Federation Special Service Citation in 1963 for his writings. He holds a graduate degree from Cornell University.

F. G. COOCH *(Snows and Blues)* is biologist in charge of Biocide Investigations, Canadian Wildlife Service, Ottawa. Prior to 1961 he served as Arctic Ornithologist for the same service for 10 years, studying snow geese on their breeding and wintering grounds. Dr. Cooch is a graduate of Cornell University.

ARTHUR H. COOK *(Better Living for Ducks—Through Chemistry)* is a private consultant on problems of wetland development and management. Prior to 1962 he was employed by the New York State Conservation Department in soil chemistry and ecology. Dr. Cook is author of more than 30 papers on wildlife management. His advanced degree is from Cornell University.

ERNEST A. CÔTÉ *(A Canadian Looks at the Future)* is Assistant Deputy Minister of the Canadian Department of Northern Affairs and National Resources, a position he has held since 1955. He is leader of the Canadian section of the International Migratory Bird Committee, and has been engaged in public service since 1945. He is a graduate of the University of Alberta.

CLARENCE COTTAM *(They also Serve)* is Director, Welder Wildlife Foundation, Sinton, Tex. He is a former Assistant Director, U.S. Fish and Wildlife Service, and has had over 30 years' wildlife experience. Dr. Cottam has received several national awards and honors, including the Aldo Leopold and Audubon medals and fellowship in the National Academy of Sciences. He is author of more than 230 published papers on wildlife. His advanced degree is from George Washington University.

WALTER F. CRISSEY *(Research, Key to Progress)* is Director, Migratory Bird Populations Station, Patuxent Wildlife Research Center, Laurel, Md. He has been associated with wildlife research for more than 30 years, and since 1947 has been concerned with waterfowl population studies. He has been closely connected with surveys of waterfowl breeding grounds and wintering areas and in analyses of the data from these surveys. He is a graduate of Cornell University.

ALBERT M. DAY *(No Place to Hide)* is Executive Director, Pennsylvania Fish Commission. He is a former Director of the U.S. Fish and Wildlife Service and has a career in wildlife that spans 45 years. He is author of a book entitled *North American Waterfowl*. He is a graduate of the University of Wyoming.

FRANK DUFRESNE *(Northern Watersheds and Deltas)* is Associate Editor for *Field and Stream*. Before turning to full-time writing, Mr. Dufresne served for over 40 years in the wildlife field, beginning in 1920 as a fur warden in Alaska, then serving as executive officer of the Alaska Game Commission, and later as chief of information for the U.S. Fish and Wildlife Service in Washington, D.C.

ALEX DZUBIN *(White-fronts)* is a research biologist with the Canadian Wildlife Service. He began his professional experience with waterfowl in 1951 with the Delta Waterfowl Research Station. He received a graduate degree from the University of British Columbia in 1953.

FRANK C. EDMINSTER *(Farm Ponds and Waterfowl)* is Assistant Director, Division of Plant Technology, of the U.S. Soil Conservation Service, Washington, D.C. He has some 34 years experience in wildlife work, the past 27 of which have been with the Soil Conservation Service. His publications include five books and more than 100 technical and popular papers and bulletins. He holds a graduate degree from Cornell University.

VERNON EKEDAHL *(Farming for Waterfowl)* is Assistant Regional Supervisor, Branch of Wildlife Refuges, Bureau of Sport Fisheries and Wildlife, Portland, Ore. He has nearly 30 years' wildlife experience, virtually all of which has been closely related to waterfowl management.

RAY C. ERICKSON *(Planting and Misplanting)* is a research staff specialist, Division of Wildlife Research, Bureau of Sport Fisheries and Wildlife, Washington, D.C. Previously, he was Chief, Section of Habitat Improvement of the Branch of Wildlife Refuges. Dr. Erickson has 25 years' professional wildlife experience, chiefly in waterfowl ecology and management. His graduate degree is from Iowa State University.

PAUL L. ERRINGTON *(Talon and Fang)* was Professor of Zoology at Iowa State University at the time of his death in 1962. He was internationally recognized for work on populations of mammals and birds, including predator-prey relationships on marshes of North Central United States. Dr. Errington was twice honored by The Wildlife Society for outstanding wildlife publications, and in 1962 was recipient of the Society's Aldo Leopold Medal. His graduate degree was from the University of Wisconsin.

THOMAS R. EVANS *(Beyond National Boundaries)*is Supervisor, Game Management Division, Illinois Department of Conservation, Springfield. He has had 28 years' wildlife experience in the Midwest. He is a graduate of the University of Minnesota.

A. MURRAY FALLIS *(Blood Parasites)* is Director, Department of Parasitology, Ontario Research Foundation, and Professor of Parasitology, University of Toronto, Canada, a position he has held since 1947. Dr. Fallis is a fellow of the Royal Society of Canada; Past President, Royal Canadian Institute; Past President, Ontario Society of Biologists; Associate Editor, Canadian Journal of Microbiology; and Councilor, American Society of Parasitologists. He received his advanced degree from the University of Toronto in 1937.

JOHN D. FINDLAY *(A Letter to a Hunter)* is Regional Chief, Division of Wildlife, Bureau of Sport Fisheries and Wildlife, Atlanta, Ga. He was formerly Chief, Branch of Management and Enforcement, Washington, D.C. His career in wildlife covers 24 years, most of which has been in administration of waterfowl resources. He is a graduate of North Carolina State College.

IRA N. GABRIELSON *(They Also Serve)*, President, Wildlife Management Institute, is a former Director, U.S. Fish and Wildlife Service, and has nearly 50 years' wildlife experience. Dr. Gabrielson has been the recipient of several national honors, including the Aldo Leopold and Audubon medals and the Distinguished Service Medal of the United States Department of the Interior. He has authored four books and coauthored three. He has written many shorter articles. He holds honorary advanced degrees from Oregon State College, Morningside College, and Middleburg College.

ANGUS GAVIN *(Ducks Unlimited)* is General Manager, Ducks Unlimited of Canada, having been associated with that organization since 1945. Prior to that, he served with the Hudson's Bay Company for 17 years, most of which was in the Arctic. Mr. Gavin is a graduate of Kanes College. He is credited with the discovery of the nesting grounds of the Ross' and the Tule goose.

FRANCIS G. GILLETT *(Federal Refuges)* is Chief, Division of Wildlife Refuges, Bureau of Sport Fisheries and Wildlife. Previously he spent 25 years as Regional Supervisor of Refuges at the Bureau's Regional Office in Minneapolis and as Chief, Division of Wildlife, at Atlanta. Mr. Gillett is a graduate of Michigan State University.

LAWRENCE S. GIVENS *(Farming for Waterfowl)* is Regional Supervisor, Branch of Wildlife Refuges, Bureau of Sport Fisheries and Wildlife, Atlanta, Ga. He was formerly a soil conservationist for that Branch. Mr. Givens received a graduate degree from Virginia Polytechnic Institute.

LESLIE L. GLASGOW *(Rice and Waterfowl)* is Associate Professor of Wildlife Management, Louisiana State University, Baton Rouge, La. His professional interest in waterfowl and wetlands management covers some 16 years. Dr. Glasgow is Past President, Southeastern Section of The Wildlife

Society. He was given an award as Outstanding Conservationist in Louisiana by the Louisiana Outdoor Writers Association in 1959. His advanced degree is from Texas A. and M. University.

FRED A. GLOVER *(Tundra to Tropics)* was appointed Leader, Colorado Cooperative Wildlife Research Unit, Fort Collins, Colo., in January 1964. For 10 years prior to this assignment, he was responsible for planning, organizing, and conducting waterfowl surveys and banding projects for the Bureau of Sport Fisheries and Wildlife. After completing his graduate studies at Iowa State University in 1949, Dr. Glover taught at Humboldt State College in California, where he was head of the Wildlife Department.

J. BERNARD GOLLOP *(Prairie Potholes and Marshes)* is waterfowl biologist for the Canadian Wildlife Service at Saskatoon, Saskatchewan. From this strategic point in the prairie country he is conducting research on waterfowl populations. Results of his research have appeared in more than 25 technical papers. His graduate degree is from Cornell University.

WILLIAM E. GREEN *(Water Off and On)* is a regional wildlife management biologist with the Bureau of Sport Fisheries and Wildlife, stationed at the Upper Mississippi National Wildlife Refuge, Winona, Minn. He has nearly 25 years' experience in marsh and water management. Dr. Green is a graduate of Colorado State University and holds an advanced degree from Iowa State University.

RICHARD E. GRIFFITH *(Forage and Truck Crops)* is Chief, Division of Wildlife, Northwest Region, Bureau of Sport Fisheries and Wildlife, Portland, Ore. He has nearly 30 years' experience in wildlife management and administration, the greater part of which has been concerned with waterfowl. He is a graduate of Syracuse University.

MERRILL C. HAMMOND *(Ducks, Grain, and American Farmers)* is wildlife biologist on the Lower Souris National Wildlife Refuge in North Dakota for the Bureau of Sport Fisheries and Wildlife. For the past 25 years he has been engaged in waterfowl management investigations in the northern prairies. He is a graduate of Brigham Young University.

HENRY A. HANSEN *(Northern Watersheds and Deltas; Honkers Large and Small),* flyway biologist for the Bureau of Sport Fisheries and Wildlife, has spent 18 years on waterfowl research and management, the past 8 in Alaska, where he has charge of waterfowl investigations. He is a graduate of Iowa State University.

ARTHUR S. HAWKINS *(Mississippi Flyway)* is Mississippi Flyway Representative for the Bureau of Sport Fisheries and Wildlife. His active career in waterfowl management spans a period of nearly 30 years with the Illinois Natural History Survey and the Bureau of Sport Fisheries and Wildlife. In 1961 he was named Twin Cities Federal Civil Servant of the year, in the contributions category. He holds a graduate degree from the University of Wisconsin.

E. E. HORN *(Rice and Waterfowl)* is Consultant, Conservation and Natural Resources, Richfield Oil Corporation, Los Angeles, Calif. Mr. Horn retired from the U.S. Fish and Wildlife Service in 1951, after 32 years' service. During most of his career he has been closely connected with waterfowl management

CARL G. HUNTER (*Green Trees and Greenheads*) is General Manager, Wingmead Farms, Stuttgart, Arkansas. Before this he was a game biologist with the Arkansas Game and Fish Commission for 13 years. He is a graduate of the University of Arkansas.

LAURENCE R. JAHN (*Plants on Parade*) is a field representative in the North Central States for the Wildlife Management Institute. His wildlife experience covers 17 years, 12 of which were with the Wisconsin Conservation Department and 5 with the Wildlife Management Institute. He holds a graduate degree from the University of Wisconsin.

DANIEL H. JANZEN (*Waterfowl Tomorrow in the United States*) is Director, Bureau of Sport Fisheries and Wildlife, Washington, D.C., a position he has held since 1957. For 10 years prior to that, he was Regional Director for the same Bureau in the Midwestern States. He has 35 years' experience in wildlife management and administration. He is a graduate of Oregon State College.

G. HORTIN JENSEN (*Western Production Areas*) is flyway biologist, Bureau of Sport Fisheries and Wildlife, Brigham City, Utah. Mr. Jensen has been with the Bureau for 25 years. He holds a graduate degree from Utah State University.

WAYNE I. JENSEN (*Botulism and Fowl Cholera*) is Chief, Section of Wildlife Disease Research, Denver Wildlife Research Center, and is stationed at Bear River Research Station, Brigham City, Utah. He has been employed by the Bureau of Sport Fisheries and Wildlife since 1955. Prior to that he was employed in the School of Hygiene and Public Health, Johns Hopkins University. Dr. Jensen's primary field of research is avian botulism. He holds an advanced degree from Cornell University.

RAYMOND E. JOHNSON (*Fish and Fowl*) is Assistant Director, Bureau of Sport Fisheries and Wildlife, Washington, D.C. Before joining the Bureau in 1952, Dr. Johnson spent 7 years with the Michigan Department of Conservation. His field of specialty during this period has been fishery biology. His advanced degree is from the University of Michigan.

SAMUEL E. JORGENSEN (*State Areas*) is Chief, Office of Foreign Activities, Bureau of Sport Fisheries and Wildlife. Previously, he was Chief, Branch of Federal Aid of that Bureau. He has been employed in some phase of wildlife conservation and management for 27 years. He is a graduate of Utah State University.

FRANCIS H. KORTRIGHT (*Cousins by the Dozens*) is a prominent Canadian industrialist who is well known for his contributions to conservation. In 1947 his book, *Ducks, Geese, and Swans of North America* won for him the Brewster Medal. He has received numerous awards, including an Honorary Chieftainship of the Cayuga Nation of the Six Nations, whose name for him translates "Defender of Wildlife." He is the founder and Past President of the Conservation Council of Ontario. He received his education in the West Indies.

FRANK M. KOZLIK *(Private Duck Clubs)* is Waterfowl Coordinator for the California Department of Fish and Game. He has been engaged in wildlife work for nearly 25 years in Wisconsin and California. He is a graduate of the University of Minnesota.

JEROME H. KUEHN *(Carp, A Sometimes Villain)* is Wildlife Survey Supervisor, Minnesota State Department of Conservation, Saint Paul. He has devoted the past 17 years to biological surveys of lakes, streams, and marshes of Minnesota. He is the author of more than 25 papers on biological surveys. Mr. Kuehn's graduate degree is from the University of Minnesota.

DONALD F. LA POINTE *(State Areas)* is Chief, Projects Investigation Section, Branch of River Basin Studies, Bureau of Sport Fisheries and Wildlife, Minneapolis. He has had 12 years' experience in fish and wildlife research and management in Eastern and Midwestern States. He is a graduate of the University of Minnesota.

DANIEL L. LEEDY *(Research, Key to Progress)* is Chief, Division of Research and Education, Bureau of Outdoor Recreation, Washington, D.C. He was Chief, Branch of Wildlife Research, Bureau of Sport Fisheries and Wildlife, before assuming this position in 1963. Dr. Leedy is Past President of The Wildlife Society. He received the American Motors Conservation Award in 1958. His advanced degree is from Ohio State University.

WILLIAM G. LEITCH *(Water)* is Chief Biologist for Ducks Unlimited of Canada. His waterfowl career started as a field biologist for that agency in 1939 shortly after graduation from the University of Manitoba. He has been Chief Biologist since 1946. Mr. Leitch also holds a graduate degree from the University of Manitoba.

A. STARKER LEOPOLD *(Mexico and Migratory Waterfowl Conservation)* is Professor of Zoology and Assistant to the Chancellor, University of California, Berkeley, Calif. He has a distinguished career in wildlife management, and has served widely as a consultant on national and international wildlife problems. Dr. Leopold is Past President of The Wildlife Society. He is author of the book *Wildlife of Mexico,* and numerous wildlife papers. His advanced degree is from the University of California.

HARRY GORDON LUMSDEN *(Northern Forests and Tundra)* is Senior Biologist, Upland Game and Waterfowl Unit, Research Branch, Ontario Department of Lands and Forests. Prior to his present assignment he was Game Management Supervisor, Fish and Wildlife Branch of the same Department. He has spent 6 years on surveys of the Canada goose breeding grounds in northern Ontario.

JOHN J. LYNCH *(Weather; Ducks in Dixie),* research biologist for the Bureau of Sport Fisheries and Wildlife, is stationed at Lafayette, La. His waterfowl career started in 1936. He was one of the pioneers in breeding ground surveys in Canada and the Northwest Territories. He is a graduate of Rhode Island College and holds an honorary Master's Degree from that Institution.

Russell G. Lynch *(No Place to Hide)* retired January 1, 1964, after 42 years on the *Milwaukee Journal,* where his last assignment was reporting on natural resources and conservation. He is the author of a widely read series "Ditches, Ducks and Dust."

Gordon E. McCallum *(Clean Water, and Enough Of It)* is Assistant Surgeon General, Public Health Service, and Chief of the Division of Water Supply and Pollution Control. He is author of more than 125 papers on water pollution control. Dr. McCallum was named by the American Public Works Association in 1963 as one of the Top Ten Public Works Men-Of-The-Year. His advanced degree is from Clemson University.

R. H. Mackay *(Our Native Swans)* is Regional Supervisor of Operations for the Canadian Wildlife Service at Edmonton, Alberta, and was formerly Dominion Wildlife Officer for British Columbia. He has 15 years' experience in professional wildlife research and management. He has conducted research on the biology of trumpeter swans along the British Columbia coast and in Alberta. Mr. Mackay is a graduate of the University of British Columbia.

L. G. MacNamara *(Water Off and On),* Director, Division of Fish and Game, New Jersey Department of Conservation and Economic Development, is one of the veteran wildlife administrators in the Atlantic Flyway. He was a member of the Black Duck Committee, the predecessor of the Atlantic Flyway Council, and served as chairman of the Council in 1958 and 1959.

John Madson *(The Cornfielders; Waterfowl and the Hunter)* is Chief of the Information Service, Conservation Department, Olin Mathieson Corporation, at East Alton, Ill. Mr. Madson holds a graduate degree in wildlife management from Iowa State University. He has served as an editor and public relations officer of the Iowa Conservation Commission and as outdoor feature writer for the *Des Moines Register.* He has authored several popular publications and books on wildlife.

G. W. Malaher *(Reservoirs)* is Director, Wildlife Branch, Department of Mines and Natural Resources, Manitoba, Canada. His experience in resource conservation dates from 1927, and he has held his present position for 18 years. He is a graduate of the University of New Brunswick.

Howard L. Mendall *(Adventuresome Waterfowl)* has been Leader of the Maine Cooperative Wildlife Research Unit since 1942. Prior to that he was a member of the teaching and research staff at the University of Maine. He is the author of 60 articles, technical papers, and bulletins on wildlife. In 1959 he received the Terrestrial Publication Award of The Wildlife Society for his book *The Ring-necked Duck in the Northeast.* He holds a graduate degree from the University of Maine.

Harvey W. Miller *(White-fronts)* is a wildlife biologist at Lake Andes National Wildlife Refuge for the Bureau of Sport Fisheries and Wildlife. Previously he was employed by the Nebraska Game, Forestation, and Parks Commission. Mr. Miller is a graduate of Colorado State University.

JOHN B. MOYLE *(Carp, a Sometimes Villain; Plants on Parade)*, Supervisor, Section of Research and Planning, Division of Game and Fish, Minnesota Department of Conservation, has 25 years' experience in research on Minnesota wetlands. Dr. Moyle is the author of more than 50 technical papers and bulletins and many semi-popular articles. His advanced degree is from the University of Minnesota.

DAVID A. MUNRO *(Survival of the Species in Canada; Research, Key to Progress)* is Chief, Canadian Wildlife Service, a position he assumed in 1964 after serving 10 years as Staff Specialist in Ornithology and Operations. For 5 years before that he studied waterfowl in British Columbia for the Canadian Wildlife Service. Dr. Munro is author of 20 or more published papers on waterfowl. He received his advanced degree from the University of Toronto.

HARVEY K. NELSON *(Adventuresome Waterfowl; Honkers Large and Small)* is Director, Northern Prairie Wildlife Research Center, Jamestown, N. Dak., for the Bureau of Sport Fisheries and Wildlife. Preceeding his appointment to this position he had 13 years' experience with waterfowl management in the North Central States. He is a graduate of the University of Minnesota and holds a graduate degree from Michigan State University

MARCUS C. NELSON *(Farming for Waterfowl)* is Regional Supervisor, Branch of Wildlife Refuges, Bureau of Sport Fisheries and Wildlife, Albuquerque, New Mexico. He has had 20 years' experience in wildlife refuge management, most of which has involved production of food crops for waterfowl. He is a graduate of Utah State University.

THEODORE A. OLSON *(Blue-Greens)* is Professor in the School of Public Health, University of Minnesota, where he has been since 1938. He is a Fellow of the Public Health Association, a graduate of the University of Minnesota, and holds an advanced degree from Harvard University.

LANSING A. PARKER *(A Letter to a Hunter)* is Associate Director, Bureau of Sport Fisheries and Wildlife, Washington, D.C. His career in wildlife management and administration spans 29 years. He is a graduate of the University of Minnesota.

ERNEST L. PAYNTER *(Waterfowl in the Canadian Breadbasket)* is Director of Wildlife of the Province of Saskatchewan. He writes from a background of close association with both agriculture and duck management and some 60 years of life in the center of Canadian duck production. Mr. Paynter is a graduate of the University of Saskatchewan. He holds honorary life memberships in the Saskatchewan Agricultural Graduates Association, the Saskatchewan Fish and Game League, and the Alberta Fish and Game Association.

CLAIR T. ROLLINGS *(Weedkillers and Waterfowl)* is a wildlife management biologist with the Branch of Wildlife Refuges, Bureau of Sport Fisheries and Wildlife, Minneapolis, Minn. His specialty for the past 17 years has been waterfowl habitat management. He holds a graduate degree from the University of Minnesota.

ROYSTON R. RUDOLPH *(Green Trees and Greenheads)* is Assistant Regional Supervisor, Branch of Wildlife Refuges, Bureau of Sport Fisheries and Wildlife, Atlanta, Ga. He has had more than 10 years' wildlife experience, all concerned with waterfowl management. He is a graduate of North Carolina State College.

J. CLARK SALYER II *(Federal Refuges)* is Staff Specialist, Wildlife, for the Bureau of Sport Fisheries and Wildlife. Before this assignment he spent 28 years as Chief of the Division of Wildlife Refuges. Mr. Salyer was a recipient of the Nash Award for Conservation in 1957 and received the Distinguished Service Award of the United States Department of the Interior in 1962. He holds a graduate degree from the University of Michigan.

GEORGE B. SAUNDERS *(South of the Border)* is wildlife biologist, Bureau of Sport Fisheries and Wildlife, Gainsville, Fla. His experience in fish and wildlife investigations covers nearly 30 years, half of which was spent as flyway biologist in the Central Flyway. Dr. Saunders initiated waterfowl surveys in Mexico in 1938 and has made surveys in all Mexican States, and in Central America. His advanced degree is from Cornell University.

GEORGE V. SCHILDMAN *(White-fronts)* is an assistant project leader for the Nebraska Game, Forestation, and Parks Commission, and is head of the white-front subcommittee of the Central Flyway Council's Technical Committee. He has been instrumental in setting up a flyway-wide program for the management of white-fronted geese. He is a graduate of the University of Nebraska.

JOHN L. SINCOCK *(Ducks in Dixie)* is Chief, Section of Wetland Ecology, Patuxent Wildlife Research Center, Bureau of Sport Fisheries and Wildlife. He has been engaged in waterfowl research since 1953 and his publication "An Ecological Study of Waterfowl Areas in Central Florida" was selected for the outstanding award by the Southeastern Section of The Wildlife Society in 1958. Mr. Sincock holds a graduate degree from Pennsylvania State University.

ALLEN G. SMITH *(Prairie Potholes and Marshes)* is wildlife research biologist, Bureau of Sport Fisheries and Wildlife. For 17 years he has devoted major attention to waterfowl production in Alberta, Canada. He holds a graduate degree from the University of Connecticut.

J. DONALD SMITH *(Stock Ponds and Dugouts)* is Chief, Section of Surveys and Banding, Division of Management and Enforcement, Bureau of Sport Fisheries and Wildlife. His career in wildlife management began in 1937, and he has been concerned with waterfowl surveys and waterfowl habitat for virtually his entire professional career. He is a graduate of the University of Minnesota.

MORTON M. SMITH *(Ducks in Dixie)* is a flyway biologist, Bureau of Sport Fisheries and Wildlife. His experience as a waterfowl biologist dates from 1951, when he obtained a graduate degree from Louisiana State University and took part in his first aerial survey of wintering waterfowl in Louisiana for the Louisiana Wild Life and Fisheries Commission.

ROBERT H. SMITH *(Northern Watersheds and Deltas)* is a flyway biologist for the Bureau of Sport Fisheries and Wildlife. Since joining the United States Bureau of Biological Survey in 1936 he has covered most of the waterfowl nesting and concentration areas between Central America and the Arctic Islands. His experience in Canada's Arctic and Subarctic regions extends over a period of 18 years. He is a graduate of Dartmouth College.

PAUL F. SPRINGER *(Insecticides)* is Leader, South Dakota Cooperative Wildlife Research Unit, Brookings, for the Bureau of Sport Fisheries and Wildlife. Before this assignment he had 15 years' experience in ecological studies of wetlands. Dr. Springer served as Chief, Section of Wetland Ecology, Patuxent Wildlife Research Center, from 1958 to 1963. His graduate degree is from Cornell University. He has authored over 45 technical papers, most of which deal with waterfowl.

J. THOMAS STEINER *(State Areas)* is Chief, Section of Lands and Development, Division of Federal Aid, Bureau of Sport Fisheries and Wildlife. He has had 15 years' experience in wildlife management with the State of Mississippi and the Federal Government. He is a graduate of Texas A & M University.

W. J. D. STEPHEN *(Waterfowl in the Canadian Breadbasket)* is wildlife biologist with the Canadian Wildlife Service, Saskatoon, Saskatchewan. He formerly was game biologist with the Wildlife Branch of Manitoba. Mr. Stephen's special field of interest is the integration of migratory bird resources with agriculture. His graduate degree was conferred by the University of Toronto.

THOMAS STERLING *(Dredges and Ditches)* is biologist, Ducks Unlimited of Canada, Saskatoon, Saskatchewan. Mr. Sterling has 15 years' experience in waterfowl habitat management and in population surveys in Canada. He is a graduate of the University of British Columbia.

JEROME H. STOUDT *(Prairie Potholes and Marshes)* is wildlife research biologist, Bureau of Sport Fisheries and Wildlife. He has given 23 years to the study and management of waterfowl, primarily in the northern prairie breeding grounds of Minnesota, the Dakotas, Saskatchewan, and Manitoba. He was awarded the degree of M.S. by the University of Minnesota.

ALLEN T. STUDHOLME *(Dredges and Ditches)* is Chief, Division of Management and Enforcement, Bureau of Sport Fisheries and Wildlife, Washington, D.C. Previously he was Regional Chief, Division of Wildlife in Boston and Minneapolis, respectively, for that Bureau. He has 24 years' wildlife experience, 19 of which were with the Federal Government and 5 with the State of Pennsylvania. He is a graduate of the University of Wisconsin and has a graduate degree from Pennsylvania State University.

LAWSON G. SUGDEN *(Potholes—Going, Going. . . .)* has been a wildlife biologist for the Canadian Wildlife Service for 15 years and is stationed at Edmonton, Alberta. Prior to that, he was for 6 years a regional game biologist with the British Columbia Fish and Game Branch. He holds a graduate degree from Utah State University.

DANIEL O. TRAINER, JR. *(Blood Parasites)* is Associate Professor of Veterinary Science, University of Wisconsin. Previously he was for 5 years Leader of the Wildlife Pathology Project for the Wisconsin Conservation Department. Since 1956 his research has been chiefly on wildlife diseases. Dr. Trainer has published more than 25 technical papers concerning diseases of wildlife. His advanced degree is from the University of Wisconsin.

FRANCIS M. UHLER *(Bonus from Waste Places; Water Off and On)* is a research biologist for the Bureau of Sport Fisheries and Wildlife, Patuxent Wildlife Research Center, Laurel, Md. His research on the food habits of waterfowl and the development of waterfowl feeding and nesting grounds spans a period of almost 40 years. He is a coauthor of *Food of Game Ducks of the United States and Canada* and more than 15 other technical papers on related subjects. Mr. Uhler received the United States Department of the Interior's Distinguished Service Medal in 1962. He is a graduate of Gustavus Adolphus College.

HANS G. UHLIG *(Stock Ponds and Dugouts)* is biologist for the Soil Conservation Service, United States Department of Agriculture, at Saint Paul, Minn. He has conducted research on wildlife in several States. His specialty is land-use planning for income-producing outdoor recreation. He is a graduate of Iowa State University and has a graduate degree from Oregon State University.

ROBERT L. WARDEN *(Weedkillers and Waterfowl)* is employed in Plant Science Research and Development, Bioproducts Department, the Dow Chemical Company, Minneapolis. He has been engaged in weed control research at Montana State College and Dow Chemical Company for 15 years. He holds a graduate degree from Montana State College.

CLARK G. WEBSTER *(Instant Nesting Habitat)* is Assistant Chief, Section of Wildlife Management, Division of Wildlife Refuges, Bureau of Sport Fisheries and Wildlife, Washington, D.C. He has been engaged in wildlife research and management for more than 15 years with major emphasis on waterfowl. He is a graduate of George Washington University.

EDWARD G. WELLEIN *(Northern Forests and Tundra)* is Chief, Section of Migratory Bird Population Studies, Denver Wildlife Research Center, for the Bureau of Sport Fisheries and Wildlife. He has had 25 years' experience in wildlife management and research with the States of Maine and Minnesota and the Federal Service and has participated as a pilot-biologist in annual waterfowl surveys in Canada. He holds a graduate degree from the University of Minnesota.

WILLIAM M. WHITE *(Reservoirs)* is Chief, Division of River Basin Studies, Bureau of Sport Fisheries and Wildlife. He has been engaged in wildlife resources management work for more than 15 years. He is a graduate of George Washington University.

CECIL S. WILLIAMS *(Botulism and Fowl Cholera)* is Director, Denver Wildlife Research Center, Denver, Colo., for the Bureau of Sport Fisheries and Wildlife. Prior to his present assignment he was Section Chief, Waterfowl Management Investigations, for the same Bureau. He has more than 33 years' experience in waterfowl research and management. He holds a graduate degree from the University of Colorado.

RICHARD K. YANCEY *(Matches and Marshes)* is Assistant Director, Louisiana Wild Life and Fisheries Commission, New Orleans. He has 15 years' wildlife experience in the State of Louisiana, most of which has involved waterfowl. He holds a graduate degree from Louisiana State University.

LEE E. YEAGER *(Fur and Feathers)* is Research Staff Specialist, Bureau of Sport Fisheries and Wildlife, and is Head of the Cooperative Wildlife Research Units. Prior to this assignment, in 1963, he served as Leader of the Colorado Cooperative Wildlife Research Unit at Fort Collins for 16 years. Dr. Yeager is author of more than 100 technical papers on wildlife and of numerous popular articles. His advanced degree was awarded by the University of Michigan in 1937.

Acknowledgements

PHOTOGRAPHS

This book is enhanced by many excellent photographs of waterfowl, waterfowl habitat, and other subjects, all of which give extra meaning to the text. They were selected from more than 3,000 made available through the generous cooperation of many organizations and individuals, to all of whom the sponsors of the book, the contributing authors, and the readers are much indebted. The names of photographers, where known, the sources of photographs, and the pages on which the photographs appear are as follows:

Erwin A. Bauer, Columbus, Ohio: page 95, 522, 711, 713 (upper).
Canadian Wildlife Service: 284, 540.
Allan D. Cruickshank, Rockledge, Fla.: 21.
Ducks Unlimited (Canada): 280, 468, 546, 549, 550, (by Robert Dodds) 547.
Florida Game and Fresh Water Fish Commission: 28, (by Bill Hansen) 669.
Grits Gresham, Natchitoches, La.: 686, 710.
Hawaii Division of Fish and Game: 26.
Humboldt State College, Arcata, Calif.: (by C. F. Yocum) 161.
Illinois Department of Conservation: 74, 590.
Iowa State Conservation Commission: 18, 441, 566, 708, (by F. A. Heidelbauer) 128; (by Jim Sherman) 563.
Louisiana Wild Life and Fisheries Commission: (by Richard K. Yancey) 622; (by Eduard Morgan) 624.
Maryland Game and Inland Fish Commission: 517.
Massachusetts Division of Fisheries and Game: 92 (upper), 97, 102, 326 (upper), 694.
Michigan Department of Conservation: 10, 25 (upper), 361.

Montana Chamber of Commerce: (by Bill Browning) 472.

Montana Fish and Game Department: 656.

Nebraska Game Commission: 42, 514.

New York Conservation Department: 571, 572.

North Carolina Wildlife Resources Commission: (by Joel Arrington) 7; (by Jack Dermid) 5, 17, 117, 120, 171, 178, 314, 502, 510, 560.

Ohio Department of Natural Resources: 309, 658.

Oregon Game Commission: (by Ron E. Shay) 645.

Remington Farms, Chestertown, Md.: (by Joe Linduska) 289, 326 (lower), 433, 521, 524, 529, 534, 647, 688, 703; (by Clark Webster) 659.

Royal Canadian Air Force: 275.

Sun Papers, Baltimore, Md.: (by Bill Burton) 376; (by Edward Nolan) 712.

Texas Game and Fish Commission: 212, 214, 317.

U.S. Department of Agriculture, Soil Conservation Service: 25 (lower), 426, 513; (by E. W. Cole) 513, 405; (by George Lowary) 650; (by Keith F. Myers) 607 (upper); (by Bradford Poe) 400; (by E. W. Rees) 429; (by Paul M. Scheffer) 532; (by G. A. Simpson) 393; (by Carl H. Thomas) 616.

U.S. Department of the Interior, Fish and Wildlife Service: (by S. T. Olson) 150; (by Rex Gary Schmidt) 31, 55, 59, 70, 87, 172, 241, 389, 461, 463, 474, 602 (upper), 621, 670, 677, 678, 684, 691, 692, 704, 713 (lower), 735; Bureau of Sport Fisheries and Wildlife: 163, 337, 414, 415, 498, 506, 586; (by Winston Banko) 8, 158; (by I. G. Bue) 394; (by Walter F. Crissey) 44; (by Herbert Dill) 20, 22, 205, 507; (by Frank Dufresne) 620, 626; (by Ray C. Erickson) 291, 581; (by E. A. Goldman) 257; (by Luther Goldman) 92 (lower), 492, 500; (by M. C. Hammond) 607 (lower); (by C. J. Henry) 229, 331; (by Tom Horn) 237; (by Eugene Kridler) 639; (by W. F. Kubichek) 82, 295, 338, 601 (upper), 673; (by John J. Lynch) 104; (by Grady Mann) 48, 372; (by David B. Marshall) 85, 126, 131, 141, 148, 162, 250, 298, 420, 436, 505, 601 (lower), 602 (lower), 608; (by F. R. Martin) 193, 674, 701; (by R. St. Ores) 277; (by George B. Saunders) 256; (by Glen A. Sherwood) 153, 544; (by Frederick C. Schmid) 34, 652, 660, 687; (by Paul F. Springer) 176; (by John H. Steenis) 183; (by James M. Thompson) 327, 501; (by Gerald Townsend) 594; (by Francis M. Uhler) 589; (by R. Upgren) 363; (by Peter J. Van Huizen) 198, 244; (by Clark Webster) 664; (by Jerald J. Wilson) 196, 286; (by Lee E. Yeager) 301, 318, 320.

Virginia Commission of Game and Inland Fisheries: (by L. G. Kesteloo) 640.

QUOTATIONS

Quotations that appear at the ends of many chapters are mostly from copyrighted publications. Authorization for reprinting here is by permission of the copyright holders, whose courtesy is deeply appreciated. The sources of the quotations, the pages in this book on which they occur, and the names of the publishers are given below:

Durward L. Allen (p. 526): *Wildlife Legacy,* Funk & Wagnalls Company, Inc.

Rudolph Bennitt (p. 88): *Journal of Geography,* September 1940, National Council of Geography Teachers.

Stuart Chase (p. 252): *Rich Land Poor Land,* McGraw-Hill Book Company.

Ding Darling (p. 322): *Proceedings of the North American Wildlife Conference,* United States Government Printing Office, 1936.

William O. Douglas (p. 494): *My Wilderness, the Pacific West,* Doubleday and Company, Inc.

Edward H. Graham (p. 232): *Natural Principles of Land Use,* Oxford University Press, Inc.

Wallace Grange (p. 356): *The Way to Game Abundance,* Charles Scribner's Sons.

Aldo Leopold (p. 272, 281, 380): *A Sand County Almanac,* Oxford University Press, Inc.

John Muir (p. 133): *The Wilderness World of John Muir* by Edwin Way Teale, Houghton Mifflin Company.

Sigurd F. Olson (p. 124): *The Singing Wilderness,* Alfred A. Knopf, Inc.

Franklin D. Roosevelt (p. 262): Message to the Congress of the United States, January 24, 1935.

Peter Scott (p. 164): *Wild Chorus,* Country Life, Ltd.

Carl D. Shoemaker (p. 681): *Transactions of the Thirteenth North American Wildlife Conference,* The Wildlife Management Institute, 1948.

Ernest Swift (p. 398): *By Which We Live,* National Wildlife Federation.

Index